Christmas
1954

PARADE OF THE ANIMAL KINGDOM

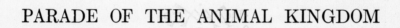

THE MACMILLAN COMPANY
NEW YORK · BOSTON · CHICAGO · DALLAS
ATLANTA · SAN FRANCISCO

MACMILLAN AND CO., Limited
LONDON · BOMBAY · CALCUTTA · MADRAS
MELBOURNE

THE MACMILLAN COMPANY
OF CANADA, Limited
TORONTO

PARADE
OF THE
ANIMAL KINGDOM

By ROBERT HEGNER, Ph.D.

Professor of Protozoölogy in the Johns Hopkins University

ASSISTED BY

JANE Z. HEGNER

Formerly Instructor in the University of Missouri

WITH OVER SEVEN HUNDRED
ILLUSTRATIONS

NEW YORK
THE MACMILLAN COMPANY
1951

CONTENTS

vi CONTENTS

PARADE OF THE ANIMAL KINGDOM

CHAPTER 1

PARADE OF THE ANIMAL KINGDOM

Noah was a lucky man. His experience would have made a naturalist wildly happy. How thrilled he must have been as he stood at the head of the gangplank and watched the Parade of the Animal Kingdom march past him into the Ark, — the beasts, the fowls, and "everything that creepeth upon the earth."

By what method the more primitive animals got into the Ark we are not going to inquire. Many of them cannot be seen with the naked eye and most of them live in either fresh water or the sea. Among them are numbered the Protozoa, the Sponges, the Polyps, Sea Anemones and Corals, and the spine-bearing Starfishes, Sea Urchins, Sea Cucumbers, and Sea Lilies. Other less primitive groups include some representatives that live on land and others that live in the water, — the Worms, the Clams, Snails and Devil Fishes, and the Lobsters, Shrimps, and Crabs.

Every well-managed Parade is led by a band and is provided at intervals with other bands, or at least with drum corps, but thus far the Parade of the Animal Kingdom was void of music and practically free from noise, since none of these lowly creatures has a voice. Perhaps Shem and Ham and Japheth played a lively march as the procession wound its way along. But the Insects provided their own music, from the strident jazz of the Crickets and Cicadas to the gentle humming of the Flies and Bees. The Spiders and Scorpions do not sing and have few attractions; they might never have reached their goal if Noah's orders had not included "every living creature."

More interesting to most of the spectators were the divisions that now hove in sight, consisting of the animals with backbones, — the Fish, the Frogs, Toads and Salamanders, the Snakes, Lizards, Turtles and other Reptiles, the Birds, and finally the Four-Footed Beasts.

Such a marvelous Parade had never before been witnessed, and such a wild cargo is unparalleled in the history of navigation. In our time and generation, Animals are widely scattered over the surface of the earth and must be sought for far and wide, and one or a few at a time. This requires an enormous amount of time and effort. Thousands of scientists have devoted their lives to the study of the Animal Kingdom with the result that we now have a rather comprehensive knowledge of the galaxy of species. It is somewhat difficult to define a species; the simplest definition is, "a species consists of a group of closely similar individuals which do not mate with individuals of other species."

If we could emulate Noah and review a Parade of the Animal Kingdom containing a pair of every species of animal known to science, and if these animals were to march by at the rate of one pair every three seconds, more than a month would elapse before the Gorilla would make his appearance. No one knows how many different kinds, or species, of animals are now living on the earth, but three million is certainly a conservative estimate. Fortunately each species differs sufficiently from every other species so that they can be distinguished one from another; and these species can be arranged in small groups on the basis of similarity in structure. Small groups of species can be gathered together into larger groups and thus order brought out of what would otherwise be chaos.

Few people realize the abundance and variety of animal life. Almost every part of the earth is inhabited by animals of some kind, and these animals are more or less restricted to certain kinds of habitats. Four principal kinds of animals may be recognized according to their mode of existence: (1) marine animals living in the salt waters of the sea, (2) fresh-water animals living in streams, ponds, and lakes, (3) terrestrial animals living on land, and (4) parasites which live on or within the bodies of other animals.

The oceans are inhabited by millions of animals of all sizes, ranging from the whale to microscopic types. Salt-water animals are restricted to certain definite regions; some float on or near the surface, and others live at various distances from the surface, until a depth is reached where light never penetrates. As a rule, animals living in salt water die almost at once if transferred to fresh water; likewise salt water is fatal to fresh-water animals.

Every pond, lake, brook, creek, and river is inhabited by a host of living animals. A pond, for example, furnishes a home for young mosquitoes; frogs and salamanders find a home amid the vegetation; crayfishes crawl about on the bottom, and wheel animalcules and many other extremely small animals swim above them. Besides these, almost every drop of pond water contains a number of animals that can be seen only with a microscope.

Terrestrial animals are better known than all others to the average person. Everyone is aware of the vast numbers of deer, wolves, field mice, snakes, insects, and other types that move about on the surface of the earth. Animals like the mole and the earthworm, which live underground, are said to be subterrestrial, and those, like the birds and butterflies, that frequent the air are called aerial.

Parasites are more widely spread than is generally known. Almost every animal is infested with others which prey upon it. Those that live on the outside of the body, such as fleas and lice, are called external parasites. Others, called internal parasites, live inside of the body; these include such species as the hookworm, tapeworm, and malaria germ. Frequently parasites are preyed upon by other parasites, — a condition known as hyperparasitism — and even the hyperparasites may be parasitized. Thus the following humorous lines contain a grain of truth:

Great fleas have little fleas upon their backs to bite 'em,
And little fleas have lesser fleas, and so ad infinitum.

Animals that have a backbone are placed together in one large group, the Vertebrates, so called because the backbone consists of a row of small bones each of which is known as a vertebra. All of the other animals, which have no backbone, are called Invertebrates. The forty thousand or more species of Vertebrates may be divided into five groups as follows:

1. *Mammals.* These are usually known as Animals or Beasts. They are covered more or less with hair, and feed their young on milk from mammary glands. Some of the representative mammals are the apes, monkeys, bats, rats, mice, rabbits, dogs, cats, cattle, sheep, horses, whales, sloths, and opossums.

2. *Birds.* Feathers are possessed only by birds, hence the members of this group are easily distinguished from other animals. Most birds are able to fly, but some of them, such as the ostrich and the penguin, have lost this power and must remain on the ground or swim about in the water.

3. *Reptiles.* Most reptiles live on land, but many of them spend much or all of their time in the water. They are usually covered with an armor of scales or bony plates. Among the reptiles are the turtles, snakes, lizards, and alligators.

4. *Amphibians.* An animal that spends part of its life in the water and part on land is said to be amphibious, a term derived from a Greek word which means "living a double life," that is, both in the water and on land. Amphibians breathe by means of gills during their young days in the water, and with lungs when they leave the water and live on land. They are not covered with scales. Frogs, toads, and salamanders are common members of the group.

5. *Fish.* Fish are true aquatic animals, spending their entire existence in the water. They breathe with gills, swim about by means of fins, and are usually covered with scales. Some live only in the salt water of the sea, others only in fresh water, but a few are able to live in both salt water and fresh water.

The Invertebrates are much more numerous than the Vertebrates both in species and in individuals. However, in spite of their enormous numbers, they are less well known than the Vertebrates. The principal groups of Invertebrates, arranged in order of their complexity, are as follows:

1. *Protozoa* (15,000 species). These are the simplest of all animals, for which reason their name, Protozoa, meaning "first animals," was given to them. They are too small to be seen with the naked eye except under special conditions. They live in water or moist earth, or as parasites inside of other animals. Each protozoon consists of a single cell. The cell is recognized by all students of plants and animals as the unit of structure of living things, much as a brick is the unit of structure in a brick building. Each cell consists of a minute mass of living substance, called protoplasm, surrounded by a wall; in the center of the cell is a spherical body, called the nucleus. All animals except the protozoa are made up of many cells, sometimes billions of them. The size of an animal is usually determined by the number of cells and not by their size. For example, the cells of an elephant are about the same size as those of a mouse, but there are vastly more of them.

2. *Sponges* (3000 species). The animals that produce the common bath sponges, and their near relatives, occupy a separate division in the Animal Kingdom. A few sponges live in fresh water, but most of them are inhabitants of the sea.

3. *Coelenterates* (4300 species). The term Coelenterate is derived from two Greek words meaning "hollow intestine." Many of them are mere sacs often with enormous quantities of transparent jelly in their bodies. Coral polyps, jellyfishes, and sea anemones belong here. Several common species live in fresh water, but all the other species live in the sea.

4. *Echinoderms* (5000 species). The term Echinoderm means "spiny-skin" and has reference to the spines of carbonate of lime embedded in the skin of many of them. The starfish is the best-known type; others are known as sea urchins, sea cucumbers, and sea lilies. They all live in the sea.

5. *Flatworms* (6500 species). Tapeworms and liver flukes are types of parasitic flatworms. Other Flatworms live in fresh water or in the sea and in moist places on land. All are wormlike in shape and have flat bodies.

6. *Round Worms* (3500 species). Moist places on land, fresh water, salt water, and the bodies of most large animals are inhabited by Round Worms. They are usually long and slender, and whitish in color. Some of them are serious parasites, for example, the hookworm and trichina. One of the commonest species lives in cider vinegar and is known as the vinegar eel.

7. *Jointed Worms* (5000 species). The bodies of these worms consist of a row of rings, or segments, sometimes over one hundred in number. They live in the sea, in fresh water, and in the soil. Well-known species are the earthworm, or angle-worm, and the leech.

8. *Rotifers* (1500 species). The presence of two circlets of moving, hairlike bristles at the front end of a number of common species suggested the names Rotifer and Wheel Animalcule for the members of this group. The term Rotifer means wheel-bearer. Rotifers live in fresh and salt water and as parasites on other animals. They are very small and can be seen clearly only with the aid of a microscope.

Often the Flatworms, Round Worms, Jointed Worms, Rotifers, and certain other animals are considered all together under the heading of Worms, as they are in Chapter 6 of this book.

9. *Mollusks* (80,000 species). Snails, clams, oysters, slugs, and cuttle fishes all belong to this group. They have very soft bodies, usually enclosed in and protected by a hard shell of carbonate of lime. The sea, fresh water, and land are all inhabited by them.

10. *Crustaceans* (20,000 species). In these animals the skeleton is on the outside of the body and is often encrusted with carbonate of lime. Most of them live in fresh or salt water and breathe with gills. Lobsters, crayfishes, crabs, barnacles, and sow bugs are common types.

11. *Myriapods* (2000 species). The term Myriapod is appropriate for the Centipedes and Millepedes belonging to this group, since the term means "myriad-footed," referring to the great number of legs possessed by these animals. Myriapods are long, slender creatures that live on land.

12. *Arachnids* (27,500 species). The Greek word for spider is used as a name for this group, but it includes scorpions, mites, ticks, and king crabs also. These are eight-legged animals many of which are provided with a sting. Some of them transmit serious diseases to human beings.

13. *Insects* (625,000 species). Insects are more numerous than all other animals taken together. They are really the dominant animals on the earth at the present time, although man is able to protect himself from noxious types and to use to his advantage beneficial types, such as the honeybee and silkworm. Some of the large

groups of insects are the grasshoppers, cockroaches, dragonflies, lice, bugs, beetles, moths, butterflies, flies, fleas, ants, bees, and wasps.

All animals, no matter how large or small or where they live, must successfully overcome certain conditions in order to exist. They must protect themselves from heat and cold, from wind and rain, and from rivals and enemies. They must find food, capture it, engulf it, and digest it. They must secrete various substances, such as digestive juices, and excrete waste products which would otherwise poison them. And most important of all, they must reproduce themselves or their race would soon die out.

One reason why Natural History is such a fascinating study is that the various species of animals have so many different methods of solving these problems. Even closely related animals exhibit activities that are extremely diverse, and the more we study these activities the more interesting they appear. Certain animals such as the elephant and the skylark have become famous in history or in literature, but there isn't a single species that is not just as fascinating to one who undertakes to observe its daily activities. We believe that everyone who tries it will heartily agree with us.

In the following pages only a small number of representative species are described and only a small fraction of what is known about each species is presented. The reader is invited to obtain further information from books containing more extensive accounts and to gain first-hand knowledge by actual observations of the animals themselves in their native haunts.

Chapter 2

THE FIRST ANIMALS — THE PROTOZOA

Nature played a naughty trick on mankind when she created the First Animals, the Protozoa, of such a minute size that these fascinating creatures can be seen only with the aid of a microscope. Furthermore thousands of generations of human beings lived and died without being aware that Protozoa existed, since they were not discovered until late in the seventeenth century. Since then they have afforded limitless hours of work and pleasure to both amateur and professional scientists.

The study of animals is usually begun with the Protozoa, and perhaps no better introduction to the Animal Kingdom is possible, hence we have placed the Protozoa at the head of the first division in our "Parade." Although Protozoa cannot be seen with the naked eye when only one or a few are present, some of them are colored and, when billions of them congregate together, give color to the water in which they live; for example, the green color often observed in fresh-water ponds may be due to a minute protozoon. Others that cannot be seen with the naked eye when alone may give a cloudy or milky appearance to the water.

When a drop of pond water is placed under a microscope, a new world of animal life is revealed. The disgusting-looking green scum is seen to be made up of countless numbers of beautiful little creatures swimming about in a carefree manner without any regard as to what we may think of them, and the "dirty, milky water" likewise disappears and such a myriad of graceful, shimmering animals are disclosed that we can hardly believe that what we see is reality and not a part of fairyland.

Protozoa are usually defined as one-celled animals, but in spite of their small size and one-celled condition, they are able to maintain themselves and their race successfully in competition with the so-called higher animals. They perform with their single cell all the functions of life characteristic of human beings. They are able to protect themselves from the weather and from their enemies. They find food, which they eat and digest. They take in oxygen and give off carbon dioxide, secrete digestive juices, cast out waste products, and reproduce themselves.

We consider ourselves the "Lords of Creation," but there are billions more Protozoa in the world than there are human beings, and they are able to live in more different kinds of habitats, and some of them not only live inside the bodies of human beings, but actually kill thousands of people every year with diseases such as amoebic dysentery, malaria, and sleeping sickness.

Protozoa will die if they are not kept moist, hence we find them in water everywhere and in damp places on land. Bodies of fresh water of all sorts are teeming with them, countless numbers live in the sea, the soil is inhabited by them to a depth of several feet, and every species of higher animal that has been properly examined has been found to harbor one or more species within its body.

The reproductive powers of Protozoa are almost unbelievable. The common Slipper Animalcule (page 22) gives rise by the division of its body to several offspring every day. These begin to reproduce within 24 hours. It has been estimated that in one month the offspring of a single Slipper Animalcule would reach the enormous number of 268 million, and if it were not for the ever-present business depression in nature that limits their food supply, these offspring would soon completely occupy the known universe. Protozoa solved the problem of mass production millions of years before the automobile was invented.

It is a very simple matter to find Protozoa for purposes of observation, but one must have a microscope in order to study them. A little scum from the surface of a pond is almost certain to contain a number of different species. These are arranged by scientists into four large groups according to the way they move about. One group, the False-Footed Protozoa, creep along by means of footlike projections of the body which they push out and then flow into. The second group contains the Whip-Bearing Protozoa which lash their way through the water with one or more whiplike flagella attached to one end. The third group, the Ciliates, are covered more or less with minute hairlike cilia that move in shimmering waves as they propel the animal along. The fourth group are Spore-Bearers that live within the bodies of other animals and do not need to move about themselves since they are carried from place to place by the animal, called the host, in which they live. The host in this case differs from a host in polite human society, since the protozoan "guests" are usually not only uninvited but unwelcome.

No one knows how many species of Protozoa there are in the world. At least 15,000 species have been described, but new species are reported by scientists almost every day, and every species of higher animal seems to harbor within its body Protozoa peculiar to itself, hence there must actually exist many times 15,000 species The Slipper Animalcule (page 22) is one of the largest species; but a specimen of average size measures only about $\frac{1}{150}$ inch in length. Some Protozoa are larger than this but most of them are smaller. In the following pages will be explained how interesting and important these minute creatures are with respect to their relations to the earth and its other inhabitants, including mankind.

Protozoa are of fundamental interest to animal psychologists, since they represent the "animal mind" in its most primitive form. Whether or not they are in any degree conscious is a question still unanswered. If Protozoa have recognizable sensations, they must be infinitely less in both quality and quantity than those of higher organisms. That their behavior may be modified under experimental conditions has been demonstrated, which indicates that Protozoa may be able to learn by experience.

A review of the facts regarding the activities of Protozoa seems to show that factors are present in their behavior comparable to the habits, reflexes, and automatic activities of higher organisms and that if Protozoa were large animals, so as to come within the everyday experience of human beings, their behavior would at once call forth the attribution to them of states of pleasure and pain, of hunger, desire, and the like, on precisely the same basis as we attribute these things to the dog.

False-Footed Protozoa. It seems hardly fair to brand a group of Protozoa with the name "False-Footed," but this type of protozoon insists on "walking" on improvised "legs" that are not legs at all and hence must take the consequences. If one is watching a specimen under a microscope, suddenly a bulge is seen at the edge of the body. This bulge grows in length until it may be as long as the rest of the animal, appearing somewhat like a finger thrust out to see what the world is like ahead. Then the rest of the body flows into this false foot, or pseudopodium, which

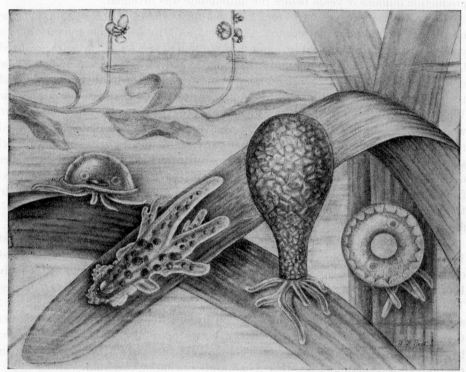

Drawn by Barbara Bradley Root

False-Footed Protozoa. Three species as they would appear under water if magnified 230 diameters. (1) Amoeba proteus is creeping along the stem of a plant. (2) Arcella is arch-shaped in side view but (3) doughnut-shaped as seen from above; a few false feet are protruding from beneath the shell. (4) Difflugia looks as though he were standing on his head, but this is his customary position.

accordingly is obliterated. A new false foot may appear at the same place as the old one or at some other point on the body.

False-Footed Protozoa cannot swim, but must have a solid object to crawl about on. Therefore, we may expect to find them under water on stones, weeds, or on the muddy bottom. Members of this group live in the sea, in the ground, and in moist places generally, as well as in fresh-water ponds. Some of them are naked and others are covered with a shell. Large numbers of them produce a very complex and beautiful skeleton which is internal, just as our skeleton of bone is inside of our bodies, but can be seen clearly because the living substance of the Protozoa is transparent. The false feet of many species are not finger-shaped, but very long and slender and may even be branched. Over one half of all the known species of Protozoa belong to this group.

Amoeba Proteus. How often do the meek and humble finish at the head of the procession! Thus the honor of leading the Parade of the Animal Kingdom is conferred upon the simplest of all the Protozoa, a shapeless mass of protoplasm known as Amoeba proteus. This name is derived from two Greek words; Amoeba means "to change," and Proteus was in classical mythology a sea-god who had the power of changing his shape. This name is well suited to the animal, since Amoeba is continually changing its shape.

Here is an animal only about $\frac{1}{100}$ inch long and almost transparent that has aroused the interest of thousands of scientists and whose activities are still under investigation, although it is not accused of committing any crime. How does it move and what stimulates motion? How does it locate its food and why does it engulf certain food particles and cast aside others that seem to us just as edible? What decides whether it shall divide or not and when? These and hosts of other questions have not yet been fully answered.

But why do we wish to know the answers to these questions? The reason is quite simple. Amoeba consists of living matter, known as protoplasm; our bodies are built up of the same substance. If we knew how Amoeba moves, we could explain the movement of our own white-blood corpuscles. If we knew how Amoeba eats, we could explain the activities of the cells in our bodies that devour minute disease germs. If we knew what forces are concerned in the division of Amoeba, we might solve the cancer problem, since cancer is due to the unlimited division of cells.

Amoebas occur in fresh water practically all over the world. They creep about in search of food, and engulf, with the aid of their false feet, other Protozoa, minute plants, and pieces of larger plants and animals that may have died and broken up. Grains of sand and many other particles that might serve as food are disdainfully ignored. When Amoeba has reached a certain size it seems to know that it ought to divide. This is a very complicated process but can be described in simple terms. First the nucleus divides into two. Then a constriction appears near the middle of the body which gradually pinches the animal into two parts. Each of these is a small Amoeba with all of the puzzling characteristics of its parent. As a matter of fact, each of the two "daughters" is one half of the mother. The mother therefore lives on in the form of her offspring. In one sense Amoeba is immortal, since if there were no enemies to eat her, nor any scientists to destroy her in their experiments, she need never die, although she always loses her individuality when she divides.

Amoeba proteus has a great influence on the microcosm in which it lives since it feeds on minute plants and other animals and in turn serves as food for slightly larger animals. That is, it is a link in a chain of events that finally ends with Man, since in many cases the animals that eat the amoebas are themselves devoured by fish and we may have fish for dinner the following Friday.

Amoeba proteus is only one of a large group of naked False-Footed Protozoa called Amoebas. They are all similar in many ways but can be distinguished one from another by their size, the shape of the nucleus, and the shape and number of their false feet.

Arcella. Many of the close relatives of Amoeba appear to be unwilling to go through life as nudists and hence secrete a shell for themselves. The cousin, known as Arcella, is one of these. The name Arcella means "a little box." This little box is to Arcella what a house is to us and what the shell is to an Oyster. It is something to retire into to escape bad weather or enemies.

The shell of Arcella is a very beautiful light-brown structure, which, when looked down upon through a microscope, reminds one somewhat of a doughnut. The upper surface is shaped like a dome. In the lower surface is a circular opening, the mouth of the shell, through which the false feet are thrust in search of food or for crawling about among the weeds in the pond where it lives.

Difflugia. Like the third little pig, the amoeba-like protozoon called Difflugia is willing to work hard to make its house impregnable, and, as a result, builds a shell of minute grains of sand which are glued together by a sticky secretion and form a firm house of stone well suited to withstand attacks by any "big bad wolf" that may be seeking to devour it. Otherwise Difflugia is similar to Arcella, and, if it were deprived of its shell, would resemble a naked Amoeba. More than a score of species of Difflugias have been described. Some are long and slender and others are short and stout; some have a round dome and others a pointed dome; and several bear spines on the dome or have teeth around the mouth of the shell.

Endamoebas. Most Amoebas live a blameless life in complete harmony with their neighbors, but some of them are bad, and when they are bad they become very horrid indeed. The prefix *End* is added to their name because they live within other animals. Almost every kind of animal that has been studied is known to be inhabited by one or more species of these parasitic Amoebas. Man is no exception, and even seems to be in high favor, since he may harbor as many as six different kinds of Amoebas.

One species lives in the mouth and may be called the Kissing Amoeba since it is transmitted from one person to another during kissing. Over 50 per cent of the population is infected with this species, and it is reasonable to conclude that those who are not infected have never been kissed. Human nature being what it is, there is no known method of preventing the spread of this organism. Fortunately it does not appear to be particularly harmful. A few years ago this Amoeba was supposed to be the causative agent of pyorrhea and our teeth were supposed to fall out because of their presence. This naturally created a great deal of excitement since no one wants to lose his teeth after going to all the pain and trouble of getting them. However, it was discovered later that no relation exists between Amoebas and pyorrhea and everybody settled down again to a calm existence.

The other five species live in the large intestine. All but one of these are supposed to be harmless. The injurious species is present in about 10 per cent of the population. Most of the infected persons, or hosts, are in the carrier condition; that

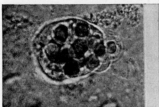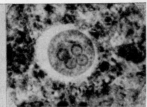

Courtesy, Army Medical Museum

Endamoeba. At the left is a dysentery Amoeba, magnified 100 diameters, creeping through excretory matter. The round bodies inside of it are red blood corpuscles. At the right is a cyst of a dysentery Amoeba containing four nuclei.

is, the Amoebas live and multiply in their large intestine but do not do any damage. Occasionally the body is unable to resist the Amoebas, which burrow into the wall of the intestine, producing abscesses and ulcers resulting in dysentery. Some of the Amoebas may enter the blood capillaries and be carried to the liver, brain, spleen, etc., where abscesses occur. The injuries to the intestine and other organs may result in death, but there are now several drugs, such as emetine, yatren, stovarsol, and carbarsone, that are known to be effective remedies.

The dysentery Amoebas, and other intestinal Amoebas, form spherical cysts which pass out of the body in the excreta and may be swallowed by susceptible persons in contaminated food or drink, — in this way infection is brought about. It is evident that the proper disposal of human excrement is very important if we wish to escape infection. Where sanitary conditions are bad the water should be boiled.

Globigerina. The idea of becoming dust, after a long and useful life, is not a particularly pleasant one, but is far less humiliating than that of becoming a bit of slimy ooze, which is the fate of Globigerina.

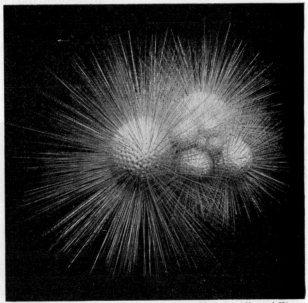

Courtesy, American Museum of Natural History

Globigerina. This enlarged model of the skeleton shows the spherical chambers of different sizes lived in by the animal as it grew larger and larger. The long spines, and pores in the shell through which it thrusts its false feet, are also visible. Magnified 70 diameters.

Globigerinas live in the sea, like homeless orphans, floating about as the waves and currents may decide. Most of their life is spent in secreting a shell of carbonate of lime in which to live. When the first globelike chamber becomes too small, another larger one is constructed until a group of different sizes is produced.   Long, slender spines extend out from the shell, and the false feet are also long and branched.   The body contains many cavities filled with a liquid, probably lighter than sea water, which give it a frothy appearance and help it float near the surface.

In course of time the animals die, and the shells sink to the bottom of the ocean, where they accumulate in such incredible numbers as to form what is known as Globigerina Ooze. The greater part of the bottom of the Atlantic Ocean is covered with it, — an area of about 20,000,000 square miles.   As the deposits increase, the ooze becomes compact and finally solidifies in the form of limestone called chalk. This occurred in various parts of the earth that were once under the sea.   For example, a layer of this chalk exists in Alabama and Mississippi 1000 feet thick in some places.   It

Sun Animalcule.   This is about what one sees when he views the living animal under a microscope.   The false feet look like spines.   Inside are several long, slender plants engulfed as food. Magnified about 100 diameters.

almost gives one a headache to try to imagine how many little specks of animated jelly were necessary to build the shells required to produce such enormous quantities of limestone.   The shells of Globigerina and its relatives may be obtained by carefully washing the sand or mud that lies between the high and low tide marks at the seashore.   A careful search of the surface of seaweeds may reveal some of them.   The sand that is sometimes placed in sponges to increase their weight also contains many different types.

Sun Animalcule.   Astronomers tell us of the vast numbers of suns that exist in the heavens above, but only a naturalist with a microscope can introduce you to the suns in the waters beneath.   The Sun Animalcule has long been recognized as one of the most beautiful of all animals, as it floats about in the waters of a pond or rolls along over water plants on the points of its rays.

Each little Sun consists of a spherical mass of protoplasm from which long, slender pseudopodia extend out like the rays of the sun.   Each ray has a central filament which holds it in place.   When other

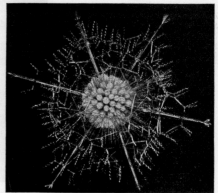

Courtesy, American Museum of Natural History

A Little Ray.   A minute bit of protoplasm secretes this marvelously intricate shell.   Magnified about 100 diameters.

minute animals in the water touch these rays, they may stick to them.   Then the neighboring rays bend over toward the prey which is carried by them down into the body.

Little Rays — Radiolaria. If Globigerina, the Sun Animalcule, and the Little Rays of the Sea were to stage a beauty contest, choosing Miss Protozoon of 1935 would be so difficult that we would not relish the position of judge. The Little Rays, or Radiolaria, float about in the sea, extending their long, slender rays much as the Sun Animalcule does.

The most remarkable thing about the Little Rays is the beauty and exquisite delicacy of the skeleton of silicon that they secrete. It seems marvelous indeed that such a simple-looking minute particle of living substance is able to extract this mineral substance from the sea water and build it up into such perfect radiant structures. When death occurs, the skeleton slowly sinks to the bottom of the sea, and so many billions of them are formed every year that in time they accumulate into a thick layer of what is called Radiolarian Ooze. This is particularly widespread in the Pacific and Indian oceans, where it covers an area of sea bottom estimated at 2,290,000 square miles.

Whip-Bearing Protozoa. So important in the lives of these Protozoa are their long, whiplike flagella that the name Flagellates is usually applied to the members of the group. In the first place, their flagella have given them immeasurably more freedom than is enjoyed by the Amoebas. Variations in number, size, and position of the flagella exist among the different species. In some, the flagella are in front and by lashing backward draw the body along through the water. In others, the flagella are behind and propel the animal forward somewhat like the screw of a steamboat. In either case the result is the ability to swim about in any direction. Whether many of these Flagellates enjoy a full dinner pail, or are doomed to die of starvation, depends also on the flagella, since food particles are drawn into the mouth-opening by their activity.

The Whip-Bearers differ from the False-Footed Protozoa in another important structural feature; the outer portion of the body is a thin, but firm, layer of protoplasm that prevents the animal from changing its shape as in the Amoebas.

Perhaps the most interesting general fact regarding the Flagellates is that many of them possess certain characteristics that are plantlike and other characteristics that are animal-like. As a matter of fact, students of plant life (Botanists) and students of animal life (Zoologists) both claim them. There is no difficulty in recognizing a tree as a plant or a dog as an animal, but this is not so easy with these minute organisms.

Flagellates are even more widely distributed on the earth than Amoebas, and occur almost everywhere where it is moist. Perhaps the easiest way to obtain free-living flagellates is to collect some of the green scum from the surface of a pond. When this is viewed under a microscope, usually myriads of brightly-colored flagellates become visible. These colored species live the way plants do, that is, by manufacturing starch by means of their green chlorophyll with the aid of sunlight. Parasitic flagellates are abundant in the cecum of the common fowl. Material from the cecum should be examined soon after the fowl is killed and should be diluted with a weak solution (0.7%) of common salt before being placed under a microscope.

Euglena. It seems too bad that the most abundant Whip-Bearer, the little green-colored Euglena, is too stupid to realize how much time and effort scientists have spent trying to find out whether it is a plant or an animal, and how it got that way.

Euglena is the commonest of the Whip-Bearing Protozoa. A single specimen, being only $\frac{1}{150}$ inch in length, cannot be seen with the naked eye, but when a great many are massed together, they impart a green tint to the fresh-water ponds in which they live. The body, when seen under a microscope, appears to be spindle-shaped, and at the anterior end is a colorless flagellum that lashes to and fro, drawing the animal forward.

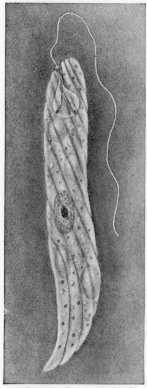

Drawn by Barbara Bradley Root

Euglena. The body is long and slender with grooves running spirally around it; the flagellum is about as long as the body; inside are a large reservoir and other bodies and near the center a nucleus. Magnified about 1000 diameters.

The green color is due to the same substance, chlorophyll, characteristic of green plants. Chlorophyll, in the presence of light, is able to break down carbon dioxide (CO_2), thus setting free the oxygen, and to unite the carbon with water, forming a substance allied to starch called paramylum.

The red eye-spot near the anterior end of Euglena is a conspicuous feature; it appears to be sensitive to light and accounts for the fact that the organism swims toward an ordinary light, such as that from a window; this is of distinct advantage, since light is necessary for the breaking down of carbon dioxide by means of chlorophyll. The multiplication of Euglena is by splitting lengthwise into two. Oval or spherical cysts are sometimes formed, the cyst wall protecting the organism from drying during a period of drought and liberating it when water is again encountered.

Euglenas are a favorite article of food for frog tadpoles. We once placed half a dozen tadpoles in a dish with a pint of water that contained so many Euglenas it looked like bright green soup. The next morning the water was perfectly clear; the tadpoles had eaten every single Euglena. The green coloring matter could be seen in the intestines of the tadpoles through the body wall when the tadpoles were turned over on their backs, a method of detecting the guilty food robber as certain as that of finding jam on the lips of a small boy who has just made a raid on the pantry.

Flagellates in Drinking Water. Some Flagellates are not content to live and die in obscurity, but advertise their presence by the taste and odor they impart to drinking water. These organisms frequently unite to form colonies, which are often spherical, or branching. A species, named Uroglena, is one of the worst offenders, giving rise to a fishy odor resembling that of cod liver oil. A branching species, Dinobryon, also produces a fishy odor.   An odor resembling that of ripe cucumbers, and a taste both bitter and spicy, is furnished by a species known as Synura.

These tastes and odors are due to aromatic oils formed within the body and liberated when the animals disintegrate after death.   An extremely minute quantity

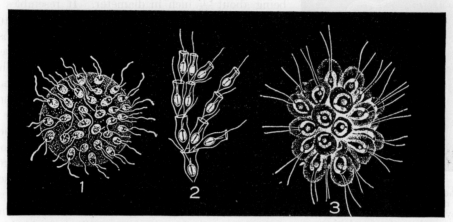

Flagellates in Drinking Water.   The three types shown here much enlarged are (1) Uroglena with many individuals embedded in a jelly-like ball, (2) Dinobryon that forms a branching colony, and (3) Synura with about 32 individuals in one cluster.

of this oil produces a perceptible odor; for example, one part of oil from Synura can be detected in 25,000,000 parts of water.   The addition of quantities of copper sulphate, small enough to be harmless to man and other animals, will destroy these Protozoa and free the water from unpleasant odors and tastes.

The Night Light — Noctiluca.   If we were accustomed to drink sea water instead of fresh water, we might find the Flagellate known as Noctiluca a nuisance, since this species sometimes occurs in enormous numbers floating near the surface of the ocean.   Frequently a steamship may sail for miles through water that resembles tomato soup, due to the orange color of billions of Noctilucas.   A gallon of such water contains as many Noctilucas as there are people in New York City.

Even more striking is the appearance of the sea when one travels over it at night, since Noctiluca is phosphorescent and glows with a bluish or greenish light when agitated.   The waves formed as the prow of the boat cleaves through the water break into scintillating, liquid flames of bluish tint, and are left behind in our wake like a fairy trail.   One can read the time on his watch a foot away from a glass full of these Flagellates.   Incidentally this light is not accompanied by the production of heat, and hence without the loss of energy, as is the case with all methods we have perfected of making artificial light.   Many other animals and certain plants possess a similar power of producing light without wasting energy, for example, the fireflies and glowworms (page 183).

The scientific name of this species is very appropriate.   Noctiluca means "night light."   The title Noctiluca was given to Luna, the Roman Goddess of the moon, whose Palatine palace was always lit up at night. The specific name Scintillans refers of course to the sudden flashing of the light when the water is disturbed. Under the microscope at night, the light is seen to come from myriads of tiny dots within the body of the animal.

The Night Light — Noctiluca. The appearance indicated here is a magnification of its delicate, daytime structure. At night many minute dots of bluish-green light glow within its body. Natural size, $\frac{1}{25}$ inch in diameter.

Noctiluca is a comparatively large Flagellate, being about $\frac{1}{25}$ inch in diameter. It resembles a crystal globe with a delicate network of protoplasmic streamers just beneath the surface. Most of the contents consist of a liquid lighter than sea water, which keeps the organism floating at the surface without the effort required when a human being tries to float. On one side is a mouth from which two flagella extend, one thin and the other a thick tentacle-like flagellum with cross bars. Other minute organisms that live in the sea serve as food for Noctiluca. Thus do these minute creatures resemble animals in general since they prey on other living organisms smaller or weaker than themselves. At one time the thick flagellum of Noctiluca was thought to represent a worm, attached to a bladder that was supposed to serve as a float.

Red Snow and Bloody Rain. No battlefield could possibly look so gory as a meadow covered with Red Snow, and nothing could be more startling than the discovery of a pool of Bloody Rain. This appearance of blood without blood shed is due to the vast gangs of a Flagellate known as Haematococcus, a term that means "bloodberry" and was no doubt given to it because it is shaped like a berry and is blood red in color. It is difficult to imagine how many of these Flagellates are necessary to impart a red color to water or snow, since they are only about $\frac{1}{500}$ inch in diameter.

In polar regions and on the tops of snow-capped mountains, Haematococcus seems to be able to grow and multiply in the snow, and when sufficiently numerous, to change its color from white to red. It has been suggested that the red color absorbs heat from the sun and thus enables this species to grow and reproduce at a low temperature.

Haematococcus also lives in rain water in hollows in the rocks or in reservoirs and frequently in ornamental urns in cemeteries. To this water it gives a red color which is responsible for the belief that bloody rain has fallen.

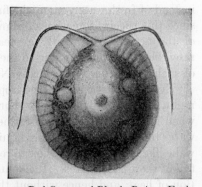

Red Snow and Bloody Rain. Each little flagellate that takes part in giving snow or rain a red color would look like this if our eyes could magnify it 2500 diameters. The horn-like projections are the flagella with which it swims about. Natural size, about $\frac{1}{500}$ inch in diameter.

Volvox. A song could easily be written about Old Man Volvox who "just keeps rolling along" through the water of ponds, like an animated ball, minding his own business, but furnishing much of interest to the curious naturalist. He is a social creature, consisting of a colony of thousands of individuals, all of whom live in complete harmony. United, he is about the size of the head of a pin; divided, he could not be seen with the naked eye.

One remarkable point in which Volvox differs from most other colonial Protozoa is the production of a type of cells, known as germ cells. These germ cells are of two kinds; some become large and egglike and are incapable of movement; others break up into many small, active, rodlike bodies resembling the spermatozoa of higher animals. The egglike female germ cell must be penetrated (fertilized) by one of the spermatozoa-like male germ cells before it is able to develop into a new colony like the parent colony. Here we encounter sexual reproduction for the first time in the animal kingdom.

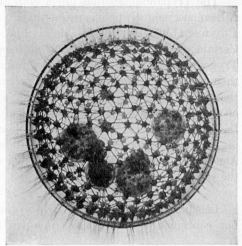

Courtesy, American Museum of Natural History

Volvox. A colony consisting of many individuals arranged in a single layer in the outer wall of a sort of hollow ball; each individual has two flagella and is connected with all its neighbors by minute strands of living matter. The bodies within are young colonies. Magnified about 700 diameters.

Volvox, after giving rise to the germ cells, sinks to the bottom and disintegrates, thus providing us with the first example of natural death in the animal kingdom. As in higher animals, the germ cells provide for the succeeding generation and the body that produces the germ cells dies.

Courtesy, Army Medical Museum

Trypanosomes. Two of the blood-inhabiting flagellates that cause African Sleeping Sickness as they appear under a microscope magnified 2000 diameters. These minute creatures bear the responsibility for a tremendous amount of human suffering.

Blood-Inhabiting Trypanosome Flagellates. If you had Aladdin's magic lamp and wanted to live a life free from care, you might wish to be a Trypanosome. Bathed continuously in blood rich with food, the Trypanosome Flagellates need not worry about the depression nor where the next meal is coming from. However, there always seems to be a "fly in the ointment," which, in this case, is the necessity of getting out of the blood of one host and into that of another. It is safe to say that only one in thousands succeeds, the rest perishing with the host.

Many animals are parasitized by Trypanosomes. The easiest way to get some for examination is to draw a drop of blood from the leg of a frog or the tail of a newt, and mount it under a microscope. The sinuous little Flagellates, if present, will be seen wriggling frantically among the blood corpuscles. Trypanosomes are carried from frog to frog by blood-sucking leeches.

The Trypanosomes that infect man are carried by blood-sucking flies or bugs. African sleeping sickness is caused by a Trypanosome that lives part of its life in a fly resembling the Blue Bottle Fly and called a Tsetse Fly (pronounced set-zee). Certain game animals, especially antelope, are also infected with this type of Trypanosome, and furnish a sort of reservoir from which the Tsetse Flies derive their infection. How destructive Trypanosomes may be is indicated by the fact that in the State of Uganda, near Lake Nyanza in Africa, over 200,000 people, out of a total population of 300,000, died of the infection in six years. Fortunately there are not Tsetse Flies in America, hence no one in this country need be afraid of becoming infected. Other Trypanosomes cause diseases in man in South America, and in cattle, horses, and other domesticated animals in various parts of the world.

Leishmania Flagellates. A trip to the Orient is very pleasant and interesting, but continued residence there involves many dangers. For example, in many

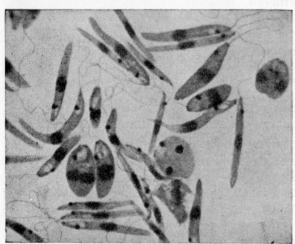

Photo by Drbohlav

Leishmania Flagellates. A little material from an oriental sore magnified 2000 diameters reveals countless numbers of long, slender flagellates each bearing a single "whip." The stout specimens are in process of division.

localities a disgusting disease called Oriental Sore is prevalent. This is due to a little Flagellate, named Leishmania after a famous British scientist, Sir William Leishman. One attack of Oriental Sore gives immunity against further attack. Usually the sores occur on the face, neck, or other exposed parts of the body; hence in Bagdad certain citizens are said to vaccinate their children on some unexposed part of the body, with material from active sores, much as we vaccinate against smallpox, so that there will be no visible scars.

Another Oriental disease of man due to Leishmania Flagellates is known as Kala-Azar. A third human disease resulting from infection with this type of Flagellate occurs in tropical America. Many lower animals are also infected with Leishmanias. The easiest way to obtain some for study is to examine the intestine of house flies or water striders in which similar Flagellates abound. Even certain plants are parasitized by Leishmanias, especially the sap, or latex, of milkweeds.

Intestinal Flagellates. If Jonah had taken a gun and camera with him, he might have had some real sport in the alimentary canal of his Whale, shooting Intestinal Flagellates. Not only whales but practically every kind of animal is supplied with this type of Protozoon. They find the alimentary canal an exceedingly favorable hunting ground and besides are protected and carried around by their accommodating hosts. Half a dozen different kinds may live in our own digestive system.

One species that lives in the mouth and one of the species that live in the large intestine, both Trichomonads, have an undulating membrane on one side. The Giardia Flagellate of the small intestine possesses a sucking disk which enables it to cling to the intestinal wall. The large intestine may be inhabited by several species.

From 10 to 50 per cent of the general population are infected with these Protozoa. Most

Drawn by Ethel Norris

Intestinal Flagellates. Three types that occur in the intestine of rats; those at the left and right are similar in appearance to human flagellates. They are shown as they appear when alive. (1) Giardia with its sucking disk; (2) Hexamitus with six flagella at the upper end; and (3) Trichomonas with an undulating membrane on the right side. Magnified about 2500 diameters.

of the species are harmless, and those that are supposed to be responsible for what physicians call flagellate diarrhea bring about this condition in only a few of those persons who are infected. We found in our experiments that a diet consisting largely of animal proteins, such as meat and cottage cheese, is of value in eliminating these Flagellates from the intestine.

Flagellates and White Ants. Not even Damon and Pythias were as closely associated, or depended as much on each other, as do certain White Ants, or Termites, and the Flagellates that live in their alimentary canal. The intestine of every one of these White Ants contains a wriggling mass of Flagellates. Transmission from one White Ant to another is practically perfect, since the mothers feed their offspring on partly digested excretory matter, known as proctodeal food, which contains large numbers of Flagellates; hence every young White Ant receives an infective dose from its parent.

White Ants may be deprived of their Flagellates by placing them in an atmosphere of pure oxygen under pressure, or in a hot chamber (incubator). This does not injure the White Ants but destroys the Flagellates. Now, White Ants feed on wood, which consists largely of cellulose, and continue to eat wood after their Flagellates have been removed; but they are unable to digest cellulose without the assistance of the Flagellates; hence they starve to death in the midst of plenty. If the starving White Ants are fed on material containing Flagellates, they are again able to digest their food and will live indefinitely.

The Flagellates in their turn are supplied by the White Ant with an abundance of the cellulose on which they feed. White-Ant Flagellates are very complex in their organization and differ from most other Flagellates in the possession of a very large number of flagella. The type of association exhibited by White Ants and their Flagellates is termed Symbiosis. The term symbiosis means "living together," and usually is applied to instances in which two different species of organisms not only live together but are mutually beneficial and unable to live when separated from each other.

Flagellate of White Ants. The intestine of the white ant contains millions of these minute flagellates. They are covered all over with long flagella, like whiskers. The cellulose food of the insect host is digested by them. Magnified about 350 diameters.

Ciliated Protozoa. The Ciliated Protozoa are the large, highly organized, and showy aristocrats of the Protozoan universe. The cilia that cover parts or all of their bodies look like minute hairs. They are not like the almost useless hairs on our bodies, however, but by their movements accomplish what we do with our hands and feet and lips. In the first place, they work in groups and their backward strokes force the body rapidly forward through the water. When seen through a microscope, these movements look like the waves that pass over a field of grain in a gusty breeze. The cilia around the mouth opening draw food within reach and drive it into the gullet. Those around the excretory pore create a current of water which carries away the waste products.

Just beneath the surface of the body in many Ciliates is a layer of minute rod-shaped organs of defense and offense; when stimulated, their liquid contents are shot out with considerable force, forming long threads which keep certain enemies from getting too close and paralyzing with a poison other small animals. Inside of the body of a ciliate are several structures of interest. There are two nuclei instead of one as in other Protozoa; one is very large and the other is very small. One or several contractile vacuoles may be present; these gather in waste matter in solution and force it to the outside through the surface of the body. Food vacuoles may also be found, each containing a particle of food in process of digestion.

Fresh-water streams and ponds abound in ciliates. If some pond weeds are gathered and placed in a dish in a warm place, and kept covered to prevent evaporation, countless numbers of ciliates will appear within a few days. Anyone examining such a "culture" with a microscope for the first time will experience a thrill of discovery almost as great as did van Leeuwenhoek, the great Dutch scientist, who invented the microscope and was the first man to see Protozoa. Van Leeuwenhoek discovered minute living creatures in rain water which he described

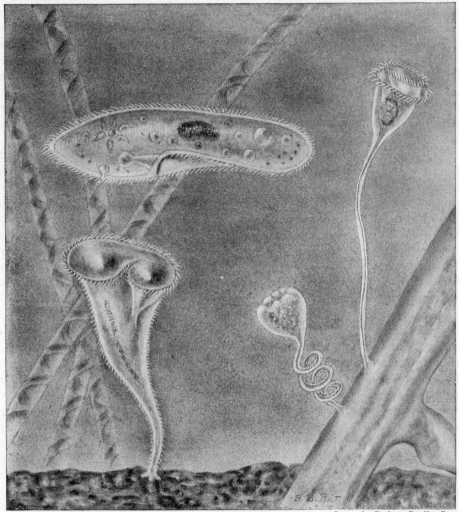

Drawn by Barbara Bradley Root

Ciliated Protozoa. Three species common in fresh-water ponds. (1) Above is Paramecium accomplishing the difficult feat of swimming through the water in a straight line; (2) at the left is Stentor extending its trumpet in search of food; and (3) at the right are Vorticellas one with its stalk and bell extended; the other contracted. Magnified about 220 diameters.

so clearly that one can now recognize them without difficulty. He was unable to determine their internal structure and hence thought that they were filled with organs resembling those of higher animals. "How marvelous," he writes, "must be the visceral apparatus shut up in such animalcula." We know now that Protozoa are single cells and not full of organs.

Slipper Animalcule — Paramoecium. The Slipper Animalcule has been "teacher's pet" ever since Protozoa have been studied, because, although only $\frac{1}{125}$ inch in length, it is comparatively large and very abundant in "infusions" of pond weeds in water. The opening in the "slipper" is really only a groove on one side at the end of which is the mouth. The Slipper Animalcule deserves a prominent position in any animal parade because it can swim in a straight line. This is a very great accomplishment. Everyone knows that when a person is lost in the woods, he walks in a circle instead of in a straight line, in spite of the fact that he can make mistakes in only two directions, right or left. The Slipper Animalcule is rotated on its long axis by its cilia, and the cilia in the groove on one side beat more strongly than those on the opposite side, hence the body is always swerving toward the weaker side. The result is a spiral path that follows a straight line.

The reactions of the Slipper Animalcules to changes in temperature, light, chemicals, etc., have been studied more than those of any other animal. When these Ciliates strike a solid object, they back away and try a new direction; they swim toward a weak acid but away from a strong acid; they try to escape when ultra-violet rays are thrown upon them; and they seek water of a temperature of about 70° F. In general, these reactions bring the animals into water that is best for their welfare. And all of these reactions do not have to be learned, but are instinctive like that of a baby crying for food. If the Slipper Animalcule were as large as a dog, it would no doubt exhibit hunger, desire, pleasure, and pain just as a dog does.

Bell Animalcule — Vorticella. If the charming little Vorticellas could only ring their Bells how much more pleasant life in fresh-water ponds would be for other aquatic animals, since these Bell Animalcules are almost as abundant as the Slipper Animalcules. They are shaped like a bell, but are fastened upside down at the end of a stalk five or six times as long as the body. The stalk is attached to some solid object, and from time to time contracts in the form of a coil spring, thus drawing the bell backward. It then straightens out again, the "bell" being pushed forward in another direction. Around the outer end of the bell is a row of cilia that produces a vortex in the water directed toward the mouth opening. This brings food particles where they can be sucked into the gullet. When danger threatens, the edges of the bell may be drawn in over the mouth.

One species of Bell Animalcule was the first Protozoon ever seen by man; it was discovered by van Leeuwenhoek in April, 1675. Some of the Bell Animalcules are colonial in habit, living in large groups, each on the end of a stalk; but the stalks are attached to one another somewhat like the branches of a tree. It is a familiar habit of these little creatures to attach themselves to the body of some larger animal in their aquatic habitat, such as a tadpole, snail shell, or turtle. They have no thumb with which to indicate in which direction they wish to be transported, but they are benefited no matter where they are carried since new feeding grounds are certain to be encountered during the travels of their animated submarine. How they select their food has long been a puzzle to scientists.

Trumpet Animalcule — Stentor. Another member of the aquatic orchestra, had Protozoa been endowed with musical ability, would no doubt have been the Trumpet Animalcule. If one were to detach a Bell Animalcule from its stalk and stretch it out a bit, he would obtain a ciliate shaped very much like a trumpet. This trumpet-like shape suggested the scientific name Stentor for this group of Protozoa. Stentor was a Greek herald in the Trojan War, who, according to Homer, had an extremely loud trumpet-like voice.

Trumpet Animalcules are usually fastened to a water plant, stick, or stone, but may swim about freely in the water, at which time they are oval in shape. Some of them contain minute green plants and hence are green in color. These plants live with the Trumpet Animalcules in perfect harmony, producing oxygen for their hosts, who in turn furnish protection and a home for them.

Opal Ciliates. Gems are often found in curious places, but the most vivid imagination would hardly select the intestine of frogs and toads as the home of the gem among Ciliated Protozoa. Verily, truth is stranger than fiction, since that is undoubtedly the residence of the Opal Ciliates. This is a very simple statement to prove since you need only to examine with a microscope some of the contents of the intestine of a frog or tadpole. Usually numerous specimens of Opal Ciliates are to be found there. These present an opalescent appearance as they swim about. Like many parasites, they are modified somewhat by their mode of life; they have no mouth, but absorb their food through the surface of the body, being continually bathed in nutriment digested by the frog. They are literally "in the soup."

In the spring the Opal Ciliates produce little spherical bodies, called cysts, which pass out of the frog's intestine into the water at just about the time tadpoles hatch from the frog's eggs. The cysts are swallowed by the tadpoles and hatch in the intestine, thus populating a new generation of frogs.

As in the other groups of Protozoa, many species of Ciliates spend their lives as parasites on or within the bodies of other animals. A simple way to get enormous quantities of parasitic Ciliates is to go to a slaughterhouse and bring back some of the material from the first or second stomach of a cow. About 40 species

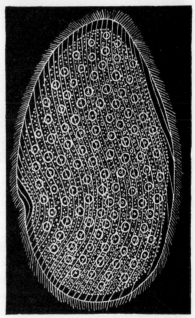

Opal Ciliate. This is what we see if we examine under the microscope the contents of the intestine of a frog, — certainly a very unusual place in which to live. Magnified about 400 diameters.

of Ciliates have been described from the cow's stomach, and you will find a wriggling mass of individuals in your material if you examine it with a microscope within an hour or two after the cow is killed.

The Human Ciliate.   The word *pig* is sometimes applied to a person who is as "dirty as a pig" or who "eats like a pig."   As a matter of fact all of us have something in common with the pig, and that is the Human Ciliate, to which the scientific name Balantidium coli has been given. This Ciliate lives by the million in the intestine of the pig. It produces ball-like cysts, which may be swallowed by human beings in dirty water, milk, or food. These cysts hatch in the human intestine, and in some people burrow into the intestinal wall, forming abscesses and ulcers and producing dysentery. It is worth while to be careful that the food you eat and the water and milk you drink are clean, especially if there are any pigs in the neighborhood. The Human Ciliate looks very much like the Slipper Animalcule, but can live only in the intestine of pigs or of human beings.

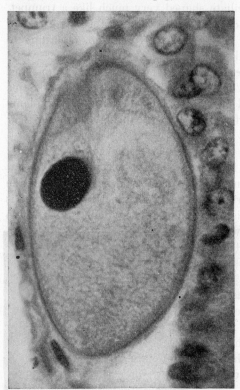

Courtesy, Army Medical Museum

The Human Ciliate. A specimen plowing its way through the wall of the large intestine. This is a "large" Ciliate about $\frac{1}{250}$ inch long. The black spot is the nucleus; above the nucleus is the funnel-shaped mouth.

Sucking Protozoa. Among human beings a sucker may be born every minute, but among Protozoa millions of suckers are continuously breeding more suckers in an endless array. These suckers are really Ciliates that have cilia when they are babies but lose them as they grow up. In their place appear sucking tentacles with which they capture other minute Protozoa, and by means of which they suck the living substance of their prey into their own bodies. Not a very pleasant occupation, but very successful, because Sucking Protozoa are very numerous not only in fresh water and in the sea, but as parasites in and on other animals.

The Tree Sucker, known to scientists as Dendrosoma radians, grows on plants in fresh water, where it forms large, treelike branched colonies. The branching trunks grow up from a creeping base and may be $\frac{1}{12}$ inch high. At the end of each branch is a cluster of sucking tentacles awaiting any luckless Slipper Animalcule or other minute animal that might chance to touch and become fastened to them. When this happens a stream of delicious food from the captive flows down each tentacle into the body, there to be transformed into the living substance of the Tree Sucker. A continuous struggle is being carried on between each little animalcule and the other little animalcules in his neighborhood and only the fortunate few survive. The survivors are, of course, the best fitted for their mode of life.

Spore-Bearing Protozoa. Many mothers with naughty or crying children would like to wrap them up securely and lay them on a shelf for a while. This could be accomplished easily if transformation into Spore-Bearing Protozoa were possible, since the young of this group are born in the form of spores with a firm and non-breakable coat.

Almost every species of animal furnishes a home for one or more species of Spore-Bearing Protozoa; in fact, all of the Spore-Bearers are parasites. They pass from one animal to another in the spore stage, hence their name. The spore is a seedlike body whose cover protects the delicate living substance within from injury while it is outside of the body of its host.

Spore-Bearing Protozoa have no locomotor organs, such as pseudopodia,

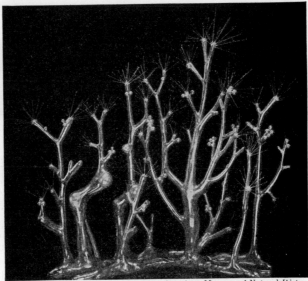

Courtesy, American Museum of Natural History

Tree Suckers. How complex Protozoa may be is illustrated by this branching Ciliate, whose cilia have given way to the sucking tentacles at the ends of the branches. Magnified about 25 diameters.

flagella or cilia, but are carried about by the animal in which they live. They have no mouth, since they live in the substance of the host and absorb this as food through the surface of their body. Only a few of the spores ever succeed in reaching a new host, hence enormous numbers of them must be produced or the race would soon die out. Human beings may be parasitized by several species of Spore-Bearing Protozoa. Other species are abundant in domestic and wild animals.

Gregarines. The house-wife whose kitchen is overrun with cockroaches, the farmer whose crops have been ruined by grasshoppers, or the miller who finds his grain riddled with meal worms might accept their afflictions with better grace if they knew that cockroaches, grasshoppers, and meal worms have something gnawing at their vitals. Practically all of these insects and many other species are parasitized by Spore-Bearers known as Gregarines. These Gregarines at first live within the cells of the intestinal wall, but as they grow larger they break out into the cavity of the intestine. Living specimens mounted under the microscope in weak salt solution glide about slowly without any visible locomotor organs; their exact method of movement has never been determined with certainty. Probably when Gregarines are very numerous they kill the insects they parasitize, but usually they do not destroy their host but simply give him a very bad "stomach-ache."

Each animal consists of two parts, the one behind containing the nucleus. Often two specimens will be found attached end to end, a condition called syzygy. They may surround themselves with a wall which they secrete, thus producing

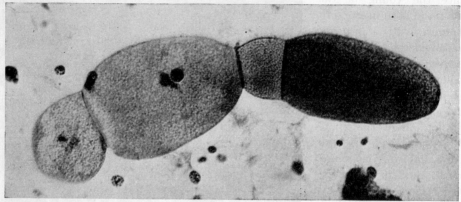

© *General Biological Supply House*

Gregarines. Two specimens, from the intestine of a cricket, attached end to end. Each consists of two parts, the hinder part contains the black-stained nucleus. They glide along, but how they do this is not known. Magnified about 300 diameters.

a cyst, in which, after a number of cell divisions, followed by cell fusions two by two, many spores are formed. These pass out in the excrement of the insect and develop into new Gregarines if swallowed by another insect.

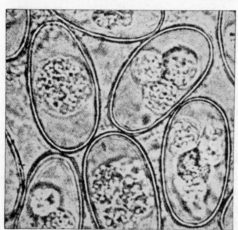

Photo by Wenyon

Coccidia. The large oval bodies are oocysts such as are found in the fecal pellets of a rabbit. The spherical bodies inside several of the oocysts will form the spores. Magnified 1000 diameters.

Coccidia. We have often been asked how anyone can be a 100 per cent American when his internal decorations consist of Intestinal Ciliates, Amoebas, Flagellates, and other similar jazz babies, to which must now be added the Coccidia. These Spore-Bearers infect not only human beings but also dogs, cats, fowls, and many other animals. The spores are swallowed in contaminated food or drink and develop in the cells of the intestinal wall. Cysts are formed in which spores develop. Human infection results in diarrhea which lasts about two weeks. Almost every pet rabbit is infested with Coccidia, but with a species that is unable to develop in man. Cysts can easily be obtained by soaking rabbit pellets in a small amount of water. Young rabbits are frequently killed by their Coccidia, as are also young chickens and other birds and mammals.

Malaria. This Spore-Bearing Protozoon has had a profound influence on human history. Malaria has been known for centuries, but the minute protozoon that is responsible for it was not discovered until 1880, by the French military doctor Laveran. The method of transmission was not determined until 1898, when Ross proved that certain mosquitoes carried the malarial organisms of birds from one to the other; later Grassi, in Italy, demonstrated that human malaria is transmitted in similar fashion. Human beings can be infected only by the bite of the females of certain species of infected anopheline mosquitoes.

The life-cycle of the Malaria Protozoon is rather complicated, but includes such a marvelous series of stages that it seems well worth describing here. The

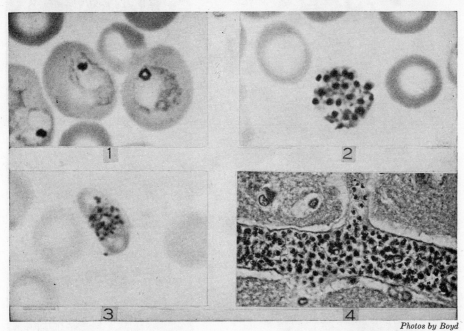

Photos by Boyd

Malaria Parasites. (1) Human red blood corpuscles; three of these are much enlarged and contain each a malaria parasite. (2) A malaria parasite breaking up into about 24 young merozoites. (3) A sexual malaria parasite. (4) A capillary in the brain filled with red blood corpuscles containing malaria parasites. All highly magnified.

diseased mosquito injects the infective stage of the Malaria Protozoon into the blood when it bites. This infective body, the sporozoite, penetrates a red-blood corpuscle, where it becomes amoeboid in shape and is known as a trophozoite. This grows rapidly until it almost fills the corpuscle. Then it divides into from 15 to 24 daughter cells, the merozoites. The corpuscle soon breaks down, liberating the merozoites, each of which attacks another red-blood corpuscle. This period of growth and reproduction takes 48 hours. When large numbers of the parasites are present and millions of corpuscles break down at one time, the patient suffers a chill followed by fever.

Mosquitoes become infected by sucking up blood from such a patient. Certain of the parasites develop in the mosquito's stomach and form little, spherical, tumor-like growths on the stomach wall.   In these, thousands of spindle-shaped sporozoites are formed.   They eventually break out, and some of them become lodged in the salivary glands of the mosquito, where they remain until they may be

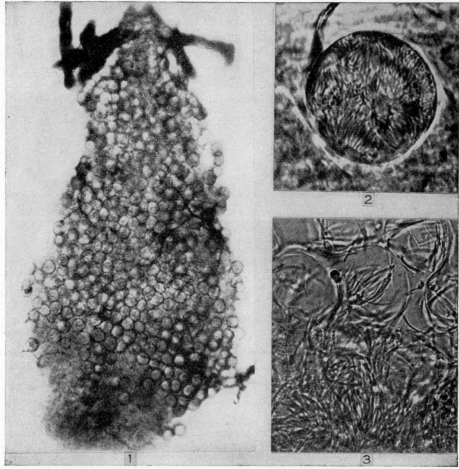

Photo by W. V. King.   Courtesy, Army Medical Museum

Malaria Parasites.   (1) View of the outside of a mosquito's stomach; each little sphere is the oocyst of a malaria parasite.   (2) A single oocyst more highly magnified showing the long, slender sporozoites within.   (3) Part of the salivary gland of a mosquito containing many slender, crescent-shaped sporozoites.   Highly magnified.

injected into the blood of another person.   Malaria has been and still is the most important of all tropical diseases.   Quinine, plasmoquine, and atebrine are some of the drugs that are generally used for the treatment of malaria.   Usually when a person goes into a malarious region he is very careful to protect himself with a bed net from mosquitoes.   The mosquitoes become active at dusk, hence "early to bed and early to rise" is a good motto for anyone living in the tropics to observe.

Texas Fever. Forty years ago when cattle in the Texas region became sick they didn't have to describe their symptoms or stick out their tongues; their owner knew only too well that they had Texas fever and would die. In course of time, it was learned that this disease is caused by a Spore-Bearing Protozoon, and in 1893, Smith and Kilborne, of the United States Department of Agriculture, discovered that a tick, now known as the Texas fever tick (see Chapter 9), carries the parasite from a sick animal to a well one. Their discovery is particularly noteworthy because this was the first insect-like animal known to transmit disease-producing Protozoa. The knowledge thus gained aided in the discovery of the transmission of malaria and yellow fever by mosquitoes.

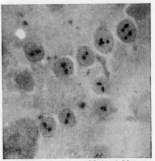

Courtesy, Army Medical Museum
Texas Fever Parasites. Nine red blood corpuscles of a cow infected with the parasites of Texas Fever. Each pear-shaped black dot is a minute parasite $\frac{1}{8000}$ inch long.

The Texas fever parasite lives inside of the red-blood corpuscles. Usually two pear-shaped parasites are present in each infected corpuscle; as many as half of all the corpuscles in an animal may be parasitized.

Pebrine. We often hear someone say he or she "feels like a worm," but no one could possibly feel as badly as a silkworm looks when it is suffering from the disease known to the French as Pebrine. This disease, which once threatened the silk industry of France, is due to a very minute Spore-Bearing Protozoon only about $\frac{1}{5000}$ inch in length. The spores, which escape from the body of a diseased worm in its excrement, infect any worm that may swallow them along with the mulberry leaf it is eating. Inside of the silkworm the spores hatch and multiply very rapidly, invading all the tissues of the body and eventually killing the worms, or moths that develop from them. As in the Texas fever parasite, the spores penetrate the eggs of the moth and infect the silkworms that hatch from these eggs.

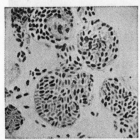

Photo by White
Pebrine Parasites. Each group of oval dots represents a mass of parasites in a cell from the stomach of a honeybee. These parasites are similar to those that cause Pebrine in silkworms. They are about $\frac{1}{5000}$ inch long.

Pasteur, in 1865, saved the silk industry of France by discovering how eggs containing parasites could be distinguished from good eggs, by means of a microscope. Diseased eggs could thus be destroyed and silkworms raised from good eggs only. This discovery nas saved the world billions of dollars. A disease due to a similar parasite is very destructive to honeybees.

CHAPTER 3

SPONGES

There are probably more skeletons in the bathrooms in this country than there are "skeletons in the closets." To prove this, we need only count the Sponges now in use for bathing purposes. The sponges that we use when we take a bath, or wash our automobile, do not look much like animals; nevertheless they are skeletons manufactured by animals, and are shaped much like the animals that built them.

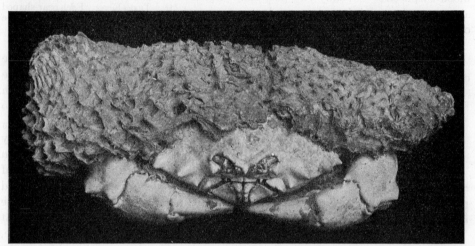

Courtesy, American Museum of Natural History

Sponge Crab. This species of crab places a sponge on his back so that he may be concealed from his enemies and may creep up on his prey without being noticed.

The Greek philosopher Aristotle (384–322 B.C.) was familiar with sponges and decided that they were animals, but thousands of scientists who followed him thought they were plants. Gerarde, in his famous Herbal (1636), says, "there is found growing upon the rockes near unto the sea a certaine matter wrought together of the foame or froth of the sea which we call Spunges . . . whereof to speak at any length would little benefit the reader, seeing the use thereof is so well known." Later, sponges were called Zoophytes, or plant-animals. Their animal nature was not finally established until the first half of the nineteenth century.

Most sponges, including the species that produce the bath sponges of commerce, live in the sea, but a few live in fresh-water ponds and streams. They are usually attached to a rock or some other solid object in the water, or to the sea bottom by

30

means of needle-like spicules, and many of them encrust stones, shells, sticks, or plants. Some are quite irregular, but others are shaped like a ball, a glove, a cup, a dome, or a cone. In size, sponges vary from species no larger than a pinhead to those three feet across and one foot thick — big enough for a mermaid to sit on. Many sponges are white or gray, but others are colored yellow, orange, brown, red, violet, green, or black. Green sponges usually owe their color to green plants that live in them. The skeletons keep the soft cells, that make up the living sponge's

Photo by Hegner

Sponge Boats. Tarpon Springs, Florida, is the center of the sponge industry in this country. These sponge boats are tied up at the wharf there and decorated with flags.

body, from collapsing into a jelly-like mass. They vary according to the species. Some consist of spicules of carbonate of lime or spicules of silicon; others of spongin fibers. Spicules are of various shapes but constant for each species, and hence of value in identifying different types. They are built up within special cells, of material extracted by the sponge from the water. The body of a sponge has many pores in the sides which open into canals leading to chambers and other canals within. At the top are one or more larger pores, depending on the size of the sponge, which are known as oscula.

Sponges are usually considered, even by scientists, to be very quiet and sluggish animals, but if a piece of living sponge is placed in a bowl of water and some powdered chalk added, currents of water may be seen entering the pores in the sides and being thrown out of the oscula like rocks from the crater of a volcano. Sponges are, in fact, among the most active and energetic of all animals, working night and day to create the currents of water that bring food and oxygen into the body and carry away waste matter, — they are veritable living dynamos. These currents of water are created by a type of cell that lines certain canals and cavities within the sponge. Each of these cells has a collar around the end from which projects an actively moving flagellum. The flagella move so as to keep up a constant flow of water. The amount of water that passes through the body of a sponge is tremendous; for example, an average-sized sponge draws about 45 gallons of water through its canal system in a single day.

Courtesy, U. S. Bureau of Fisheries

Bath Sponges. The sponge at the left is a Grass Sponge and the other a Sheep's Wool Sponge; they grew together on one base. Reduced in size.

Sponges commonly reproduce themselves by means of buds, which remain attached to the parent and thus bring about the formation of large masses. In certain species, especially in the autumn, a number of cells congregate to form a gemmule, which separates from the parent and develops into a sponge the following spring. Eggs and spermatozoa may also be formed. The fertilized egg develops into a young sponge which possesses movable cilia, and is therefore capable of swimming about; in this way sponges are distributed throughout bodies of water before they settle down for life.

Very few animals eat sponges because of their skeletons of spicules or spongin. Besides this, many sponges, when alive, give off a strong, unpleasant odor, and some even secrete poisonous substances. Probably for this reason, as well as for purposes of concealment, certain species of crabs are accustomed to place sponges on their backs or on their legs. Other animals find the body of the sponge an excellent place in which to retreat for protection. The number and variety of these are indicated by the results of an examination of twelve living bath sponges reported by Pearse in the Dry Tortugas Islands near Florida. These twelve sponges, which ranged from two to eight inches in diameter, contained 683 other animals belonging to 15 or more species, including jointed worms, brittle stars, crustaceans, and bivalves. Oysters and other bivalves are sometimes starved to death by an encrustation of sponges, but, for the most part, sponges are of value to man.

That sponges are lowly organized creatures is indicated by their ability to grow even though cut up into small pieces. Even more remarkable was the discovery that if a broken-up sponge is strained through fine bolting cloth so as to separate the cells, these cells will fuse together on the bottom of the dish and gradually develop into a sponge of the type broken up. No wonder sponges are so abundant when they are so hard to kill.

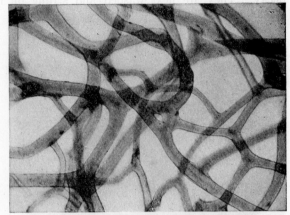

Courtesy, Nature Magazine, Washington, D. C.

Sponge Fibers. The common bath sponge is made up of a network of horny fibers that look like this when highly magnified.

> The sponge is not, as you suppose, a funny kind of weed;
> He lives below the deep blue sea, an animal like you and me,
>   Though not so good a breed.
> And when the sponges go to sleep, the fearless diver dives;
> He prongs them with a cruel prong, and, what I think is rather wrong,
>   He also prongs their wives.
> I know you'd rather not believe such dreadful things are done;
> Alas, alas, it is the case; and every time you wash your face,
>   You use a skeleton.   (From A. P. H. in "Punch")

Bath Sponge. Prehistoric man probably enjoyed the use of Bath Sponges as much as we do today, and was perhaps more in need of them. Their many uses were known to the Greeks and mentioned by Homer in the *Iliad* and *Odyssey*. Glaucus of Anthedon, a character in Greek mythology, was a sponge diver. Passages in the Bible prove that sponges were in common use in Jerusalem. The Roman soldiers sometimes used sponges instead of cups for drinking purposes, which probably accounts for the fact that a sponge was used to soak up the vinegar offered by them to Christ during the crucifixion.

Bath sponges all came from the Mediterranean Sea until 1841, when the Bahama Islands became another source of supply. Later, sponge fishing off the coast of Florida was begun.

Fishing for sponges is carried on by divers, either with or without a diving suit, or in shallow water by men in boats, who secure them with hooks. The latter method is used in the Bahamas and Florida, the hooks consisting of curved prongs.

Living bath sponges resemble somewhat a piece of raw beef liver, being slimy to the touch and fleshy-looking. They may be grayish-yellow in color, or various shades of brown to black. The sponges are killed by being trodden under the bare feet of the fishers. Then they are hung up and the soft parts allowed to decay. They are next washed and strung on ropes in bunches. The sponges consist of a skeleton of horny material, called spongin, which contains several of the same substances as those in silk. Some sponges are bleached with chemicals, but are not as durable as those untreated. Commercial sponges are of various types. Sheep's-wool sponges comprise about 90 per cent of the value of American sponges. The best Mediterranean sponges are known as Turkey-cup and Turkey-solid sponges. Other types are called yellow, velvet, grass, glove, wire, reef, hardhead, Turkey-toiled, and honeycomb sponges.

Courtesy, American Museum of Natural History
Urn Sponge. Several Urn Sponges have attached themselves to the shell of a clam. These are among the simplest of all sponges. Size about one inch long.

Urn Sponge. No one would consider a vacation at the seashore successful without a sandy beach, but "such quantities of sand" might become monotonous, and a few tide pools among the rocks in which to look for sea-anemones, crabs, sponges, and other denizens of the marine world are very desirable. One of the simplest of the sponges that are often common in tide pools is the Urn Sponge. This species is named Grantia in honor of Robert Grant, who, in 1825, proved that sponges are animals. Grant was examining a sponge, when he noticed the movements of particles in the water. He says, "I beheld, for the first time, the splendid spectacle of this living fountain vomiting forth from a circular cavity an impetuous torrent of liquid matter, and hurling along in rapid succession opaque masses which it strewed everywhere around. The beauty and novelty of such a scene in the animal kingdom long arrested my attention. . . ."

Urn Sponges grow in clusters. They are about $\frac{1}{2}$ inch high and dull yellow, gray, or drab in color. The sides are dotted with hundreds of pores which open into canals that penetrate the thick walls. Each sponge has a large central cavity opening through a large osculum at the upper end. The wall is held up by spicules of carbonate of lime, some straight and pointed at each end, others with three rays, and others T-shaped.

Fresh-Water Sponge. The sea does not have a monopoly on sponges, but, as though to satisfy the desires of inland naturalists, a few species have acquired the ability to live in fresh water. More than 20 species of Fresh-Water Sponges occur in the United States. They are usually to be found in clear water, encrusting stones, sticks, and plants, and are mostly yellow, brown, or green in color. The green color is due to minute green plants that live in the sponge. The most abundant species is a branching form of Spongilla that lives in the sunlight in running water and is green in color. Another species prefers standing water and avoids the light. A third species lives in shallow water, usually under stones or roots, and is gray in color.

Fresh-Water Sponges produce gemmules in the fall. These are spherical bodies with a shell and air spaces that make them light enough to float. They carry the race through the winter and distribute the species by floating about in the currents far and wide. When they hatch, a delicate creamy film emerges, which manufactures a framework of spicules on which a sort of skyscraper of beautiful silicon is erected.

Courtesy, American Museum of Natural History

Fresh-Water Sponges. These specimens have grown around twigs which keep them off the bottom and in clear water.

Fresh-Water Sponges furnish a home for the young of a family of nerve-winged insects, called Spongilla Flies because they depend on the Spongilla type of sponge for a living.

Venus's Flower-Basket. Everyone will readily admit that the Goddess of Beauty and Love should be properly adorned, hence any product of the sea that is particularly beautiful is named after Venus. Thus, the most beautiful sponge skeleton, an object that is more or less familiar in museums, is known as Venus's Flower-Basket. It is shaped like a cornucopia and is about a foot long. Its gleaming silver color is due to a fine network of silicon resembling spun glass. The work required to build this marvelous structure is almost unbelievable. The silicon present in solution in sea water is about $1\frac{1}{2}$ parts in 100,000; hence to extract one

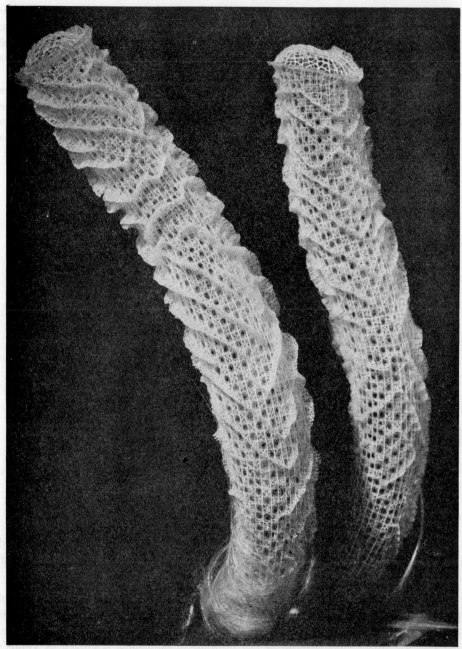

Venus's Flower-Baskets. These cornucopias are the skeletons built of "spun glass" by sponges. They are about a foot long, and fastened in the mud of the sea bottom by threadlike spicules at the lower end.

ounce of skeleton, at least a ton of sea water must be drawn through the pores of the sponge and forced out again through the oscula.

In some of these sponges a pair of pink-colored crabs make their home. In Japan, according to Ijima, Venus's Flower-Basket is in great demand for marriage ceremonies. The name in Japanese means "Together unto old age and unto the same grave"; this name is sometimes changed slightly as a joke so as to mean "Two lobsters in the same cell."

The sponges that construct these beautiful "baskets" live in the sea near the Philippine Islands, where they are fastened in the mud of the sea bottom by a mass of long siliceous threads at the lower end.

Other Sponges. Sponges resemble one another in their principal features, but vary so greatly in form and habits that one is tempted to believe they deliberately set out to furnish work for unemployed naturalists. A number of species are more or less branched.

Courtesy, American Museum of Natural History

Red Sponge. The body of this sponge consists of short, fleshy branches rising like a crimson forest from a rock or shell lying on the sea bottom.

The Finger Sponge grows to a height of about six inches and consists of a flattened stalk, which is attached to a rock or shell, and a number of finger-like, lobed branches. The living substance is dull orange-red, but the skeleton is whitish. Finger sponges live on our North Atlantic coast at depths of fifteen feet or more.

Another species with branches, that may be found along our Atlantic coast, is the Red Sponge. The young form incrustations in shallow water on oyster and scallop shells, etc., and send up branches in clusters that may be four inches high and six inches in diameter. They are brilliant crimson in color.

Boring Sponges occur near shore from South Carolina to Cape Cod. They form irregular masses and are bright sulphur-yellow in color. Their name has reference to their habit of attaching themselves to the shells of oysters, clams, etc., and boring them so full of holes that in time the shells are entirely broken up.

The Sulphur Sponge is bright yellow in color, rather massive in appearance, and has a smooth surface. It lives on sandy bottoms south of Cape Cod in shallow water.

CHAPTER 4

COELENTERATES — POLYPS, JELLYFISHES, AND CORALS

How would you like to be nothing but an animated stomach, with perhaps a load of superfluous jelly to make you look stout and prosperous? If you think this would please you, we suggest that you study the group of animals we call Coelenterates, a word that means "hollow intestine."

However, in spite of their lowly structure, the Coelenterates have managed to make themselves a conspicuous part of the life at the seashore. Many of them are attached to rocks and are often collected as seaweeds, which they resemble very closely; others, called jellyfish, pulsate slowly as they are carried by in the currents; and the sea anemones congregate in the tide pools, where they furnish a flower-like riot of color. Sea fans, sea pens, corals of many sorts, and comb-jellies are also numbered among the 5000 or more species in this group of animals.

In fresh-water ponds lives a very common species named Hydra that is well known to all students of Zoology. Somewhat similar forms that live in the sea are known as hydroids or polyps. Jellyfishes are similar in fundamental structure, but are bloated out of shape by their enormous accumulation of jelly, of doubtful value after they go to all the trouble to get it. Sea anemones and corals are of the polyp type.

It gives one something of a shock to learn that such flower-like creatures are predatory, shooting with their poison darts any unsuspecting small animals that approach too close, and stuffing their helpless prey into their capacious mouths with their writhing tentacles.

Coelenterates are on a somewhat higher level than sponges; they have muscle fibers, and some of them can swim about; they have simple types of nervous systems and are sensitive to light, temperature, chemicals, touch, and gravity. The phenomena of polymorphism and alternation of generations, which they exhibit, will be described later. Many Coelenterates are luminescent when disturbed at night.

Hydra. Hydra, the mythological nine-headed dragon slain by Hercules, was a monstrous creature; for this reason our heartfelt sympathy is freely offered to its harmless little namesake, the fresh-water Coelenterate, so unjustly called Hydra. If some pond weeds are gathered and placed in a glass dish full of water, Hydras may be found later clinging to the plants or sides and bottom of the dish. They are easily seen with the naked eye since they range from about $\frac{1}{10}$ inch to one inch in length. They resemble a short, thick white thread, the stalk, frazzled at the unattached outer end to form a number of long tentacles. Both the stalk and tentacles are capable of remarkable expansion and contraction because of the muscle fibrils in many of the cells.

In nature, Hydra clings by one end, called the foot, to a leaf or other solid object, or hangs down from the surface from a balloon-like float that it secretes at the base of the foot. Hydra's method of capturing and devouring the small animals it uses as food is quite remarkable. On all parts of the body, but especially abundant on the tentacles, are little wartlike projections containing large and small stinging capsules, like a battery consisting of cannons surrounded by smaller machine guns. A trigger-like spine sticks out from each capsule.

When a small food animal is so unfortunate as to come within reach of a Hydra, the stinging capsules are exploded and the animal "shot." A poison in the capsule is forced out through a minute tube into the victim, which is immediately paralyzed. So powerful is this poison that it can even dissolve the extremely hard shell of an insect. When captured, the prey is carried by the tentacles to the mouth, which opens to receive it. The edges of the mouth close around the victim and force it into the digestive cavity. This cavity occupies the entire stalk and continues into the tentacles. Particles that are not digested are forced out through the mouth by a very sudden squirt. Hydras will not eat unless they are hungry.

© General Biological Supply House

Hydra. A specimen with two buds. When photographed, this animal was in a contracted condition; if extended, it would be three or four times as long, both as regards stalk and tentacles. The buds are about to separate from the parent. Magnified about 15 diameters.

Hydra has no skeleton and is so delicate that it must frequently become injured. This does not send the Hydra to the hospital to be stitched up, because the body rapidly grows into a normal animal again, a process known as regeneration, or the power of restoring lost parts. A single Hydra may be cut into many pieces, each of which will grow into an entire animal if it is not too small. No wonder Coelenterates were considered plant-animals (Zoophytes) by the naturalists of the eighteenth century.

The gentle reader may be surprised to learn that grafting is accepted by Hydras without a murmur.   To be sure, this does not occur in nature, and the "grafting" is not like that practiced by certain human beings.   The facts are that, under certain conditions in the laboratory, parts of two Hydras, if held together, will soon grow together, just as a part of one plant may be grafted upon another plant.   Pieces of Hydra too small to grow into a complete individual may fuse together and then develop into a typical specimen.   This wonderful power of growth under adverse circumstances is a great advantage in the struggle for existence of such a delicate and easily injured animal as Hydra.

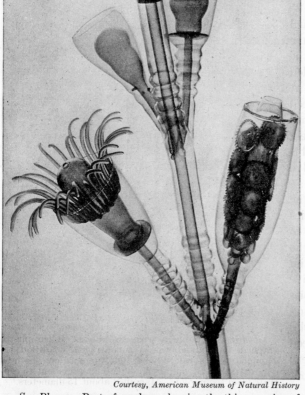

Courtesy, American Museum of Natural History

Sea Plume. Part of a colony showing the thin covering of the stalks and polyps. At the left is an individual resembling a Hydra, and at the right a sac full of minute jellyfish in various stages of development. Magnified about 50 diameters.

Sea Plume. At the seashore at low tide the tide pools appear as veritable menageries of strange and wonderful animals. Many of the rocks and seaweeds may be covered with delicate-looking Sea Plumes. Growing over the surface of the rocks are "roots" from which slender stems about six inches long develop. Each stem gives rise to many branches; some of these resemble the Hydra just described, being flower-like polyps with a mouth in the center surrounded by about thirty tentacles.

Near the base of some of the branches are slender sacs in which minute jelly-fish, or medusas, develop; these escape in course of time into the boundless sea, where they lay eggs. The eggs become ciliated and swim about, but finally attach themselves to a rock and grow into Sea Plumes.

Thus a generation of Sea Plumes, attached to the rocks and multiplying by the formation of stems and branches, alternates with a generation of jellyfishes that multiply by means of eggs; this is a good example of what is known to biologists as the alternation of generations.

Hedgehog Hydroid.   Only an overworked imagination could conceive of such a bizarre place to live as the top of a snail shell inhabited by a hermit crab.   It reminds us of a Japanese dinner we attended in Tokio that seems to us equally fantastic, the first course consisting of pickled squids smothered in starfish eggs. However, both the Hedgehog Hydroid, that lives on top of the shell, and the hermit crab, that lives within the shell, are content with their companionship; in fact, they are real messmates.

Hedgehog Hydroid.   A colony containing three types of individuals.   At the left are the much-bent protectors of the colony; rising above the rest are the individuals that capture and digest food; and among the others are a few reproductive members bearing bunches of organs that resemble coconuts.   Magnified about 10 diameters.

The Hydroid coats the top of the shell with a thin layer of living substance, from which arises a miniature forest of polyps about $\frac{3}{8}$ inch high.   These polyps are of three types; the tallest of them resemble Hydra, with a mouth at the end surrounded by tentacles, and spend their time capturing and swallowing food; the second type has short, blunt tentacles and a bunch of reproductive organs around the stem that look like a cluster of diminutive coconuts.

Of particular interest is the third type of polyp; these grow around the edge and are heavily loaded with stinging cells.   They twist about actively so as to meet, at least half way, any enemy that may approach the colony.   Incidentally the hermit crab is also protected by these warlike polyps.   In return for this service, the crab carries the Hedgehog Hydroid around on its back and doesn't object if some of the food particles that escape from its jaws are appropriated by the polyps of the Hydroid.

Portuguese Man-o'-War. Everyone who has encountered this curious creature on the high seas agrees that its name is fully warranted. It is a floating battleship,

small, but well provided with arms and ammunition. The "ship," or float, is a bag of gas with a puckered crest that serves the purpose of a sail. It is only about four inches long, but when the wind blows, the slender, sinuous tentacles that hang down from it may trail along for a distance of fifty feet or more. The surface of the float shimmers with beautiful iridescent colors, blues, pinks, violets, and purples, and the crest may glow with vivid carmine.

The Portuguese Man-o'-War consists of several types of individuals that develop from a single egg and form a colony. Each type has a certain role to play in the life of the colony. Some individuals are short and blunt, with a mouth in the end for engulfing fish and other small marine animals; these are captured by the long, flat tentacles. The latter are armed with batteries of poison darts that shoot and soon paralyze their prey. The tentacles then contract so as to bring their victim within the grasp of the mouth, whose lips spread over it, forming a sort of digestive sac. Swimmers are often painfully stung when they chance to come in contact with these warlike tentacles.

The Portuguese Man-o'-War must, of course, reproduce itself, this duty being performed by individuals resembling grapelike clusters that hang down among the greedy mouths and stinging tentacles. A colony such as this, consisting of several types of individuals, is known to biologists as polymorphic, which means "many forms." We could hardly expect an animal so low in the scale of life to furnish more of interest than the Portuguese Man-o'-War. One may expect to see specimens floating about in tropical seas, or in the Gulf Stream, where they are often quite common.

Courtesy, Amer. Mus. Nat. Hist.

Portuguese Man-o'-War. The float on top of the water is about four inches long; from it hang down the several types of tentacles.

Moon-Jelly. To many seashore visitors jellyfishes are nasty messes in a half putrid condition lying on the beach; we can hardly blame them for shuddering at the mere mention of the name. Swimming jellyfishes give an entirely different impression, as they slowly throb their way through the water, sparkling in the sunshine. They create a still lovelier light of their own at night, when they send out a greenish-golden illumination, as lustrous as that of the brightest glow-worm. If you but dip your hand into the water on a calm summer night, it breaks into shining drops at your touch.

One of the commonest jellyfishes along the coast from Maine to Florida is the Moon-Jelly, a species that grows to be about a foot in diameter. It is a weak milk-blue in color, with four horseshoe-shaped reproductive organs near the center, yellowish-white or pinkish, as seen through the almost transparent jelly. In shape, the Moon-Jelly resembles an umbrella with eight shallow lobes in the margin and a fringe of small tentacles around the edge. In the center of the under surface is the mouth, around which hang down four long, narrow lips with folded margins. The mouth opens into a "stomach" from which small canals radiate out to the edge of the disk. Between the marginal lobes are sense organs of equilibrium which enable the Moon-Jelly to maintain an upright position in the water.

The jellyfish, or medusa stage, in the life history of the Moon-Jelly, is more conspicuous than the polyp stage, contrary to what occurs in the Sea Plume (see page 40). Its eggs are produced in the summer or fall, and develop into a ciliated form which falls to the bottom, where it spends the winter as a minute polyp

Courtesy, American Museum of Natural History
Moon-Jelly. The umbrella-shaped jellyfish is swimming slowly with the much-extended lips and long slender tentacles trailing behind. The "umbrella" grows to a diameter of one foot.

attached to a stone or dead shell. In the spring this polyp gives off a succession of little medusas that gradually grow into fully-developed jellyfishes.

Although jellyfishes are about 99 per cent water, certain people, especially the Japanese, dry them, and, when needed, cut them into strips, soak them in water, and flavor them. As for us, we do not envy anyone his dish of jellyfish.

Sea Anemones. The most beautiful and conspicuous inhabitants of tide pools along the seacoast are the Sea Anemones. When fully expanded they form a sea garden filled with flower-like crowns of various colors, resembling not so much the anemones after which they were named, but more closely chrysanthemums or dahlias.

The Brown Sea Anemone is the commonest species along our northeastern seacoast. It has a smooth column, which may be three inches wide and four inches high, and a wider crown of hollow tentacles arranged in a number of circlets around

Courtesy, Nature Magazine, Washington, D. C.

Sea Anemones. Pinks and dahlias in the garden of the sea. Those in the foreground have the column contracted but show the mouth and its surrounding tentacles. In the background are fully extended specimens.

the central, slitlike mouth. The skin is soft, and both column and tentacles are contractile. When disturbed, this sensitive "flower" may be drawn into a shapeless mass rather easily overlooked, and long white threads bearing poison darts are extended through minute pores in the side to drive away enemies. This species is usually brown in color but may be white, pink, or orange. In general the Sea Anemones of the warmer, tropic waters are more highly colored than those farther north.

In nature, Sea Anemones are far from flower-like. They serve as death traps for any small animal that comes within reach of their tentacles, which may be beautiful in color but wield their batteries of stinging cells with deadly effect. The prey is carried through the greedy mouth into the body, which is hardly anything more than a digestive sac.

The eggs of the Sea Anemones develop, as in other Coelenterates, into a ciliated ball, which swims about for a time, and then settles down, becomes attached to a

Photo by Harris. Courtesy, Nature Magazine

Corals from the Great Barrier Reef of Australia. Here is a group representing many types of skeletons built up by Coral Polyps.

rock or shell, and grows into another anemone. Saville-Kent's Anemone that lives on the Great Barrier Reef of Australia is two feet across and is inhabited by small red and white fish; these swim in and out through the mouth without being injured in any way by the poison darts.

Corals and Coral Reefs. The Coral Polyp is a real Wonder of Nature. A single polyp is usually but a fraction of an inch in size, and would be hardly noticeable by itself; but when thousands, or millions, or even billions, live together, their accomplishments are almost incredible. The bicarbonate of lime extracted from the sea water and formed into a skeleton by the coral polyp is what we know as Coral. The

Coral Polyp is not an insect, as frequently stated, but a Coelenterate resembling in structure the Sea Anemone. The skeleton it builds up is necessary to support the delicate tissues of the polyp.

Corals abound in the warm waters of the tropics, but a few occur in temperate regions and even in the Arctic.   Some corals live a solitary existence, but many of them, by division, form enormous colonies. Of special interest are the corals that build coral reefs and islands.   These occur in many parts of the world.

Courtesy, American Museum of Natural History

Star Coral.   This is the way Coral Polyps look when fully expanded and enlarged from ⅔ inches to 1½ inches high.   The coral skeleton into which they can contract is hidden beneath them.

Coral reefs are of three general types, fringing reefs, barrier reefs, and atolls. A fringing, or shore, reef is a ridge built up from the sea bottom so near the land that no navigable channel exists between it and the shore.   Frequently breaks occur in the reef, and irregular channels and pools are created, which are often inhabited by many different kinds of animals, some of them brilliantly colored.   A barrier reef is separated from the shore by a wide, deep channel.   Often a barrier reef entirely surrounds an island.   An atoll is a more or less circular reef enclosing a lagoon.

The origin and growth of coral reefs have been studied for many years.   Charles Darwin proposed the subsidence theory to account for the presence of coral at great depths, since the living polyps are not found below 300 feet, whereas coral exists 1000 or more feet below sea level.   Darwin believed that the sea bottom, on which the corals were living, gradually sank and that the polyps built up the coral just as rapidly as this took place.   The Great Barrier Reef of Australia is probably the most extensive of all coral reefs, being over 1250 miles long, covering an area of

200,000 square miles, and enclosing a channel from 10 to 25 fathoms deep, and in some places, 30 miles wide.

The life on such a coral reef is indescribably colorful. Corals of all shapes and colors form the background, and every color that occurs among flowers on land is represented among the coral polyps. Besides these, almost innumerable other animals live in the holes and cavities among the reefs, some simply seeking shelter and others feeding on the polyps. Coral-reef fishes are famous for their gaudy colors and bizarre shapes. Worms, crustaceans, giant clams, snails, cuttlefishes, sponges, sea anemones, sea fans, and many other types of animals add their variety of shape and color to the gorgeous ensemble.

Star Coral. All the heavenly bodies have their counterparts in the sea, including Sun Fish, Moon Fish, and Star Coral. The Star Coral is a species that occurs along the seashore as far north as Cape Cod, encrusting stones and dead shells. A colony consists of from five to thirty glossy white and translucent polyps. These build up a mass of bicarbonate of lime in the form of little cups with partitions radiating out from the center; these cups may form a mass two inches high and four inches in diameter. When disturbed, the polyp retracts into the cup.

Each polyp, when expanded, is about $\frac{3}{8}$ inch high and $\frac{1}{8}$ inch wide. The tentacles are long and tapering and number from 18 to 24. They end in a whitish knob and are covered with batteries of stinging cells. Each colony arises from a single young coral by a process of budding.

Photo by Hegner

Branching Coral. This coral skeleton is similar to that produced by the precious Red Coral.

Red or Precious Coral. Skeletons are obviously valuable to animals while they are alive and able to use them, but in some cases are more desirable to us after their builders are dead. This is true of both the Bath Sponge and the Red Coral. The latter constructs the most precious skeleton in the world. This is a branching type of coral that is dredged at depths of from 90 to 900 feet, and as far as six or eight miles from shore.   It is composed of carbonate of lime secreted, as in other corals, by little flower-like polyps which ornament its crimson branches.   The most important coral banks lie off the coast of Algeria, Tunisia, and Sicily.   Precious coral is also obtained near the coast of Japan.

Manufacturing coral into beads, cameos, and other types of jewelry is carried on principally in Italy and Japan.   In Torre del Greco, in Italy, over 3000 persons are engaged in this work, and a school has been organized by the government known as the Royal School for Coral Engraving.   Dark-skinned people, such as Italians, Spanish, Portuguese, and East Indians, are especially fond of coral ornaments because they appear to particular advantage against their darker type of skin.

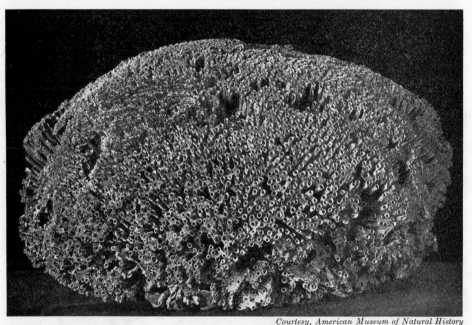

Courtesy, American Museum of Natural History

Organ-Pipe Coral.   The dome-shaped skeleton of reddish organ pipes built by a colony of emerald-green Coral Polyps.

Precious Coral has been known and esteemed at least since the time of the ancient Greeks and Romans, and has been used for various curious purposes, such as to protect children from disease, to guard the wearer from the evil eye, and to protect homes from lightning, plagues, and other calamities.   It is needless to state that it has none of these occult powers.

Organ-Pipe Coral.   Like a pipe organ in form, but unable to utter a sound, is the Organ-Pipe Coral.   Each polyp builds a cylindrical tube and neighboring tubes are bound together by cross bars.   From the open ends of the reddish tubes extend the emerald-green tentacles of the polyps.   The colony builds a dome-shaped skeleton of tubes which may become eight inches or more in diameter.   This mass is attached to stones, shells or other corals in various regions of the tropical seas.

Marine Animals Attached to the Piles of a Wharf. Among the types shown here are the Red Sponge (1), Sea Anemone (2), Starfish (3), Flower Worms (4), Barnacles (5), Edible Mussels (6), and Sea Squirts (7).

CHAPTER 5

SPINY–SKINNED ANIMALS — ECHINODERMS

The sheltered life we live is brought home to us when we study some of the lower animals. We are practically free from the attacks of other species of animals and from the ravages of the elements. Whereas protection from the weather and from their voracious neighbors comes foremost in the lives of the Echinoderms, and has resulted in the development of a skin filled with spines of various sorts. These "spiny-skinned" animals all live in the sea, and are seen by "land-lubbers" only in museums or on visits to the seashore. They form a conspicuous element in the life along the coast and may be found all over the globe from the shore-line to deep water.

The approximately 5000 known species are separated into five classes, the Starfishes, Brittle and Basket Stars, Sea Urchins, Sea Cucumbers, and Sea Lilies, or Crinoids. All of them have certain features in common, although they do not resemble one another very much superficially. Besides their spiny skin, their principal characteristic is probably their radial symmetry. This is very clearly seen in the Starfish, with its central disk, or hub, from which rays extend out like the spokes of a wheel. Some of them have a well-developed skeleton of calcareous plates, but others possess only a few of these in the body wall.

Photo by Hegner

Starfish. A typical specimen with five arms. This is a large species photographed on the coast of California, and is shown draped over a large stone. It measured over a foot across the arms.

A unique feature of Echinoderms is the water-vascular system, especially the tube feet. This system consists of tubes filled with water. The tube feet project from the body, and when their ends are pressed against an object and the water in them is drawn out, they cling to the object by suction; when the water is again forced into the tube feet, they relax. The tube feet are used for locomotion, for capturing prey, for breathing, and as organs of touch. A Starfish or Sea Urchin would be as helpless without tube feet as we should be without arms, legs, and lungs.

Young Echinoderms differ so much from the adults in appearance that they were at one time supposed to belong to another group of animals. They are bilaterally symmetrical, and swim about in the water near the surface, thus serving to distribute the species far and wide. The adults live mostly on the bottom, creeping slowly about, or burrowing in the sand. Some of them are permanently attached by a stalk. When injured, they are capable of regenerating various parts of the body, even some of the internal organs. Their colors are often brilliant, including red, orange, and purple.

Photo by Hegner

Starfish. A pentagonal type with arms united in such a way as to be hardly recognizable as a Starfish. Diameter in life about 5 inches.

Starfish. Our tendency to give inappropriate names to various things has been carried into the Animal Kingdom, and accounts for the name Starfish for an animal that is not related in any way to the true Fishes. However, it is the commonest of the Echinoderms and the type best known to most people. Starfishes usually have five arms; these are movable in spite of the calcareous plates that make them seem so rigid. In some species the arms are more numerous, but in these the number is usually a multiple of five.

During the day, Starfishes rest quietly among the rocks, but when night falls, they become active, moving slowly about in search of food. Their athletic powers can be demonstrated by turning one over on its back; it will bend its arms so as to turn a sort of handspring, which brings it right side up again. One scientist claims that he taught Starfishes to use one particular arm in turning over. We accept this as true, and not just another "Starfish" story.

Starfishes are not only carnivorous animals, but decidedly voracious. They are especially injurious to oysters and clams. Opening an oyster or clam shell is a real, man-size undertaking. The Starfish accomplishes it by humping itself over the shell, attaching its tube feet to the sides, and then exerting a steady pull that eventually opens the shell. It is the length of the pull that does the trick. The Starfish then turns its stomach inside out and inserts it into the shell. The body of the clam or oyster is soon digested away, and the Starfish moves on to another victim, leaving nothing but the cleaned shell behind. We admit that this really does sound like a fish story, but there is no question about the facts.

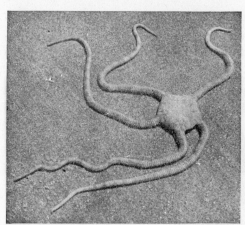

Brittle Star. Lying on the sand with long, serpent-like arms. The disk was about 1 inch in diameter and the arms about 4 inches long.

Photo by Hegner

Some Starfishes have long, slender arms, and often more than five of them; others have such short arms as to be almost pentagonal, like that shown in the accompanying photograph.

Brittle Star. The loss of an arm to a human being is a great calamity, but Brittle Stars have arms especially constructed so that they can easily break them off if they become injured. Perhaps if we could grow a new arm as readily as the Brittle Star does, we wouldn't mind a little accident now and then.

Brittle Stars move about comparatively rapidly, can climb, and almost "run" along the sea bottom. This is because of the activity of the arms, which almost seem to writhe like serpents, hence the name Serpent Star sometimes applied to this type of Echinoderm.

The feeding habits of Brittle Stars are very different from those of Starfishes. Minute organisms and decaying matter that lie on the mud of the sea bottom are scooped into the mouth by means of special tube feet; rows of spines extend over the mouth opening and serve as strainers, keeping out particles that are too large. About 2000 species of Brittle Stars have been described.

Basket Star. Certain species in nearly every group of animals become so complicated that they hardly seem to belong to the same family. Witness, for example, how the Basket Star has developed from a simple Brittle Star. Each of its five arms branches near the base, and each of these soon branches again, and this continues almost

Sea Urchin. An almost spherical shell bears a large number of long, sharp, movable spines. About 5 inches in diameter.

Photo by Hegner

indefinitely. In fact, one species is said to branch so often that the tiny end branches reach the enormous number of 80,000; when all of these are actively writhing about they resemble a huge family of baby snakes.   Not only are these branches graceful as they curl about, but they are also useful as a means of clinging to seaweeds and corals, and in capturing small animals.   Fish are sometimes caught by the Basket Star much as they are in a purse net by a human fisherman.

The species illustrated here occurs in shallow water off the coast of California. It is covered with a soft skin and is flesh-colored with orange markings.   When it wishes to change its position it walks along on its branching arms as though on tiptoe.

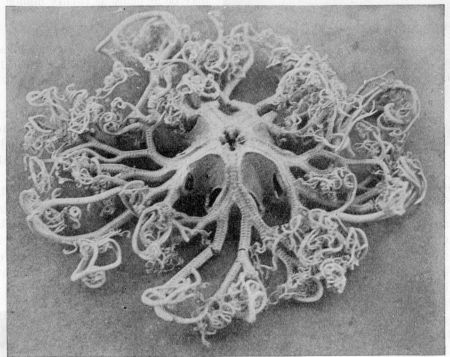

Photo by Hegner

Basket Star.   The division of the arms gives rise to a large number of very active tentacle-like branches which writhe like a bunch of serpents.   This specimen was 10 inches in diameter.

Sea Urchin.   Wading at the seashore is an agreeable diversion, but must be practiced with caution in regions where Sea Urchins abound.   These hedgehogs, or porcupines, of the ocean are covered with long, sharp spines that effectively protect them from most of their hungry marine neighbors.   Not only are the spines sharp, but in some species they are poisonous.

Sea Urchins live mostly near shore.   Some of them grind cavities in the rocks, where they lie concealed from possible enemies, and incidentally also escape the pounding of the surf.   The shell of the Sea Urchin is made up of rows of plates closely fitted together, forming a rigid, hollow ball flattened at each end.   From the hole in one flattened end protrude five shiny teeth connected with a complicated structure within the shell called Aristotle's Lantern.   Such an elaborate mechanism seems hardly necessary just for eating sand, but is used largely for this purpose. Animal and vegetable matter that has fallen to the bottom and become mixed with the sand is digested out by the Sea Urchin and the sand, which is ground nice and smooth, is cast out.

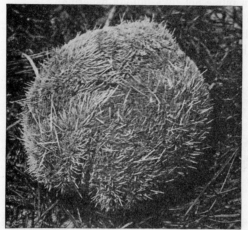

Photo by Hegner

Heart Urchin. The spines that cover this species are so short they do not conceal the groove and point that give it the shape of a heart. About 3 inches in diameter.

The internal organs of Sea Urchins are used as food in some countries, especially in France and Italy. They consist largely of eggs, of which there may be as many as twenty million in a single Urchin.

Sand Dollar. If we could inflate the American dollar until it reached a diameter of three inches and a thickness of $\frac{3}{8}$ inch, and cover it with so many small spines as to give it a velvety appearance, it would look very much like a Sand Dollar. Such a dollar might well wish to bury itself in the sand the way the Sand Dollar does.

The flat shape of the Sand Dollar prevents currents of water and shifting sands from rolling it about or turning it over. On a hard surface the Sand Dollar cannot turn a somersault to right itself, but it is able to do so in sand. In general structure and habits, Sand Dollars resemble Sea Urchins. They live on top of or in the sand, from low water mark to 800 fathoms or more. With mouth side down, they move about with the aid of their spines, engulfing sand out of which they digest minute plants and animals. All together they do not seem to us to lead a very exciting life. How they must crave to go places and do things!

The Sand Dollar illustrated in our photograph is a species that lives along the Pacific coast of North America. It is purple in color when alive but changes to a greenish hue after death. An indelible ink can be prepared from Sand Dollars by grinding up the spines and skin and mixing it with water.

Sea Cucumber. Anyone who sets out to collect Sea Cucumbers to add to his salad will be doomed to disappointment, because Sea Cucumbers have a thick leathery skin more like rubber than like succulent vegetation. However, in the Far East they are col-

Photo by Johnson and Snook

Sand Dollar. The shell is flat and three inches in diameter, and the spines are very small, giving the surface a velvety appearance.

lected in large numbers, cooked, dried in the sun, and sold as trepang, or bêche-de-mer (worm of the sea). This is considered a great delicacy, especially by the Chinese, who use it in making soup.

Sea Cucumbers are worm-shaped Echinoderms that have no spines and only a few small pieces of skeleton embedded in their skin. They lie on their sides with their long branched tentacles extended around the mouth. In some species these

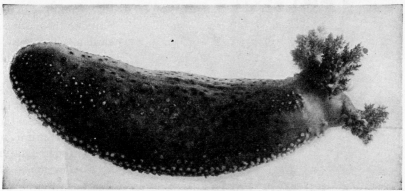

Courtesy, American Museum of Natural History

Sea Cucumber. A common species on the Atlantic coast, showing cucumber shape and branching tentacles. About 5 inches long.

tentacles resemble seaweed, and small animals come to rest on them. "When one tentacle has got a sufficient freight, it is bent round and pushed into the mouth, which is closed on it. It is then forcibly drawn out through the closed lips so that all the living cargo is swept off."

Certain Sea Cucumbers display a most remarkable method of protecting themselves from their enemies. Their breathing organs, which are treelike in form, may be cast out of the body, where they swell up in the sea water into a mass of tough white threads in which the enemy becomes entangled. A lobster may be rendered perfectly helpless as a result of rashly interfering with a Sea Cucumber. A new set of breathing organs soon grow in to take the place of those cast out. Over 500 species of Sea Cucumbers are known. The common brown-colored species along the Atlantic coast is about five inches long and an inch and one-half thick. It is very sensitive to changes in

Photo by Hegner

Sea Cucumbers. Specimens drying on a mat on the wharf at Jolo in the Philippines. They will be sold as bêche-de-mer and made into soup.

the intensity of the light and will contract its body if an object passes between it and the source of the light. It moves away from a strong light and buries itself in the mud. This apparently does not entirely satisfy the sense of protection of the Sea Cucumber, since it will also cover its body with seaweed.

Sea Lilies. The Echinoderms do their part to add beauty to the sea bottom by contributing the Sea Lilies, or Feather Stars, to the marine flower garden. The Sea Lilies are attached to the bottom, and their arms, which branch near the base, extend upward, forming a sort of net of feather-like sprays, beautiful to see, but forming a fatal trap for small animals. Sometimes a Sea Lily may break away from its stalk and swim about by movements of its arms.

The fossil remains of Sea Lilies are very abundant in limestone formations. They are known to geologists and paleontologists as crinoids, and crinoid stems are among the most numerous of the fossils to be found in certain regions. In early geologic times they were the most numerous of all Echinoderms. Now only a remnant of a former flourishing group remain alive.

About 600 living species are known. The Basket Sea Lily lives along our Atlantic coast in from 35 to 600 fathoms of water; it has ten arms, each with twenty-five or thirty branches, and is about two and one-half inches in diameter.

Courtesy, Science Service

Sea Lily. A stalk that was attached to the sea bottom bears five arms which branch three or four times, forming a trap for small animals.

CHAPTER 6

WORMS

"Only a worm" is a common expression that indicates fairly well where worms belong in popular opinion. Any small creature that is long and slender, that crawls, and is without conspicuous limbs, is usually called a worm. In this sense the term is applied to several species of snakes and lizards, to certain mollusks, and to the young of insects, as well as to several entire groups of animals.

Five of the larger assemblages of animals that are sometimes included by scientists under the heading of Worms are the Flatworms, Round Worms, Wheel Animalcules, Moss Animals, and Segmented Worms. Representatives of each of these groups will be described in the following pages. They differ so much from one another that very few general statements can be made about them. Although very abundant, they are mostly small and inconspicuous and our attention is seldom attracted to them. They are usually regarded as repulsive, and we confess that it is difficult to get enthusiastic about some of them, but others are extremely interesting, and many are among the most beautiful of all living things.

Worms burrow in the earth, or crawl over the ground, or swim in the water, or build tubular cases attached to stones under water, or live attached to the outside, or snugly housed inside, of other animals.

Many uses for the word *worm* have been introduced into the English language. Because some worms crawl or wriggle on the ground, the term has been applied to the cringing type of person, with a meaning of contempt or disgust. Worms creep along quietly and stealthily, hence it is common to speak of one "worming his way" along, when he creeps on his belly through the grass toward some living creature he wishes to approach unnoticed. Figuratively speaking, one may worm his way into another's favor.

All together, probably 20,000 or more species of Worms have been described. The relations of many of them to human welfare are intimate and important. Some, such as the Earthworm, are of great value; others, such as the parasitic Hookworm, are the cause of great suffering to hundreds of thousands of people.

Fresh-Water Flatworm. Life cannot be very exciting to the Fresh-Water Flatworms, or Planarians, since they spend much of their time modestly concealed beneath a stone in some sluggish stream. They are soft, flat, and unobtrusive; most of them are very small, but some may reach a length of half an inch or more. The body is covered with cilia and filled with muscles, so that they can swim a little, and also creep along slowly. The parts of the body do not radiate out from the center, as in the Coelenterates and Echinoderms, but are arranged in pairs on either side of a central axis, a condition known as bilateral symmetry. Five pairs of eye spots are present near the forward end, but there is very little of interest to see, and not much light to see with, where Flatworms live. Anyway they probably don't see images as we do, but only differences in light intensities.

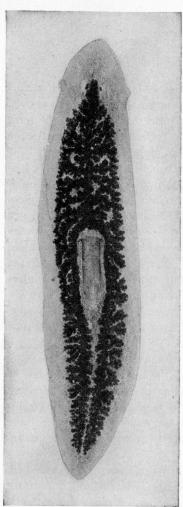

© General Biological Supply House

Fresh-Water Flatworm. This specimen was stained and then photographed. The eyes, "ears," black-stained intestine, and proboscis near the center of the body show clearly. Magnified 10 diameters.

The feeding habits of Fresh-Water Flatworms are really interesting. Other small animals are eaten; these are captured with a long proboscis that is extended out through the mouth near the center of the underside of the body. The prey, if small, is covered with slime and then swallowed, or if large, digestive juices are poured out through the proboscis and the digested particles are pumped back into the intestine. This proboscis is almost as useful to its owner as is a trunk to an elephant.

The intestine consists of three main stems, each with many branches. The excretory system is also much branched, each branch ending in a cell that contains a flickering group of cilia, and on this account is known as a flame cell. The cilia create currents through the branches which carry wastes to the outside.

Fresh-Water Flatworms are capable of regenerating an entire animal from very small pieces, and pieces from one animal can easily be grafted onto another (see page 40). They must frequently be injured by their enemies, such as fish and young insects, or by movements of the rocks; hence their ability to grow into a complete animal, although severely injured, is very valuable in the struggle for existence.

Starvation has no terrors for Fresh-Water Flatworms; they simply live on the substance of their own bodies. For example, one specimen which was half an inch long was starved for nine months, during which time it gradually became smaller and smaller until it was only $\frac{1}{7}$ inch long. When given food, it regenerated all the parts it had used up, and became a perfectly normal worm — believe it or not.

Three large groups, or classes, of Flatworms are recognized by scientists. The free-living Flatworms, that is, those that are not parasitic, live in fresh water, salt water, or in moist places on land. About 1500 species of these have been described. The other two classes are the Flukes and the Tapeworms, all of which are parasitic.

Liver Fluke. The life history of the Liver Fluke makes that of the Fresh-Water Flatworm, or even our own lives, seem very colorless indeed. How any of them survive is almost a mystery. The adults live in the bile ducts of the liver of sheep, cows, and pigs, and occasionally in human beings. Their principal duty seems to be that of laying eggs. One Fluke may produce 500,000 eggs, and since there may be 200 or more Flukes in the liver of a single sheep, over 100,000,000 eggs may be laid in one parasitized animal.

The eggs are carried out of the body of the host in its excrement. If they chance to reach water, they hatch into larvae that look something like the Slipper Animalcule (see page 22). These die unless they encounter a snail of a certain species into which they can burrow. Inside of the snail the baby Flukes divide again and again until each one has become the parent of thousands; these break out of the snail, and if they chance to reach water, they swim about awhile, and then each one rounds up into a ball, and secretes a wall around itself, thus becoming a cyst. If a sheep or other animal drinks water containing these cysts, the cysts hatch in the intestine and the young that emerge creep up the bile passages into the liver. There are a good many "ifs" in this story. That any of the eggs ever complete their mission in life and give rise to adult Flukes seems to us one of the most remarkable phenomena in all nature.

Flukes injure and sometimes kill the animals in which they live. In China, Japan, and Egypt, the infestation of human beings by Flukes is a serious problem; thousands become sick every year and many die. These Flukes may live in the intestine, the liver, the lungs, or the blood. Many species of lower animals are parasitized by Flukes; in fact, about 3000 different kinds of these worms are known to science.

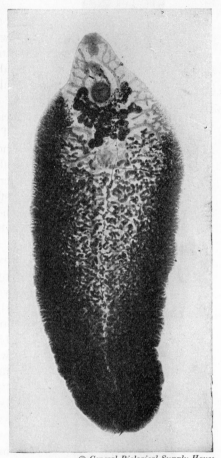

© *General Biological Supply House*

Liver Fluke. A stained specimen highly magnified. The black-stained branching organs are the intestines and reproductive organs.

Pork Tapeworm of Man. You may not be aware of the fact, but human beings and pigs have much in common. For example, if it were not for our association with pigs, we need not be bothered with the Pork Tapeworm. The fully grown Tapeworm is usually from six to ten feet long, but may reach a length of twenty-five

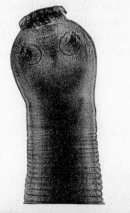

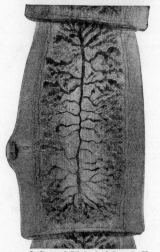

feet. It is whitish in color and flat, resembling a long piece of dirty white tape, divided, by grooves running crosswise of the body, into from 600 to 2500 segments. The head is about $\frac{1}{25}$ inch in diameter, and has a circlet of hooks on the end and four suckers on the sides with which it attaches itself to the wall of the small intestine in which it lives. The segments are about $\frac{2}{5}$ inch wide and $\frac{1}{5}$ inch long. They are almost completely filled with eggs.

Tapeworms are degenerate animals physically, but well adapted to their mode of life. They have no locomotor organs, since they do not need to move about. A mouth is also absent, and none is necessary, because the creatures live in a more or less continuous stream of nutritive material digested by their host. This is absorbed through the surface of the worm's body.

The eggs pass out of the host's body in the excrement; those that chance to be swallowed by pigs hatch in the small intestine, and the young burrow into the intestinal wall until they gain entrance to a blood vessel. They are carried in the blood to various parts of the body, eventually burrowing into the muscles, where they produce egg-shaped cysts. Flesh infested by these young Tapeworms is called "measly pork." If this is eaten by human beings when raw or not cooked sufficiently to kill the cysts, a Tapeworm develops from each cyst and attaches itself to the wall of the small intestine. Cysts may develop in man as well as in pigs, and sometimes get into the eyes or brain with disastrous results. Several other species of Tapeworms also use man as a host.

Tapeworms are widely distributed among the lower animals. As a rule the adult worms live in some species of vertebrate and the larval forms in a different kind of animal, called the intermediate host. About 1500 species of Tapeworms have been described.

Pork Tapeworm of Man. Three small parts of a worm 10 feet long are shown here highly magnified. The head bears hooks at the end and suckers at the sides. Back of the head are very young segments. The next section shows a half-grown segment; and the third section an old segment; each of these is full of reproductive organs.

Vinegar Eel. If you wish to enjoy vinegar on your salad, you had better not examine it too closely, because one of the commonest Round Worms lives in cider vinegar, and vast numbers are usually present at the bottom of the vinegar cruet. These Vinegar Eels are visible to the naked eye when a test tube containing them is held up before a bright light, but a microscope is necessary in order to see them well. Even then very little can be observed except a slender, threadlike worm

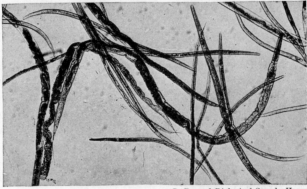

about $\frac{1}{10}$ inch long, whipping about by contortions of the body and making no progress whatever; certainly a great waste of energy, but perhaps as good for the worm as "setting up" exercises are for us.

The female Vinegar Eel brings forth her young alive in the form of minute worms about $\frac{1}{100}$ inch long. They soon become full grown and live for about a year. A near relative

© *General Biological Supply House*

Vinegar Eel. A group of round worms taken from a vinegar cruet and photographed. Magnified about 50 diameters.

of the Vinegar Eel has been found only in the mats used in Germany to rest beer steins on between drinks. To some people this might seem like an ideal type of existence, since the worms are continuously bathed in the beer that spills over the edge of the glass.

Round Worm of Man. Cleanliness is not only next to godliness, but is also greatly to be desired in order to escape infestation with Round Worms. The adult Round Worms of man live in the intestine, and are especially abundant in children who are not as clean as they should be. They are milk-white or reddish-yellow in

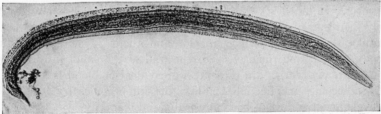

© *General Biological Supply House*

Round Worm of Man. This milky-white worm migrates through the lungs of infested human beings and into the intestine, where it secretes poisonous substances. It ranges from 5 to 11 inches in length.

color and from five to eleven inches long and $\frac{1}{4}$ inch in diameter. In some people they are so numerous as to obstruct the intestine. The nervous system of those infested may be affected by poisonous substances secreted by the worms. The worms may be removed quite easily by treatment with oil of chenopodium or hexyl-resorcinol.

The eggs escape from the body in the excrement. When swallowed by a human being, they hatch in the small intestine; the young burrow through the intestinal wall, enter the blood vessels, and are carried to the lungs; from there they make their way up the windpipe into the throat and are swallowed again. Finally they reach the intestine, where they grow into adults. When large numbers of the young worms pass through the lungs, they set up an inflammation which may result in a generalized pneumonia.

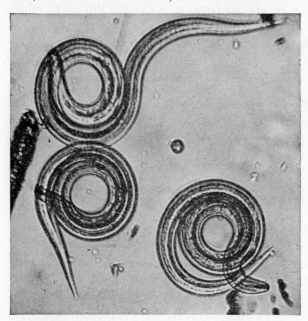

Hookworms. Three specimens photographed with the help of a microscope. Magnified about 200 diameters.

The Round Worm of Man is widespread and very abundant in some localities; for example, recently in southwestern Virginia, 60 per cent of the children and 30 per cent of the adult inhabitants were found to be infested. Other species of Round Worms that live in man are the Guinea Worm, Whip Worm, Hookworm and Pin Worm. Lower animals are also infested by large numbers of species, several thousand of which have been described. Fortunately in most cases the species of worms that live in these lower animals cannot live in human beings.

Hookworm. In localities where Hookworms abound laziness may not be a sin, but merely the result of infestation with these insidious little round worms. They are threadlike in appearance, white in color, and about $\frac{1}{25}$ inch long. Within the human body they attach themselves to the wall of the small intestine and suck blood. When many worms are present, a great deal of blood is lost and the infested person becomes anemic, dull, and lazy, his skin becomes dry, his breath short, and his development retarded, both physically and mentally.

The eggs pass out of the body in the excrement of the host. They develop in moist soil, and the young worms usually gain entrance to a new host by boring through the skin of the feet. In localities where Hookworm Disease is common, many people go barefoot. The young bore into the blood vessels, are carried to the heart, and from there into the lungs. They then make their way through the windpipe into the throat, are swallowed, and, after passing through the stomach, become attached to the wall of the small intestine

It is estimated that even in the United States, where we are supposed to be especially enlightened, there are 2,000,000 persons suffering from Hookworm Disease. The most important methods of control are to dispose of human excrement properly, to eliminate worms from the body with such drugs as oil of chenopodium, carbon tetrachloride, or tetrachlorethyl; and to wear shoes so as to prevent infestation through the feet.

Trichina Worms. The consciousness that one's muscles are riddled with little worms makes an infestation with Trichina Worms seem even more painful than it is. Such an infestation, like that with the Tapeworm, is due to our fondness for pork. Rats may also be involved. The history of the disease known as Trichinosis is as follows.

Rats are highly infested with Trichina Worms; in some parts of the United States more than three fourths of all the wild rats have them in their muscles. Pigs sometimes eat rats and thereby acquire an infestation; from 1 to 2 per cent of the pigs in this country harbor Trichina Worms. If the flesh of these pigs, without being cooked sufficiently to kill the worms, is eaten by human beings, the worms are released from the pork and burrow into the wall of the small intestine. Here, each female worm, which is about $\frac{1}{6}$ inch long, gives birth to large numbers of young, which are only about $\frac{1}{250}$ inch long. These young enter the blood vessels and are carried to all parts of the body in the blood. They

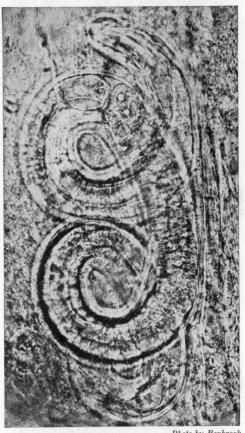

Photo by Benbrook

Trichina. Here is a worm coiled up in a bit of muscle and magnified about 400 diameters.

eventually burrow through the wall of the blood vessels into the muscles, especially the muscles of the diaphragm, tongue, and eyes. Here they coil up and each forms a lemon-shaped cyst about $\frac{1}{50}$ inch long.

If a large number of Trichina Worms are eaten by a person, the infestation will cause intestinal disturbances, pain in the muscles, and continuous fever. There is no remedy for this disease, and about 10 per cent of those suffering from it in the United States die. The label "U. S. Inspected and Passed" is no guarantee that pork is free from Trichina Worms, since they may be overlooked even on microscopical examination. The only way to guard against infestation is to eat well-cooked pork.

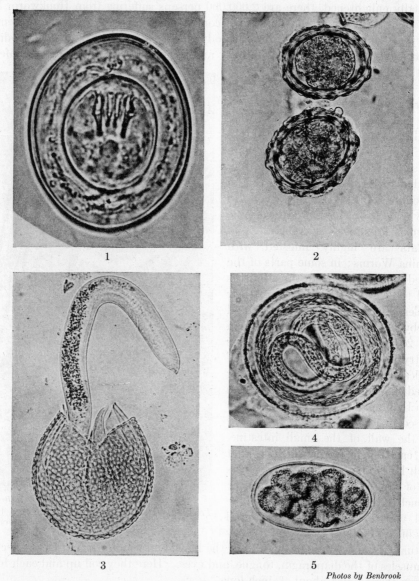

Eggs of Parasitic Worms. (1) Egg of a tapeworm. (2) Eggs of a Round Worm. (3) Round Worm egg hatching. (4) Round Worm egg with young ready to hatch. (5) Hookworm egg. Highly magnified.

Earthworm. Mankind accepts without much thought, and certainly without thanks, the many benefits derived from what we call "lower" animals. Could anything be more lowly than an Earthworm? Yet Earthworms are continually honeycombing the soil beneath our feet, making it more porous and insuring better penetration of air and moisture, and like miniature plowmen are working over the surface layers of earth making it more fertile. Darwin found that one acre of ground may contain over 50,000 Earthworms, and that these 50,000 worms carry more than 18 tons of earthy castings to the surface in a single year. At this rate in 20 years a layer three inches thick would be transferred from the subsoil to the surface.

Earthworms are soft and naked, and hence must live in moist earth; for this reason also they venture out of their burrows chiefly on damp nights. They are

Photo by Howes.   Courtesy, Nature Magazine

Earthworm. At the left is the pointed anterior end. The rings of the body are clearly shown. The eggs are contained in the light, swollen area back of the head. The entire body is kept moist with shiny mucus. Much enlarged.

never "rained down" but are "rained up" out of their burrows. The burrows usually extend about two feet underground. Have you ever watched a Robin pulling an Earthworm out of its burrow; or perhaps you have tried to do so yourself? It is no easy task, because short, stiff bristles extend out from the sides of the body into the walls of the burrow.

Earthworms can force their way through soft earth, but must eat their way through harder soil. The earth eaten passes through the alimentary canal and is deposited on the surface as "castings." Decaying vegetable matter in the soil provides food for the worms, as well as leaves and other vegetation on the surface which the worms drag into their burrows at night.

The Earthworm is a representative of a group of worms that are said to be segmented; that is, the body consists of a linear series of rings, or segments, that are similar in structure. Most of the segmented worms live in the sea, but many species occur in fresh water. The Leeches are parasitic. All together about 5000 species of these worms are known.

Clam Worm. Clam Worms are among the most abundant and largest of all marine worms. They have been named Nereis by scientists after the Nereids or sea-nymphs, but this name is not very appropriate, since the worms neither look nor act like sea-nymphs. During the day time, Clam Worms remain in the burrows which they make in the sand near low-water mark; these are kept from collapsing by a lining of mucus. At night they emerge, and swim actively about like eels in search of the small animals on which they prey.

Courtesy, Nature Magazine

Clam worm. The body consists of a row of segments each with an "oar" on either side. At the left end is the head bearing several pairs of tentacles. About one-half life size.

Clam Worms are really fierce and voracious animals. They are provided with a proboscis armed with a pair of formidable horny jaws. This proboscis is thrust out through the mouth, the jaws are fastened into the prey, and the latter is then quickly torn to pieces. All of which is quite gratifying to the worm, but not a very pleasant experience for the victim.

The Clam Worm reaches a length of a foot or more. It is dull bluish-green in color and somewhat iridescent. The body consists of a row of similar segments. On each side of each segment is a leaflike extension in which are embedded two groups of bristles. These serve as oars in locomotion and also as respiratory organs. The head is provided with four eye-spots and several tentacle-like sense organs.

Bristle-Winged Tube-Dwelling Worms. Many groups of animals including the Worms number torch-bearers among their numbers. The Bristle-Winged Tube-Dweller, when disturbed, emits an azure blue to greenish phosphorescence that is so bright one can read his watch by the illumination. Most of the time this species remains in its tube, safe from many would-be enemies. This tube is parchment-like and formed of a secretion from the worm. It is U-shaped and has two openings that extend slightly above the sand or mud in which it is embedded.

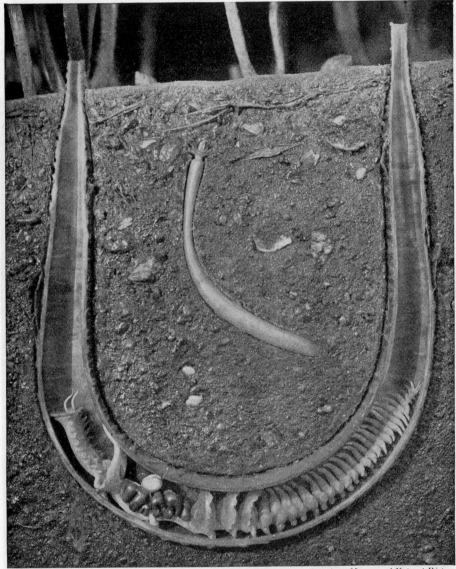

Courtesy, American Museum of Natural History

Bristle-Winged Tube-Dwelling Worm. The tube is secreted by the worm and opens at both ends above the surface so a current of water can be drawn through it with the bristle wings near the middle of the worm. Slightly larger than natural size.

The body of the worm is quite complex, as shown in our illustration. Near the center are flaps or "wings" projecting from some of the segments. These wings move back and forth creating a current of water through the tube. Food particles that are carried in with the current are entangled in mucus secreted by the worm, and this mucus loaded with food is slowly rolled into a ball and engulfed by the mouth. The species illustrated here is about six inches long.

Flower Worm.   No group of marine animals seem to have a monopoly on flower-like beauty, but it requires some stretching of the imagination to conceive of a blooming Worm.   Nevertheless, there are such, and among the most ornamental of them all is the Flower Worm.   This handsome species attaches itself to rocks or shells in shallow water along the seashore from Cape Cod to New Jersey.

Courtesy, American Museum of Natural History

Flower Worm.   The beautiful feathered gills of two worms are shown here projecting from the ends of the tubes in which the rest of the worms are concealed.   Ten times natural size.

In order to protect its soft body from hungry neighbors and dashing waves, it builds a white, coiled tube of calcium carbonate about three inches long and $\frac{1}{8}$ inch wide.   At one end is a circular opening that can be closed with a closely-fitting door when danger threatens.   The body of the Flower Worm is wormlike, but at the anterior end it bears a wreath of feathered gills; these are variable in color but oftenest purplish-brown.   A group of these Worms with gills extended and spread out present as exquisitely lovely a bit of animated nature as exists in all the world.

Medicinal Leech. Formerly physicians were referred to as Leeches and the medical profession was alluded to as Leechcraft. Luckily, at present better methods of letting blood are employed than the use of bloodsucking Leeches.

The body of the Medicinal Leech is about four inches long but can be much contracted and extended. At each end is a sucker. The leech moves along by extending the body, attaching the forward sucker, and then bringing the back sucker up to it, thus forming a loop. The forward sucker is then loosened and extended. Leeches live in fresh-water ponds, in the sea, or in damp soil. Many of them suck

Photo by Cornelia Clarke

Leeches. Black sinister-looking worms shining with mucus. They are proficient bloodsuckers.

blood, but the wounds they make are slight and no one need be afraid of being poisoned by them. If present in sufficient numbers, they are capable of killing any animal by sucking out most of its blood.

The Medicinal Leech can swallow three times its own weight of blood at one meal; but since it takes about nine months to digest this amount, meals are few and far between. We have often been attacked by leeches while bathing in the "old swimming hole," or during excursions into the tropical jungles in the Philippines where leeches are very abundant and voracious. The persistence of leeches when they once attach themselves has led to several unpopular uses of the term; for example, a person who gets control of another and holds on for sordid gain is often called a leech.

Vulture-Headed Moss-Animal. Moving day has no terrors for the Moss-Animals, because they become attached to some solid object in the water when quite young, and remain there the rest of their lives. Most of them occur in the sea, but a few live in fresh-water ponds and streams. They are colonial in habit; a large colony may be a foot or more in height and resembles a patch of dull and inconspicuous moss. When examined with a microscope, however, they are found to be not only interesting, but also beautiful.

Vulture-Headed Moss-Animal. A branch separated from the colony looks like a floating spray of silvery cornucopias.

The Vulture-Headed Moss-Animal, for example, looks, when highly magnified, like a forest of glittering trees with bright orange trunks and pearly-white or yellowish tufts of branches at the top. These may be up to a foot in height. The "common people" in such a colony are protected by a transparent sheath and look as though they were wrapped in cellophane; their duty is to capture with their tentacles minute organisms that can be used as food.

The "privileged class" of the colony are among the strangest of all freaks of nature. They resemble the head of a vulture and are attached to the branches by a flexible neck. Like an army of alert scouts, they keep their heads moving about in all directions, and with wide-open jaws snap viciously at any intruding animals, holding them with bulldog tenacity. We wouldn't relish a swim in such a forest if these Vulture Heads were as large as they are ferocious.

Comb Moss-Animal. Naturalists who live inland need not feel grieved because most of the Moss-Animals inhabit the sea, since a number of interesting species may be found in fresh-water ponds and streams. One of these is the Magnificent-Comb Moss-Animal. Like its marine cousins, this species lives in colonies attached to solid objects in the water. The base is gelatinous in consistency and from it arise short stalks bearing a horseshoe-shaped crown of from 60 to 84 tentacles.

These Moss-Animals increase by forming buds; the buds may be external and grow into individuals like their parents, or internal, becoming what are known as statoblasts. A statoblast consists of a small mass of tissue surrounded by a wall containing air spaces. When statoblasts escape from the colony, they float at the surface and may be carried long distances; eventually they hatch and each of the young settles down to form a new colony.

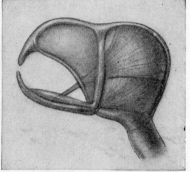

Vulture-Headed Moss-Animal. One of the "Vulture Heads" with jaws ready to bite any intruder. Greatly enlarged.

Wheel Animalcules — Rotifers. The "wheels" of these minute animals are successful locomotor organs and "keep on rolling" continuously, but are constructed very differently from wagon or automobile wheels. The spokes are really cilia which move in such a way as to simulate a rotating wheel, hence the name Rotifers applied to the Wheel Animalcules. Rotifers are so small that they must be studied with a microscope. They are then found to be fairy-like creatures, often fantastic in shape, brilliantly colored and exceedingly animated. Most of them live in fresh water, and can be found in large numbers in ponds, streams, ditches, and almost any pool of water, where they swim about among the vegetation or creep over the surface of water plants.

For the most part Rotifers are elongated. At the anterior end is a thin disk, called the corona, often indented to form lobes; cilia moving along the edge of these

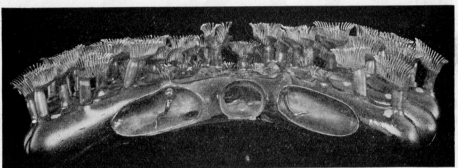

Comb Moss-Animal. Model of a colony from a fresh-water pond. Each stalk bears a crown of many tentacles. Much enlarged.

lobes give the impression of revolving wheels. Back of the corona is the pharynx, or mastax, in which are jaws working vigorously back and forth, as one can see through the transparent body wall. The posterior end is called the foot; this is often divided to form two "toes." Glands in the foot secrete a sticky substance, which passes out of the ends of the toes through small pores, and anchors the animal whenever it desires to rest awhile.

Courtesy, American Museum of Natural History

Wheel Animalcule. A colony of tube-building Rotifers each in its gingerbread tube constructed of pellicles of food. A ciliated corona projects from the end of each tube. Highly magnified.

Some Rotifers form a tubelike house into which they can retreat from danger. The species shown in our illustration is rather common on water plants, and is about $\frac{1}{30}$ inch long. It is famous for its large, four-lobed corona and for its gingerbread house. Minute particles of food are gathered and cemented together into little balls; when a ball has reached the right size, the Rotifer bends down and adds it to the edge of the tube. Such an animal should be able to maintain a hunger strike for a long period. In case of drought, Rotifers may dry slowly, secreting in the meantime a gelatinous envelope that prevents complete desiccation. When water becomes available, they awake into bundles of activity again as though nothing had happened.

CHAPTER 7

MOLLUSKS

Mollusks. Without Mollusks the world would not be as pleasant a place in which to live even for one who is not interested in nature, because Mollusks furnish us with oysters, clams, and abalones to eat, with pearls of great price, and with pearl buttons and various kinds of ornaments. No banquet is complete without oysters on the half-shell, and no theater party without a few pearls scattered about here and there.

To the naturalist, Mollusks constitute a group of unique animals, differing in many ways from all others. Their name is derived from the Latin word *mollis*, meaning "soft," and their bodies certainly live up to this name. However, most of the Mollusks secrete a shell of calcareous material, within which their soft bodies are protected from other animals, and from injury due to physical agents in their environment, such as dashing waves or lack of moisture.

The Mollusk's body consists usually of the head, the visceral mass, and the foot, and is more or less surrounded by a membranous covering called the mantle. This mantle secretes the shell. Mollusk shells are always interesting, and often beautifully shaped and exquisitely colored. Collecting them has been, and is, a favorite pastime for large numbers of people. The study of these shells is known as Conchology. The foot is generally a flat, creeping organ, but in the Cephalopods, or Head-Footed Mollusks, it is divided up into arms, such as those of the Devil Fish.

Mollusks are distributed almost everywhere on land and sea. Many Snails and Slugs crawl about on land, breathing by means of a sort of lung. Fresh-water ponds and streams furnish a favorite haunt for many species of both lung-breathing and gill-breathing snails. Many of the most gorgeous seashells are built by snails, some of which live among the rocks, and others in the sand or mud.

The Bivalves are likewise widespread in their distribution. Well-known species are the Fresh-Water Mussel, the Oyster, the Cockle, and the Hard-Shell and Soft-Shell Clams. A third group contains the Head-Footed Mollusks already mentioned; the best known of these are the Squids, Cuttle Fishes, Nautilus, and Devil Fishes. And finally, there are two groups of Mollusks that are not encountered as often as these three larger classes, namely, the Coat-of-Mail Shells, and the Tooth Shells.

Mollusks usually feed on vegetation, or on microscopic plants and animals, but some of them are quite voracious, capturing and tearing to pieces relatively large animals, such as crabs. All together the five classes of Mollusks include about 80,000 known species. Anyone who has time on his hands which he wishes to employ in an interesting way could do much worse than to spend it studying this fascinating group of animals.

Coat-of-Mail Shells. Like the knights of old, the Chitons, or Coat-of-Mail Shells, protect themselves with an armor of plates. Eight plates are present in a single row, arched above and overlapping like shingles on a roof. When detached

Photo by Hegner

Coat-of-Mail Shell. A chisel is necessary to pry the Coat-of-Mail Shell from the rock to which it clings. Eight arched armor plates protect the body. About natural size.

from the rocks to which they cling, they roll up like an armadillo, with the soft parts practically covered by the hard shell. Beneath the shell are the delicate organs of the animal, and the entire lower surface is occupied by the flat, muscular foot.

Coat-of-Mail Shells live on rocky shores mostly in water less than 25 fathoms deep. They usually rest quietly by day, clinging tightly to the rocks by means of the suction of the foot. At night, they become more active, creeping about sluggishly in search of seaweed and other vegetable food. Although only from $\frac{1}{2}$ inch to six inches long, Coat-of-Mail Shells are sometimes collected and eaten just as are clams and snails. Collecting them for market, however, will probably never be very profitable.

Land Snails. If we were forced to carry our house on our back as the Snail does, we would probably move about at a "snail's pace." But although "slow motion" may be a disadvantage, the possession of a strong shell to live in is an equal advantage; in fact, it is better to move slowly and arrive a little late, than never to arrive at all.

Photo by Cornelia Clarke

Land Snails. They look as though they were having a race with foot fully extended and "horns" stretched out to their fullest extent. About natural size.

The Snail's shell is secreted by the animal and consists of calcium carbonate obtained from the food and water in the Snail's habitat. This means that a shell can be built, and the animal can live, only where there is plenty of lime. The shell of the Edible Snail is about two inches long and two inches wide. It is twisted into a low, conical spire of about five whorls, and is cream-colored, with from three to five pale brown bands. The Snail is protected from injury by the shell and also from drying. In dry weather it retires as far back as possible and secretes a parchment-like wall across the opening which prevents moisture from evaporating.

The fleshy part of the body on which the Snail moves is called the foot. Loco-motion in the Snail is most interesting. A slime gland at the forward end of the foot deposits a film of mucus on which the Snail moves by means of wave-like contractions of the foot muscles. It thus lays its own pavement ahead of itself, which is always the same whether the path is rough or smooth, uphill or downhill. Progress is therefore always about the same; it may be 2 inches per minute, 10 feet per hour, and 240 feet per day, provided the animal keeps going continuously

Courtesy, American Museum of Natural History

Land Snails. These snails have retreated into their shells, secreted a door across the opening, and are taking a nice long nap (hibernating).

— not a bad snail's pace at that. Anyway it is fast enough to satisfy the snail.

The head of the Snail bears two pairs of tentacles or "horns." Each of the longer pair has an eye at the end; these are drawn in like the fingers of a glove if disturbed. The shorter tentacles are knobbed at the end and are probably organs of smell. Snails can find food that is hidden as far away as eighteen inches. Beneath the tentacles is the mouth. Edible Snails are vegetarians. Small pieces of lettuce and other plants are cut off by the small, brown, knife-like jaw and rasped into fine bits by the thousands of minute, backward-pointed teeth that cover the bandlike tongue.

The Edible Snail lays eggs in June. A pit about four inches deep is dug in the ground and about forty white eggs, each the size of a pea, are deposited in it. Then the eggs are covered with earth and allowed to hatch with-out any further attention from the mother.

Photo by Cornelia Clarke

Land Snail. These pearly white eggs of the snail are laid among the moist moss and lichens all ready to be strung as a fairy necklace.

When the young Snails hatch, they eat their egg shell, and are then ready for life in the outer world. In the winter, Snails dig themselves into the ground, secrete a wall across the opening of the shell, and sleep peacefully until spring arrives. The idea of eating Snails is unpleasant to most people, but anyone who can eat an oyster without getting sick could certainly eat the much less disgusting Snail.   In France, Italy, and Spain Snails are considered a delicacy, and are even reared for market on Snail farms, or "snaileries."   Usually they are not eaten until they are well fattened with meal, bran, and vegetables.

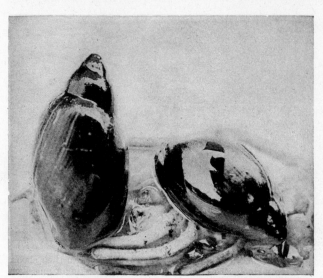

Photo by Cornelia Clarke

Tadpole Snails with shining shell creeping over a dead crayfish.

The Edible Snail is only one of many Snails that live on land.   There are, for example, the Oval Amber Snail (Succinea) with its fragile, transparent shell about an inch long; the White-Lipped Snail (Polygyra) with yellowish-brown shell an inch in diameter and slightly less in height; and the Pyramid Snail (Pyramidula) with thin brownish shell only $\frac{5}{16}$ inch in diameter and $\frac{1}{8}$ inch high.

Fresh-Water Snails. Snails may be slow, but "they get there just the same"; in other words, they have succeeded in populating their share of the earth's surface, including fresh-water ponds and streams.   So numerous are they that anyone who wishes to study them can obtain specimens in abundance by visiting almost any near-by creek or pool.   Most of them are right-handed and the rest left-handed; that is, if they are held with the opening

Photo by Cornelia Clarke

Wheel Snails.   The irregularities in the shell on the left indicate unfavorable growth periods.

of the shell toward you, this opening will be on the right-hand side or on the left-hand side according to the species of Snail.   The shell is chuck full of Snail, the body being twisted so as to penetrate to the extreme apex.   Some Fresh-Water

Snails possess gills with which they breathe under water, whereas others have a sort of lung cavity and must come to the surface from time to time for air.

The Great Pond Snail (Lymnaea) is a right-handed species $2\frac{1}{2}$ inches long. Its long, slender spire consists of six or seven whorls. It may be found creeping along on the underside of the surface film of the water, or feeding on living or dead plants in quiet ponds or slowly-moving streams.

The Tadpole Snail (Physa) is left-handed and much smaller, with a very large whorl surmounted by a short, sharp-pointed spire. Threads of mucus, like fairy ladders, are secreted by this species extending from the surface to the bottom of the pond so that they can creep

Photo by Cornelia Clarke

Ponderous Snail. Most of the dark, outer coat has been worn off of these heavy shells.

rapidly up or down. Since Snails are "light" in water this requires little effort.

The Wheel Snail (Planorbis) builds a shell that forms a flat coil $\frac{5}{6}$ inch in width with the spire in the center. Very few pools of stagnant or slowly running water are without dozens of this type of snail.

The Ponderous Snail (Campeloma) secretes a heavy shell, greenish or blackish in color and $\frac{3}{4}$ inch long and $\frac{5}{8}$ inch wide. This species breathes with gills. The eggs hatch within the shell of the parent and the young escape some time later.

Courtesy, U. S. Bureau of Entomology

Spotted Garden Slug. The skin is kept moist with mucus; the "horns" are fully extended; the shell is beneath the slight hump just in front of the center of the body. Slightly less than life size.

Slugs. A favorite nightmare entertained by certain people is that of suddenly finding themselves on the public street without any clothes on. That must be exactly the way a Slug feels when the board under which he is hiding is turned over into the light of day.   Slugs are closely related to the Land Snails, but nevertheless are completely naked.   They may have a shell, but this is only a thin, calcareous plate entirely concealed beneath the skin.

Courtesy, American Museum of Natural History

Bushy-Backed Sea Slug.   A forest of breathing organs ornament the back and help conceal the animal in the seaweed.   Magnified about 5 diameters.

To keep from drying up, Slugs must live in a moist place, such as is afforded under boards and stones and in holes in the ground.   At night they come forth to feed on vegetation, which they grind up with their rasping tongue, selecting, especially, delicate young lettuce, celery, and potato plants.   They often visit the same plant night after night.   Behind them is left a slimy trail which reveals their midnight forays even though they themselves are well hidden.

About thirty species of garden Slugs occur in the United States. Some, like the Giant Slug which was introduced from Europe, may be six or seven inches long.   The Common Garden Slug is usually about one inch long.   In winter, Slugs burrow into the ground, where they coil up for a nice long winter's sleep.   Those that live in warm greenhouses remain active all winter unless put out of existence by the proprietor.

Courtesy, Nature Magazine

Papillate Sea Slugs.   Mother and baby covered with delicate, glistening, tubular papillae.   About natural size.

Sea Slugs.   The Sea Slugs have demonstrated the fact that, although absolutely naked, they can compete successfully with spiny sea urchins, hard-shelled clams, and armor-plated barnacles.   This is due to their shape, color, and habits.   They live among seaweeds, which they resemble so closely that it is practically impossible to see them. Sea Slugs are shaped much like Land Slugs and have no shell.

A common species, the Bushy-Backed Slug, is about one inch long. At the forward end are two antler-like projections and on the back are two rows of delicate, much-branched extensions that look like an avenue of miniature trees. These serve in part as breathing organs and in part to render the Slug invisible amid the seaweed. Sea Slugs spend their lives in shallow water and are present along both the Atlantic and Pacific seacoasts. They live on seaweed, and are active in habit,

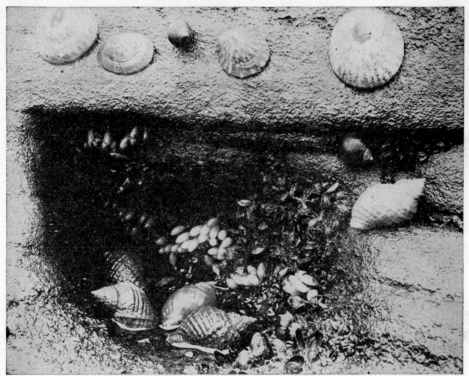

Courtesy, Nature Magazine

Whelks, Periwinkles, and Limpets. Seaweeds and Snails in a crevice in the rocks at the sea-shore. The larger snails with prominent ridges are Whelks; above are two smaller, darker-colored, smoother-shelled Periwinkles; at the top, tightly clinging to the rocks, are four Limpets.

crawling about on their foot, or swimming slowly with an undulating motion. The eggs are laid in a gelatinous string that is fastened to the rocks or to sea plumes and seaweeds. The young are covered with a delicate shell, which they lose as they grow up.

Another species that is common along the North Atlantic coast is the Papillate Sea Slug. On the back of this form are many rows of simple tubular papillae.

Whelks and Periwinkles. Among the commonest of the smaller marine snails are the Whelks and Periwinkles. Whelks are to be found from just below low-tide mark to deep water from New Jersey to Greenland. The shell reaches a length of three inches; it is grayish or yellowish brown in color outside and white or golden yellow inside. The outside has about a dozen longitudinal ridges crossed by a number of raised, revolving ribs. In Europe, where Whelks reach a larger size than in this country, they are widely used as food. They also serve as bait in fishing for cod.

Periwinkles appear to have come to us from Europe in recent times, populating our Atlantic coast from Long Island northward during the latter half of the past century. They are abundant on the rocks and seaweeds between tide levels. In

Courtesy, American Museum of Natural History

Oyster Drill. No oyster is too large to discourage an attack from the Oyster Drill Snail. Here is a snail in the act of drilling a hole through the shell of a living oyster.

order to live in such a boisterous location the shell must be thick and heavy. A horny operculum on the foot is used to close the shell, making of it an "impregnable fortress." Periwinkles are about ¾ inch long and conical in shape. The shell is dark brown or yellowish with dark spiral bands. The tongue is a remarkable structure 2½ inches long and bearing 600 concentric rows of sharp, curved teeth, seven in each row. With such a formidable array of teeth "all the better to bite you with," the Periwinkle can find nothing better to eat than seaweed.

Oyster Drill. The maxim "handsome is as handsome does" is not recognized by the Oyster Drill, since he looks like an ordinary Snail but has developed perfectly atrocious habits. Although less than one inch long, he does not hesitate to attack oysters and clams many times his size. Selecting a place near the hinge of the oyster's shell, he rasps a hole through it, and then sucks the soft, living tissue of the oyster through the hole.   Perhaps we wouldn't feel so sympathetic toward the oyster if we didn't want him for our own use.

Oyster Drills must be very successful, because they are common along the Atlantic coast from Maine to Florida, living in shallow water and down to sixty feet in depth.   Naturally they are especially abundant where there are oyster beds.

Queen Conch.   One of the largest Mollusks in America is the Queen Conch that lives in the Atlantic, being especially common along the shores of the Florida Keys and West Indies. The shell may be a foot long and weigh five pounds. It has a small spire, a very large lower whorl with a much-expanded lip, and protuberances extending out from the ridges. Conch shells are favorite ornaments and are also used as dinner horns in some localities.

The body of the Queen Conch is used by the natives as food. This habit has resulted in the bestowal of the name "Conch" on the inhabitants of certain of the Bahama Islands. The snout is long and the eyes large; one eye is located on the end of each of a pair of long stalks. The foot is provided with a clawlike operculum.

"The conch is impulsive in temperament. It does not glide, but jumps along, striking the sharp claw into the sand, and

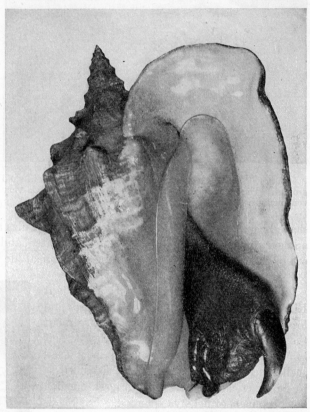

Courtesy, American Museum of Natural History

True Conch.   The shell is nearly a foot long and very massive. The snail is extending its foot with the claw on one side that is used when it leaps.

flopping the shell from side to side as it proceeds.   A most astonishing sight is a frightened conch taking long leaps, and making quick turns to escape capture when pursued.   If placed on its back, it rights itself by a somersault."   (Rogers.)

About one hundred species of Conchs belong to the group which includes the Queen Conch.   They can be attracted by placing a piece of meat in a wire cage, so as to protect this bait from fish, crustaceans, and other carnivorous marine animals, and lowering it into the water where it should be left over night.

Channel Shell. Also called a Conch is the Channel Shell, a species found only along our Atlantic coast from Cape Cod to the Gulf of Mexico, living in shallow water and often very abundant. It is not as massive as the Queen Conch, being only about seven inches long, but is nevertheless one of our largest marine snails. The shell has a short spire and a very large lower whorl from which extends a long channel. The whorls have flat shoulders and deep grooves where they meet. The color of the shell is brownish outside and yellowish within. On the outside are many revolving lines. Hermit Crabs find these shells very satisfactory as a place in which to live. The eggs of the Channel Shell are laid in lens-

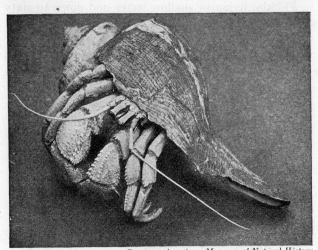

Courtesy, American Museum of Natural History

Channel Shell. The Hermit Crab is dragging this old shell around. The "channel" at the right end of the shell is very conspicuous.

shaped capsules about one inch wide; these capsules are arranged along a cord in a linear row. The eggs do not become separated, and since all of the young break out of the capsules at about the same time, social life is provided for the young.

Ear Shell — Abalone. If Jack the Giant Killer had cut off one of the giant's ears and fossilized it, he would have had a trophy about the size and shape of an Abalone shell. Certainly no one would recognize it as a snail shell, since the spire is so greatly flattened as to be practically wiped out, and the opening has become enormously expanded. Ear Shells were famous for their beauty long before they were found to be good to eat. The inner surface of the shell is pearly, iridescent, and lustrous, and the outer rough surface, when polished, makes the title of aurora, or rainbow, shell seem well deserved. Besides being ornamental, the shells are made into buttons and buckles and used for inlaying.

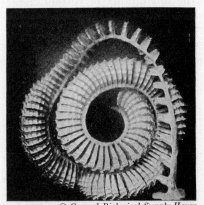

© *General Biological Supply House*

Eggs of the Channel Shell. The eggs are laid in lens-shaped capsules, each about one inch wide, and fastened in a row to a cord.

When alive, the ten-inch Abalone shell is well filled by the animal. The foot is flat, and when attached to a rock, holds fast, more firmly even than that of the Limpet. The Japanese, and others who collect Abalones at depths of from 20 to 60 feet or more, dislodge them by forcing a chisel under the foot. The food of these marine snails consists of vegetation scraped from the rocks with their rasping tongue. The row of little holes near one edge of the shell are entrances to the breathing chamber.

Abalones when cooked in the form of steaks, stew, or chowder compete favorably with other types of shellfish. The Orientals cook, dry, and smoke them. A steadily decreasing supply has necessitated legislation for their protection. Half a dozen species of Ear Shells live on the Pacific coast, and two species on the Atlantic.

Limpet. The spiral characteristic of the snail shell is absent from that of the Limpet and what is left is a rather high-arched disk full of fleshy animal. The European Limpet digs a smooth, shallow pit in a rock the exact size of its shell; here it clings so tenaciously that a force estimated at over 60 pounds is required to break its hold. A sudden blow, however, is sufficient to dislodge an unsuspecting Limpet, since it must lift its shell slightly in order to breathe.

Photo by Hegner

Abalone or Ear Shell. The iridescent material of the shell is concealed by the rough surface. The volcano-like ornaments are barnacles. At the left near the edge are the breathing pores. About one-third natural size.

Limpets possess a "homing" instinct, returning to their citadels each night after foraging over the rocks for algae and other vegetable food.

When an insurance agent is particularly persistent, you may truthfully say of him, "He stuck like a Limpet to a rock."

The accompanying photograph is of the Giant Key-Hole Limpet that occurs along the coast of California. It is a large species, reaching a length of over four inches. The name is derived from the

Photo by Hegner

Key-Hole Limpet. The shell is covered over with a shining black mantle in the living animal. About one-half natural size.

presence of an oval hole near the top of the shell.   The shell has many fine ridges radiating out from this opening.   Most or all of the shell is covered in the living animal by the black mantle; the huge, yellow foot spreads out beneath it.

Slipper Shells.   The under surface at the left reveals the shelf that covers the "toes."   The shell from above is seen at the right.   About natural size.

Photo by Hegner

Slipper Shell.   For many years Slipper Shells have attended Princeton University, and, although none of them has ever been granted a college degree, they have added much to our knowledge of animals, since one of the famous professors at that institution has spent much of his life studying them.   As in the Abalone, the spire of the Slipper Shell, or Boat Shell, is very much flattened.   The aperture is half closed by a horizontal plate so that when the shell is placed on its back it reminds one of a boat containing one seat.   Slipper Shells move very slowly. They occur on both the Atlantic and Pacific coasts and are one or two inches long.

Sea Butterfly (Clione).   Many Sea Butterflies, or Wing-Footed Mollusks (Pteropods), are shell-less "shell-fish"; they spend their lives on the ocean waves, never coming to shore nor sinking to the bottom.   They are about $1\frac{1}{4}$ inches long, pale blue in color, and almost transparent.   Sea Butterflies swim actively with their wing-like fins, but are really at the mercy of the waves and currents.

They are never lonesome since they live in vast schools, sometimes covering the sea for many miles. This sociable habit leads to their destruction, since whales find it possible to make a substantial meal of them with little effort.   In this case, "united we stand, divided we fall" appears to be a poor policy.   So important an element of the whale's diet are these beautiful little creatures that they are known to many only as "Whale's Food."

Drawn by M. Palmer

Sea Butterfly.   Above are the "wings" with which she swims about near the surface of the sea, — an invitation for the whale to come to dinner.   About twice natural size.

Tooth Shells.   The small, white, cylindrical shells that one sometimes finds washed up on the sea beach are not the teeth of an animal, but are the former homes of Mollusks.   The occupants lived buried in the sand beyond the low-tide mark. Here with their breathing tube just above the surface of the sand they spent a placid existence.   The shells are tubular and open at both ends.

Fresh-Water Mussel, or Clam.   Only one who has put his finger between the open valves of a healthy Mussel can appreciate the expression "to shut up like a clam."   The two parts of the Clam's shell, the valves, open and close on an elastic

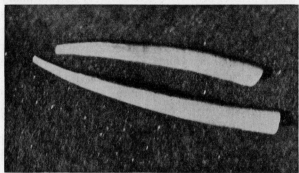

Photo by Hegner

ligamentous hinge. Between the valves are two sets of powerful muscles, one set near the front and the other near the back. When these muscles relax, the elastic hinge expands and opens the shell, and when they contract, the valves are brought together with an almost irresistible force. The shell is built up mostly of carbonate of lime extracted from the water by the Clam. On the outside is a thin, horny membrane that resists the acids in the water, and on the inside is a layer of mother-of-pearl

Tooth Shells.   These are not the sharp teeth of a predatory animal but were once full of a living mollusk and buried in the sand.   Slightly enlarged.

that has an iridescent sheen.   The concentric ridges on the outside of the shell are lines of growth and represent intervals of rest between successive periods of growth.

Inside the shell is a cold, moist animal that well deserves to be called "clammy." The foot is the most conspicuous organ.   It is extended from the anterior end of the open shell, and thrust like a wedge into the sandy or muddy bottom of the pond or stream in which the Clam lives.   If the shell is on its side, it is brought into an upright position and the foot then plows its way slowly along the bottom.   At the

Photo by Cornelia Clarke

Fresh-Water Mussels.   The animal that secreted the shell at the left has departed this world and the valves have sprung open.   The horny covering near the hinge of the shell has worn away, revealing the carbonate of lime underneath.   The shell on the right is tightly closed by the clam within.   Lines of growth are plainly visible on both shells.   About two-thirds life size.

posterior end of the Clam, two little fleshy tubes, called siphons, extend out through the crack in the shell.   A current of water enters the lower siphon and another current comes out of the upper siphon.   These currents are created by the movements of vast numbers of cilia within the shell.   The water that enters carries with it oxygen and minute animals and plants on which the Clam feeds.   The water expelled from the body is loaded with excretory substances.   The shell is not entirely filled with the Clam's body, but the lower part contains a cavity into which hang down on each side two sets of gills with which the animal breathes.

Reproduction in the Fresh-Water Mussel involves a series of very extraordinary events. The eggs are not cast out of the shell, but are deposited in the hollow gills of the mother. Here they develop, and spend the winter, as little bivalves. They break out in the spring, and if they chance to meet a fish, they seize hold of its fins or gills. The tissues of the fish grow around the young Clams, forming what are called "worms" or "blackheads." After feeding on the tissue of the fish for a while, they break out, fall to the bottom, and gradually grow into adult Clams. The greatest advantage derived by the Clam from its association with the fish is the wide and rapid dispersal of its young.

More than 500 species of Fresh-Water Mussels live in the United States; of these about 40 are of commercial value because of their shells. The mussel

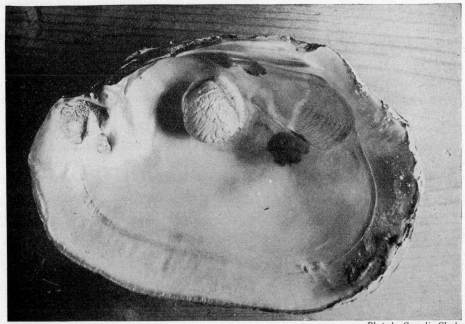

Photo by Cornelia Clarke

Fresh-Water Mussel. Inside of the shell is the iridescent mother-of-pearl, — in this case engaged in forming a pearl. The principal muscle was attached near the upper, right-hand portion of the shell.

fishery is limited almost exclusively to the Mississippi Valley where the rivers flow through a limestone region. The shells are made into pearl buttons, and 50,000 tons or more of them have recently been cut up in a single year. The pearls produced by Fresh-Water Mussels are only second in value to the shells. These pearls are formed around the young of parasitic flatworms. Mussels eat vast quantities of organic particles that pollute fresh-water ponds and streams, and hence are of importance as scavengers.

The man had sure a palate cover'd o'er
With brass or steel, that on the rocky shore
First broke the oozy oyster's pearly coat,
And risk'd the living morsel down his throat. (Gay)

Oyster. We take off our hat to this man; he must have had not only a brass palate, but also a cast-iron stomach. We suspect that he lived in the dim prehistoric past, since vast heaps of empty oyster shells, known as kitchen middens, occur in various parts of the world where they were left by prehistoric man, after

Photo by Hegner

Pearl Oyster. The rough outside and smooth inside of a shell are shown here. Pearls are made of the mother-of-pearl secreted on the inside by the oyster. About one-third natural size.

their contents had been devoured. We know that the Greeks and Romans were fond of Oysters, and that the cultivation of Oysters, as recorded by Pliny, dates at least from the first century B.C.

Many species of Oysters have been described, some of them reaching a length of three feet. Such an enormous species should, of course, live in either Florida or California, but as a matter of fact, is an inhabitant of Japan. Adult Oysters are unable to move about, being attached by the left valve to some solid object on the bottom near the seacoast. Correlated with its inability to move is the absence of a foot. Oysters feed in much the way fresh-water mussels do. Organic particles are carried into the shell in currents of water and certain of these are selected by the Oyster and swallowed. If the water contains dangerous germs, such as those of typhoid fever or cholera, they may lodge in the Oysters and cause disease in anyone eating them.

The only feature that keeps Oysters from extinction is their prolificness. A single Oyster may deposit as many as 60,000,000 eggs in one season; these develop in the Oyster's gills into little ciliated spheres, called spat. After escaping from the shell of the mother, the spat swim about for a day or two and then settle down on some solid object, there to rest for the remainder of their lives.

Oyster farming consists in the preparation of beds which are strewn with empty oyster shells for the spat to settle on.   The young oysters grow into "fry" about an inch long by the end of a year.   In from three to five years they are ready for market. During this time they may be transplanted several times, and are at all times protected from starfish, oyster drills, and other enemies.

Pearls are sometimes found in our oysters, but the best pearls occur in the Pearl Oysters of tropical seas.   These pearls are not natural secretions, but are formed around some foreign body, such as a young tapeworm.   They consist of the same substance as the inner layer of the shell.

Edible Sea Mussel.   One of our "inexhaustible resources" that has not yet been exploited is the Edible Sea Mussel.   This is due not to lack of advertising on the part of the Mussels, since at low tide acres of them are exposed on mud flats

Courtesy, American Museum of Natural History

Edible Sea Mussels.   Mussels and barnacles often struggle for a place of attachment to the rocks on the seashore, resulting in such masses as shown here.   The Mussels fasten themselves to the rocks with bunches of threads.

and on rocky shores with pebbly bottoms.   It is the result of our fondness for oysters.   Take away the oyster and the Edible Mussel will "come into his own," unfortunately for the Mussel.   In Europe these Mussels are not only regularly used as food, but are even reared for the table.

The shell of the Sea Mussel is wedge-shaped and glossy black or bluish in color.

It reaches a length of about four inches and is about an inch thick. Perhaps the most interesting difference between it and the fresh-water mussel is the presence of a group of threads which serve to anchor the animal to the mud, or to a rock or to the shell of another Mussel. If it becomes desirable to move, these threads can be cast off and new ones thrown out. This type of progress is slow, but time means nothing to a Mussel, and the enormous beds that exist prove that their rate of locomotion is sufficient for the preservation of the race. The family of Edible Sea Mussels contains several hundred species which are distributed widely throughout the world.

Hard-Shell Clam. The names given by scientists to the common Hard-Shell Clam are Venus mercenaria. Mercenaria is appropriate, since wampum, the money of the Indians, was made from the shell of this Mollusk, especially from the purple patch on the margin. The appelation Venus, the goddess of beauty, promises something worth looking at, but the dirty white shell leaves much to be desired. However, beauty is only skin deep, and the contents of the shell taste just as good regardless of the dingy covering. The menu card may call this species the Little-Neck Clam. Other names for it are Round Clam and Quahog.

Photo by Johnson and Snook

Hard-Shell Clam. An edible species with a hard shell; it can close its shell very tight and remain alive within it for a long time out of water.

Hard-Shell Clams are most abundant in shallow water on sandy or muddy bottoms, especially in bays and estuaries. They burrow to some extent, and crawl about rather rapidly with their strong foot. Clammers usually fish for them from boats with a rake. The shell is very hard and solid, and about three inches long and two and one-half inches wide. Hard-Shell Clams can live a long time out of water, especially if kept cool, and hence are often shipped long distances to market. Several hundred species have been described in the family to which Hard Shells belong; these are distributed in salt water far and wide.

Soft-Shell Clam. Our fondness for the Soft Shell, or Long-Neck, Clams is due in part to the ease with which we gather them on the beach in front of our summer cottage on Mount Desert Island, Maine. Here they live between tide limits buried in the pebbly mud, usually about four inches beneath the surface. They certainly make excellent soup and chowder. Their delicious flavor, however, is not a modern discovery, since all the evidence indicates that the Indians enjoyed clam bakes long before the Puritans arrived on our shores. The shell is much thinner than that of the Hard-Shell Clam, and the neck may reach a foot in length. This neck consists of the two water ducts, or siphons, joined together and surrounded by a leathery skin. It might better be called the "tail," since the head end of the Clam is at the opposite end of the shell.

The neck projects just above the surface when the tide is in, and food is gathered as in the fresh-water mussel. At low tide, holes in the sand or mud indicate where the Clams are buried, or little jets of water may be shot up into the air here and there as the Clams draw in their necks. Sometimes these Clams lie so close together they seem to form a continuous mass. One observer counted 163 animals, from one to two inches long, in an area of one square foot. Besides being a valuable article of food, Soft-Shell Clams are used as bait by fishermen.

Photo by Woodworth. Courtesy, Nature Magazine

Soft-Shell Clam. This "goeduck" clam reaches a length of seven inches and a weight of six and one-half pounds. It burrows in the bottom and extends its long neck above the surface.

Scallops. Shellfish would certainly be puzzled if they were to study our food habits as industriously as we do theirs. We capture Scallops and throw away all of the body except the large muscle that closes the shell; this is white and tender and considered a great delicacy. On the other hand, we throw away the muscle of the Oyster and eat the rest of its body. We don't eat the shell of the Scallop, but the cook finds its arched and rounded valves admirably adapted for "scalloping" other shell-fish. Each valve has two winglike "ears" near the hinge of the shell, and from this region radiate out about twenty ribs. These are crossed by many lines of growth.

The common Beaming Scallop is provided around the edge of the shell with a row of tiny eyes, dark iridescent blue in color, that glow with a beautiful fluorescence. That these eyes are sensitive to light can be proved easily be casting a shadow over the animal and noting how quickly it closes its shell. Scallops do not burrow in the sand nor plow their way along the bottom, hence the foot is very small. They either rest on their right valve or swim through the water. When swimming, the shell is opened and closed by the powerful muscle, and the jet of water squirted out forces the shell forward, sometimes several feet at a time.   Young scallops may skip about actively in the water or attach themselves temporarily by means of an anchor of threads.

Scallops occur in the ocean in many parts of the world, from shallow water to several hundred fathoms. Over two hundred species have been described.

Heart Shells, or Cockles. Cockles are famous for their edible qualities, but who wants to be famous at such a price.   In most places there are not enough of them to make commercial fishing profitable, hence they are left in peace.   Perhaps after all it might be better to be a Cockle than an Oyster.   The shell of the Cockle when viewed from the end is heart-shaped. That of the Spiny Cockle is approximately five inches long, five inches high, and four inches

Photo by Hegner

Scallop. The outside of this valve shows the small "ears" and the prominent ribs that radiate out from the hinge. The Circular Scallop illustrated here is about two inches long.

in diameter. It has about forty ridges radiating out from the center, each bearing a large number of conspicuous spines near the margin of the shell.

Photo by Hegner

Spiny Cockle. The shell is heart-shaped and covered with ridges that bear short spines. Cockles are thus well protected as they lie in the sand of the seashore.

The foot of the Cockle is long and bent and very strong. It may be thrust out to a considerable distance, and, as the result of a vigorous twist, pulls the shell forward several inches in a sudden leap. About 200 species of Cockles are known. They live partly buried in sand or mud in shallow water along the seashore.   Their food consists of microscopic organisms which they filter out of a current of sea water that is drawn into the shell by means of minute cilia.

Ship Worm. The animated augurs we call Ship Worms begin their nefarious carpenter work soon after they hatch from the egg and are no larger than pinheads. As they grow up, the holes they bore in the bottom of wooden ships, in the piles of wharves, and in any other wood that chances to be handy, become larger and larger, and eventually the largest timbers are so honeycombed that they crumble to bits. All this hard work seems to be done for purposes of protection, since the wood removed is not used as food, although it passes through the alimentary canal of the Ship Worms.

Really the Ship Worm is a bivalve Mollusk that has gone astray. The valves of the shell are about $\frac{1}{4}$ inch long and $\frac{1}{12}$ inch wide, and the entire "worm" becomes from six inches to two feet in length. The tube is usually from $\frac{1}{4}$ to $\frac{2}{5}$ inch in diameter and lined with calcareous material secreted by the animal. The valves are provided with tiny teeth which rasp away the wood when the shell is rotated. The burrows generally follow the grain of the wood, avoid knots, and seldom break into neighboring burrows. At the outer end of the tube are the ends of the long siphons which protrude from the opening; when these are withdrawn the doorway is closed by two little calcareous plates.

Photo by Hegner

Ship Worm. Here is a piece of wood riddled with the burrows of Ship Worms. The burrows are about $\frac{3}{8}$ inch in diameter; no matter how many of them there are they don't break into one another.

Steel ships have deprived Ship Worms of what formerly was a favorite place to dig a home. Methods of protecting timbers in wharves, etc., from attack, have also been devised, such as impregnating them with creosote. Only one good deed can be attributed to Ship Worms; they destroy sunken timbers and other wood that might become a nuisance in harbors.

Squids, or Sea Arrows. That the Sea Arrows, shooting back and forth through the water like animated shuttles, and the slow-motion clams are "sisters under the skin" is a little difficult to believe, yet fundamentally their internal workings are arranged on the same general plan. The shell of the Squid has almost disappeared, being represented by an internal scale shaped like a pen. The submarine-shaped body is built for rapid progress through the water. The fins are largely used for steering purposes, but may also propel the body slowly backward or forward.

What appears to be the head of the Squid corresponds largely to the foot of other Mollusks. In the Head-Footed Mollusks, the foot is divided into a siphon and ten arms. Eight of the arms are provided each with two rows of sucking disks;

the other two are longer and have four rows of sucking disks on their expanded ends. Small fish and other small marine animals are captured by swift backward darts, the prey being clasped firmly in the flexible arms and held securely by the cup-shaped suckers.

Squids are famous for their color changes. Pigment cells filled with blue, purple, red, and yellow color are present in the skin, and when these become larger or smaller, the color changes rapidly as though the animal were blushing. These chameleon-like changes in color harmonize with the color of the background, resulting in concealment of the animal.

The two eyes of the Squid are very conspicuous. They resemble somewhat in structure the human eye, but have no lids. Beneath the head is the siphon, a sort of flexible tube which can be bent in any direction, and through which water or "ink" can be forcibly ejected. Water is expelled through the siphon so powerfully that the Squid is propelled like an arrow in the direction opposite that toward which the siphon is pointed. Within the body is a sac filled with a dark fluid resembling ink. When attacked by an enemy some of this ink is discharged through the siphon, forming a cloud like a smoke-screen behind which the Squid makes his escape.

Squids are used as food in Oriental countries, and are eaten in enormous quantities by fish and especially by whales. They are very valuable as bait; about one half of the bait used in fishing for cod on the Newfoundland banks consists of Squids.

The Common Squid that lives along the Atlantic coast of North America is from six to nine inches long. Near the coast of Newfoundland, however, Giant Squids are occasionally encountered. These may be fifty feet or more in total

Courtesy, American Museum of Natural History

Squid or Sea Arrow. Squids are pointed behind and swim backward. Small animals are caught and held by the sucker-studded arms. The siphon is located just back of the arms on the lower surface; it propels the animal backwards by expelling jets of water and through it "ink" may be ejected.

length with arms as large as a man's legs, and suckers as big as tea-cups. Probably certain sea-serpent stories are founded on the sudden and unexpected appearance of these monsters. Incidentally the Giant Squid is the largest living Invertebrate animal known.

One of the relatives of the Squid has a name that is well known, the Cuttle Fish. This species secretes a calcareous, internal shell, which has been found to be of value in raising canary birds, since it furnishes them with lime. The cigar-shaped, fossilized shells, called Belemnites, were formed by extinct relatives of the Squid.

Chambered or Pearly Nautilus.   Fortunate indeed is he whose praises are sung by a famous poet.   The Chambered Nautilus would be "just another Mollusk" had not Oliver Wendell Holmes immortalized him in his incomparable poem.   The feature that especially distinguishes him is the shell.   This is coiled like a watch spring and divided by cross-walls into a series of compartments.   A new, and larger, chamber is built when the old compartment is outgrown, and a new wall secreted behind it.   A calcareous tube connects the walls, and through this extends

Courtesy, American Museum of Natural History

Chambered Nautilus.   The animal is shown here in its last and largest chamber, having lived successively in each of the other chambers during its growth.   About natural size.

a strand of living tissue, called the siphuncle.   The empty chambers are filled with a gas which renders the shell buoyant and allows the Nautilus to move more rapidly through the water.

> *Year after year beheld the silent toil*
> *That spread his lustrous coil;*
> *Still, as the spiral grew,*
> *He left the past year's dwelling for the new,*
> *Stole with soft step its shining archway through,*
> *Built up its idle door,*
> *Stretched in his last-found home, and knew the old no more.*
>
> (O. W. Holmes)

The Chambered Nautilus lives in the sea at depths of 100 feet or more, near some of the islands of the South Pacific. It does not swim at the surface, but hunts near the bottom for crabs and other animals that serve as food. As in the squid, jets of water ejected from a tube, the siphon, force the animal backward through the water. The shell of the Chambered Nautilus is from four to six or more inches in diameter, with two and one-half coils in the adult. It is smooth and white outside, with stripes of reddish brown, and pearly inside. Extending out from the last and largest chamber are almost a hundred tentacles; these are not provided with suckers, as in the Squid, but nevertheless cling firmly to solid objects. On the back of the head is a hood that partially closes the opening of the shell when the animal withdraws into it.

The Nautilus belongs to a family of ancient lineage, in fact, only a few species survive of the many that lived in the Eocene period of the Earth's history. Many of the extinct species left fossilized shells behind them "so that we would be certain not to overlook them." Among these are the Ammonites that secreted highly decorated shells coiled as are those of the Chambered Nautilus. The Paper Nautilus does not belong to the Chambered Nautilus family, but is more closely allied to the Devil Fishes.

© *General Biological Supply House*

Paper Nautilus. The female Paper Nautilus, a near relative of the Octopus, secretes a delicate shell which is a perambulator, serving as a cradle for the developing young.

Octopus, or Devil Fish. If we were the devil we should not feel flattered to have the Octopus named after us, for no more repulsive and sinister-looking animal ever lived, and the imaginations of our most creative artists have failed to picture anything more horrible and bizarre. The ferocity of the Octopus and its readiness to attack man have not added to its charms.

Devil Fishes live in dark caves in the rocks and in crevices in coral reefs, preferring the warm waters of the tropics to the cooler waters of northern regions. Most of them are not large enough to harm a human being, but the Giant Devil Fish of the Pacific reaches a diameter of twenty-eight feet and is really dangerous.

The body of a Devil Fish is soft and rounded, and the eyes, with their slit-shaped pupils, are prominent and full of hate. The long, flexible, sucking arms are, of course, the most terrifying and disgusting feature of the Devil Fish. Eight in number, each with two rows of sucking disks, they are more active than an elephant's trunk and wonderfully effective as organs of attachment. They are connected near the base by a membrane, so that when spread out, a sort of umbrella is formed with the arms representing the ribs. By opening and closing this umbrella the body is given a backward, gliding movement.

Photo by Hegner

Octopus. A large part of the body of an Octopus consists of arms that bear cup-shaped suckers. The eyes are conspicuous. The mottled appearance of the body is well shown here. This was a living young specimen about eight inches across the arms.

Devil Fishes can walk forward on the sea bottom on their arms, but ordinarily swim backward like a Squid, using water ejected from the siphon as a driving force, much as escaping gas propels a skyrocket into the air. As in the Squid, ink can be emitted through the siphon, forming a smoke screen behind which the Devil Fish can retire, and startling changes in color may occur, such as from brown to pink, yellow, or black.

The regular diet of the Devil Fish consists of crabs; these are paralyzed by the injection into their breathing chambers of a poison produced in the salivary glands of the Devil Fish. The arms and parrot-like beak then tear the crab into pieces. Strange as it may seem, the loathsome Devil Fish is very good to eat, and is considered a great delicacy in certain countries, especially in Italy.

CHAPTER 8

CRUSTACEANS

If success were judged by numbers, the Joint-Footed Animals, or Arthropods, would be given first place without a rival in sight, since this group contains more different kinds of animals than all the rest of the Animal Kingdom taken together. It includes the Crustaceans, Insects, Spiders, Mites, Millepedes, and Centipedes. All have a skeleton on the outside of the body, not inside as in human beings. This skeleton is secreted by the animal and consists of a hornlike substance known as chitin. It is not a solid piece, but is thin in places so that movements of various

Courtesy, Nature Magazine

Amphithoë. The armor plates along the top and sides of this Crustacean protect it from injury; the feelers (antennae) are long and branched; each segment of the body bears a pair of jointed appendages. Magnified about 10 diameters.

parts of the body are possible, just as in a coat of armor. All Arthropods are provided with jointed legs or other appendages.

The Crustaceans include the Fairy Shrimps, Water Fleas, Fish Lice, Barnacles, Sow Bugs, Beach Fleas, Prawns, Lobsters, Crayfish, and Crabs. Many of them have calcium carbonate in their shells, which gives them a crustlike consistency, and suggested the name of the group. Crustaceans live mostly in the sea, but many inhabit fresh water or damp places on land, and others are parasitic in or on other

97

animals.   They may be microscopic in size or as large as twelve feet or more from the tip of one leg to that of the opposite leg.   They may be solitary, like Lobsters, or congregate in vast shoals, like Shrimps.   In size, shape, color, and activities they are adapted to many different kinds of habitats.

Crustaceans breathe by means of gills.   Two pairs of feelers, or antennae, serve as sense organs of touch.   In many the skeleton of the forward part of the body is in one piece, forming a head-thorax (cephalothorax).   A large number of paired appendages are present, each, typically, with two branches.   About 20,000 species are known.

The relations of Crustaceans to other animals are interesting and important. Many of them feed on decaying plants or animals and are valuable scavengers, keeping the seashore clean and purifying the water.   They in their turn furnish almost the only food of many other animals, such as fish and some species of whales. Such forms as lobsters, crayfish, and crabs are relished by human beings and furnish a livelihood for many fishermen.

Fairy Shrimps.   Nothing in early spring seems more surprising than the discovery of a collection of Fairy Shrimps, only about an inch long, swimming about on their

Photo by Peltier.   Courtesy, Nature Magazine

Fairy Shrimp.   To these fairy-like little creatures the World must seem upside down because they swim on their backs.

backs in a pool of cold water.   How did such delicate little Crustaceans spend the winter, and how did they find their way into the pool?   The answer demands a knowledge of the life-history of these little leaf-footed fairies.

The pools in which Fairy Shrimps live dry up in the summer, and the race would perish except for the fact that the eggs they lay in the summer become buried in the mud at the bottom and remain alive there in spite of summer's drought and winter's cold. Thus when the snow melts in the spring and the pools fill up with water, the eggs are all ready to hatch and give rise, as if by magic, to semi-transparent, pinkish-colored Fairy Shrimps. This does not explain why they swim on their backs. We don't know the answer, but we can assure you that they do so with rare grace, waving their leaflike feet rhythmically back and forth.

Fairy Shrimps are among the most primitive Crustaceans. Most species live in fresh-water ponds or pools, but a few live in salt water; one of them is especially famous for its ability to live in water more salty than sea water.

Water Fleas. Those who in their travels have encountered fleas, for example, as we did a few years ago in a Mexican hotel, will be sorry to learn that there are Water Fleas as well as land fleas. But Water Fleas don't bite; they simply resemble real fleas somewhat in appearance. To the naked eye they look like minute specks, since they are only about $\frac{1}{10}$ inch long.

The microscope reveals a semi-transparent, oval, bivalve shell enclosing a heart that beats regularly, as a heart should, and behind the heart, a brood pouch full of eggs. At the forward end, a single eye looks down into the depths, while above it, extending out of the shell, are two enormous antennae; these are not sense organs, as

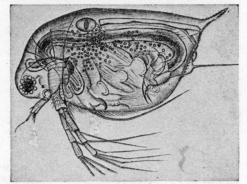

Water Flea. The body is protected by a transparent, bivalve shell and the antennae are used to swim with. Water Fleas do not bite. Size, about $\frac{1}{10}$ inch long.

in many other Crustaceans, but serve for swimming, while the weaker legs create a current that brings food and fresh water into the shell. Our common Water Flea has a prominent beak on the underside of the head and a long spine at the posterior end.

Water Fleas are very prolific, producing a brood of young every two or three days. Their numbers are kept down by aquatic insects and fish that consume them by the tens of thousands. In summer, thin-shelled eggs are laid, but as autumn approaches, thick-shelled winter eggs are deposited; these are capable of withstanding cold weather and so preserve the race until the following spring. In some species the winter eggs are provided with air cells which keep them at the surface where they are distributed far and wide by the currents. Several hundred species of Water Fleas are known; most of them live in fresh water.

Cyclopes. The Cyclopes of Greek Mythology were giants with a single eye in the center of their foreheads. The modern Cyclopes are "little giants" in the sense that in competition with other animals they are pre-eminently successful. Wherever life exists in fresh water or in the sea, there one will find swarms of Cyclopes, or members of their class, appearing like little whitish specks, as they jerk their way through the water.

The body of Cyclops is pear-shaped and about $\frac{1}{8}$ inch long.   At the anterior end are two long, antler-like antennae, and at the posterior end, a forked tail. Much of the time, the female carries a well-loaded egg sac on each side of her tail.   The single eye is red.

As in the Water Flea, Cyclops lays summer eggs that hatch quickly, and more resistant winter eggs that carry the race through periods of cold and drought. Only animals and plants that are microscopic in size are accepted as food.   The Cyclopes, in turn, furnish a large part of the menu of larger aquatic animals.   Some of their relatives that live in the sea form the principal food of certain species of whales, and are often so numerous that the water is colored red by them for miles around.

Some of the relatives of Cyclops have developed frills on their feet that are both useful and ornamental. These frills are often beautifully colored, but we suspect that they are designed so as to enable their owners to swim about easily in the ocean currents.

Not all of the Cyclopean relatives are really respectable.   Some of them live within the bodies of other aquatic animals, such as the sea squirts, and a number of them become attached to the skin or gills of fish, or actually burrow into the flesh of fish thereby becoming real parasites.   These fish lice possess suckers as a means of attachment. They live both in fresh water and in the sea.

Frilled Oar-Foot.   The feet of this near relative of Cyclops are beautifully frilled; they are efficient swimming organs.

Rock Barnacles.   The most important event in the life of a Barnacle is the selection of a favorable place to attach itself, since when once fastened to a rock it is fixed there for life.   So many Barnacles cover the rocks between high and low tide levels along the seashore that no more empty spaces seem available.   Almost 3000 Barnacles have been counted on one square foot of rock.

Rock Barnacles secrete for themselves a calcareous shell resembling that of the Mollusks so closely that early naturalists thought they belonged to this group. Later, they were proved to be Crustaceans capable of swimming about when young, but sessile in the adult stage.

The common Acorn Barnacle surrounds itself with a shell of six thick pieces, joined together by thinner ones. It reaches a length of two inches. When the tide goes out, the shell is closed, but when covered with water, six pairs of delicate, curling legs are thrust out and become busily engaged in kicking food into the mouth; this food consists of minute organisms. Although Rock Barnacles usually become fastened to rocks, they may also attach themselves

Photo by Hegner

Rock Barnacles. When the tide is out, the Rock, or Acorn, Barnacles hide in their shells and close the door, but when covered with water, they extend their feet from the open door and kick food particles into their mouths. Since they are fastened to the rocks, they must depend on food brought to them by the ocean currents. About two-thirds natural size.

to the timbers of wharves, to seaweed, and to large marine animals. Whales are often so intensely irritated by Barnacles that have cemented themselves to their skin, they are said to "leap like lambs."

Goose Barnacles. It seems curious indeed that Barnacles and Geese ever became associated in the minds of men. According to a story prevalent in the Dark Ages, there were Barnacle trees, the fruit of which "if it falleth on land dieth, but if it falleth into the water it liveth, and becomes the familiar Barnacle Goose." Perhaps the fact that the breeding places of Barnacle Geese were unknown led to the idea that they hatched from Barnacles.

Goose Barnacles are also called Ship Barnacles because of their habit of

Photo by Hegner

Goose Barnacles. A large group are here shown hanging down from a piece of wood floating in the sea. Their sizes indicate their age. The delicate, curved legs are extended from the shells of some of them. About one-half natural size.

attaching themselves to the bottoms of ships.   They may be found hanging down from many other objects floating about in the sea.   At the end of a long stalk is the bluish-white, faintly-striated shell, usually of five pieces.   As in the Rock Barnacle, six pairs of bristly feet may be protruded from the shell; these comb the surrounding water for the small organisms that they carry into the mouth.   About forty species of Goose Barnacles are known.   The commonest species has a shell up to two inches long, and a stalk from two to six inches long.

Sow Bugs.   Very few Crustaceans live on land but among those that do are the Sow Bugs.   Because they possess only gills to breathe with, they must live in moist places, hence we find them under logs, stones, bark, and in various sorts of debris where it is damp.   Sow Bugs are elliptical in shape and flat, which enables them to creep into crevices.   Some species can roll themselves up into a ball, but one of the

Photo by Cornelia Clarke

Sow Bugs.   Moist places under stones and boards furnish a home for these terrestrial crustaceans.   The antennae are long; on the upper surface are a series of tuberculated plates. and the lower surface is provided with many pairs of legs for running.   About ⅗ inch long.

most common species can not; the latter appears to get along just as well as the others in spite of the absence of this accomplishment.

Sow Bugs are gray or of a dark slate color and about ⅗ inch long.   The female lays her eggs in a pouch, or marsupium, on the under surface of the thorax; here they develop and produce young, which emerge from the pouch looking like miniature adults.   The food of Sow Bugs consists principally of decaying vegetation, but often young, tender plants are attacked and the Bugs then become a pest. Poison bait containing Paris green is advocated for their destruction.

Beach Fleas. Although Beach Fleas are remarkably agile and can leap even better than real fleas, they do not bite. This is fortunate for visitors to sandy sea beaches, for here the Beach Fleas congregate in enormous numbers, hiding beneath seaweed thrown up on the sand, or burying themselves in the sand just below high-tide mark. If a clump of seaweed is moved, the Beach Fleas will scatter in all directions and quickly dig into the sand head first until well covered.

The common Long-Horned Beach Flea is white, gray, or brownish in color, possesses very long antennae, and measures about an inch in length. The body is flattened from side to side,

Beach Flea. This harmless burrower in the sand on the seashore is shaped like a flea and jumps like a flea. The antennae are very long. About 2½ times natural size.

like that of a flea, and the hind legs are adapted for jumping. Beach Fleas are among the most valuable scavengers of the seashore, feeding on both decaying animal and vegetable matter. Swimming is not indulged in unless necessary; then they may swim about on their sides or backs, as well as in an upright position.

Most of the 2500 species in the group to which the Beach Fleas belong live in the sea, but some of them are common in fresh-water ponds and streams.

Shrimp. He lies on the sand beneath the water ready to dash swiftly backward out of danger with a flip of his tail. His long antennae are sensitive and warn him of an enemy's approach.

Edible Shrimp. The dictionary defines a Shrimp as a "small, wrinkled person"; this, however, does not describe the kind of Shrimp we are interested in. Our Shrimps belong to a group of 6000 or more species of Crustaceans distinguished by the possession of ten walking legs.   Lobsters, crayfish, and crabs also belong to this group.

Shrimps are elongated and the abdomen is well developed.   The antennae are whiplike, and as long or longer than the body; they serve as organs of touch. Shrimps live in both shallow and deep water; some have been collected from a depth of four miles.   They are very agile, shooting backward with quick jerks of the swimming fin at the end of the tail.   Both animal and vegetable matter are eaten by them, and they are being constantly preyed upon by fish and other marine animals.

The Edible Shrimp that lives along our northwestern seacoast is about two inches long and light in color with dark markings, closely resembling the sandy bottom on which it lives.   When disturbed it seeks shelter beneath the sand, keeping in touch with the outer world by thrusting its eyes and antennae above the surface.   Small Crustaceans of the Shrimp type are often called Prawns.   A number of species of both types are used as food in various parts of the world. The Shrimp industry of the United States is especially valuable in Louisiana and California.

Crayfish.   The Crayfish seems to be one of those animals that doesn't care where he is going but wants to know where he has been, because his principal method

Photo by Cornelia Clarke

Crayfish.   The eggs of the mother are glued to the swimmerets under the tail, where they are well protected until they hatch.   Shell, pincers, antennae, walking legs, and the rostrum between and above the eyes are all shown in this photograph.   About natural size.

of locomotion is backward.   At the end of the tail is a swimming fin that is brought forward beneath the body with great force by the large muscles in the abdomen, thus driving the animal backward with surprising speed.   Crayfishes also walk, either forward or backward.

Crayfishes live in fresh-water lakes, ponds, and streams, where they conceal themselves under logs or rocks, except when out searching for decaying animal and vegetable matter to eat for their dinner. They face the opening in their hiding places with their eyes on the watch for food and enemies, and their antennae, which are sensitive organs of touch, waving back and forth. Their food is grasped by the large pincers on the first pair of legs, is then crushed by the jaws, and swallowed. In the stomach are a group of teeth, called the gastric mill, that grind it up into fine particles.

The breathing organs of Crayfishes are gills, resembling those of fish. These are lodged in a chamber on either side of the thorax formed by a fold of the skeleton. A constant current is kept flowing through these chambers, bathing the gills with fresh water.

The eggs, or "berries," of Crayfishes are laid in April and fastened with a sticky secretion to the appendages beneath the abdomen. They are carried and protected until they hatch, and the young still cling to their mother for about two weeks. Their span of life is about three years.

Lobsters. The phrase "as red as a boiled Lobster" is very expressive, since boiled Lobsters are certainly red, and that is the condition of most of the Lobsters we see. However, in nature these big brothers of the Crayfishes are usually dark green in color with red and blue mottlings. They resemble Crayfishes in structure and habits, but are much larger. Their great claws are particularly well developed.

Courtesy, U. S. Bureau of Fisheries

Lobster. The claws of the Lobster are comparatively enormous. The swimming paddles at the end of the tail are shown here spread out, and also the egg masses under the tail. About one-fourth natural size.

Lobsters may grow to a length of over two feet and a weight of over thirty pounds, but they have been fished for so persistently that most specimens are now under ten inches in length and less than two pounds in weight. They are found along the Atlantic coast from North Carolina to Labrador, being especially abundant off the coast of Maine. In summer they live in shallow water on rocky or sandy bottoms, but as winter approaches they move into deeper water.   Like others of their relatives they are scavengers, and are easily caught in traps, called Lobster pots, built like an old-fashioned rat trap and baited with decaying organic material.

The skeleton of Lobsters, and other similar Crustaceans, is rigid, and growth is impossible unless it is shed occasionally ; then it splits down the back and the animal that creeps out has a soft, elastic skin.   This skin expands and then becomes rigid. Young lobsters spend much of their time changing their skeleton ; eight times the first year, five times the second year, and three times the third year.   After that, growth is slower ; the males change twice and the females once each year.

Spiny Lobsters.   Animals that live among the rocks in shallow water along the seacoast are like a Daniel in a den of lions ; their first and most important problem is that of protection from their merciless associates. The lobster's pincers are formidable enough to frighten away almost any marine animal. Spiny Lobsters, which have no pinching-claws, are fortified by sharp spines, especially on the top of the thorax and sides of the abdomen. Another interesting characteristic is the great length of their antennae, which enable them to feel their way a considerable distance ahead, and thus to dart back out of danger before an enemy gets too close.

Courtesy, U. S. Bureau of Fisheries

Spiny Lobster.   It is easy to see why this species is called the Spiny Lobster.   Note the absence of pincers and the enormous size of the antennae.   About one foot long.

One species of Spiny Lobster lives along the coast of Florida and in the West Indies.   Another species is a favorite article of food in California and Western Mexico. They are common on coral reefs and in tide pools where they hide in crevices or among the sea weeds. Decayed fish is very attractive to them hence they are easily captured in lobster pots. In California laws have been passed regulating their capture.

Blue or Edible Crab.   Those of us who live in Baltimore or Crabtown (Annapolis) are thoroughly familiar with Edible Crabs in the form of crabmeat or Soft-Shelled Crabs.   The latter are Crabs that have just shed their hard skeleton.   If not disturbed, the new skeleton becomes hard in a few days; but in the meantime the Crabs are particularly delicious.   Edible Crabs rank in value next to the Lobster in our markets.   They are known as Blue Crabs in the North and as Sea Crabs in the South.

A muddy bottom, covered more or less with eel grass, in a shallow bay or estuary furnishes a favorite habitat for Edible Crabs.   Here they creep or swim about

Photo by Hegner

Edible Crab.   The large claws protect him from many of his enemies, but not from Man. Note the beady eyes and rakish way he holds his short antennae.   About life size.

searching for decaying matter, or for anything alive that they can catch and devour. They are rather belligerent and will fight any other animal regardless of size.

The body of the Crab differs markedly in shape from that of the Crayfish or Lobster.   It is flat, short, and broad, and the abdomen is bent forward under the head-thorax.   The shell of the Edible Crab reaches a breadth of six inches, and is distinguished by a sharp spine that projects out from each side.   The first pair of legs bear large, strong pincers, and the fifth pair of legs are much flattened, forming efficient swimming organs.   The upper part of the body and the claws are dark green, but the feet are blue, hence the name Blue Crab.

Edible Crabs " are very active and can swim rapidly.   They also have the habit of pushing themselves backward into the mud for concealment.   They are predaceous and pugnacious, and have great strength in their claws, which they use with dexterity.   They not only fight their own kind, but show a bold front to all enemies, including man."   (Arnold.)

Crabs of various sorts live in many parts of the world, in the sea and on land, in shallow water and in deep water, in sand and among the rocks.   Some of the better known species are Spider Crabs, Lady Crabs, Oyster Crabs, and Fiddler Crabs.

Hermit Crabs. The wisdom of the snail in carrying his house on his back is obviously appreciated by the Hermit Crab, since the latter is willing to burden himself with a marine snail's shell for the sake of the protection it affords. The habit of appropriating empty snail shells in which to live has brought about several curious modifications in the structure of these Crabs. The abdomen is soft, and is twisted

Courtesy, Shedd Aquarium, Chicago

Hermit Crab. All we usually see of the Hermit Crab are the legs, antennae, and eyes that he chooses to extrude from the snail's shell in which he lives. The eyes are on the end of long stalks between the bases of the antennae. Slightly less than life size.

so as to fit the coils of the snail's shell. One pair of abdominal appendages develop into hooks which anchor the body in the shell; the other abdominal appendages become degenerate.

The right-hand pincer, which is used to capture and crush its prey, is constructed so as to close the opening in the shell. The smaller left-hand pincer fills any crevices in the opening left by the other claw. The second and third pairs of legs drag the shell around. Hermit Crabs, unlike snails, move about rapidly and with great freedom.

One peculiar difficulty encountered by Hermit Crabs is that of their own growth, which makes it necessary for them to go house-hunting periodically for larger quarters. After

Photo by Hegner

Sponge Crab. This Spider Crab attaches small sponges on its legs and back which help conceal it as it wanders about in the seaweed. About natural size.

much strenuous scouting, a suitable shell is found and the Crab darts quickly from the old to the new so as to be exposed as short a time as possible to the dangers outside of the shell.

Not content with the protection afforded by the snail shell, Hermit Crabs often place hedgehog hydroids (see page 41), or sea anemones, or sponges on top of the shell. Even more remarkable than this is the case of a Shore Crab in the Indian Ocean that always carries a sea anemone in each pincer which it can thrust into the face of an approaching enemy. The stinging cells of the sea anemone are, of course, as effective as a burst of shrapnel.

Spider Crabs. These appear to be the weak sisters of the Crab family, but their method of maintaining themselves in the struggle for existence is quite novel.

Photo by Hegner

Spider Crab. This type of Crab has a shell that is pointed in front and rounded behind. The long, spindling legs are the most conspicuous characteristic and are responsible for the creature's first name. The legs of this species have a spread of over 2 feet.

They are sluggish, have feeble claws, long, slender legs that look as though they could only be in the way, and are apparently very stupid. But in reality, certain Spider Crabs are as clever at protecting themselves from their enemies as any animals known.

Those that live among seaweeds collect some of these with their pincers, add to them a sticky secretion from the mouth, and then place them on their backs where there are hooked hairs that help to hold them there. Thus covered with "shrubbery," the Spider Crab can crawl about among the seaweeds without being observed.

Living animals may also be used for this purpose, such as hydroid polyps and sponges. The Crabs select some type of organism that grows in the region where they live. If removed to a different setting, the Crabs may remove one set of decorations and replace them with a set from the new surroundings. One little Spider Crab attaches sponges not only on its shell, but also in patches on its legs. This species occurs on the Pacific coast from Monterey Bay to Panama. It creeps along slowly and unnoticed among the seaweeds and other marine flora and fauna.

The Spider Crab shown in our illustration lives along the coast of California and is only $\frac{2}{5}$ inch long and $\frac{1}{5}$ inch broad. It has decorated itself with many small pieces of sponge. Other Spider Crabs may be much larger, reaching that of the species from Japan which measures twelve feet across its outspread legs. The body of Spider Crabs is rounded behind and drawn out to a point in front. Their most distinguishing feature, however, is the length of their slender legs.

Fiddler Crabs. The antics of a colony of Fiddler Crabs are certain to amuse the most blasé seashore visitor. You are accordingly urged to visit a mud-bank just above high tide where the ground is riddled with burrows. When disturbed, every little Fiddler runs sideways to the nearest hole, brandishing its enormous right claw in a threatening but ludicrous manner. If everything is quiet, the crabs soon appear again at the entrance to their burrows with the large claw still held in readiness for combat. This claw is sometimes waved slowly back and forth, which accounts for the name Fiddler. The left claw is small, but is usefully employed in picking particles of food out of the mud and sand.

Photo by Hegner

Fiddler Crab. His right claw is enormously overdeveloped; his left claw small. He fiddles the air with his right claw in a threatening manner, which no doubt has the effect of keeping enemies at a safe distance. About natural size.

The burrows are about an inch in diameter and may be a foot or more deep. No earth is evident around the burrows because the material excavated is made up into small pellets and carried several feet away from the entrance.

"After peering cautiously about, the crab emerges, and carries its load four or five feet away before dropping it; then again looks about before quickly running back; and, finally, turning its stalked eyes, looks in all directions and suddenly disappears, soon to return with another load." (Arnold.) The males are very pugnacious. "They lock the two large chelae together as if they were shaking hands and then each apparently tries to break off his opponent's claw by a sudden twist. Sometimes there is a tearing sound as though the claw had been broken off. We have heard the sound a number of times but we have never seen a claw really broken off. However, we have found several claws on the beach which would indicate that the struggle sometimes ends disastrously. Frequently we have seen the combat terminated by one of the fighters losing his hold and being thrown back over his opponent for a distance of a foot or more." (Johnson and Snook.)

Trilobites. Our study of Nature, strange as it may seem, began with fossil Crustaceans that lived about 500 million years before we were born. We accompanied our big brother on his trips in search of fossils and frequently returned with trilobites. These primitive animals once lived in the seas throughout the world, but for some unknown reason became extinct, and are now known only by their skeletons embedded in rocks. This skeleton was in life much like that of the Crayfish, but the body was flat and could be rolled up like a rug. A conspicuous shield covered the head; this was divided into three lobes by longitudinal grooves, hence the name Trilobite. Most of them were from one to three inches long.

A species that was common in the seas covering northeastern America and northern Europe in bygone ages is called the "daddy longlegs" of Trilobites because its many legs were unusually long. It was probably a carnivorous animal feeding on living and decaying animals. The living relatives of Trilobites have not been located with certainty, but are probably represented by the Fairy Shrimps and other Leaf-Footed Crustaceans.

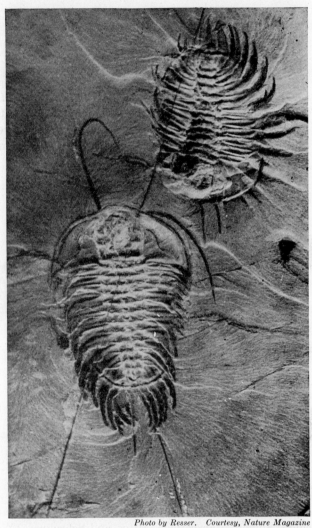

Photo by Resser.   Courtesy, Nature Magazine

Trilobites. Crustacean-like animals of the past preserved as fossils in a slab of shale. They were about 5 inches long when alive.

CHAPTER 9

ARACHNIDS

"Among the wonders of Natural History, few things are more remarkable than is the multitude of small many-legged animals, often of beautiful structure, striking habits, and complex life-histories seldom obtruding themselves upon our notice. Down among the grass roots, under the drifted leaves and amid the fallen pine needles lives a Lilliputian populace, fighting and slaying, mating and bringing forth young, pursuing a life vivid, intense, and fierce, of which the Brobdingnagian

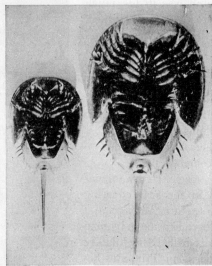

© *General Biological Supply House*

King Crabs. "Living fossils," the last survivors of a group of ancient lineage, difficult to kill because of their effective hard-shelled armor. Almost 2 feet long.

mammal is in most cases quite unaware." (Savory.) A large proportion of these elusive animals belong to the group known to the Greeks as Arachnids, which includes Spiders, Harvestmen, Mites, and Scorpions. We are adding the Centipedes and Millepedes as an appendix to the Arachnids.

A few Arachnids are aquatic, but most of them live on land or as parasites on other animals. Characteristics that are common to many of them are the presence of four pairs of legs, from two to twelve simple eyes, breathing organs, called book lungs, containing "leaves," and a sucking stomach. The body usually consists of two parts, the head and thorax fused together in front into a cephalothorax, and behind this the abdomen. Feelers, or antennae, are absent. Most Arachnids lay eggs but some of them bring forth their young alive. About 30,000 species are known to science.

112

King or Horseshoe Crab. Any animal shaped like a horseshoe should be lucky and apparently the Horseshoe Crab has profited by his shape. In bygone ages the Horseshoe Crab lived in the primordial seas with many other peculiar animals. Now all his former comrades have died and been fossilized, so we might know about them, and only he has persisted as a living type. His exact position in the Animal Kingdom is in doubt, but most scientists who are interested in him consider him an Arachnid, a problem he himself doesn't need to worry about.

King Crabs live in shallow water along the eastern coast of North America, where they burrow in the sand or mud. The head-thorax is a heavy, arched, horseshoe-shaped piece, with two pairs of eyes on the upper surface. The abdomen is also covered by a single piece of skeleton. At the posterior end is a long, heavy spine. On the under surface may be seen the various appendages that enable the animal to capture food, to crawl about, and to burrow in the sea bottom.

Courtesy, U. S. Bureau of Entomology

Scorpion. The body is thick but the tail is slender and flexible with a bulb full of poison and a sting at the end. The scorpion evidently believes in preparedness since the front end is also protected by two formidable pincers.

King Crabs are dark brown in color and reach a length of almost two feet. They move about actively at night feeding on clam worms and other small animals. When placed on their backs, they shove their long spine into the sand so as to turn the body enough to allow the feet to reach the bottom, and then with a mighty heave, turn over. Four other species of King Crabs are known; these all live along the eastern coast of Asia.

Scorpions. The Scorpion is famous for his sting. He does not go out looking for trouble, but will sting any animal that molests him. The insects and spiders on which Scorpions feed are seized by the large pincers, and, if too vigorous to handle, are stung. The poison is secreted by glands located in a bulbous-like swelling in the last segment of the abdomen, and is ejected through an opening near the end of the curved sting. Ordinarily this sting points downward, but when it is to be used, the tail is bent over the back and the sting points forward.

No Scorpions that live in the United States are dangerous to human beings, but in the tropics, where some of them grow to a length of eight inches, their sting is sometimes fatal.   In children the sting of a large scorpion causes vomiting, convulsions, and even death.   Scorpions are not affected by their own poison, hence never commit suicide by stinging themselves.

Courtesy, American Museum of Natural History

Scorpion. A mother with young on her back, with her pincers open for business and the sting on the end of her tail in position for instant action if necessary. About three inches long.

Scorpions are solitary animals except during the mating season. If two are found together "one is either courting or eating the other." The female often devours the male after mating. Scorpions do not lay eggs but bring forth their young alive; the young ride around on the back of their mother for about a week, and then shift for themselves. Scorpions are active at night and seek a hiding place at dawn. For this reason, while traveling in the tropics, it has always been our custom to shake out our shoes and clothing carefully in the morning before putting them on. About 300 species of Scorpions have been described; of these about 25 live in our eastern and southern States.

SPIDERS

Most people don't like spiders. Housewives must wage war against them continuously; those who wander through the woodlands often encounter their webs and must remove them from face and clothing; and practically everyone is afraid of their poisonous bites. Nevertheless, to nature lovers Spiders are among the most interesting of all animals. They occur all over the world and are very numerous both in number of species and number of individuals. About 15,000 species have been described and separated into 60 families; representatives of about 30 families and 1500 species live in the United States. Spiders are provided with poison claws with which they kill their insect prey, but with the exception of the Black Widow Spider of the South and the Tarantulas of the Southwest, are no more harmful to human beings than are beetles or ants.

Spiders are not insects; they can be distinguished from them easily because they have four pairs of legs instead of three pairs as in insects. Usually four pairs of eyes are present but some have a lesser number. Nature has provided Spiders with a digestive system that is a sort of food reservoir. Enormous quantities of blood can be taken in at one time and stored in the abdomen, being used up slowly as needed. This enables Spiders to live without food for periods up to a year or more in length.

The eggs of Spiders are laid in a cocoon or egg-sac made of silk. The cocoons are attached to some object or carried about by the mother. Within the cocoon the young prey upon each other so that only the most vigorous survive. This cannibalistic habit is not uncommon among Spiders in general; often, but not always, the female devours her smaller and weaker mate. As in insects, the Spider's body wall is rigid, hence in order to grow in size, it must be cast off at intervals. Usually the skin is molted eight or nine times before the full size is reached, and thereafter sometimes once per year.

Perhaps the most interesting activity of Spiders is web-building, although a type known as Hunting Spiders do not construct webs. The webs are woven of a fluid secreted by glands in the abdomen and forced out through several pairs of spinnerets. This fluid hardens into a silk thread on contact with the air. Cobwebs are of four principal kinds.

1. The flat webs are closely woven of long threads, crossed by finer ones in all directions, and connected with a tubular nest, where the spider hides and from which it runs out on the upper side of the web after insects that may fall upon it.

2. The netlike webs are made of smooth threads in large meshes, sometimes in a flat or curved sheet held out by threads in all directions. The spider lives on the underside, back downward.

3. The round webs are made of threads radiating from a common center and crossed by circular loops and spirals, part of which are adhesive.

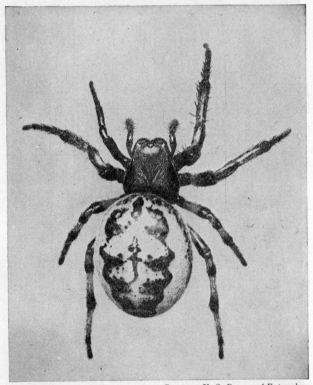

Courtesy, U. S. Bureau of Entomology

Spider. Spiders possess four pairs of legs, not three pairs as in insects; the head and thorax are fused together and the abdomen is often globular. Many spiders are beautifully colored.

4. The webs of certain species are composed in part of loose bands of silk. (Emerton.)

Some of the most common Spiders belong to the following seven groups:

1. *Tarantulas and Trap-Door Spiders.* Tropical and subtropical species, large, dark-colored, and hairy; the claws move up and down; about 40 American forms.

Photo by Spencer. Courtesy, Nature Magazine

Spider Web. A structure made by an orb weaver, photographed while beaded with dewdrops.

2. *Funnel-Web Spiders.* Species mostly large, and brownish, with long legs; webs in the grass or in the corners of buildings, flat in shape with a funnel-shaped tube near the middle in which to hide; about 50 American species.

3. *Comb-Footed Weavers.* Small, light-colored species with a comb on the last pair of legs for spreading silk over the insect prey; web more or less irregular, in corners of rooms, on plants, and fences; include the common House Spider and poisonous Black Widow Spider.

4. *Orb Weavers.* Large, often brightly colored, with long legs; web round and regular; about 120 American species.

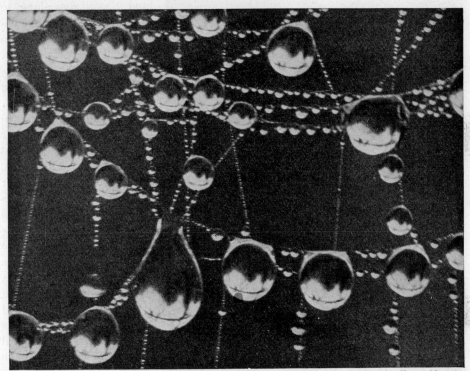

Photo by Spencer.   Courtesy, Nature Magazine

Spider Web. The threads spun by the spider when bejeweled with dewdrops in the early morning resemble strings of fairy pearls with here and there a glistening pendant.   Much enlarged.

5. *Crab Spiders.* Body short, broad, and crablike in shape; can walk sideways or backward as well as forward; do not spin a web, but lie in wait and pounce on prey; about 125 American species.

6. *Wolf Spiders.* Large, dark-colored, and hairy, with long, strong legs fitted for running; capture prey by pursuing it; no web, but line hiding place with silk; about 125 American species.

7. *Jumping Spiders.* Species with short body and legs fitted for running and jumping; can jump sideways and backward as well as forward; no web; they hunt for and spring on their prey.

Garden Spider. The web of an orb weaver, such as the Garden Spider, ranks high among the Wonders of Nature. We are apt not to appreciate the ingenuity and skill of the builder, nor the beauty of the web when completed, because Garden Spiders and their handiwork are so common. The plan of such a web is as follows: "After making the outer framework the radiating lines are formed. A line is stretched across the space so as to pass through the point which is to be the center of the orb. In doing this the spider may start on one side, and be forced to walk in a very roundabout way on the outer framework to the opposite side. It carefully holds the new line up behind it as it goes along, so that it shall not become entangled with the lines on which it walks; one or both hind feet serve as hands in these spinning operations.

The spider then goes to the point where the center of the orb is to be, and fastening another line there, it walks back to the outer framework, and attaches this line an inch or two from the first. In this way all of the radiating lines are drawn. The next step is to stay these radii by a spiral line which is begun at the center, and attached to each radius as it crosses it. The turns of this spiral are as far apart as the spider can conveniently reach, except at the center of the web. All of the threads spun up to this stage in the construction of the web are dry and inelastic. The spider now proceeds to stretch upon this framework a sticky and elastic line, which is the most important part of the web, the other lines being merely a framework to support it. In spinning the sticky line the spider begins at the outer edge of the orb, and passing around it fastens this line to each radius as it goes. Thus a second spiral is made. The turns of this spiral are placed quite close together, and the first spiral, which is merely a temporary support, is destroyed as the second spiral progresses." (Comstock and Herrick.)

Photo by Cornelia Clarke

Garden Spider. When at home he rests on a reinforced section of his web waiting for a fly to enter his parlor; then he rushes out and makes his captive secure.

Spiders differ in their methods of capturing insects. They may rest quietly in the center of the web, or retire to a nest at one side until an insect becomes entangled in the sticky thread. Then they rush out, sting their victim, and spin threads around it until all struggles cease. The spider itself never seems to become entangled in its own web. This is probably due in part to the skillful use of the claws and hairs on the feet. When the captured insect has become quiet, its juices are sucked out by the Spider.

Garden Spiders are mostly rather large, some of them reaching a length of one inch. They often possess long legs and a rounded abdomen. A number of species are brightly colored, as though to warn possible enemies to keep away from sudden death.

Photo by Cornelia Clarke

House Spider.   The villain that spins his web in the particular corner that doesn't get dusted before the tea party; a nuisance to every housewife.   Near by are several egg sacs.

House Spider.   At least one species of spider is universally considered to be a nuisance; this is the House Spider.   "It makes a large web in the corners of rooms, under furniture, and in the angles of fences and between stones.   It usually stands in the most sheltered part of the web, where a part of it is more closely woven than the rest, but not enough so to conceal the spider.   It occasionally makes the web in an open place where there is no shelter above, and then it sometimes carries a piece of leaf into the web and hides under it, as is the usual habit with some allied species. The webs of the young are usually more regular in form than those of adults.   A male and female often occupy the same web for a long time.   The eggs are laid in brownish pear-shaped cocoons, several of which are made in the same season by one spider and hang in the web."   (Emerton.)

House Spiders are about ¼ inch long, the male being smaller than the female. The abdomen is broad near the center, tapering to a point at the posterior end; in side view the abdomen appears much thicker than when seen from above.   No claims of beauty can be made by this species; the general color is dirty white to almost black; and the various marks of orange, brown, and black are often obscure.

Long-Legged Spider. Houses may be infested by another species that belongs to the same family as the common House Spider; this is the Long-Legged Spider which has such long legs that it is often confused with Harvestmen and called Daddy Longlegs. The body of this Spider is only about ¼ inch long, but the legs may be eight times as long as the body, as our photograph demonstrates. The cephalothorax is nearly round, and the abdomen slender. The body is generally pale brown in color.

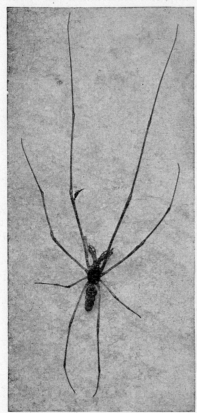

Photo by Cornelia Clarke

Long-Legged Spider. Fortunately this species of house spider prefers the cellar and hence does not deface the living rooms with its unsightly webs. We should think he might get tangled up in his extraordinarily long legs.

"This is a house spider, common in America and Europe, and probably imported. It lives in cellars where there is but little light and makes large, loose, flat webs, horizontal where there is a convenient place, or irregular to fit into surrounding objects. The spider hangs in the web with the abdomen directed upward, and when alarmed swings itself around rapidly so that it can hardly be seen. The egg cocoon is so thin that it does not conceal the eggs and is carried about in the spider's mandibles until the young hatch out." (Emerton.)

Crab Spiders. If all types of Spiders were lined up in a row, what amazing differences would be exhibited in size, shape, length of leg, color, hairiness, and in other physical characteristics! The behavior of the various species, if known, would be found to be equally varied. Thus Crab Spiders are short and flat, and the hinder end of the body is much wider than the front. The legs extend out on the sides and not forward and backward as in many species. Such an animal would certainly be mistaken at first sight for a Crab if it were observed creeping about the rocks at the seashore.

Crab Spiders not only look like Crabs but also walk like certain species of Crabs, that is, with a sidewise gait. They live in open places and frequent flowers. "They stand among the flowers, holding by the hind legs, with the front legs extended or bent in stiff and awkward positions, and wait for insects to alight on the flowers within reach." They are said to favor flowers of the same color as themselves; for example, white Spiders on white flowers and yellow-colored individuals on yellow flowers. The Crab Spiders in our photograph are representatives of one of the largest species, reaching a length of ½ inch and a leg spread of 1½ inches.   They occur all over this country and in Europe also.

Jumping Spiders.   The stay-at-home Spiders that build webs and then rest while their victims blunder into their "parlor" may enjoy all the comforts of a home, but the Jumping Spiders that live in the wide open spaces can boast of a freedom that is truly enviable.   They live in the tops of low plants, some of them spinning tubes in which to hide, lay their eggs, or spend the winter.   Among their accomplishments is the ability to walk sidewise and backward as well as forward.   Many of them are able to jump for considerable distances.

Jumping Spiders are from about ⅙ to ⅖ inch long.   They are stout and have a large cephalothorax which is broad in front.   The front legs are thicker than the

Photo by Cornelia Clarke

Crab Spiders.   The yellow one on the left seems to realize that it is difficult to see when resting on the yellow center of the daisy, and the white one on the right, when resting in the midst of the white petals.

others and no doubt play an important role in jumping.   The three pairs of eyes are peculiarly arranged; the front pair are very large and close together, whereas the other two pairs are much smaller, wider apart, and farther back.

Studies of Jumping Spiders have revealed the fact that these little creatures are as ardent and put on as much display in their love-making as larger animals, such as birds, do.   The courtship of a species only ⅙ inch long is thus described : "When some four inches from her he stood still, and then began the most remarkable performances that an amorous male could offer to an admiring female.   She eyed him eagerly, changing her position from time to time, so that he might be always in view. He, raising his whole body on one side by straightening out the legs, and lowering it on the other by folding the first two pairs of legs up and under, leaned so far over as to be in danger of losing his balance, which he only maintained by sidling rapidly towards the lowered side. . . . Again and again he circles from side to side, she gazing towards him in a softer mood, evidently admiring the grace of his antics.

Photo by Cornelia Clarke

Jumping Spider. The strong, stout legs of this species enable him to jump as well as to walk sidewise, backward, and forward. The largest pair of eyes shine like headlights and must terrify the unfortunate insect that gets too close.

This is repeated until we have counted a hundred and eleven circles made by the ardent little male. Now he approaches nearer and nearer, and when almost within reach whirls madly around and around her, she joining with him in a giddy maze. Again he falls back and resumes his semicircular motions, with his body tilted over; she, all excitement, lowers her head and raises her body so that it is almost vertical; both draw nearer; she moves slowly under him, he crawling over her head, and the mating is accomplished." (Peckham.)

Tarantulas and Bird-Eating Spiders. Thanks to the general use of bananas, we frequently have an opportunity to see Tarantulas and Bird-Eating Spiders that remain hidden on the trip north from Central or South America, but are widely advertised in the daily press when they suddenly emerge from a bunch of this tropical fruit. These Tarantulas do not belong to the same family as those of Italy after which the dance called the Tarantella was named. They are the giants of the Spider world, dark-colored and hairy. One species that lives in South America has a body two inches long and legs that spread out over seven inches. The largest of all Spiders belongs to this group; it lives in Guinea and has a body three and one-half inches long. Such Spiders are definitely known to catch small birds occasionally, although their regular diet consists of insects.

During the day Tarantulas live under stones and logs and in cavities in trees. At night they go on hunting expeditions, preying especially on large beetles. One of the best-known species lives in the southern and southwestern states. By many its bite is supposed to be deadly, but experiments indicate that it is no more serious than a bee sting. In spite of their size and strength, Tarantulas fall a prey

Tarantula. Very few spiders are larger than this one which lives in Honduras. Such hairy creatures are known to capture small birds as well as large insects. Life size.

to wasps. The wasp throws the Spider on its back and stings it in the nervous system so as to paralyze it; then it stores it up, still alive but helpless, as food for its young.

Trap-Door Spider. Even the fiercest of Spiders feel the need of protection, and many curious methods of obtaining security from enemies have been devised. Among these is that of the Trap-Door Spider, which builds a trap door not for the purpose of capturing its prey, but to keep from being preyed upon. The Trap-Door Spiders belong to the same family as the Tarantulas. Their jaws are provided with a special row of teeth and thus adapted for digging.

The Common Trap-Door Spider of California is $1\frac{1}{8}$ inches long and of a dark, chocolate-brown color. It digs a tunnel in the ground slightly wider than itself and about six inches deep. The walls of the tunnel are covered with a layer of silk so as to prevent it from collapsing, and the opening is closed with a lid of silk hinged

Photo by Hegner

Trap-Door Spider. At the left, above, the burrow in the ground is shown covered with a circular door somewhat larger than the cent lying near by. At the left, below, the door is pushed back on its hinge revealing the entrance. When dug out, the burrow is found to be about six inches deep and lined with whitish spider web; the spider is near the bottom at the right.

to the lining of the wall. In this species the lid is rather thick and has a beveled edge which fits into the top of the tunnel very snugly. Opposite the hinge are two little holes in the lid into which the Spider inserts its claws in order to hold the door shut. The top of the lid is covered by the Spider with earth or moss or grass like that of the surroundings so as to conceal it from view. These Spiders really seem rather timid as they venture forth on a hunting expedition only to scoot back into their burrows at the first sign of danger.

Wolf Spiders. All Spiders are hunters, but the hunters *par excellence* are the Wolf Spiders. The members of this family are not content to spin a web and wait for prey to come to them, but venture forth from their hiding places and chase down their victims. This habit was recognized by the ancient Greeks who gave them the name Lycosa, which means "wolf." Many of the common Spiders that we see running about through the grass with an egg sac attached to their spinning organs are Wolf Spiders. The young that hatch from these eggs are carried about on the back of their mother for some time before they are ready to shift for themselves.

Photo by Howes.   Courtesy, Nature Magazine

Face to Face with a Spider. When a spider is viewed from in front and highly magnified, the enormous legs and underslung body, combined with three pairs of glaring eyes and a bristling "chin," provide a monster we should not like to meet after dark, or any other time.

Photo by Howes.   Courtesy, Nature Magazine

Wolf Spider. Although endowed with a fierce disposition, the Wolf Spider takes good care of the young which are carried on the back of the parent. About 3 times life size.

One of our common species resembles very closely the true Tarantula of Southern Europe, which is a Wolf Spider. The name Tarantula was derived from Taranto, a city in southern Italy, where these Spiders are common. From the fifteenth to the 17th century an hysterical malady, called Tarantism, supposedly due to the bite of the Tarantula Spider, prevailed as an epidemic in the region around Taranto. The remedy for this disease was popularly believed to be violent dancing. This gave rise to the rapid, whirling dance called the Tarantella.

Silk Spiders. There are no family quarrels among the Silk Spiders because the wife is so much larger than her husband that no arguments are possible. The female of one species that is widely distributed in our southern states is about an inch long, whereas the male is only $\frac{1}{4}$ inch long. The difference in size between male and female is even more pronounced in a species that lives in the tropics; the female is two inches long and weighs 1300 times as much as the male, which is $\frac{1}{10}$ inch long. These comparatively gigantic wives are undoubtedly the Amazons of the Spider world.

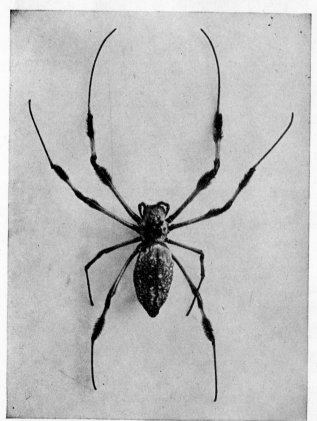

Courtesy, U. S. Bureau of Entomology

Silk Spider. The female of this species spins a great quantity of strong silk and constructs a web two or three feet in diameter. Three pairs of her legs are ornamented with tufts of hair. Natural size.

The male of our southern species is allowed to live in the web of his mate. This web is very large — two or three feet in diameter — and is supported by very strong threads of silk. This silk surpasses in strength that of the silkworm, and large quantities of it are produced, hence the name Silk Spider. The webs are built in shady forests and account for much of our discomfort when we run into spider webs while walking among trees. The legs of the female Silk Spider are very long; three of the four pairs are covered with tufts of hair.

Silk is used by certain Spiders as a method of transportation. On sunny days in autumn, large numbers of fine threads, the so-called gossamer threads, may be seen floating about over fields and meadows. On some of these threads, if we examine them, we shall find a small (young) spider. This aerial vehicle is of the creature's own construction, having been produced in the following manner: Having ascended some elevated spot, such as a clod of earth, the spider spins a few short threads, which are fastened to the ground. These it grasps in order to obtain a firm hold. Next it once more presses the silk glands against the supporting surface and elevates its abdomen. In this way a thread is formed, which, soon being seized by the wind, is drawn out longer and longer, is blown hither and thither, and thrown into tangles, so that finally a small raft is produced. At last the wind lifts both the raft and its maker up into the air, and the aerial journey begins. Perchance the

Courtesy, Nature Magazine

Black Widow Spider. This villain of the spider tribe is responsible for most of the human cases of poisoning due to spider bites. Near by is the egg sac. About 1½ times natural size.

little ship will be stranded — agreeably to the wish of its navigator — in some spot where the latter may enjoy its winter rest in security, in order in the following year to spread its species. (Schmeil.)

Black Widow Spider. The bad reputation suffered by Spiders in general is due largely to the crimes committed by the Black Widow. This species is dressed in velvety-black widow's weeds, and spends a large part of her time as a widow, since she eats her husband; these facts account for her name. The hour-glass-shaped, bright red spot on the under side of the abdomen is a conspicuous and easy mark of identification, and is responsible for another name for this species, that is, the Hour-Glass Spider.

Apparently nearly all cases of severe illness or death as a result of Spider bites may be attributed to Black Widows. Various parts of the world are inhabited by them, especially the tropics. They occur in considerable numbers in our southern states. The female has a globose abdomen and is about ½ inch long. She belongs to the Comb-Footed Weavers and makes a large web with a funnel-shaped retreat in the center.

Much ink has been shed in an effort to convict or acquit the Black Widow. The verdict is "guilty." Recently 150 cases were carefully studied, twelve of which had ended fatally. It was found that the bite results in acute pain, restlessness, nausea, labored breathing, and constipation. Treatment consists in administering a sedative and hot applications to lessen the pain, ammonia or strychnine to stimulate heart action, and a purgative.

Harvestmen, or Daddy Longlegs. These nomads of the fields are most frequently seen at harvest time when forced out of their hiding places or when wandering about at dusk in search of small insects. Their home is where they happen to

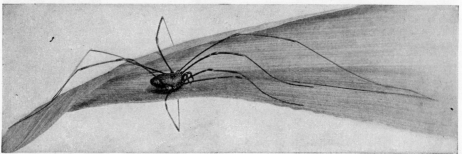

Photo by Cornelia Clarke

Daddy-Longlegs. The small, oval body hangs down in the center of the four pairs of long, slender legs.

be, since they have no silk glands and do not prepare a nest or hiding place as most Spiders do. In fact, they are not True Spiders, but are relegated to a separate group by themselves.

The extremely long legs of Daddy Longlegs are bent near the middle, and the small oval body hangs down among them as though surrounded by a fence of thin poles. These legs may afford some protection, but the continued existence of Harvestmen is no doubt due to the offensive odor of the fluid secreted by their stink glands. That certain legs are sensitive organs of touch is indicated by the fact that the second pair are waved about in the air like the cane of a blind man to aid in deciding where to go next. The legs become separated from the body very easily, as everyone who has tried to catch a specimen knows.

The eggs of Harvestmen are laid during the summer or autumn in the ground or in moist places under stones. They hatch in the spring. Where the weather becomes very cold in winter, most of the adults die in the autumn, but in warm climates, they may hibernate until spring arrives. About 75 species of Harvestmen have been reported from America.

MITES AND TICKS

Although of small size Ticks and Mites are of great importance to man because some of them inflict painful bites and others serve as carriers of disease germs. The parts of the body are all fused into one piece, and in most species this is oval in outline and somewhat flattened. Mites and Ticks are to be found almost everywhere. Some of them live in fresh water, others in salt water; some live on the ground, others on vegetation; some live on the outside of the body and others burrow into the body of other animals. Animals and plants, either living or dead, serve them as food; the parasitic species live largely on blood. Some of the more interesting families are as follows:

1. *Gall Mites.* Small, slender species that feed on plant juices and stimulate the plant to form growths called galls. Example, Pear-Leaf Blister Mite.

2. *Hair-Follicle Mites.* Small, slender forms that live in the sebaceous glands and hair follicles of man and domestic animals. Example, Hair-Follicle Mite.

3. *Bird Mites.* Species parasitic on birds, especially domestic fowls. Example, Chicken Mite.

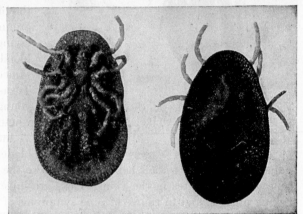

Photo by Herms

Fowl Tick. The head, thorax, and abdomen of ticks and mites are all fused into one piece. Four pairs of legs are visible on the under surface. The body of the Fowl Tick is soft. Its food is the blood of fowls. Magnified 5 diameters.

4. *Itch Mites.* Many forms parasitic on man, mammals, and birds. Examples, Human Itch Mite, Sheep Scab Mite.

5. *Harvest Mites.* Red, hairy species, common in the southern states. Example, Chigger, or Red Bug.

6. *Red Spiders.* Species destructive to fruit trees, house plants, and various crops. Example, Clover Mite.

7. *Fresh-Water Mites.* Many brightly colored species that live in fresh-water ponds. Example, Water Mites.

8. *Soft Ticks.* Parasitic forms that suck the blood of warm-blooded animals and transmit various disease germs. Example, Relapsing Fever Tick.

9. *Hard Ticks.* Species with a hard shield on the back; parasitic on mammals, birds, and reptiles; many of them carry disease germs. Examples, Texas Fever Tick, Rocky Mountain Spotted Fever Tick.

These are only a few of the twenty-six families into which mites and ticks are divided. All together about fifteen thousand species have been described and fifteen hundred of these are known to live in the United States.

Texas Fever Tick. The United States Department of Agriculture has many accomplishments to its credit, but few of them are more interesting or more far-reaching in their influence on human welfare than the discovery in 1893 that Texas Fever in cattle is carried from one animal to another by the common Cattle Tick.

Photo by Herms

Texas Fever Tick. The parasites that infest cattle and transmit the minute protozoans responsible for Texas fever in these animals. Adult female at the left and male at the right.

The annual loss in the South from Texas Fever has in the past reached over $60,000,000. Now, thanks to the discovery of the guilty Tick, an easy method of controlling the disease has been devised.

The Ticks gorge themselves on the blood of cattle, then drop to the ground and lay eggs, each female laying from 1000 to 5000. If the blood swallowed by the parent contained the parasites responsible for Texas Fever (see page 29), the young "inherit" some of them. These young "Seed Ticks" are about $\frac{1}{32}$ inch long. They climb up on a blade of grass, and when cattle brush against them, cling to their hair, creep down to the skin, and begin to suck blood. Some of the parasites in the young Ticks are injected into the cattle during the sucking process, and in course of time symptoms of Texas Fever develop.

The control of Texas Fever is quite simple. The adult Ticks die after they have laid their eggs. The young Ticks that hatch from these eggs will die in a few months if there are no cattle to feed on. Hence a pasture becomes free from Ticks if cattle are kept away from it for a few months. The Ticks can be removed from cattle by dipping the animals in a vat of crude petroleum or an arsenical mixture.

Rocky Mountain Spotted Fever Tick. If Ticks confined their attentions to the lower animals they would be obnoxious enough, but when they attack human beings

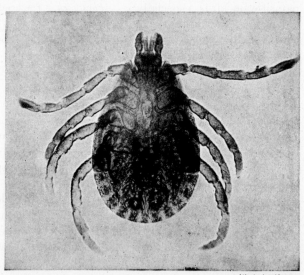

Photo by Hegner

Rocky Mountain Spotted Fever Tick. Ticks have four pairs of legs. This species lives on several different types of hosts and may transmit Spotted Fever to human beings.

and transmit terrible diseases they become a menace that demands eradication. The first step in the control of such a scourge as Rocky Mountain Spotted Fever is to learn the life history of the Tick that transmits it.   This has been done and the facts are quite astounding.

The disease is primarily that of gnawing animals, such as ground squirrels, chipmunks, woodchucks, and rabbits.   One female Tick lays from 2000 to 8000 eggs on the ground.   The young climb upon a blade of grass or into a bush until an animal comes within their reach.   They attach themselves, become engorged with blood, and drop to the ground again.   After digesting their meal they go through the same process again.   By this time they have developed into the adult stage and now seek out a third host, which is usually a cow, horse, or some other large mammal, and sometimes man.   The first two hosts are most often smaller, gnawing mammals.   This life-cycle requires two years for completion.   As in the Texas Fever Tick, the disease germs of Rocky Mountain Spotted Fever are passed on from parent to offspring in the egg.

Another important disease of man that is transmitted by Ticks is Typhus Fever.   This disease occurs especially in the southwestern United States, in Mexico, Central and South America, Europe, Asia, and Africa.

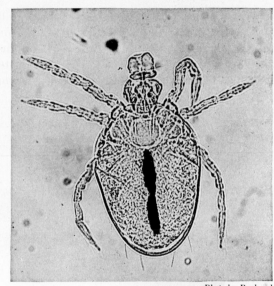

Photo by Benbrook

Harvest Mite, or Chigger.   Young Mites have only three pairs of legs.   They insert their beak into the skin and cause severe itching.   Enlarged 130 diameters.

Harvest Mites, or Chiggers.   The attacks of Harvest Mites remind us of the old woman who said there was one thing she never could resist and that was temptation.   We believe that no living man has sufficiently strong will power to resist scratching the intense itching of a Harvest Mite's bite.   These mites do not often assault us in the north, but in our southern states and in the tropics they may be such a pest as to take all the joy out of life.   Once in Darien, Panama, and again in the jungles near the southern boundary of Costa Rica, we were attacked by such large numbers that our bodies were covered with red blotches and the intolerable itching made sleep almost impossible.

Harvest Mites, or Chiggers, are not adults, but young Mites with three pairs of legs.   Being red in color they are often called Red Bugs.   They live on or near the surface of the ground and crawl up on any part of the body that comes near them. Since they are almost microscopic in size, they easily penetrate clothing, settling down usually around the ankles, knees, and waist.   Here they attach themselves to the skin, insert their piercing mouth parts, and begin to suck. After a few hours we become aware of their presence by the severe itching, and begin to scratch. A blister appears in the center of the red blotch in about a day, and in course of time a scab forms. The itching may last for several days.

Man is only an incident in the life of Chiggers, their normal hosts being small mammals, birds, reptiles, and amphibians. The best way to prevent their bites is to stay away from where they live. Otherwise sulphur sprinkled inside of one's clothing is said to repel their invasions. The itching can be reduced by hot salt baths, or by the application of alcohol, sulphur ointment, or carbolized vaseline.

Water Mites.   Mites apparently try not to be partial in their attentions, since they occur all over the world and attack not only animals that live on the earth but also those that live in the water. Thus the curse of many aquatic insects is the Water Mite. This species is closely related to the Harvest Mite, but has developed bristles on the legs, which aid in swimming, and has acquired the ability to stay under water for a considerable period. The young attack their prey and suck juices much as young Chiggers do.

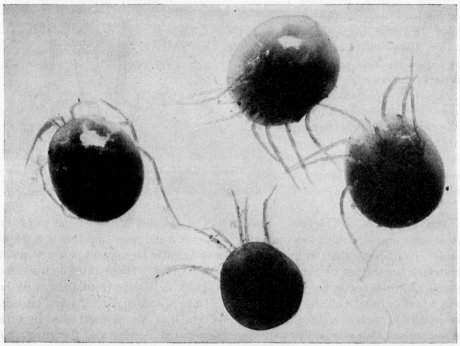

Photo by Cornelia Clarke

Water Mites. The body is a sort of dark red sac with four pairs of slender legs and a sucking beak.

Of the 500 species in the Water Mite Family, about 100 occur in America. A species common in pools and sluggish streams has a soft, oval, dark red body and is about $\frac{1}{3}$ inch long. They swim actively, or creep about over water plants, coming to the surface from time to time to breathe.   Apparently the chilliness of the water does not affect them, because they may be found late in the season when ice has already formed on the surface.

Other Mites.   Itch Mites are little whitish creatures just large enough to see. They burrow into the human skin and lay eggs under the surface.   If not destroyed by proper treatment, the young make fresh tunnels of their own and "seven-year

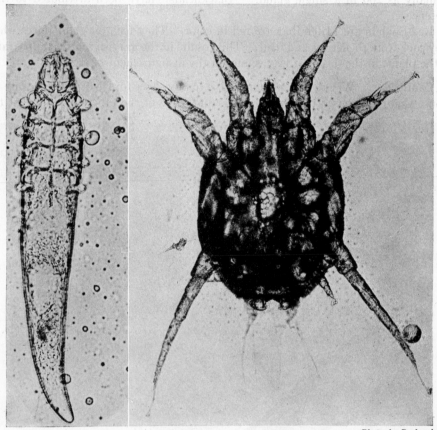

Photos by Benbrook

Follicle Mite, at the left.   A slender species that lives in the hair follicles and subaceous glands of the skin.   Magnified 100 diameters.

Scab Mite, at the right.   This species attacks the ears of rabbits and may cause their death.   Magnified 100 diameters.

itch" results.   Cleanliness prevents attack and sulphur ointment eradicates the Mites.   A nearly related species produces mange in horses, dogs, and rats.

Scab Mites do not burrow into the skin of their hosts, but cling to the outside, sucking blood.   In order to relieve the intense itching the afflicted animals rub the spot, thereby causing wounds on which scabs form.   Horses, cattle, and especially sheep are frequently attacked by these Mites.

Chicken Mites are a serious pest of poultry in some parts of the country.   During the day they hide in crevices, but at night come out and suck the blood of poultry. They are about $\frac{1}{20}$ inch long and gray in color, except when engorged with blood, which gives them a reddish tinge.   A 20 per cent kerosene emulsion will destroy them.

Face, or Follicle, Mites are elongated in shape and extremely small, being only about $\frac{1}{75}$ inch long and $\frac{1}{500}$ inch wide.   They live in the hair follicles and sweat glands of man and certain other animals, lying with their heads down, sometimes as many as 200 in a single gland.   "Blackheads" have been attributed to their presence.

Red Spiders are Mites that are red in color.   They feed on plant juices which they suck from the leaves and fruit.   This results in the grayish mottled appearance of the plant, in the death of leaves, and in the disfigurement of fruit.

Centipedes.   We are glad we don't have to buy shoes for Centipedes because the House Centipede has fifteen pairs of legs and some of the others have almost two

Photo by Cornelia Clarke

House Centipede.   Fifteen pairs of long legs give this species an overburdened appearance. It is active at night but can run rapidly and thus escapes capture.   About twice natural size.

hundred pairs. No wonder "hundred-legged worms" can run fast. About 1000 species of Centipedes are known. The body consists of a row of segments, each with a pair of long legs. The head bears a pair of long antennae and just back of the head are two curved poison claws. The body is flat, so that Centipedes can hide in crevices under logs and stones where they spend the day. At night they become very active and ferocious as they search for their living animal prey. The poison

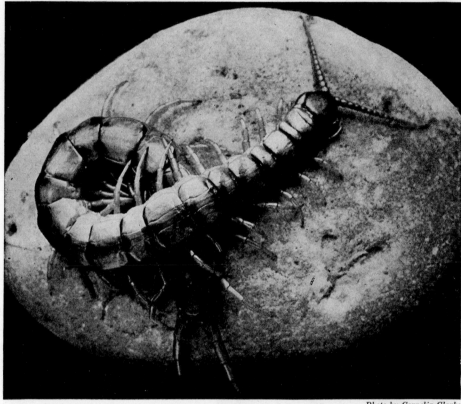

Photo by Cornelia Clarke

Garden Centipede. Twenty-one segments and the same number of pairs of legs give this species a flexible body and plenty of speed. Enlarged.

that can be ejected through the openings in the ends of the poison claws will kill small animals but is not dangerous to human beings.

The largest Centipedes live in the tropics; one species that occurs in the East Indies may reach a length of over one foot. The House Centipede lives in damp places in houses, especially in cellars. It is about an inch long and has very long legs, the last pair being two inches long. So delicate is this species that it cannot be captured without being injured. We ought to welcome the presence of this species since it feeds on cockroaches and other insects. The Garden Centipede is only about $\frac{1}{4}$ inch long. It lives in the soil and may injure flowers and vegetables by feeding on their roots.

Millepedes. Why "thousand-legged worms" should be endowed with so many legs is something of a mystery, since they are sluggish creatures and move very

Photo by Cornelia Clarke

Centipede. Under surface of the head greatly enlarged, showing the beadlike tentacles and the strong, black poison claws.

slowly. Some of them even prefer to roll up into a ball rather than attempt to escape. Nature is not accustomed to provide more legs for her children than are

Photo by Brownell

Millepede or Thousand-Legged Worm. Each segment bears two pairs of legs, yet Millepedes are sluggish creatures; they prefer to hide rather than run away from danger.

necessary, yet the "lords of creation" have only two, whereas Millepedes have two pairs on almost every segment of their bodies and may possess over a hundred segments. The body is cylindrical and the antennae short. Air enters through pores near the legs.

Millepedes live in dark, moist places and feed on decaying animal or vegetable matter, although some of them may eat the roots of living plants. The skeleton is hard and no doubt protects them from many enemies. Besides this they possess stink glands which emit a very unpleasant odor; in some species these glands secrete prussic acid. Millepedes lay their eggs in damp earth. The young have only three pairs of legs when they hatch but acquire more as they grow up. The common species in the Eastern and Central United States is about 1½ inches long and possesses thirty pairs of legs.

CHAPTER 10

INSECTS

Certainly God loved Insects or He would not have created so many of them. In no group is the abundance of animal life more strikingly demonstrated than in the Insects. Scientists for many years have been describing new species daily and at an ever-increasing rate, and about 625,000 different species are now known; probably three or four times that many are still to be discovered. The number of individuals is beyond all computation.

To most people the term Insect means any small living creature, and is often applied to animals that are not insects, and even to certain human beings who are considered beneath contempt. To scientists, on the other hand, Insects constitute a well-defined group of animals with certain characteristics that set them apart from all other animals. These characteristics include a body divided into three parts, head, thorax, and abdomen; a pair of feelers, or antennae, attached to the head; usually one or two pairs of wings and three pairs of legs attached to the thorax; and breathing apparatus consisting of a network of hollow tubes connected with the internal organs and opening to the outside by means of pores on the sides of the body. Insects do not breathe with any organs in their heads as we do through our nose and mouth.

The wings and legs of Insects enable them to fly, run, or crawl about with great freedom, and their small size makes it possible for them to live in all sorts of crevices. It is not strange, therefore, to find Insects living all over the world in almost every conceivable type of environment. Many of them spend much of their time flying about in the air; others walk or crawl about on the surface of the ground or on plants and other objects; a surprising number live under the ground; a very interesting group find fresh water a satisfactory habitat; and most of the higher animals serve as hosts for Insects that have taken up a parasitic mode of existence.

In order to live successfully in these various habitats and to leave offspring behind them when they die, many curious modifications are necessary. The variety of these modifications seems almost infinite. Many of them are referred to in the descriptions that follow, but in general the mouth parts, wings, and legs furnish the most conspicuous adaptations.

In most cases the mouth parts are adapted either for biting or for sucking. The majority of Insects with biting mouth parts, or mandibles, live on vegetation and have jaws capable of crushing their food; the rest live on animals and possess jaws that are sharp and pointed and fitted for biting or piercing. The Grasshoppers, for example, are provided with crushing jaws and the Tiger Beetles with piercing jaws. The other mouth parts help keep the food between the jaws while it is being ground up. Sucking insects, such as Mosquitoes, possess jaws for penetrating the tissues of plants or the skin of animals, and other mouth parts which form a tube through which juices are sucked into the body.

Wings are not always present. Some of the more primitive Insects, such as the Fish Moth, have no wings. In other Insects, such as the Bedbug and Flea, the wings have become lost as a result of degeneration. Typical Insects have four wings arranged in two pairs, but the True Flies have only two wings. The fore wings of Beetles are hard and sheathlike and are stationary during flight like the wings of an airplane, and the fore wings of Grasshoppers are leathery. Wings consist of outgrowths of the skin and are strengthened by a framework of minute tubes called veins. These veins are not blood vessels, but serve only to give rigidity to the wings. They are arranged differently in different species of Insects but are alike in individuals of the same species, hence they are of great value to scientists who wish to separate one species from another.

The legs of Insects are adapted for many purposes. Cockroaches and other running Insects are provided with long, slender legs; the Praying Mantis has fore legs for grasping other Insects; Grasshoppers have the hind legs much enlarged for leaping; the fore legs of the young Cicada are modified for digging; the hind legs of the Water Beetle are oarlike swimming organs; and the legs of the Honeybee are adapted for gathering pollen.

The eggs of Insects are of various sizes, shapes, and colors, and often very beautiful, although usually too small to be seen well without the help of a microscope. Some Insects resemble their parents when they hatch from the egg, but most of them do not; the latter undergo various changes in appearance before the adult form is attained. These changes constitute what is known as metamorphosis, a term meaning " change in form."

When such Insects as the Grasshopper hatch from the egg, they are without wings. As they grow they must shed their skin from time to time in order to accommodate their enlarging body. Finally wings grow out and the young, or nymph, becomes an adult. This type of metamorphosis is said to be incomplete. Complete metamorphosis, as in the Potato Beetle, involves a wormlike, active larva, which changes into a stationary pupa, inside of which the adult develops. Grubs are the larvae of Beetles, and Caterpillars the larvae of Butterflies and Moths. The pupae of butterflies are called chrysalids.

Losses due to Insects are enormous, reaching hundreds of millions of dollars every year in this country alone. Agricultural industries are the principal losers. Most of our insect pests have been introduced from foreign countries. Among these are the Hessian Fly, Elm Leaf Beetle, Leopard Moth, Gypsy Moth, Brown Tail Moth, Mediterranean Fruit Fly, Codling Moth, European Corn Borer, Bean Weevil, San Jose Scale, Cottony Cushion Scale, Japanese Beetle, Cotton-Boll Weevil, Argentine Ant, and a host of others.

The study of Insects is known as Entomology. Entomologists have been able to arrange all of the 625,000 or more known species of Insects into about 22 orders. It is difficult to list these without referring to their scientific names, but the derivation of the scientific names is given here as an aid to non-scientific readers. It will be noted that all insects are not "Bugs" but that the True Bugs are all included in one order. Various types of flies are listed, but only one order, the Diptera, contains True Flies with two wings.

Order 1. Thysanura (tassel tail).   Bristle Tails, Silver Fish, etc.
Order 2. Collembola (glue bar).   Springtails.
Order 3. Orthoptera (straight wing).   Cockroaches, Crickets, Grasshoppers, etc.
Order 4. Isoptera (equal wing).   Termites or White Ants.
Order 5. Neuroptera (nerve wing).   Dobson Fly, Ant Lion, etc.
Order 6. Ephemerida (ephemeron, a may fly).   May Flies.
Order 7. Odonata (a tooth).   Dragon Flies.
Order 8. Plecoptera (plaited wing). Stone Flies.
Order 9. Corrodentia (gnawing). Book Lice, etc.
Order 10. Mallophaga (wool eater). Bird Lice.
Order 11. Thysanoptera (fringe wing). Thrips.
Order 12. Anoplura (unarmed tail). Sucking Lice.
Order 13. Hemiptera (half wing). Bugs.
Order 14. Homoptera (same wing). Plant Lice, Scale Insects, etc.
Order 15. Dermaptera (skin wing). Earwigs.
Order 16. Coleoptera (sheath wing). Beetles.
Order 17. Mecoptera (length wing). Scorpion Flies, etc.
Order 18. Trichoptera (hair wing). Caddis Flies.
Order 19. Lepidoptera (scale wing).   Moths, Skippers, and Butterflies.
Order 20. Diptera (two wing).   True Flies.
Order 21. Siphonaptera (tube without wing).   Fleas.
Order 22. Hymenoptera (membrane wing).   Bees, Wasps, Ants, etc.

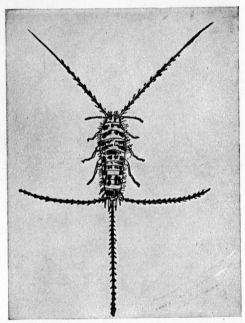

Silver Fish. An insect without wings but with silvery, fishlike scales covering the body. Two long feelers extend out from the head and three long bristles from the tail.

Silver Fish. Because of its primitive nature, the Silver Fish is accorded the honor of leading the largest division in the Parade of the Animal Kingdom. Like many other animals, it shuns publicity, not because of modesty, but because it has something to conceal. Thus when exposed to the light, it darts like a flash into some safe hiding place. Housekeepers are often horrified by the number of these insects they find in their closets or among their books at housecleaning time, but although Silver Fish enjoy eating the starch in book bindings, clothing, and even wall paper, they do very little, if any, real damage.

A close examination of a Silver Fish reveals a body covered with silvery scales, a condition that is responsible for the names Silver Fish and Fish Moth applied to the members of the group. Attached to the head are two long feelers, or antennae; and extending backward from the posterior end of the body are three bristle-like threads; these account for the name Bristle Tail, with which this little insect is also burdened.

We seldom see Silver Fish because they come out to feed only at night. A near relative of the Silver Fish is called the Fire Brat because it frequents hot places, especially the neighborhood of stoves and fireplaces.

Photo by Snyder

Termite or White Ant. The adults possess gauzy wings crowded with a network of veins. There is nothing whitish about the body of this fellow.

Termites, or White Ants. The social life of some groups of insects is surprisingly complex and rigidly organized. Whether such a fixed type of division of labor will ever evolve in human society even professors of sociology cannot be expected to prophesy with certainty. Termites are among the most interesting of these social insects. They are not "White" Ants, but are called by this name because they resemble ants somewhat in shape and habits and are often light in color.

A termite colony includes a female, the queen, one or several males, many soldiers, and a multitude of

Photo by Spencer

Termite or White Ant. The worker Termite has no wings; she does all the work while the queen lays the eggs and the soldiers guard the colony.

workers. The queen loses her wings when she starts a colony, and becomes a sort of egg-laying machine, with enormously enlarged abdomen. She lays all the eggs in a colony and is fed and cared for by the workers.   The workers are wingless and weak, but gather food, dig tunnels, and build nests, accomplishing marvels by their united efforts.   The soldiers have very large heads and strong jaws; it is their duty to protect the colony from attack by true ants and other enemies.

The food of Termites consists largely of wood and wood products.   They are very injurious in many tropical countries and even in parts of the United States, because they eat the wood in buildings and feed on books and various other articles made of wood pulp.   Termites work only in the dark and build tunnels for this purpose. They may bore away the inside of a timber in a building, leaving only a shell, or may eat away the inside of a book. In the tropics, railroad ties and many other objects are made of metal or concrete to prevent their destruction by Termites.   Buildings can be constructed so as to be Termite proof, but it is difficult to eliminate Termites when they have once established themselves.

Courtesy, American Museum of Natural History

Dobson Fly.   The adult has large, thin wings filled with veins; also formidable-looking jaws which, however, are probably never used.

Dobson Fly.   Fishermen are familiar with the nymphs of the Dobson Flies, which they call hellgrammites or crawlers.   The adults are large, measuring four or five inches across the expanded wings.   The wings are grayish-white and well-netted with veins.   The life of the adults is short; probably no food is eaten, but the important business of laying eggs is consummated.   Several thousand eggs are laid in a mass on some twig or stone.

The nymphs live under stones in rapidly flowing streams.   They possess strong jaws with which they capture other aquatic insects.   When fully grown, which requires three years, they are two or three inches long and dark brown in color. They are especially useful as bait for bass fishing.

Aphis Lion and Lace-Wing Fly. It is difficult to believe that the Aphis Lion is the offspring of a beautiful and dainty creature with delicate, gauzelike wings. "Its mother, the golden-eyed lace-wing fly, is a dear, sweet thing, that you would think fit only to go on an Easter card, so pale and aesthetic are her light-green wings. But her children are such regular little 'divvels' that she dare not lay her eggs in one mass, for the first one out would eat up all the rest. So she spins a lot of stalks of stiff silk and sticks one egg on the end of each, thereby giving each young one a chance for its life." (Sutherland.)

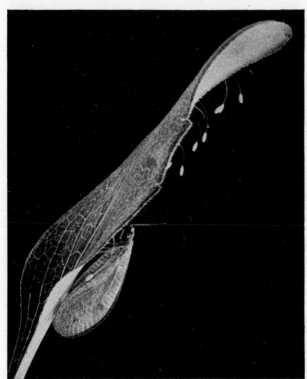

Courtesy, Nature Magazine

Lace-Wing Fly. The wings are thin and the many veins and cross-veins give it a lacelike appearance. Above are her eggs, each fastened to the end of a slender stalk.

The voraciousness of the Aphis Lions is not at all pleasant for the aphids, or plant lice, on which they feed, but is of great benefit to us, since aphids are very destructive to vegetation. In fact, we are coming to depend more and more on predaceous insects like the Aphis Lions to protect us from other insects that are injurious.

Aphis Lions are dark-colored, and about $\frac{1}{4}$ inch long. Their jaws are very large and pincer-like, well fitted for piercing the bodies of plant lice and sucking out the juices. Their mothers, the Lace-Wing Flies, are about an inch long and very fragile-looking. Their odor, however, is not as dainty as their appearance.

May Flies. Most of us look back upon our childhood as the happiest time of our lives. If the childhood period of the May Flies is correspondingly happy, we need not sympathize with them because they exist as adults for only a day or a night. The young, or nymphs, of the May Flies live at the bottom of ponds and streams, feeding on vegetable matter and minute animals. Three long, feathery filaments extend backward from the posterior end, and a row of delicate, platelike, fringed gills is attached on each side of the abdomen. These gills are filled with air-tubes, called tracheae, and are hence known as tracheal gills; they are present on several types of aquatic insects and serve to obtain oxygen from the water.

May Flies.   These delicate creatures live as adults for only a day and a night.   The slender body is terminated by two very long filaments and the fore wings are large and thin with many veins.

After two or three years of aquatic life, the May Fly nymphs creep out of the water, spread their newly developed wings, and fly forth. The May Flies differ from all other insects in one respect, and that is they shed their skin after they acquire wings; no other insect is known to do this. Large droves of adult May Flies often appear in the spring or early summer and carry out a sort of mating dance. Many of them are attracted to bright lights and go astray. The rest dance through part of the night and die before morning. The females, in the meantime, lay their eggs in sticky masses on submerged stones, and the nymphs that hatch from them in about a month spend the following two or three years growing up.

The wings of May Flies are delicate and contain many veins. The fore wings are much larger than the hind wings and when spread are about $1\frac{1}{4}$ inches across. Two or three very long, threadlike appendages extend backward from the posterior end of the abdomen. Their mouth parts are rudimentary and probably no food is consumed by the adults. They are indeed ephemeral as their family name Ephemeridae suggests.

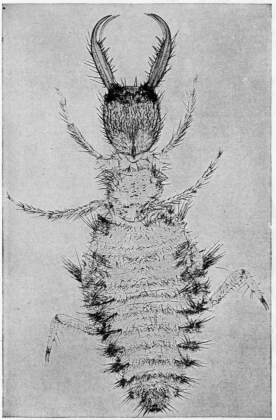

Courtesy, Ward's Natural Science Establishment, Inc.
Ant Lion. This larva of a harmless gauzy-winged insect has long, sharply-pointed jaws which are used to capture ants and other insects.

Ant Lions. The parents of the Ant Lion, like those of the Aphis Lion, are delicate insects with a slender body and long, gauzy wings. The larvae, or Ant Lions, however, are anything but delicate, and are furnished with a pair of the most deadly-looking jaws imaginable. The pitfalls of the Ant Lions "are usually found in sandy places that are protected from rain, as beneath buildings or overhanging rocks. In making these pitfalls the sand is thrown out by an upward jerk of the head, this part of the body serving as a shovel. The pits differ greatly in depth, according to the nature of the soil in which they are made. Their sides are as steep as the sand will lie. When an ant or other wingless insect steps upon the brink of one of these pits, the sand crumbles beneath its feet, and it is precipitated into the jaws of the ant-lion, which is buried in the sand, with its jaws at the bottom of the pit. In case the ant does not fall to the bottom of the pit, the ant-lion undermines it by throwing out some sand beneath it." (Comstock and Herrick.)

Dragon Flies and Damsel Flies. The Flying Dragon of the insect world fully lives up to his name not only as an aerial adult, but also as a youthful, aquatic nymph. The adult darts about with baffling rapidity, like "a living flash of light," as he leaves his perch to capture a mosquito or fly. His wings are large and gauzy,

Photo by Cornelia Clarke

Dragon Fly. The large, net-veined wings are held out like this when at rest. The head consists almost entirely of eyes.

always held out horizontally and never folded. His enormous eyes are made up of from 10,000 to about 30,000 minute facets and his vision is probably keener than that of any of the other animals in his habitat.

The nymphs of Dragon Flies differ from their parents in everything except their bloodthirstiness. They are rather sluggish, as they wander about on the bottom of a pond, or lie concealed among the debris waiting for some small animal to come within reach. Then, like a flash, the long, jointed lower lip is shot forth; the victim is impaled on the hooks at the end of it and drawn into the mouth, where the jaws soon cut it to bits. The nymphs breathe in a peculiar way. Water is drawn into and expelled from the posterior end of the intestine, and oxygen removed from it. Incidentally the nymph can propel itself forward by forcibly ejecting the water.

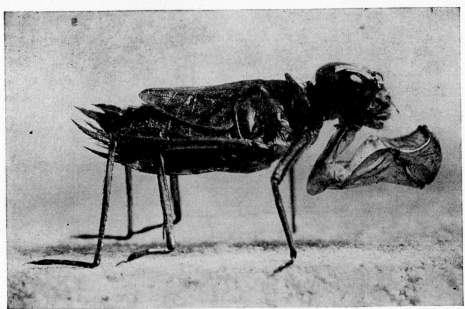

Dragon Fly. The nymph of the Dragon Fly is a Water Dragon. Under the head is a huge, jointed lower lip with hooks on the end that is extended for capturing its victims.

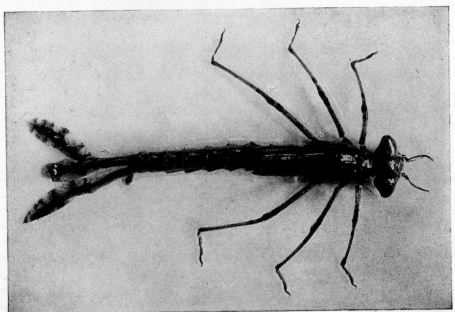

Damsel Fly. This nymph has at the end of the tail three flat gills with which it breathes.

The wings of the common green darner Dragon Fly are about two inches long and filled with finely netted veins. The abdomen is long and slender. The eggs are laid in the stems of water plants just below the surface, and the nymphs become one or two inches long.

Damsel Flies belong to the same group as the Dragon Flies, but are comparatively weak. The wings are held vertically over the back and the head is small.

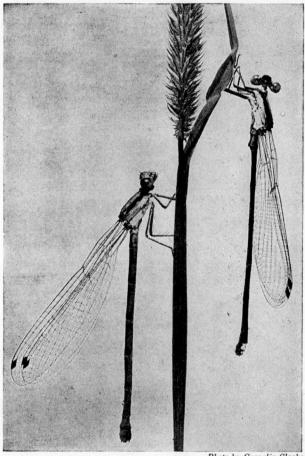

Photo by Cornelia Clarke

Damsel Flies. The abdomen is long and slender; the wings are held together over the back; and the head bears two large beadlike eyes.

They are to be found near streams and ponds. The eggs are laid in the stems of water plants and the nymphs live in the water; they have three flat gills at the posterior end. Some of the Damsel Flies are beautifully colored a metallic blue or green. They never stray very far from home, but can usually be found near the body of water in which they lived when they were nymphs. In flight they are slow and feeble but very graceful.

Stone-Flies. Very few habitats afford as much of interest to naturalists as small streams with quiet pools and stretches of swiftly running water. Many of the insects that are common among the rocks where the water runs most rapidly

are the nymphs of Stone-Flies. Many of them are about an inch long. They have flattened bodies, two filaments on the end of the tail, and threadlike tufts of gills at the bases of the legs.

Adult Stone-Flies are less interesting than the nymphs. They live in trees, but for only a short time, eating little or nothing. Their wings are folded in such a way as to extend down the back like a narrow band of network. The eggs are laid in the water.

Photo by Cornelia Clarke

Stone Fly. The nymph of the Stone Fly has a short body, two long feelers, and two filaments at the end of the abdomen. It lives in clear running water.

Caddis Worms and Caddis Flies. Houses in which to retire for rest or for protection are recognized as desirable by many of the lower animals, but especially by those that live in the water. Among these are the Caddis Worms. These

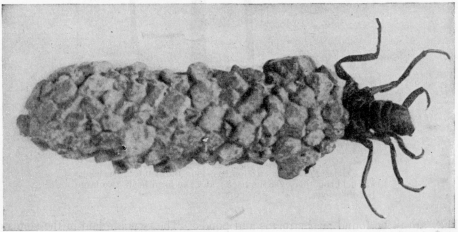

Photo by Essig

Caddis Worm. The larva of the Caddis Fly builds itself a stone house which it drags about and into which it can withdraw its head and legs when desired.

caterpillar-like larvae of the Caddis Flies build a long cylindrical tube, adding material in front as they grow larger, and dragging it with them as they crawl about on the bottom of a fresh-water stream or pond. Each species uses some particular kind of building material, such as grains of sand, small leaves, or minute sticks; these are glued together with saliva and lined with silk. At the hind end of the body are hooks which hold the Caddis Worm in its case.

Adult Caddis Flies are mothlike in appearance and range in size from about $\frac{1}{8}$ to over one inch in length. Their bodies are soft and the wings are held over the back like a slanting roof. They are seldom seen except around bright lights to which they are occasionally attracted in large numbers. Otherwise they are to be found on vegetation and stones near bodies of water. One interesting species spins a funnel-shaped web of silk in running water in which minute particles of food are captured as they are carried downstream.

Photo by Hegner

Bird Louse. This wingless parasite was found among the feathers of a crow. Size, $\frac{1}{10}$ inch long.

Bird Lice. Almost everyone at some time or other gets the idea that he could make a comfortable living raising poultry. When he attempts to put this idea into operation, he soon learns what Bird Lice are like. His chickens become restless and irritable and not the contented egg-layers of his dreams. When examined, little creatures about $\frac{1}{10}$ inch long and yellowish in color are glimpsed as they run about among the feathers.

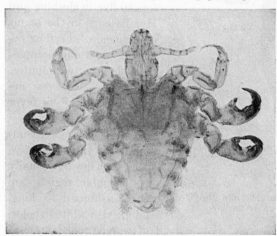

Photo by Hegner

Crab Louse. This grayish-white louse has particularly strong claws for clinging to hair. It lives on human beings.

These Bird Lice are wingless parasites. The body is flat and the chewing mouth parts strong enough to cut up bits of feathers and dead scales. The claws on the feet of the Lice scratch the skin, and the constant running about annoys the birds. The eggs are laid at the base of the feathers and the young become mature in about a month. Sodium fluoride is a practical drug to use to free the birds from the Lice. Painting the perches with nicotine sulphate is effective, and clean dust baths aid in getting rid of these little pests.

Sucking Lice. Delousing is a favorite pastime among monkeys and primitive people. We have seen monkeys in cages, Indians in La Paz, Bolivia, and Tagalogs in the Philippines picking Lice out of each other's hair, crushing them, and sometimes eating them with relish. However, these disgusting parasites are no longer found among intelligent people, except in unusual situations such as army camps. Many animals serve as hosts for Sucking Lice, but those we are most interested in are the three species that live on human beings.

Head Lice are most numerous above the ears and on the back of the head. They are about ⅛ inch long and gray in color. The legs are stout and the strong, recurved claws are fitted for clasping and holding hairs. The mouth parts form a tube in which are the piercing organs. The eggs, called nits, are cemented to the hair. The female lays six or seven eggs per day and about 250 all together.

The Body Louse is the "Cootie" famed in the annals of the A.E.F. It is similar to the Head Louse, but slightly larger. It prefers to live in clothing and lays its eggs in the seams of garments. Feeding occurs at night and occupies from three to ten minutes. Body Lice are very active, especially on fever patients.

Crab Lice are less common than the other two species. They live usually in the pubic region, are nearly as broad as long, and grayish-white in color.

Photo by Hegner

Body Louse, or Cootie. The Cootie is larger than the Head Louse and more famous, but otherwise similar.

Usually they are content to cling to one spot instead of wandering about.

Head Lice and Body Lice, especially the latter, are responsible for the transmission of several important diseases. Among these are typhus fever, trench fever, and relapsing fever. Heating clothing to a temperature of from 130° to 140° F. for ten minutes kills both adults and eggs.

The hog louse lives on domestic animals, especially swine. The dog louse, blood-sucking horse louse, and short-nosed ox louse are other common types.

Fleas. Fleas are perhaps the champion jumpers of the Animal Kingdom. A Human Flea can jump eight inches vertically and thirteen inches horizontally, that is, about 150 times its own length along the ground and 100 times its own length up into the air. Crickets, grasshoppers, and kangaroos are obviously outclassed. Fleas not only avoid capture by jumping, but possess smooth bodies flattened from side to side, which enable them to slip easily from between one's fingers. They are degenerate creatures without wings and with a minute head, but are admirably constructed for moving about freely among the hairs of the animal on which they live. They are bloodsuckers.

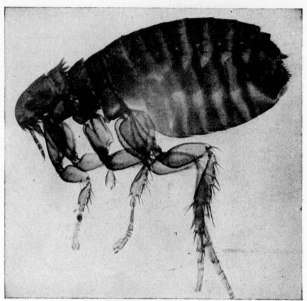

Photo by Hegner

Dog Flea. This species may also live on human beings. The head is extremely small and the legs are fitted for jumping.

To us the most interesting Fleas are the Human Flea, the Dog and Cat Flea, and the Jigger, Chigoe, or Sand Flea. All three species will attack man as well as other warm-blood animals. Human Fleas are reddish-brown in color and nocturnal in habit. They live in cracks in the floor, in rugs, and other places of concealment. Both these and the Dog and Cat Flea occur all over the world. Young Fleas are legless and eyeless and seem quite helpless, nevertheless they find enough food among dust particles to grow to maturity.

Fleas are pests not only because of their bites, but because certain species carry disease germs from one animal to another. The most guilty is the Rat Flea, which carries the germs of plague from rat to rat and from rat to man. Other gnawing animals, including ground squirrels, may be infected with plague and pass it on to man through the agency of their Fleas.

The Sand Flea, Chigoe, or Jigger is the smallest Flea known, measuring only $\frac{1}{25}$ inch long. It is a native of the New World, but has been introduced into other countries. The females burrow into the skin, especially under the toenails and between the toes. Here they swell up until they are as large as a pea. The wounds are inflamed and painful and may become ulcerated.

CHAPTER 11

STRAIGHT–WINGED INSECTS OR ORTHOPTERA

It is difficult for anyone to escape either seeing or hearing some of the Straight Winged Insects, since they are rather large, are frequently found around the house or garden, and many of them are quite noisy. They may be divided into six families. Three of these are adapted for walking or running; these are the Cockroaches, Walking Sticks, and Mantids. The other three families are adapted for leaping; these are the Short-Horned Grasshoppers, Long-Horned Grasshoppers or Locusts, and Crickets.

Most of the members of these six families possess four wings; the fore wings are often thickened and parchment-like, and the hind wings are folded like a fan beneath them. The mouth parts are fitted for chewing, and in all but one family are used for grinding up living vegetation or dead organic substances. The Mantids are carnivorous, living largely on other insects. The young of the Orthoptera are nymphs, which gradually take on the appearance of the adults as they increase in size.

Photo by Doten

Cockroach. The living Roach is feeding on a dead companion. He has a flat body, slender legs for running, and long feelers.

Cockroaches. Obscurity is very desirable to a Cockroach, for no one is too tender-hearted to step on a Cockroach, and the Roaches seem to know this. They work while we sleep, and hence may escape our notice unless we get hungry during the night and turn on the light in the kitchen unexpectedly. Fortunately sodium fluoride dusted where they spend their evenings will soon destroy them. A combination of flour and plaster of Paris has been used effectively, especially when water was placed close by; the mixture makes the Roaches thirsty; they drink water, and the plaster hardens in the stomach, giving results that are most gratifying.

Cockroaches are adapted for running, and also for hiding in small crevices; their feet are slender and their bodies very flat.   Most any kind of food will satisfy them.   "Moist articles are preferred, and a warm, wet dishrag which is not washed after using has almost irresistible attractions."   We object to Cockroaches not so much because of the small amount of food they eat but because of their disgusting odor.

Four kinds of Cockroaches may inhabit our houses, the most common being the yellowish-brown German Cockroach. This species was imported from Europe and first noticed in connection with the Croton aqueduct in New York City and hence sometimes called the Croton Bug. The other three species are the American Cockroach, Australian Cockroach, and Oriental Cockroach, or "Black Beetle."

To fully appreciate Cockroaches one must travel in the tropics, since in hot moist countries they reach their largest size and greatest number.   Many a night we have heard them fly about our room hitting the wall with a bang, and have found them hiding in our boots at daybreak.

Short-Horned Grasshoppers.   The feelers of certain Grasshoppers are short and project out from the head like horns, hence the name of this family group. Short-Horned Grasshoppers are common everywhere in field, meadow, garden, and roadside.   They leap quickly out of the way when disturbed by an intruder or fly up at our approach.   The femurs of the hind legs are much enlarged to accommodate the muscles which are required for a jumping animal of this type.

Courtesy, U. S. Bureau of Entomology
American Locust.   The feelers, or "horns," are short, the hind legs are fitted for leaping, and the wings are folded over the back.

The vegetation eaten by the Grasshopper is held between the two grinding jaws by the upper and lower lips.   Near the anterior end of the abdomen on each side is an organ of hearing.   The eggs of Grasshoppers are laid in a hole in the ground about an inch below the surface.   Here they remain during the winter.   In the spring the young emerge from the eggs as nymphs, resembling their parents in many ways, but differing from them especially because of their large heads and absence of wings.   As growth proceeds the wings grow out and the adult condition is attained.

The American Locust is a species about three inches long that occurs in the southern states and north to Connecticut and west to Iowa.   A more widely distributed species is the Red-Legged Locust.   The Carolina Locust is also common and widespread.   The Locusts we read about in the Bible are likewise members of the Short-Horned Grasshopper family.

Photo by Cornelia Clarke

Grasshopper.   A bug's-eye view from in front.

During our childhood in the Middle West the Rocky Mountain Locust was frequently mentioned in no uncertain terms, for he was loved by none and hated by all.   At that time, in Kansas, Iowa, Nebraska, and neighboring states, hordes of these large Grasshoppers were brought by the northerly winds from their breeding grounds in the northwest, and proceeded to eat up all the crops, "lock, stock, and barrel."   Nothing green was left, and on several occasions what almost amounted to a famine resulted.

"Falling upon a cornfield, the insects convert in a few hours the green and promising acres into a desolate stretch of bare, spindling stalks and stubs. . . . Their flight may be likened to an immense snowstorm, extending from the ground to a height at which our visual organs perceive them only as minute, darting scintillations, leaving the imagination to picture them indefinite distances beyond. . . .   In alighting, they circle in myriads about you, beating against everything animate or inanimate, driving into open doors and windows, heaping about your feet and around your buildings, their jaws constantly at work, biting and testing all things in seeking what they can devour."

No method of checking the ravages of migrating locusts has been devised, but the eggs and young are being destroyed in the regions where breeding occurs, and hence no more devastating migrations are expected.   The young that hatch from eggs laid by the insects after their migration do not thrive in their new home and die before reaching the adult stage, hence the spread of this destructive species is prevented.

Katydids. "*Katy did; she didn't; she did.*" These belligerent notes come from the branches of the trees where Katydids spend the night.   It is the males only that carry on the argument, and on dark cloudy days, as well as at night, the hostile, rasping song is repeated *ad infinitum.*   Next morning, if we look sharply, we may find Mr. Katydid the exact color of the leaf upon which he sits, and see his

Photo by Cornelia Clarke

Katydids.   The male is at the right and the female at the left.   The hind legs look like jointed stilts.

beautiful, finely veined wings folded close over his body, and the long, threadlike antennae moving airily above his waggish green eyes.

Katydids are classed among the Grasshoppers.   They live chiefly on leaves or twigs but will take animal food if accessible.   Their chief enemies are birds, and very still they keep in the daytime when birds are about.   The "song" is produced by rubbing together the bases of the wing-covers.

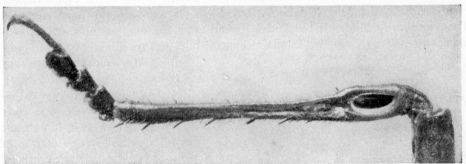

Photo by Cornelia Clarke

Katydid.   The leg of the Katydid is enlarged just below the joint at the right so as to accommodate the hearing organ or "ear."

In the autumn the flattened, slate-colored eggs are laid in two rows along a twig. These eggs hatch the following spring.   The young, as well as the adults, feed on the foliage of trees.

Katydids belong to the family of Long-Horned Grasshoppers, a family which includes also the Meadow Grasshoppers, Cricket-like Grasshoppers, and Shield-

Backed Grasshoppers. They have very long, slender antennae, and the females are provided with a swordlike egg-laying apparatus, the ovipositor.

Not all Grasshoppers have wings. Some of the wingless species have the back

Photo by Cornelia Clarke

Camel Crickets. These look like Crickets but are really Grasshoppers without wings.

arched, the head bent down between the fore legs, and a low-slung abdomen. This gives them the appearance of crickets and the name Camel Crickets. They live under stones and boards, in caves and cellars, and in other dark, moist places, coming out at night to forage.

Crickets. What good cheer is associated in our minds with the word *cricket!* Thanks to Dickens, we feel that a cricket on our hearth signifies hospitality and home comfort. Yet most of the members of the Cricket family are injurious to vegetation. The common species of Crickets may be divided into Tree Crickets, Field Crickets, and Mole Crickets. The Field Crickets are the most common. These are brown to almost black and abound everywhere in pastures and gardens under stones or in the earth. In all Crickets the hind legs are thickened for jumping, and by means of leaps they can elude their enemies.

Courtesy, Nature Magazine

Mole Cricket. A front view reveals the powerful fore limbs that are used for digging in the ground. Enlarged.

Crickets are very catholic in their tastes, as their dietetic range includes fruit, vegetables, grass, carrion, or even their weaker brothers, for we regret to admit that our cheerful Cricket is a cannibal. "Of about forty imprisoned together in a box, at the end of a week but six were living, the heads, wings, and legs of their dead companions showing that the fittest had survived."

During the late summer the chirping of the Crickets is incessant. This chirp is really the love song of the males calling to their mates.   The sound organ is most interesting, being an adaptation of the wings.   Each wing-cover is provided with a file and a scraper.   When the Cricket makes his chirp, "he elevates his wing-covers

Photo by Cornelia Clarke

Tree Crickets.   These delicate-looking, light-colored inhabitants of trees are persistent "musicians."

at an angle of about 45° with the body; then, holding them in such a position that the scraper of one rests upon the file of the other, he moves the wing-covers back and forth sidewise, so that the file and the scraper grate upon each other.   This throws the wing-covers into vibration, and produces the call."

Photo by Ramme.   Courtesy, Nature Magazine

Hedgehog Locust.   A face view of this African species makes us thankful this insect is only a Grasshopper.

Walking Sticks.   Did you ever see a stick walking?   Well, we have.   It is not a very exciting performance.   The eye notices rapidly moving bodies more readily than stationary objects, hence the method adopted by Walking Stick Insects to escape the attention of their enemies is to move very slowly and furtively.   When at rest, they are easily overlooked, so closely do they resemble a twig in both shape and color.   Some species of Walking Sticks are further protected by a secretion that can be ejected from certain glands, a secretion that only one word in the English language describes satisfactorily, the word *stinks*.

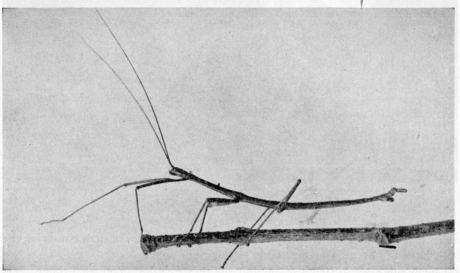

Photo by Cornelia Clarke

Walking Stick.   The body is colored and shaped like a twig and the long legs and antennae are moved so slowly that they seldom attract the eye.   These characteristics serve to conceal this insect in the trees where it lives.

Housekeeping in the Walking Stick family is the least of their troubles.   They live in trees, and breakfast, luncheon, and dinner consist of green leaves containing plenty of vitamins.   The children are neither heard nor seen.   The mother drops her eggs one by one, and the young hatch out on the ground; they never know what mother-love is.   Where Walking Sticks are abundant the eggs dropping on the leaves below make a sound like the pattering of rain drops.

In the tropics, Walking Sticks develop wings and become Walking Leaves or Leaf Insects.   Their wings may be green and resemble living leaves, or brown and resemble dead leaves.   Our common northern Walking Stick is about three and one-half inches long, brown or green in color, and with long, slender legs.   Certain species that occur in the tropics grow to a length of ten inches and are among the largest living insects.

Praying Mantis.   "What's in a name?" is demonstrated by the sanctimonious Praying Mantis which holds his fore legs in an attitude of prayer while waiting for some other insect to happen along that he can capture with them and devour.   Preying, not Praying, Mantis would be a more suitable name for this little hypocrite. The fore legs are not used for walking but devoted entirely to capturing insects; they are large and provided with strong spines which adapt them for grasping and holding their prey.

"There are few more striking insects than a Mantis in its natural habitat waiting for food; balanced on the two pairs of legs, it looks from side to side, turning the head with quick motions and seeming to look intently from the large eyes; the antennae active, moving constantly, the fore legs drawn up under the head but

Courtesy, Nature Magazine

Praying Mantis.   The fore legs are held in an attitude of prayer, but are provided with spines used to capture other insects.   Size, 3 inches long.

ready to dart out; the creature is so intent, the attitude so expectant and yet suggestive of cunning; in an instant it stiffens, becomes rigid, every part still, the long fore legs extended; should its prey alight near, it moves stealthily, stalking it as a cat does a bird, gradually drawing nearer till its fore legs strike and the insect is held securely, drawn up to the mouth and devoured."   (Lefroy.)

Mantids are more abundant and generally larger in the tropics than in the north.   Our common northern species is two or three inches long and grayish-brown or greenish in color.   The eggs are laid in small groups and surrounded by a protective covering; these cases of eggs are attached to twigs in the fall and hatch the following spring.

The devout attitude of Mantids combined with their predatory habits has stimulated many superstitions. The ancient Greeks attributed supernatural powers to them. In some countries they are believed to be soothsayers, and in the East they are said always to face toward Mecca.

Earwigs. For hundreds of years Earwigs have been accused of crawling into the ears of sleeping persons. Why they were selected instead of some other insect is a puzzle, since entomologists have exonerated them from all guilt. Earwigs are easily distinguished by the large pincers they carry on behind; the function of these is practically unknown. Their front wings are thick and too short to cover the body, and the hind wings are concealed under them, being folded with the aid of the pincers both lengthwise and crosswise. Our common species are about ⅔ inch long.

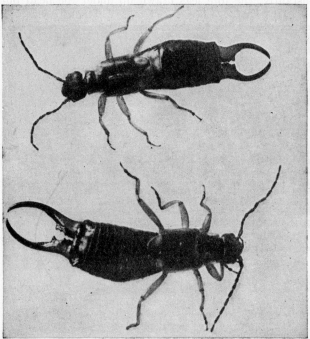

Photo by Essig

Earwigs. The wings are very short. The pincers at the end of the abdomen are harmless and do not pinch. Size, ⅔ inch long.

Earwigs hide under stones and logs, or in holes in the ground during the day, and come out at night to dine. Their breeding habits are unique. The oval, pearly-white eggs are laid in the earth and the mother sits on them like a hen. If removed and the eggs scattered, she gathers them together again with her jaws and continues her sitting. The young, when hatched, use the mother as chicks do a brooding hen, crowding under her and remaining there for several hours.

CHAPTER 12

TRUE BUGS OR HEMIPTERA

To most people any insect is a bug, but to an entomologist all bugs are True Bugs and belong to a large group of Half-Winged Insects. Many of the True Bugs have no wings, but the typical species have two pairs, the fore wings being thickened about half way out from the base, hence "half-wing," and the hind wings membranous and folded beneath the fore wings. The mouth parts are adapted for piercing and sucking and form a beak within which are the slender, piercing organs. The young hatch as nymphs which gradually grow to the adult condition. Many True Bugs live on vegetation; others are aquatic and prey on small animals in the water; and some are parasitic on birds and mammals.

A few of the families of True Bugs are the Water Boatmen, Back Swimmers, Water Scorpions, Giant Water Bugs, Water Striders, Bedbugs, Assassin Bugs, Lace Bugs, Chinch Bugs, Squash Bugs, and Stink Bugs.

Photo by Cornelia Clarke

Giant Water Bug. This is the familiar Electric Light Bug. The front legs are used for grasping other insects; the hind legs are effective swimming organs.

Another large group of insects were formerly combined with the True Bugs, but are now separated from them by entomologists. These are the Cicadas, Spittle Insects, Tree Hoppers, Plant Lice or Aphids, Scale Insects, and many others. A

161

large number of these are wingless. If wings are present, the fore wings are not thickened at the base. As in the True Bugs, the mouth parts are adapted for piercing and sucking, and the young are nymphs.

Giant Water Bugs, or Electric Light Bugs. Some of us may think we are henpecked, but we have certainly not descended to the indignity some of the Giant Water Bugs have to submit to. The high-handed frau fastens her eggs on her husband's back with water-proof glue, and he meekly and ingloriously resigns himself to this mortifying load. The process is well worth recording. "The female places herself on top of the male, her thorax extending outward and her legs hooked

Photo by Cornelia Clarke

Water Bugs. The female of this species fastens her eggs to the back of the male, where he carries them about until they hatch.

under him; now starting somewhere near the middle and sidling along every little while, she works her way around him as she fastens her eggs on his back by means of the water-proof glue secreted for that purpose. The male all the while hangs from the surface, back up, with his legs curled up under him, bravely bearing up under his burden." (Torre-Bueno.)

Many of us are familiar with these large bugs because they are attracted by lights and sometimes collect in large numbers around electric lamps. They are giants among their kind; some of them are over four inches long, and are the largest living Bugs. Other aquatic insects, snails, and small fish are captured with the first pair of legs, which are adapted for grasping, and then killed with the strong beak.

Water Boatmen. Another group of Bugs that are easy game for the amateur fresh-water biologist are the Water Boatmen. These are oval in outline, with a flattened, gray and black-mottled body usually less than $\frac{1}{2}$ inch in length. The middle legs are long and slender and have two claws at the end. The hind legs are also long, but flattened, forming oarlike swimming organs.

Water Boatmen are excellent swimmers. They can be distinguished easily from their near relatives, the Back Swimmers, because they swim in the correct, upright position, whereas the back swimmers swim upside down. In order to breathe under water the Boatmen "dive down with their bodies wrapped in a glistening blanket of air and being so much lighter than the water they have to anchor in order to stay below. They do this by almost imperceptibly catching one claw of the middle leg into some plant stem and hang there atilt in the water for long intervals. Indeed they spend a good part of their time on the bottom for they feed upon the soft vegetable ooze which gathers there, diatoms, desmids, filamentous algae, and the like." (Morgan.)

Sometimes Water Boatmen occur in enormous numbers. Many years ago we secured funds for a collecting trip to Mexico on condition that we would return with at least 20,000 insects for the University of Chicago, under whose auspices the expedition was organized. Soon after reaching Mexico City we visited Lake Texcoco, where we found the water near shore so crowded with Boatmen that we collected hundreds of them in our insect net in a few minutes and could have fulfilled our obligation, with respect to the number of insects to be secured, in half an hour had we so desired. At that time, biologists were more interested in variations of individuals within a species than they are now, hence it was perfectly legitimate to collect large numbers of one species.

The natives of Mexico are said to use the eggs of Water Boatmen as food. They float bundles of sedges

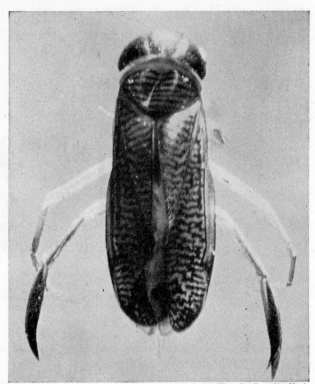

Photo by Cornelia Clarke

Water Boatman. A handsome water bug with legs long and oarlike.

in the water in localities where these Bugs breed; the Boatmen lay their eggs in the bundles in enormous numbers; then the bundles are taken out of the water and dried. The eggs are shaken off, gathered together, ground up into a sort of flour, and baked. The gregarious habits of the Boatmen lead to the destruction of large numbers of them, since thousands can be collected easily in a few minutes. Both eggs and adults are harvested and used extensively as food for birds and fish.

Back Swimmers.   The back of the Back Swimmer is shaped like the keel of a boat.   True to their name they swim on their backs, thus distinguishing themselves from all other aquatic Bugs.   Back Swimmers are rather small, being from $\frac{1}{5}$ to $\frac{1}{2}$ inch long.   The fore and middle legs are not much modified, but the hind legs are extremely long and fringed on the edge, forming very efficient swimming organs.   The colors are usually a combination of bluish-black and creamy white. The eggs are laid in the stems of plants in slits cut by the ovipositor of the mother. Egg-laying occurs from March to June.   As many as two hundred and fifty two mature eggs have been counted in a single female.   The adults live for at least one year.

"The favorite attitude of the back-swimmers is floating on the surface of the water, back downward, with the hind end of the body projecting sufficiently to admit of air being drawn into two air chambers on the ventral side of the body.   There are two longitudinal furrows on the ventral side of the abdomen arched over by

Photo by Cornelia Clarke

Back Swimmers.   Famous because they swim on their backs, these bluish-black and creamy-white bugs propel themselves through the water with their extremely long legs.

long hairs thus forming two tubes into which air is taken.   The spiracles open into these tubes."   (Comstock and Herrick.)

Back Swimmers are "extremely active, with strong grasping fore legs and a beak with which they can inflict a burning sting, the effect of which may last for some time in persons susceptible to poisons.   Although they are themselves predaceous, their young are preyed upon by nearly every other carnivorous insect including adults of their own kind."   (Morgan.)

Water Strider.   Walking on the water is considered to be a miracle, but the insects belonging to the Water-Strider Family spend a large part of their lives skating about on the surface of fresh-water pools.   Their bodies are slender and light in weight and the second and third pairs of legs are very long and thin.   They do not sink, because their legs are so long they spread out over a large area and are covered with hair that does not become wet.

The surface film thus holds them up while the second pair of legs push ahead and the hind pair do the steering. The front legs are held up ready to capture any insect that comes within reach. Often the dimples made by the legs cast large shadows that move about on the bottom and are usually more conspicuous than the Striders themselves.

The eggs are laid in the water and the nymphs resemble "frisky young spiders." Frequently Water Striders are parasitized by little, young, red, water mites that cling to their bodies while changing into adults.

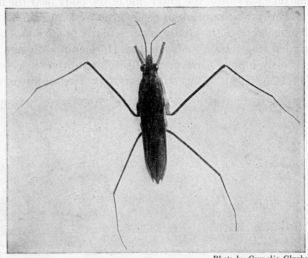

Photo by Cornelia Clarke

Water Strider. The middle and hind legs are so long and slender they sustain this bug as it rests on the surface of the water. The front legs are held up ready to capture small insects.

Stink Bugs.   Aquatic Bugs are relatively easy to deal with since they are much restricted in their distribution by reason of their habitat, and seem to the layman to differ from one another more distinctly than do the Terrestrial Bugs.   Many of the latter are of about the same shape and size and do not seem to differ much in appearance, whereas others are bizarre in shape and possess color patterns that are unique and beautiful.   Some of the principal families are the Shield Bugs, Stink Bugs, Squash Bugs, Plant Bugs, Soldier Bugs, and Leaf Bugs.

Perhaps Stink Bugs are better known to most people, at least by their odor and taste, than any other type of terrestrial species.   "We learn the flavor in one experience, and conclude that once is enough for a lifetime.   To those who live in cities it may always remain a mystery why one berry looking just like another should taste and smell so differently; but all barefooted boys and sunbonneted girls from the country who have picked the wild strawberries on the hillsides or scratched their hands and faces in raspberry patches know well the angular green or brown bugs that leave a loathsome trail behind them; and they will tell you, too, that the bugs themselves are worse than their trail, for it is a lucky youngster that has not taken one of these insects into his mouth by mistake with a handful of berries.

" It should not be concluded, however, that only members of this family possess this disagreeable odor; for most of the Heteroptera protect themselves by rendering their bodies unpalatable in this way.   Doubtless birds soon learn this fact and leave such bugs alone.   But it is to members of this family that the expressive name given above is commonly applied.

" This nauseous odor is caused by a fluid which is excreted through two openings, one on each side of the lower side of the body near the middle coxae." (Comstock.)

Many of the Stink Bugs live on vegetation and some feed on other insects. One member of the family is particularly obnoxious since it is destructive to various garden vegetables.   This is the Harlequin Cabbage Bug, or Calico Bug, which seriously injures cabbages, radishes, turnips, etc., especially in the South.   It is a handsome black insect with markings of red, orange, or yellow on the back.   The

Photo by Cornelia Clarke

Stink Bugs.   These are in the wingless stage.   Too bad such beautiful insects should produce such a bad odor.   Below is a group of their eggs.

eggs are shaped like a barrel, and are white with black rings.   The nymphs bear the same colors as the adults, but differently arranged.

The Southern Green Stink Bug is also an injurious species.   It is usually light green in color and shield-shaped, as are most of the Stink Bug family.   It measures about $\frac{1}{2}$ inch in length.   This is a very widely distributed species, living in our southern states and in nearly all of the tropical and subtropical countries in the world.   These bugs injure especially truck and cover crops, such as radishes, and peas.   Inside of the beak are a pair of jaws and a pair of auxiliary jaws; these are long, slender needles called stylets.   The stylets are thrust out of the beak and drawn back very rapidly and sink in deeper and deeper until the sap is reached and can be sucked up.

Terrestrial Bugs. Of the Terrestrial Bugs, other than those that belong to the Stink Bug family, the Spotted Milkweed Bug is one of the most distinctive. It is about ½ inch long, rather slender, and tapers toward either end. The color on the upper surface is orange or bright red with three large black spots. The bright colors and abundance of these bugs on milkweed plants render them easy for anyone interested to find.

The Leaf-Footed Plant Bug is a slender species about ¾ inch long. It is brown in color with a yellow line across the middle of the wings when at rest. Its most distinctive feature, however, is the expansion of the tibiae of the hind legs into leaflike projections. This type of bug is more prevalent in the tropics than in the temperate zone but some species occur in the United States. The one shown in

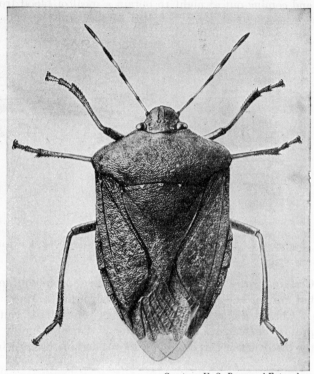

Courtesy, U. S. Bureau of Entomology

Southern Green Plant Bug. A widely distributed species in the tropics and subtropics; injurious to various species of plants. Size, ½ inch long.

our photograph ranges from South America northward as far as New York and westward to Arizona. When the leaflike expansions on the hind legs become very broad, the name Airplane Bug is applied to the species.

Courtesy, U. S. Bur. Ent.

Harlequin Cabbage Bug. A beautiful bug, but injurious to garden vegetables.

Among the predaceous Terrestrial Bugs are certain species called Soldier Bugs. These insects are usually beneficial since they prey on other insects, most of which are injurious; for example, the specimen shown in our photograph is attacking an Asparagus Beetle. Soldier Bugs occur all over the United States and their united efforts must accomplish much of value to man during the growing season for plants.

One group of blood-sucking bugs are called Kissing Bugs because they bite human beings on the face. Of these, the Cone-Nosed Bugs are of particular interest because in South and Central America they transmit a serious disease from man to man or from armadillo to man. In Brazil they are known as "Barbeiros," or Barbers, because they favor the face as a place to bite; and in Spanish America are called "Chinchas Voladoras," or Flying Bedbugs. They inhabit the houses of the natives, living in crevices in the walls and coming out at night to obtain a meal of blood from a sleeping human being.

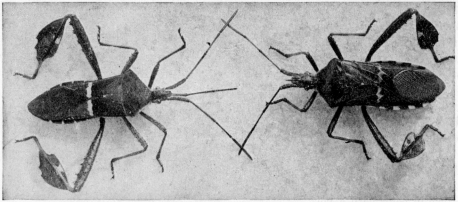

Photo by Cornelia Clarke

Leaf-Footed Plant Bugs. One joint of each hind leg is expanded so as to look like a leaf. Size, ¾ inch long.

Certain species of Cone-Nosed Bugs live in our southern and southwestern states but are not known to transmit disease germs to Man.

Chagas disease, which these bugs transmit, is caused by a minute flagellate protozoon (see page 17) that lives in the intestine of the insect. The history of the discovery of this disease is of considerable interest because we usually recognize

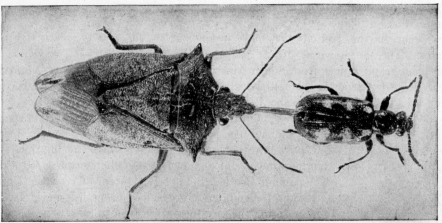

Photo by Drake

Soldier Bug. This is a beneficial species. The specimen shown here is attacking an asparagus beetle with its long beak.

a disease and then try and find the causative agent. In this case the flagellates were first found in the bugs and then the disease was recognized in children. Experiments then demonstrated that the bugs transmitted the flagellates.

Chinch Bug. The pictures one sees of Chinch Bugs, and their notoriety, give one the impression that they are large insects, whereas they are quite small, being only ⅙ inch long. What they lack in size they make up for in numbers. They multiply in fields of small grain until millions of them are present; then they migrate to corn fields, walking over the ground although they have wings. This method of migration is a bad habit, since it furnishes a point of attack for the farmer. He needs only to plow a furrow and put some petroleum in the bottom; the Chinch Bugs dive right in and their tired feet are put to eternal rest.

The body of the Chinch Bug is black and the wings, which are folded over the back, are white. The eggs are laid on the roots or stems of plants. The young are red in color; they reach their adult size in about six weeks. Corn plants and other field plants are seriously injured by the thousands of Chinch Bugs that suck out their juices. Losses due to these Bugs, especially in the Mississippi Valley, are estimated at over half a billion dollars.

Buffalo Tree Hopper. "Nature must have been in a joking mood when tree-hoppers were developed, for these little creatures are most comically grotesque in appearance. In general outline they resemble beech-nuts, except that many have humps on their backs. The prothorax is prolonged backward like a roof over the body, often quite covering it. If the young entomologist wishes to laugh, let him look at the faces of tree-hoppers through a lens. Their eyes always have a keen, droll look, and the line that separates the head from the prothorax gives them the appearance of wearing glasses. In some cases the prothorax is elevated above the head, so that it looks like a peaked nightcap; in others it is shaped like a tam-o'-shanter; and sometimes it has horns, one on

Photo by Cornelia Clarke

Chinch Bugs. An adult above and a nymph below sucking the juices from a plant. Size, ⅙ inch long.

each side, which have given one species the name of the Buffalo Tree-hopper."
(Comstock.)

The Buffalo Tree Hopper is about $\frac{1}{3}$ inch long and light green in color with whitish
dots.   It is the best-known species in America and widely distributed.   It feeds on
a large variety of plants and sometimes makes a pest of itself, especially on nursery
stock and young fruit trees.   The eggs are laid in the bark of stems in crescent-
shaped slits made by the insect; these slits heal so as to leave large unsightly scars
on the branches.   The young look more like normal insects than do the adults.
Some species excrete "honeydew," resembling plant lice in this respect.

Photo by Hillman.   Courtesy, Nature Magazine

Buffalo Tree Hopper.   A grotesque bug, light green in color with whitish spots.   The "buffalo
horns" extend out from the front corners above the eyes.   Size, $\frac{1}{3}$ inch long.

Bedbugs.   According to an old song, the Bedbug hasn't any wings but he gets
there just the same.   This is correct Natural History, since Bedbugs are wingless
and occur wherever there are human beings.   Rats, mice, and birds may also be
attacked.

The body of the Bedbug is broad and flat, about $\frac{1}{5}$ inch long, and reddish-brown
in color.   The proboscis is a piercing and sucking organ.   The distinctive and
offensive odor is due to the secretions from stink glands.   One meal lasts a long
time and life may continue for as long as a year without food.   People differ with
respect to their susceptibility to Bedbug bites; some suffer severely whereas others
seem to escape entirely.

During the day, Bedbugs hide in crevices, under wallpaper and in cracks in wooden beds or in the floor. Their eggs are laid in such locations; they are pearly-white and number from 75 to 200 for each female. Bedbugs can be eradicated by cleanliness, the elimination of cracks, the application of insecticides, or by fumigation.

Photo by Doten

Bedbugs. These specimens are piercing the human skin. They are flat and wingless. Size, ⅕ inch long.

Periodical Cicada, or Seventeen-Year Locust. If patience is a virtue, the Cicada is certainly the most virtuous of animals, since he must live in an underground dungeon for seventeen years before he emerges into the sunshine. All this preparation for life in the upper world seems hardly worth while, since he enjoys his freedom

Photo by Cornelia Clarke

Cicada. The adult at the right emerged from the nymphal skin at the left through a slit in the back.

for only a few days, and then dies.   During these few days he makes as much noise as he possibly can, "singing" loudly and shrilly.   He is lucky in one respect, because sound-making organs are not present in the female, and as the philosopher Xenarchos remarked, "Happy is the Cicada, since his wife has no voice."

The eggs are laid in slits in twigs made by the swordlike ovipositor at the end of the abdomen.   In a few weeks the young hatch and fall to the ground, into which

Photo by Cornelia Clarke

Cicada. The nymph of the Seventeen Year Locust lives in a cell underground and sucks juices from roots.

they burrow.   They puncture the rootlets of plants with their sharp beaks and suck out the sap.   When it gets too cold to work, they hibernate.   Year after year this tedious process goes on until finally they feel an urge to free themselves from their bondage, and dig their way to the surface.   After climbing up a bush or tree, the skin splits and the adult Cicada emerges.   Other species of Cicadas, known as Harvest Flies, live for a shorter time underground.

Plant Lice, or Aphids. The presence of lice on animals is taken as a matter of course, but that plants may also be lousy comes as a sort of shock. Everyone who tries to raise vegetables, flowers, fruit trees, or field crops knows to his sorrow how destructive these Plant Lice, or Aphids, can be. Their ravages are the consequence of their marvelous powers of reproduction.

Photo by Doten

Alfalfa Plant Lice. The larva of a two-winged fly is feeding on them, having just grasped one in his jaws.

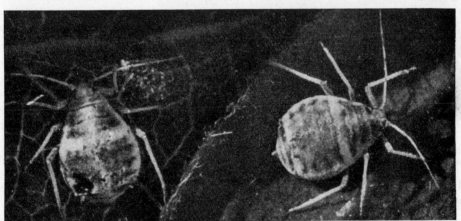

Photo by Essig

Plant Lice. Two wingless specimens with their beaks inserted into the leaf of a plant.

Aphids hatch from eggs in the spring as wingless females. These thrust their piercing mouth parts into a plant and suck out the juices. Soon they begin to bring forth female young alive; these young in a short time are also busily engaged in giving birth to young female Aphids. This continues until enormous numbers are produced. If food becomes scarce, females with wings are born; these fly to other plants and start another series of wingless females. Toward the end of summer both males and females appear, and the fertilized eggs that are then laid lie dormant over winter, thus preserving the race for the next season.

Aphids are usually greenish in color and not over $\frac{1}{10}$ inch long. Associated with them are usually to be found ants which feed upon the drops of "honeydew" secreted by the plant lice. The relations between various kinds of Aphids and Ants are often very complex. Sometimes the Ants cover the Aphids with a protecting "shed" of mud. It has been shown that the eggs of the Corn-Root Louse are collected by Ants in the autumn and stored in their underground nests, where they are cared for until spring, when the newly hatched Aphids are carried to the roots of the corn. This relationship, termed symbiosis, is mutually beneficial; the Aphids are protected by the Ants, and the Ants are repaid for their trouble with honeydew. The enemies of Aphids include ladybird beetles, insect parasites, and the larvae of flower flies.

Courtesy, American Museum of Natural History

Spittle Insect, or Frog Hopper. The bugs are hidden beneath the white froth which is manufactured by the insect and attached to stems of grass and weeds.

Spittle Insects, or Frog Hoppers. The little masses of white froth clinging to weeds and grass were supposed to be the spittle of tree frogs until it was discovered that each contained one or more little insect nymphs. The adults are leaping insects about $\frac{1}{4}$ inch long and are known as Frog Hoppers.

Both nymphs and adults suck sap. The nymphs exude part of the liquid they take in, mix it with a sticky secretion, and blow it full of air bubbles. They live in the midst of this froth, sucking juice from the plant, until they reach the adult stage.

San Jose Scales and Terrapin Scale. Scale Insects, or Bark Lice, do their part to furnish work for the unemployed, since much time and enormous effort are necessary to prevent them from ruining the fruit crop, and from destroying plants in greenhouses and out of doors. They are a family of True Bugs with sucking mouth parts, about 450 species of which occur in the United States. The males usually have wings, but lack mouth parts and are hence doomed to starvation. The females are wingless, and, in many species, secrete a sort of scale under which they live during much of their lives. Among the best-known Scales are the Cottony-Cushion, or Fluted Scale, from which the Australian Ladybird Beetles saved the fruit industry of California, the Terrapin Scale, the Pine-Leaf Scale, the Cottony-Maple Scale, the Oyster-Shell Scale, and the San Jose Scale.

Courtesy, U. S. Bureau of Entomology

San Jose Scales. The miniature "volcanoes" are female Scales. The small, whitish bodies are very young females. The tiny, oblong white bodies are male Scales.

San Jose Scales are pernicious little sap-suckers about the size of a pin head. They are perhaps the most important of all fruit-tree pests. They appeared in 1880 near San Jose, California, and from there became distributed over the United States on young trees. The adult female lies underneath a small, grayish scale formed in concentric circles. Because of their small size and protective covering, they often are not noticed until so numerous as to be very destructive. Their powers of reproduction are remarkable; it has been estimated that the progeny of a single female would number over three billion in a single season if all were to survive.

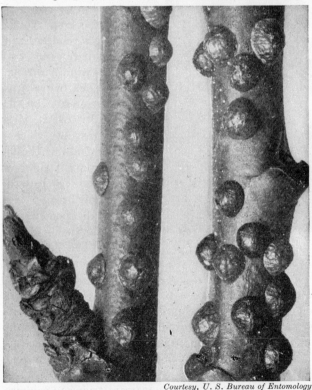

Courtesy, U. S. Bureau of Entomology

Terrapin Scales. The insects live under a protecting scale that resembles a minute turtle or terrapin.

Scale insects possess very long, slender, piercing mouth parts, which are inserted into the plant to suck out the sap. Not only does the tree become weakened because of the loss of sap, but it is also poisoned by a secretion injected into it by the insect. Two principal methods have been devised to destroy scale insects. One method is to spray the infested plants, during the winter when they are dormant, with a strong solution of lime-sulphur mixture or kerosene oil; the other is to cover the fruit trees one by one with a sort of tent and generate beneath this hydrocyanic acid gas, which quickly kills the scale insects.

Terrapin Scale Insects secrete a scale shaped somewhat like the shell of a Tortoise or Terrapin.   They attack especially the twigs of trees such as maples, sycamores, and poplars.   From the dried bodies of certain Mexican scale insects the red dye known as Cochineal is obtained.   Another scale insect of value to man is the Lac Insect of Asia, which secretes a wax that is made into shellac.

Cottony-Cushion or Fluted Scale.   The history of the Cottony-Cushion Scale in this country has made it one of the most interesting of the scale family.   An insect, the Australian Ladybird Beetle, or Vedalia, was introduced with the object of preying on the scale; the success of this venture was so great that it not only represents the first experiment of the kind to give favorable results, but is now recognized as the standard example of the biological control of an insect pest by means of an introduced insect.

Courtesy, Nature Magazine

Cottony-Cushion or Fluted Scale.   The white, fluted egg sac is attached to the posterior end of the body.

"In 1868 some young orange trees were brought to Menlo Park (near San Francisco) from Australia. These trees were undoubtedly infested by the fluted scale, which is a native of Australia.   These scale immigrants throve in the balmy California climate, and particularly well probably because they had left all their native enemies far behind.   By 1880 they had spread to the great orange-growing districts of southern California, five hundred miles away, and in the next ten years caused enormous loss to the growers.   In 1888 the entomologist Koebele, recommended by the government division of entomology, was sent at the expense of the California fruit growers to Australia to try to find out and send back some effective predaceous or parasitic enemy of the pest.   As a result of this effort, a few Vedalias were sent to California, where they were zealously fed and cared for, and soon, after a few generations, enough of the little beetles were on hand to warrant trying to colonize them in the attacked orange groves.   With astonishing and gratifying success the

Vedalia in a very few years had so naturally increased and spread that the ruthless scale was definitely checked in its destruction, and from that time to this has been able to do only occasionally and in limited localities any injury at all." (Kellogg.)

The Vedalias are often too successful; they completely destroy the Fluted Scales and then starve to death. For this reason the California State Insectary maintains a few specimens which can be sent to any locality where the scales appear. This precaution has prevented serious outbreaks and insures the fruit growers from the loss of their crops in future years.

Mealy Bugs. Some of the Scale Insects are called Mealy Bugs because they become covered with a white, powdery wax usually extending as a fringe of filaments along the sides, with two longer filaments at the posterior end. The species shown in our photograph reaches a length of about $\frac{1}{4}$ inch. The body of the female is oval, and as in other members of the family, wingless. However, legs are present and slow movement from place to place takes place.

Plants are attacked with the sucking mouth parts either above or below ground according to the species, some of which are more or less serious pests. Greenhouses are favored as a habitat, because Mealy Bugs like a moist, warm climate. The males are much smaller

Photo by Essig

Mealy Bugs. Each bug secretes waxy filaments that give it a "mealy" appearance. They suck juices from plants.

than the females and possess wings, but no functional mouth parts. They are particularly abundant in the late afternoons and evenings during the summer and fall.

CHAPTER 13

BEETLES OR COLEOPTERA

Next to the butterflies and moths, Beetles are preferred by most insect collectors. And there are plenty of them; probably 250,000 species have been described, about 20,000 of which live in North America. Some of them are dull-colored, but many species not only sport beautiful color patterns, but are embellished with brilliant metallic hues.

Adult Beetles have the fore wings hardened into sheaths which meet along the center of the back and effectively protect the membranous wings that are folded beneath them and also the body which they largely cover. The mouth parts are fitted for chewing. The young are more or less wormlike larvae many of which are called grubs. When full grown the larvae change into quiescent pupae. Within the pupa the adult develops.

Our space does not allow us to list the families of even the more common Beetles, but some of the most representative species are described in the following pages.

Tiger Beetles. Their legs are long and slender and fitted for running; and their bodies are metallic green in color.

Tiger Beetles. "With all your faults I love you still" sings the insect collector as he chases Tiger Beetles. Although among the most rapacious and greedy of insects, they are great favorites. Why, you ask? Because, like movie queens, they are beautiful and graceful, on account of which they are forgiven all. Their stylish coats of black or bronze or metallic green, banded or spotted with yellow, elicit our admiration. Look for Tiger Beetles on bright, hot days in dusty roads and on the shores of streams. Their agility, both afoot and on the wing, makes catching them a sporting proposition. At night they find rest and concealment underneath stones and in holes in the ground.

The larvae of Tiger Beetles inherit their parents' rapacity but not their charm. They are ugly "snipers," waiting at the top of their tunnels in the ground for some unwary insect to pass by; then the body is thrown forward and the prey seized by the powerful jaws. The larva is even equipped with curved hooks located on a hump of the abdomen in such a position that they prevent the body from being pulled out of the burrow by a strong antagonist.

Ground Beetles. The Smith family among insects is represented by the Ground Beetles, since their family tree is large and spreading and includes over 2000 known species in North America alone. Unlike the Tiger Beetles, they are mostly dark-colored and are active at night, hiding by day under stones, logs, etc. Their legs are slender and adapted for running over the ground, and their jaws and dispositions are of the predatory type. In fact, most of them are beneficial and some very valuable to us because of the other insects they destroy. For example, the Searcher is a species that climbs trees and slays caterpillars, and a near relative has been

Photo by Cornelia Clarke

Ground Beetle. The legs are fitted for running. The wing covers are lined with parallel grooves.

introduced from Europe into New England to prey upon the caterpillars of the gypsy moth and brown-tail moth.

Ground Beetles are rather flat and broad, which makes it easy for them to hide in small crevices. As in beetles in general, the front wings are stiff covers that protect the more delicate hind wings underneath. During flight, the front wings are held up over the body out of the way of the hind wings that do the work. The species mentioned above are slightly over an inch long.

The Bombardier Beetles also belong to the "Smith" family. They not only secrete an obnoxious fluid, as so many other insects do, but this fluid changes to a gas smoke screen when squirted out into the air.   The enemy may be bombarded with several shots in succession with "a sound like that of a tiny pop-gun."   The gunner escapes before the foe recovers from his bewilderment.

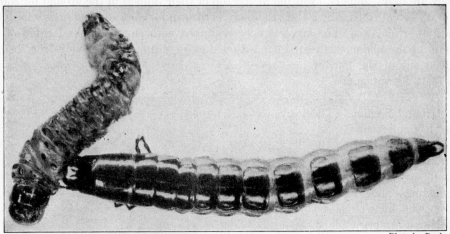

Photo by Drake

Ground Beetle Larva.   Both adult and larva of the Ground Beetle capture and devour cater-pillars.   This larva is about to have a juicy meal.

Water-Scavenger Beetles.   Fresh water would not remain fresh very long if it were not for the services of Water-Scavenger Beetles and other aquatic animals that dispose of decaying organic material and devour the microscopic plants and animals that would otherwise overrun everything.   These beetles may be found swimming or crawling about in ponds.   They are black and shiny and their antennae are club-shaped, but usually hidden beneath the head.   The second and third pairs of legs are flattened and provided with bristles which make them effective swimming organs.

The Giant Water-Scavenger Beetles are widely distributed throughout North America.   They are about $1\frac{2}{5}$ inches long.   Their eggs are enclosed in a case that is smooth, brown in color, and has a curved mast that extends above the water when the egg case is floating; otherwise the egg case is attached to a water plant.   The adults may be scavengers, but the young demand live meat, which they get even if they are forced to devour each other.

Adult Water-Scavenger Beetles breathe air, but since it is to their advantage to remain under water for long periods, they have developed a method of carrying fresh air down with them.   They come to the surface and thrust out their antennae, with which they capture a bubble of air; this they carry under the body where it spreads out like a silver mantle and can be used until more air is needed.

Whirligig Beetle.   "As familiar to the country rover as the gurgling of the brook, or the flecks of foam on its 'golden-braided centre,' or the trailing ferns and the rustling rushes on its banks, are these Whirligigs on its pools.   Around and around each other they dart, tracing graceful curves on the water, which vanish almost as soon as made. They are social fellows, and are almost always found in large numbers, either swimming or resting motionless near together. They rarely dive, except when pursued; but are so agile that it is extremely difficult to catch them without a net. Many of them when caught exhale a milky fluid having a very disagreeable odor. They feed upon small flies, beetles, and other insects that fall into the water, and are furnished with well-developed wings, with which they fly from one body of water to another." (Comstock.)

The behavior of the Whirligigs reveals their identity without further effort, but several points

Photo by Cornelia Clarke

Water-Scavenger Beetle. The outside of this species is black and glossy. The middle and hind legs are flattened and fringed for swimming purposes.

Photo by Cornelia Clarke

Whirligig Beetle. The body is shaped like a submarine. Each eye is divided into two, one for use in the air and the other to see with under the water.

regarding their structure are of considerable interest. The oval, flattened body is very smooth, hence movement through the water is accomplished without much opposition. The hind legs are flattened into paddles and fringed so as to offer as much resistance as possible to the water when forced backward as an oarsman rows a boat. The eye on each side of the head is divided into two parts; one lies above the surface of the water and no doubt sees what goes on in the air above; whereas the other is under the surface and sees what happens in the waters beneath.

The larvae of Whirligigs are as retiring as their parents are conspicuous. They hatch from eggs that are glued one by one to the under side of the leaves of pond weeds. "They are pale, slender creatures which crawl over the bottom trash or swim through the water with a sinuous motion of their bodies which is aided by eight heavily fringed gills which hang from each side of the abdomen.   They are adepts at clambering backwards or forwards.   On the tip of the abdomen there are four sickle-shaped hooks which they catch into anything convenient and pull themselves backward after the manner of caddis worms."   (Morgan.)

Carpet Beetle, or Buffalo Moth.   How often among insects respectable parents give rise to offspring with vicious habits.   The Buffalo "Moth," which is really a Beetle, is an excellent example.   The adults are rather good-looking beetles $\frac{3}{16}$ inch long, mostly black with irregular white spots, and with a red line along the center of the back.   They feed on the pollen of plants and are apparently quite harmless.

The larvae are numbered among our common household pests because they feed on furs and woolens, especially on carpets that are tacked down to the floor and left in place for a year or more.   The name Buffalo Moth was given to them

Photo by Essig

Carpet Beetle, or Buffalo "Moth."   A group of the harmless black and white beetles and several of their injurious larvae.

because of their coat of shaggy, brown hair.   They are about $\frac{1}{4}$ inch long and very voracious.   When they reach full size, they change into adult beetles, which fly at once to doors or windows in their endeavors to get outside.

Click Beetles. The acrobatic performances of Click Beetles, or Skip Jacks, are known to most boys who live in the country. When disturbed, they draw in their legs and fall on their backs. They lie still for a while and then suddenly, with a click, spring into the air several inches and alight on their feet. Most Click Beetles are rather long and flat and from $\frac{1}{10}$ to $\frac{3}{4}$ inch long. A few reach a lengh of over an inch.

One of the larger species of the 500 or more that occur in North America is called the Eyed Elater. This species has two eyelike spots on the upper surface just back of the head; these are not true eyes. In the tropics some of the Click Beetles have two luminous areas in place of these eyelike spots. Those we encountered in Puerto Rico were called automobile bugs, because at night these spots resemble the headlights of miniature automobiles. Luminous Click Beetles are said to be used as ornaments by the ladies in certain tropical countries.

The larvae of Click Beetles are called Wire Worms. They are long and narrow, yellowish or brownish in color, and covered with a hard skin. Some of them feed on the roots of plants and on seeds and are often very destructive.

© G. B. S. H.

Click Beetle. This species is called the Eyed Elater because of the two eyelike spots on the back of the thorax. The clicking mechanism is on the under surface. Natural size.

Fire Flies and Glow Worms. The luminescence of Fire Flies and Glow Worms constitutes one of the marvels of Nature. Especially puzzling is the fact that this light is accompanied by almost no heat and is thus produced without waste of energy. Fire Flies are not flies but beetles. The larvae and wingless females are called Glow Worms.

Adult Fire Flies are about $\frac{1}{2}$ inch long. Their bodies are softer than those of most beetles and their colors dull. The light-producing organ is opaque-whitish in color, and located on the underside of the abdomen, hence the Fire Fly carries his headlight on behind. The lights are not continuous, but appear and disappear like the rhythmical flashing of fairy lamps. The flashes enable the Fire Flies to find their mates in the dark.

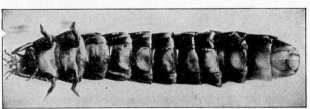

Courtesy, Nature Magazine

Glow Worm. The larva of the Fire Fly is called a Glow Worm. This is a view of the under surface showing the row of whitish luminous organs.

Sometimes the Fire Flies in one locality seem to flash all at the same time. This has been noticed especially in the Philippines, where thousands have been seen to flash in unison over 100 times per minute. Similar observations have been made in this country, but the explanation as to how the flashing is regulated is still unknown.

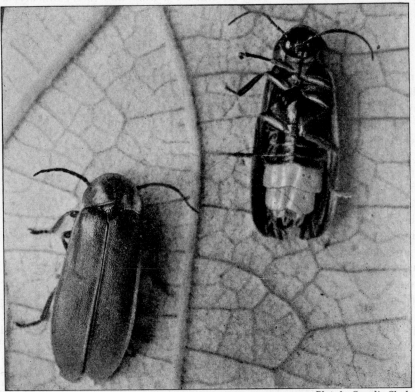

Fire Flies. The Fire Fly is a Beetle. The upper surface is of no particular interest but the end of the abdomen when seen from below is a whitish light organ. Size, about ½ inch long.

Dung Beetles, or Tumble Bugs. The activities of the Dung Beetles seem distinctly disagreeable to us, but no one will deny that they are exceedingly interesting. They belong among the scavengers, and unlike most of their kind, do not shun the light of day. The habit that is most conspicuous, and is responsible for the name Tumble Bug, is that of rolling balls of dung. The ball is pushed backward with the hind legs, often being rolled long distances and over difficult obstacles.

In some species, each beetle has his own ball and when two beetles are found together, one is trying to purloin the ball from the other. In other species, a pair of beetles unite in ball-rolling, the female pushing and the male pulling. When the ball is completed and a suitable place is found, the earth is removed beneath it so as to bury it below the surface.

These balls of dung are sometimes used as food by the beetles that roll them, or an egg is laid in each and the larvae that hatch from these eggs find a well-stocked larder, which lasts until they become adult beetles.

In ancient Egypt, Dung Beetles, or Scarabs, were considered sacred.   They were painted on sarcophagi, carved in stone, and used as a model for gems.

Photo by Howes.   Courtesy, Nature Magazine

Dung Beetles, or Tumble Bugs. A pair are rolling a "snow ball" of dung in which to lay an egg.

May Beetles and White Grubs.   Some call 'em June Bugs and others May Beetles, but to the gardener their larvae are known as White Grubs, and no affection is wasted on them.   The adults are stout, brownish beetles almost an inch long. They often appear in May in large numbers and frequently enter rooms where there are bright lights.   In the evening they leave their hiding places in the grass or earth and fly into the neighboring trees, on the leaves of which they feed.

The larvae hatch from pearly-white eggs that are laid in the soil. They feed voraciously on the roots of plants until winter comes ; then they burrow down below the frost line. The following summer is spent in eating roots, and growing, and a second winter is passed below the frost line. The adult stage is reached during the next summer, but the beetles do not emerge until the spring of the third year. The White Grubs become quite plump. They have a brown head and a swollen and darkened abdomen. The body is soft and curved when at rest, as indicated in the accompanying photograph.

Courtesy, U. S. Bureau of Entomology

White Grub. This is the larva of a May Beetle. It lives underground. The end of the abdomen is large and dark-colored.

Japanese Beetle. If we could deport undesirable insects as we do undesirable citizens, the Japanese Beetles would be on the first list selected for expulsion. They were introduced from Japan probably in the earth surrounding the roots of plants and were first discovered in New Jersey in 1916. Efforts to prevent their spread were begun in 1919, but they have succeeded in invading over 20,000 square miles of land in the eastern United States.

Courtesy, U. S. Bureau of Entomology

Japanese Beetles. A mass of these beetles and one green May Beetle on an apple.

The adult beetles are known to feed on about 200 species of plants, but they prefer apple, quince, peach, sweet cherry, plum, grape, blackberry, clover, and corn. They also attack the foliage of shade trees and shrubs. The larvae damage lawns and the roots of such plants as strawberries and cabbage. The eggs are laid in the ground. The larvae, which are white grubs, hibernate in the ground, and the adults emerge about the middle of June. They are $\frac{3}{8}$ inch long and bright metallic green in color. Their natural spread is from ten to fifteen miles per year. The larvae can be destroyed in lawns by treatment with lead arsenate. Adults can be trapped in enormous numbers. On a single property in New Jersey nearly a ton were collected in 1929.

Rose Chafer. Some insects seem to have no aesthetic sense and no respect for beauty, and will even attack the most gorgeous flowers. The Rose Chafer, or Rose Bug, is of this type. He is a slender beetle about $\frac{1}{3}$ inch long, and owes his yellow color to a thick coating of yellow, scalelike hairs. The legs are long and spiny and pale red in color. The adults have voracious appetites and do a great deal of damage when present in large numbers. The larvae live in the ground, where they feed on the roots of grass and weeds. Other flowers besides roses are attacked, as well as the leaves of fruit trees and other plants. Hand-picking and spraying with arsenate of lead are recommended for their control.

The Rose Chafer is not the only insect guilty of injuring our rose bushes. Plant lice attack both wild and cultivated roses, infesting the buds and terminal shoots. The leaves of roses serve as food for the nymphs and adults of the Rose Leaf Hopper. The Rose Scale is distributed throughout most of the United States; and the Rose Snout Beetle, or Rose Curculio, drills small round holes deep into the buds for purposes of obtaining food and laying eggs.

Rhinoceros Beetle. Considering how pestiferous or injurious some of the smaller insects are, it is comforting to know that our largest beetles are perfectly harmless. The Rhinoceros Beetle of our southern states is about 2½ inches long

Courtesy, U. S. Bureau of Entomology

Rose Chafer.   A group feeding on chestnut blossoms.   Size, about ⅓ inch long.

and has a forwardly directed horn in the middle of its head.   The larvae live in decaying wood.   The West Indies boasts of a still larger species, the Hercules Beetle, which is six inches long.

Photo by Howes.   Courtesy, Nature Magazine

Rhinoceros or Hercules Beetle.   Terrifying in appearance, but harmless, is this huge insect of the West Indies.   About one-half life size.

Colorado Potato Beetle.   When human beings interfere with Nature almost anything may happen.   For example, before 1850 what we now call the Potato "Bug" devoted its attention to sand-bur plants.   Then the settlers in the West introduced it to the succulent potato plant and the trouble began.   The beetles traveled eastward at an ever increasing rate until by 1874 they had reached the Atlantic coast, and acquired a new name, the Colorado Potato Beetle.

Colorado Potato Beetle.   Most people call him a Potato Bug, but he is just as injurious by either name.

There are two broods of beetles per year in most parts of the United States. The yellow eggs are laid in groups of twenty to seventy-five on the under-surface of potato leaves. The larvae which hatch from the eggs feed on the leaves until they are full-grown ; then they burrow into the ground, change into pupae, and finally emerge as adults. Paris green, an arsenical preparation, has proved to be a practical and effective remedy, for when sprinkled on the potato plants this poison is taken into the beetle's stomach with the leaves and quickly kills the insect.

Round-Headed Apple-Tree Borer. Considering the remarkable number of insects that live on the fruit, leaves, bark, and other parts of apple trees, we are lucky to get apple pie to eat and cider to drink. The Round-Headed Apple-Tree Borer

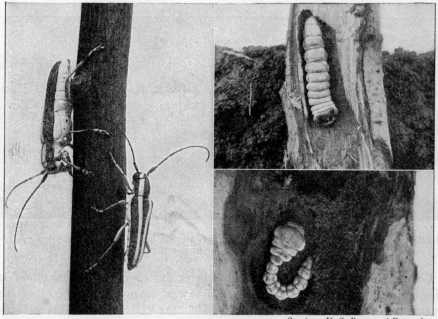

Round-Headed Apple-Tree Borers.   These are "long-horned" beetles with long, slender antennae. The adult female is at the left and the male at the right. The round-headed larva, at the right above, is in the stem of a small tree. The larva of a Flat-Headed Borer is shown at the right below to compare with the Round-Headed Borer. Magnified slightly.

is the larva of a beetle that bores into the wood of the tree near the base, with disastrous results. The front part of its wormlike body is rounded, hence the term Round-Headed to distinguish it from another type of larva which is flattened in front and called Flat-Headed.

The adults are called Long-Horned Beetles because their antennae are usually longer than the body. They are slender beetles, handsomely striped with three broad, cinnamon-brown bands along the back. The female measures about $\frac{3}{4}$ inch long and the male $\frac{1}{2}$ inch. The eggs are laid in the bark near the base of the tree. The female cuts a little slit with her jaws into which she forces her abdomen and then lays an egg. The little, legless, cream-colored larvae dig tunnels into the wood and may, in time, kill the tree. When full-grown, they are about $1\frac{1}{4}$ inches long. Digging proceeds for several years before this size is attained, and the complete life-cycle usually requires three years.

Ladybird Beetles. Dedicated in the Middle Ages to the Virgin, the "Beetles of Our Lady" have come down to us as Ladybird Beetles or Lady "Bugs." Almost all of them are very beneficial because they destroy other insects that are injurious, but several have gone astray and feed on plants. Lady Bugs are almost hemispherical in shape and usually less than $\frac{1}{4}$ inch long. They are usually colored red, yellow, or black with black, white, red, or yellow spots. The young as well as the adults feed on other insects or their eggs. For example, the cottony-cushion scales that were ruining the fruit trees in California were brought under control by introducing certain Ladybird Beetles from Australia where these scales originally came from.

Courtesy, U. S. Bureau of Entomology

Ladybird Beetles. This is the Mexican Bean Beetle. Both the adults and larvae feed on leaves and are injurious. Most Ladybirds are beneficial because of the other insects they destroy.

The Bean Ladybird is one of the black sheep of the family. Its home is in the southwestern states but in 1919 it started to travel and has since become distributed throughout most of the eastern states. The wing-covers are yellowish or brownish in color and each is ornamented with eight black spots. Bean plants are eaten and destroyed by both larvae and adults.

Blister Beetle, or Spanish Fly. Neither the young Blister Beetles nor their parents belong in polite insect society. The adults develop in their body-fluids a substance, named cantharidin, which has the peculiar property of raising a blister on the human skin. This substance is extracted from the dried bodies of the beetles, and was in years gone by much favored by physicians. When taken internally certain organs are stimulated to greater activity. In southern Europe Blister Beetles are known as Spanish Flies. An extract from them has in the past been the essential basis of "love philters."

Courtesy, U. S. Bureau of Entomology

Blister Beetle. This species is harmful because it feeds on leaves. Size, about ½ inch long.

Adult Blister Beetles are about ½ inch long, are usually dull gray or blackish in color, and often marked with yellow stripes. They may be found on leaves and flowers on which they feed. The larvae have an extraordinary history, too complex to describe here, but involving more than the usual number of changes. Some of them are parasitic in the nests of bees, and others feed on grasshoppers' eggs.

Cotton-Boll Weevil. Cotton is produced in this country over a region 600 miles from north to south and 2000 miles from east to west. It is attacked by the Boll Weevil, Pink Bollworm, Leaf Worm, Louse, Flea Hopper, and many other insects of less importance. The Boll Weevil does the greatest damage. It now covers 90 per cent of the cotton area and in recent years has destroyed about 15 per cent of the entire crop. It is indirectly controlled by increasing the productivity of the plants and by hastening the maturity of the plants before the weevils become abundant.

Dusting with calcium arsenate has been found to be effective and profitable as a control measure.

Boll Weevils are about $\frac{1}{4}$ inch long. They belong to a large group of Snout Beetles, so called because the front of the head is drawn out into a beak or snout with minute jaws at the tip. The antennae arise from the sides of the snout and are bent, or "elbowed," near the center. Cotton-Boll Weevils hibernate during

Courtesy, U. S. Bureau of Entomology

Cotton-Boll Weevil. Larvae at work in a cotton boll. At the left is an adult weevil in the resting position.

the winter. In the spring they feed on the buds of the cotton plant. Later in the summer they lay eggs in the bolls, which are eventually destroyed by the growing larvae.

Some of the destructive relatives of the Cotton-Boll Weevil are the Plum Curculio, Strawberry Weevil, Chestnut Weevil, and Bean Weevil. The Bean Weevil lays

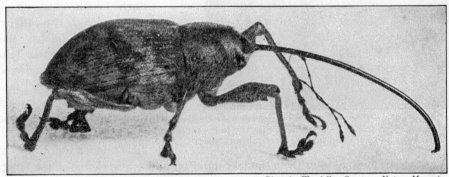

Photo by Wendell. Courtesy, Nature Magazine

Hazelnut Weevil. The snout is as long as the body; at the end are a pair of minute jaws. The feelers arise near the base of the snout.

its eggs on the surface of dried beans, and the larvae bore into them. When mature, they emerge through the little round holes that are the sign of "wormy" beans.

The Plum Curculio is a Weevil that attacks peaches, cherries, and apples as well as plums. The adults are about $\frac{1}{6}$ inch long, brown in color, and rough in appearance. The eggs are laid in young fruit and then a crescent-shaped flap is cut around and under the puncture in which it was deposited.

Bark Beetles. Trees are engaged in a "world war" with insects from the time the seeds are planted in the ground until they reach maturity. Seeds, roots, stems, leaves, buds, fruit, all have their insect destroyers. Among the most pernicious of these are the Bark Beetles, from which very few, if any, species of trees are immune.

Courtesy, U. S. Bureau of Entomology

Burrows of Bark Beetles. The female digs the horizontal burrows and her offspring, the vertical burrows.

A common species of Bark Beetle devotes its energies to the white pine. This species is a little black and brown midget only $\frac{1}{12}$ inch long, but is "as strongly built as a bulldog and has a similar tenacity." With his powerful jaws, the male cuts a hole in the bark of a tree, and tunnels through to the wood where he excavates a chamber. Female beetles are attracted to the simple home, sometimes as many as two or three sharing the chamber together. The male now spends his time guarding the entrance while the females proceed to raise their families.

Each female digs an egg tunnel an inch or two in length and lays eggs in niches along its sides. The larvae that hatch from these eggs excavate tunnels at right angles to the egg tunnel, and as they grow in size the width of their tunnels increases. By the time these are from $\frac{3}{4}$ to $1\frac{1}{2}$ inches long, the larvae are full-grown; they pupate in their tunnels and after about a week the adults emerge and begin to eat wood and bark. Soon they cut a round exit hole and seek out a new tree to test their jaws on. By examining the engravings made on the surface of the wood, one can determine the number of eggs laid, the number of larvae hatched, and the amount of wood consumed by each larva. Trees are killed or seriously injured by Bark Beetles and the economic loss from their ravages mounts into millions of dollars every year.

cover their backs and possess threadlike antennae that thicken into a club at the ends. Some Butterflies are called Skippers because they skip about abruptly from place to place. Their antennae have a club near the end, but the tip is curved back in form a sort of hook. The Moths fly by night, usually hold their wings horizontally when at rest and possess antennae that are threadlike or feather-like, and without a club near the end.

Swallow-Tails. Because of their great size and beauty, the Swallow-Tail flies, the Swallow-Tails are easily the most conspicuous, and we still consider them the most

Chapter 14

BUTTERFLIES AND MOTHS, OR LEPIDOPTERA

The gorgeous colors of Butterflies and Moths are due to their covering of scales. If the wings are rubbed gently, the colored scales come off in the form of dust. The scales are arranged so that they overlap like shingles on a roof, thus protecting as well as beautifying the insect. The mouth parts of Butterflies and Moths form a long tube for sucking up the nectar of flowers. When not in use, this tube is coiled underneath the head like a watch spring. The larvae are called cater-

Courtesy, Nature Magazine, Washington, D.C.

Tiger Swallow-Tail. A gorgeous yellow butterfly with black stripes and a "tail" at the posterior end of each hind wing.

pillars. The caterpillars of Moths spin a cocoon in which they pupate; whereas those of Butterflies do not.

About 10,000 species of Butterflies and Moths belonging to about 60 families occur in the United States. The Butterflies fly by day, hold their wings vertically over their backs and possess threadlike antennae that thicken into a club at the end. Some Butterflies are called Skippers because they skip about abruptly from place to place. Their antennae have a club near the end, but the tip is curved back to form a sort of hook. The Moths fly by night, usually hold their wings horizontally when at rest, and possess antennae that are threadlike or feather-like, and without a club near the end.

Swallow-Tail Butterflies. When we first began to collect Butterflies, the Swallow-Tails especially attracted our attention, and we still consider them the most striking members of this group of insects. Collecting Swallow-Tails with a net often resulted in broken wings and "tailless Swallow-Tails," so we set out to collect the caterpillars and rear fresh, uninjured adults from them for our collection. This is surprisingly easy to do.

Courtesy, U. S. Bureau of Entomology
Larva of a Swallow-Tailed Butterfly.
The larva of the Black Swallow-Tail is green, ringed with black and spotted with yellow. It feeds on caraway, parsnips, and other plants.

Among the common species are the Black, Tiger, Zebra, and Giant Swallow-Tails. The adults of all of these are distinguished by a "tail" at the end of each hind wing. The Black Swallow-Tail develops from a naked caterpillar, green in color, with black rings around the body and yellow spots. It feeds on the leaves of caraway and parsnip plants.

The larva of the Tiger Swallow-Tail feeds on the leaves of a variety of trees and shrubs. The adult has bright yellow wings with four black bars on the fore wings. In the southern part of its range two types of females occur, one with yellow wings and the other with black wings. Zebra Swallow-Tails may appear in any one of three different forms, two of which were once supposed to be separate species. The larvae feed on papaw.

Cabbage Butterfly. Among the pests with which we are obliged to deal are a large number of foreigners including the Cabbage Butterfly and its greedy caterpillar the Cabbage Worm. This species is not indigenous to this country but was unintentionally introduced from Europe about 1860, when it first appeared near Quebec, Canada. By 1868 it had reached the Gulf states; since then it has made its way all over the country.

The Cabbage Butterfly is white with black near the tips of the fore wings, and is about two inches across when the wings are expanded. The caterpillars are velvety green in color and resemble the foliage so closely as to be hardly distinguishable from it. When full-grown they are about one and one-fourth inches long. Spraying or dusting with Paris green kills them, but some people are afraid to do this for fear that the cabbage may be poisonous when it is eaten.   This fear, however, is unfounded, since it is estimated that one would have to eat twenty-eight entire heads at one sitting to feel any poisonous effects from the Paris green. Many cabbage worms are annually destroyed by parasites, one of which, a braconid

Photo by Cornelia Clarke

Cabbage Butterfly.   Above at the left is the larva, or Cabbage Worm; above and at the right, the pupa.

fly, is especially interesting because it was imported from Europe in 1883 for this very purpose and has "made good."

The Cabbage Butterfly is more injurious to agriculture in this country than any other species of butterfly.   This is due in part to the fact that three broods are reared in the North and even more in the South.   One can hardly ever visit a cabbage patch without seeing the whitish adults fluttering about, or the partially eaten leaves which reveal the presence of the caterpillars.   The eggs are laid on the cabbage plant and the larvae become full-grown in about two weeks. The species pass the winter as chrysalids, these being attached to the plants or to near-by objects.

Monarch or Milkweed Butterfly. Only those who have become famous or notorious can expect to be mimicked. In this class belongs the Monarch, a butterfly that appears to be so distasteful to its bird enemies that it is mimicked by another species, appropriately named the Viceroy. The Monarch is large and showy with wings of light reddish-brown. The larva, which feeds on milkweed plants, is also conspicuous, being greenish-yellow in color with glossy black bands and a pair

Photo by Hegner

Courtesy, Natural History Society of Maryland

Monarch Butterfly. Clinging to a twig, with wings closed. Compare with the Viceroy Butterfly.

Viceroy Butterfly. Note general resemblance to Monarch Butterfly but difference in arrangement of wing veins.

of curious filaments near each end. The chrysalis is bright green and ornamented with golden dots.

Monarchs have the unusual habit, for butterflies, of congregating in vast numbers in the fall and migrating southward. Only a few of them apparently return to the north the following spring. "This butterfly is a great migrant, and within quite recent years, with Yankee instinct, has crossed the Pacific, probably on merchant vessels, the chrysalids being possibly concealed in bales of hay, and has found lodgment in Australia, where it has greatly multiplied in the warmer parts of the Island Continent, and has thence spread northward and westward, until in its migrations it has reached Java and Sumatra, and long ago took possession of the Philippines. Moving eastward on the lines of travel, it has established a more or less precarious foothold for itself in southern England, as many as two or three dozen of these butterflies having been taken in a single year." (Holland.)

Monarch Butterflies.   Vast numbers of them gather together in the fall and migrate southward.

Mourning Cloak Butterfly. Often on the first sunny days of spring we are surprised to see Mourning Cloak Butterflies flitting about as though the long, cold winter meant nothing to them; and we ask ourselves where they came from and how they got here so early. The answer is simple; this species of butterfly hibernates in the adult stage during the winter in some sheltered spot, and is just as anxious to spread its wings when spring arrives, as we are to welcome the sun and warmth of a new season.

Mourning Cloaks are among our best-known butterflies. They have a wing expanse of about $2\frac{1}{2}$ inches. The underside of the wings resembles a dead leaf. The upper side is purplish brown with a broad yellow border dotted with brown on the outer margin, and just within this border, a row of blue spots.

The caterpillars are about three inches long, velvety black with orange-red spots, and protected from birds and other enemies by rows of branching spines on the upper surface. They feed on the leaves of willow, elm, poplar, and other trees, and since they are gregarious, entire branches are sometimes stripped of their foliage. The eggs are laid in masses encircling the twigs of the trees on which the caterpillars feed.

These butterflies occur all over the Northern Hemisphere. They are known as Camberwell Butterflies in England. In this country two broods are reared each year.

Courtesy, American Museum of Natural History
Mourning Cloak Butterflies. Upper surface, above; lower surface, like a dead leaf, below.

Kallima or Dead-Leaf Butterfly. In the animal world the best policy, if you are good to eat, is to conceal yourself as thoroughly as possible. Attempts to do this appear to have led to some remarkable cases of mimicry, the most marvelous of which is that of the Kallima Butterfly. Certain Butterflies that live in trees in various parts of the world, but especially in South America and India, resemble leaves so closely that they can hardly be seen when at rest. The Kallima of India is the most famous of the Leaf Butterflies.

When at rest it holds its wings up over its back, thus exposing the underside. The wings are shaped like a dry or half-withered leaf. They are pointed at the anterior end and prolonged at the posterior end into what looks like the stalk of a leaf when applied to a twig. A midrib extends from this stalk along the center of the wings, and side ribs spread out from this like those of a leaf. The general color of the under surface is brownish, but dark spots are present simulating patches of fungus, and several clear spots are present that look like holes. The forward part of the body, including the head and antennae, is concealed between the fore wings. The upper side of the wings, that are exposed when in flight, are conspicuously colored with purple and orange.

Courtesy, American Museum of Natural History

Kallima Butterflies. From above the colors are brilliant when the wings are spread. When at rest the resemblance to a dead leaf is almost perfect.

These color patterns would be of little value if the Kallima Butterfly did not behave properly; its behavior is little less wonderful than its coloration. When flying, the Kallima is able to escape being captured by birds, hence the bright colors of the upper surface of the wings are not a disadvantage. When it settles on a twig it does so abruptly, so as to appear to vanish "into thin air." It comes to rest with head up, with wings together over the back exposing the dead-leaf-like under surface, and with the "leaf stalk" applied to the stem. How this has all evolved has puzzled scientists for many years and is still subject to violent debate. According to the theory of Natural Selection some Kallimas look more like leaves than others. Those that most closely resemble a dead leaf escape their enemies and can therefore leave progeny like themselves. This type of selection practiced century after century finally led to the perfection of the Kallima of today.

Clothes Moths. Our forefathers little knew how much trouble they were preparing for the housewives of this country when they brought Clothes Moths with them from Europe. We now have three species of them to contend with, — all of them introduced from the Old Country. The adult Moths are very small,

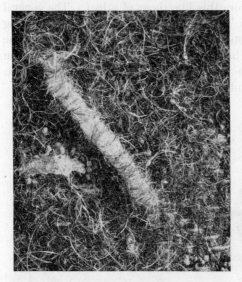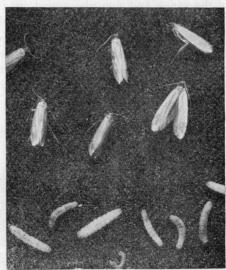

Courtesy, U. S. Bureau of Entomology

Clothes Moths. Several adults and larvae of different ages on a piece of woolen cloth, at the right. The case made by the larva in which it lives most of the time, at the left.

only about ½ inch across with the wings spread. The narrow wings are fringed with long, slender scales.

The eggs are usually laid on woolen clothing or fur. The larvae of one of the commonest species, the Webbing Clothes Moth, spin a silky, transparent tube in which they make their home. They also spin a sort of web on the material they feed on. The mature larva spins a cocoon. In warm houses two generations are usually produced in a year.

Clothes Moths are not modern pests. They are mentioned in the Book of Job, and were well known to the Romans. Various methods of control are available, such as sunlight and air, naphthalene flakes, cedar chests, moth-proof paper bags, and cold storage. A constant temperature of 40° F. keeps the larvae in an inactive condition.

Codling Moth. The larva of the Codling Moth is probably, next to house flies and mosquitoes, the insect most widely known. For who among us has never

Courtesy, U. S. Bureau of Entomology

Codling Moth. The adult is a handsome moth but the larvae are the worms that ruin our apples.

found a "worm" in his apple, or still worse, half a "worm." If the apple growers didn't keep constantly fighting this worst of all apple pests, we would encounter much more "wormy" fruit than at present, or perhaps no fruit at all.

The adult Codling Moth is inconspicuous, flies about at dusk, and hence is seldom seen and little known. It is less than half an inch long, with grayish wings that blend perfectly with the color of the bark. The eggs are laid on the leaves and the newly hatched larvae soon crawl to the young fruit. They bore into the apple at the calyx and feed near the core until fully grown. Then they leave the apple and spin a cocoon in some hiding place. The moths emerge in about ten days. The larvae that hatch from their eggs again attack the apples. These larvae also leave the fruit when mature, but hibernate over winter. They transform into moths in the early spring, just in time for their offspring to start work on the young apples. A well-arranged spraying program is necessary if good apples are to be grown.

Sphinxes, or Hawk Moths. When one mistakes a moth for a humming bird he becomes interested in the gay deceiver. Both shape and habit are responsible for the error. Sphinx Moths have a trim body and long, slender wings. Some of them have a wing spread of four or five inches. With rapidly vibrating wings they hover like a humming bird before a petunia or honeysuckle flower and thrust their extremely long proboscis down to the bottom to suck up the nectar.

Tobacco Sphinx. When resting on the trunk of a tree these moths are difficult to see. The caterpillar feeds on the tobacco plant.

When at rest the proboscis is coiled up underneath the head like a watch spring. As in other moths and butterflies the sucking apparatus is a tube formed by the two auxiliary jaws each of which is shaped like a half cylinder. When these are brought together they form a complete tube through which the nectar can be drawn into the stomach.

White-Lined Sphinx.   A common species.   Three stages in the life cycle are shown here, the adult, the green caterpillar, and the pupa.

The caterpillars are usually large, naked, and "disgusting."   A harmless "horn" is often present near the posterior end. When not feeding on leaves, these larvae raise the front part of the body and bend the head forward in such a way as to resemble an Egyptian Sphinx, hence their name.

About one hundred species of Sphinx Moths live in the United States. Among the common species are the Tomato-Worm Sphinx, the Tobacco-Worm Sphinx, the Pandorus Sphinx and the White-lined Sphinx. The color pattern of the last-named species is shown in our photograph. The general color is olive-brown, with conspicuous white or buff lines on both the body and wings. The larvae are usually yellowish-green with a row of spots on each side of the

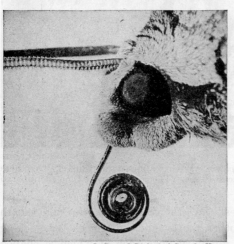

Sphinx Moth.   When not in use the tongue is coiled up like a watch spring and lies close up underneath the head.

back.   The pupae are provided with a "handle" which is really the case for the long proboscis.

Canker Worms, or Measuring Worms.   The caterpillars of certain moths are much more conspicuous than their parents.   This is certainly true of the members of the family Geometridae, whose larvae are known to almost everyone as Measuring Worms, Span Worms, or Loopers.   A number of them are known also as serious pests, especially the Spring and Fall Canker Worms.

"While walking beneath the trees in May most of us have found dark greenish-gray caterpillars an inch or less in length, dangling in the air, hanging by a thread. If you stop to watch one of them closely you may witness a gymnastic exhibition of rope climbing.   Bending his head to one side and grasping the silken thread with the front legs and jaws, he lifts up his body far enough to loop the thread about the third pair of legs.   He repeats this action again and again until the entire thread by which he hung from the branch above has been wound about his legs

Courtesy, U. S. Bureau of Entomology

Fall Canker Worms.   Called Measuring Worms, Inch Worms, or Span Worms, because the center legs are absent and the caterpillar must loop along.   Eggs on twig at left.

and he has regained the branch.   Then he breaks off the thread from the coil about the third legs, and stepping out of the coil, walks away.   Can you think of a sailor as able to climb a rope and while climbing coil up the loose rope below him? This caterpillar is not only able to coil his thread while climbing it but he can manufacture his thread while descending it.   He can start from a branch with one inch of thread and add to the lower end of that thread liquid silk from his mouth then drop until the liquid stiffens and checks his fall, then add more liquid silk and drop again, repeating this until he finds himself 15 feet or more below the branch." (Wellhouse.)

Canker Worms feed on the leaves of apple, elm, plum, cherry, and of various other trees and shrubs. They do not travel about in groups, but each worm lives an independent existence. Most of the life of the Canker Worm is spent under ground. The worms become full-grown in about a month. Then they burrow into the ground until about an inch below the surface. Here they remain for approximately nine months, changing into pupae and then into adult moths, which wriggle to the surface and emerge some evening at dusk.

The moths are gray or brownish-gray in color, and possess rows of red spines across the upper surface of the abdomen. The female has no wings. She lays her eggs in masses in crevices in the bark of trees. Canker Worms lack the central legs characteristic of other moth caterpillars and hence walk with a looping gait. They are not clothed with hairs or ornamented with bristles, and hence prove especially desirable to birds that feed on them with evident relish.

Courtesy, U. S. Bureau of Entomology

Fall Canker Worm. The female is wingless; her eggs are laid in rows in a single layer.

Gypsy Moth. When an animal from abroad is introduced into this country he finds himself in a new environment practically free from his natural enemies. Thus the Gypsy Moth, which was injurious to forest trees in the Old World, when introduced into Massachusetts in 1869, multiplied unchecked until it became necessary to employ all possible agencies to bring it under control. Within the past two decades millions of dollars have been spent in an effort to check the spread of the moths and destroy those specimens already present.

The caterpillar is hairy and about two inches long. It feeds on all sorts of leaves, including pine needles, and does not restrict its diet to one plant or a few plants, as do many other kinds of insects. In 1929 over 262,000 acres of New England forest land were defoliated by these caterpillars. The adults are brownish and inconspicuous, with a spread of wings of $1\frac{1}{2}$ inches. The female is too heavy to fly and therefore lays her eggs near the place where she emerges from her cocoon. The caterpillars can be prevented from reaching the leaves of trees by surrounding the trunk with a burlap band or a ring of sticky "tanglefoot."

Army Worm. If any species of animal were allowed to multiply without check the Balance of Nature would soon be destroyed. An excellent example of

Courtesy, U. S. Bureau of Entomology

Gypsy Moth. Caterpillars grouped beneath a burlap band tied around a tree to prevent them from crawling up and eating the leaves.

this is evident in the case of the Army Worm. Under ordinary conditions Army Worms feed on grass and other plants, but in such small numbers as to be unnoticed. Occasionally, because of the failure of the weather, or of their enemies, to keep them in check, they multiply so rapidly that they soon devour all the vegetation in their usual habitat. Then they march across the country *en masse* as a sort of army seeking new fields to conquer. When this happens the areas invaded are denuded of all foliage and the crops become a total loss.

The Army Worm is about two inches long when full-grown. The

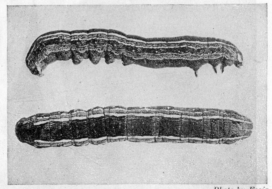

Photo by Essig

Army Worm. Side view and top view of Army Worms. About natural size.

body is grayish; three yellow stripes run down the back and a wide greenish-yellow stripe along each side. The parents are Moths, dull-brown in color and measuring about 1½ inches across the expanded wings. On each fore wing is a small white spot. The female lays about 700 eggs at the base of leaves of grass. Army Worms have spread all over the world, except in the coldest regions, but no one knows where they came from originally.

Giant Silkworm Moths. More children are probably introduced to Natural History by means of the Giant Silkworm Moths than in any other way, since their large, conspicuous cocoons are easily collected from trees and shrubs during the winter after the leaves have fallen, and the huge adult moths reared from them in the schoolroom or at home. The names of many of them are quite familiar, such as the Luna, Cecropia, Polyphemus, Promethea, and Io Emperor. They are all giants among Moths since they are the largest that occur in this country. Their bodies are heavy and covered with hair and their wings are wide and strong.

Photo by Haller.   Courtesy, Nature Magazine

Luna Moth.   The wings are light green in color, making her the "pale empress of the night."

Photo by Cornelia Clarke

Cecropia Moths. The male, with large bushy antennae, is at the left; the female, with slender antennae, is at the right; a curved row of eggs is at the extreme right.

The Luna Moth, or Pale Empress of the Night, is a particular favorite with all amateur naturalists. Its wings are tinted a delicate green and have a spread of four and one-half inches. The larva feeds on the leaves of various trees including hickory and walnut; it is three inches long when full-grown, pale bluish-green in color, with a light yellowish stripe on each side of the body.

The Cecropia is our largest species, with a wing spread up to six inches or more. Near the center of each dusky-brown wing is a crescent-shaped white spot bordered with red. The larva grows to be three or four inches long and has six rows of tubercles along the back.

The Asiatic Ailanthus Moth is a species that was introduced into this country about 1861, probably with the idea that its silk might be of commercial value. Like certain other introduced insects it has proved not only to be of no value but in certain localities is even injurious. The larvae feed on leaves of the ailanthus trees and when sufficiently numerous do considerable damage. They also feed on cherry, linden, sycamore, and other plants. The cocoon is spun on a leaf, the leaf being first fastened to a branch with silk.

The Buck Moth has wings that are semi-transparent due to the small number of scales covering them.   The eggs are laid around a twig; the larvae develop in them, but do not emerge until the warm days of spring.   Each larva is armed with branched spines that are poisonous.

Photo by Cornelia Clarke

Cecropia Moth.   The caterpillar is pale green in color; the tubercles on the back are blue, coral red, or yellow, and those along the side are blue.

Polyphemus has a "window" in each wing; the larva feeds on the leaves of various trees; the cocoon is usually covered by a leaf; and the silk can be unwound and used in weaving.   The cocoon of the Promethea Moth is also enclosed in a leaf, but some of the silk is used to fasten the leaf to the tree and hence the leaf

Photo by Doten

Buck Moth.   These caterpillars have just hatched from the eggs; their spines are poisonous.

does not fall off during the winter, making the detection of this type of cocoon easy for the collector.   The larva of the Io Emperor Moth has poisonous spines along the back, similar to those of the Buck Moth, and hence should be handled with care.

Silkworm.   If we had to pay Silkworms for the time and labor involved in the production of silk, only the wives of millionaires could afford to wear silk stockings and far greater efforts would be made to prevent "runs" in them.   The Chinese were probably the first to make use of silk; they are known to have carried on its production as an industry as early as 2600 B.C.   From China the art was carried to Japan, where a large proportion of the world's supply of raw silk is now produced. The business of raising Silkworms was introduced into Europe about 530 A.D. Silkworms could be reared in this country, but the high cost of labor makes it economically impossible.

The Silkworm is really a domesticated animal, just as much as the horse, dog, or cat.   It is the caterpillar of a moth.   The female moth lays about 300 eggs on

Photo by Cornelia Clarke

Silkworm Moths.   Two females clinging to a cocoon.

pieces of cloth or paper provided for it.   When the caterpillars hatch, they begin to feed at once on leaves of the mulberry, osage orange, or lettuce.   At the end of about six weeks they begin to spin their cocoons.

The fluid which forms the silk is produced in the silk glands of the caterpillars; it passes out from the spinnerets and hardens on coming into contact with the air. The caterpillar first attaches the thread to a near-by object and then forms an oval structure about itself by winding round and round a single thread 1000 feet in length or thereabouts.   The adult moth develops within this cocoon and emerges in about two weeks if undisturbed.   To get the silk, however, it is necessary to kill the animal within the cocoon, since if this is not done, the moth destroys one end of it when it comes out.

After the animal is killed quickly in boiling water or by dry heat, the loose silk is cleared away and the end of the thread found and unwound. Silk thread consists of several of these threads from the cocoons spun together. The threads from about 25,000 cocoons are necessary to make a pound of silk. Large quantities of raw silk are produced in China and Japan, and much of it is exported to the United States. Japan alone ships over 6,000,000 pounds per year to America.

Although no native species belonging to the Silkworm family of moths occur in this country, a closely related family, the Giant Silkworm Moths, are common

Photo by Cornelia Clarke

Silkworms. A tray containing mulberry leaves on which silkworms are feeding.

and well known. The silk produced by the caterpillar of the Polyphemus Moth can be unwound from the cocoon and used for thread and cloth.

Tent Caterpillars. Animals that are strong and fierce can afford to be solitary, but the individuals of many species band together and lead a social life, not so much apparently because they enjoy each other's company as for mutual protection. The Tent Caterpillars that hatch from a single batch of three or four hundred eggs unite in the spinning of a web that often takes the form of a tent. Into this they retire every evening and from it they emerge every morning at sunrise when they start out on their foraging expeditions in search of leaves. The tent is enlarged as they increase in size.

The Apple-Tree Tent Caterpillar is a common species that lives on apple trees and other fruit trees. Their parents are reddish-brown Moths. Eggs are laid in a mass around a twig early in the summer, and are covered with a brownish glue which protects them until they hatch about nine months later the following spring. The full-grown caterpillars are about two inches long, black in color with a white stripe down the middle of the back and a spot on the side of each segment of the body. They are sparsely clothed with yellowish hairs.

Tent Caterpillars injure trees by defoliating them, and the nests they build are very unsightly. Spraying the foliage with arsenate of lead will destroy the feeding caterpillars. The tents should be cut down, not burned, since burning may seriously injure the tree.

Corn Ear Worm. Many insects will eat one kind of plant and no other although they may be in the midst of an abundance of vegetation. This may prove to be a great disadvantage

© *General Biological Supply House*

Tent Caterpillars. A brood of caterpillars gathered together on a "tent" that they have united in spinning.

and may lead to death and extermination. The Corn Ear Worm is a type that is not handicapped in this way, since it may feed on cotton, thus becoming the Cotton-Boll Worm, or on tomatoes, becoming the Tomato-Fruit Worm. Other plants may also be attacked by this easily satisfied Worm. On account of their variety of tastes they are able to live in many localities and hence are injurious pests throughout the entire country. The adults have a wing expanse of about $1\frac{1}{2}$ inches, are fawn colored with brown markings, and nocturnal in habit.

Photo by Cornelia Clarke

Corn Ear Worm. A caterpillar about $1\frac{2}{3}$ inches long feeding on an ear of corn.

Courtesy, U. S. Bur. of Ent.
Corn Ear Worm Moth.
The delicately marked male resting on a leaf.

The larvae feed on the tips of the ears of sweet corn and in some localities it is difficult to get corn fit to serve on the table. They are about $1\frac{2}{5}$ inches long when full-grown. The adult of the Corn Ear Worm is a greenish-yellow Moth about $1\frac{1}{2}$ inches across the expanded wings.

Bag Worm. Practically the entire life of the Bag Worm is spent in a sack. The larva, soon after it hatches, spins a sort of bag in which it lives, making it larger as it grows, and attaching pieces of leaves to the outside. When full-grown the bag has reached a length of about two inches. Then the larva fastens the bag to the tree on which it has been feeding and changes inside of it into a pupa. Male Moths emerge from their bags, but the females remain inside, lay their eggs, and soon die.

The best-known species is the Evergreen Bag Worm which feeds on red cedar, arbor vitae, and other species of trees.

Courtesy, U. S. Bureau of Entomology

Bag Worm. This branch of a pine tree has been defoliated by a group of worms. Each bag contains a pupa.

Yucca Moth. One of the most remarkable associations between a plant and an animal is that of the Yucca or Pronuba Moth and the yucca plants of the south-western states and Mexico. The flowers of the yucca plant depend entirely upon this Moth for their cross-pollination.   The little white moth visits the flowers in the evening.   It scrapes some pollen from a stamen, holds it underneath its head, and carries it to another flower.   It clings to the pistil of this, and, thrusting its ovipositor through the wall of the ovary, lays an egg.   It then mounts the pistil, and forces the pollen it has brought down into the stigmatic tube.   Another egg

Photo by Cornelia Clarke

Yucca Moth.   A yucca flower visited by the little white moth that fertilizes it.

is laid in another part of the ovary, and more pollen is inserted into the stigmatic tube.   These processes may be repeated half a dozen times in a single flower. The advantage to the flower is, of course, the certainty of being cross-pollinated and of producing seeds.   These seeds provide a supply of food for the larvae that hatch from the eggs laid by the moth in the ovary.   The seeds are so numerous that the few eaten by the larvae may well be spared.

CHAPTER 15

FLIES, OR DIPTERA

Flies seem to be able to fly as well with two wings as other insects do with four wings. The wings, when present, are delicate membranes; they are absent entirely in many species. The hind wings are represented by two threadlike structures knobbed at the end, called halteres; these serve as balancing organs. The mouth parts are fitted for sucking and in some species for piercing. The larvae are often called maggots. The pupae are usually naked, but in some species are enclosed in a cocoon.

The differences in form and habits exhibited by the various groups of Flies are quite remarkable. Mosquitoes, Punkies, and Black Flies are pests because of their bites; Blow Flies are excellent scavengers; Bot Flies, Warble Flies, and Louse Flies are parasites of domesticated animals; the House Fly is a carrier of the germs of typhoid fever and other diseases; and many species are destructive to vegetation.

Crane Fly. When we complain about mosquito bites, we are trifling with our luck; how terrible life would be if Crane Flies could bite. Crane Flies look very much like giant mosquitoes and are often mistaken for them. One distinguishing feature that easily identifies them is a V-shaped mark on the top of the thorax. As in mosquitoes, the body is long and slender, the wings narrow, and the legs very

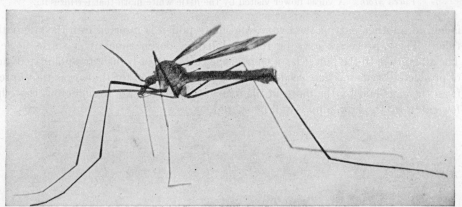

Photo by Cornelia Clarke

Crane Fly. It resembles a giant mosquito but is perfectly harmless.

long. The adults are to be found in damp, weedy places; they fly slowly and, in spite of their long legs, are poor pedestrians. "My six long legs, all here and there, oppress my bosom with despair."

For many years we have used the larvae of Crane Flies to introduce students to the science of Entomology, because they illustrate so beautifully the structure of the digestive, nervous, and respiratory systems.   These larvae live as scavengers

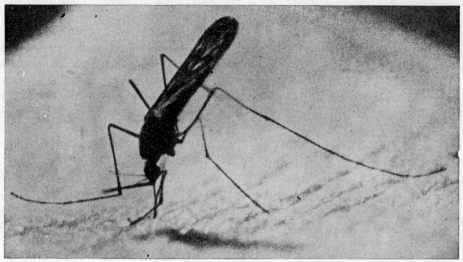

Courtesy, Science Service

Anopheline Mosquito.   Her proboscis is inserted in the skin and blood is sucked out.   She holds her body in an oblique position characteristic of the Malaria Mosquito.

in water, mud, or in the soil.   They have a tough skin and are sometimes called Leather Jackets.   About 500 species of Crane Flies have been described from North America.   Not all of these are giants; some are no larger than certain mosquitoes

Mosquitoes.   The Mosquito ranks as Insect Public Enemy No. 1 so far as human welfare is concerned.   Furthermore the damage is due entirely to "girl bandits," since only the female Mosquito sucks blood; the male is content with nectar and other plant juices.   The painfulness of mosquito bites is the least important result of their transgressions. Human malaria is carried from one person to another only by Mosquitoes; Yellow Fever, Dengue Fever, and Elephantiasis are other serious human diseases that are distributed by Mosquitoes.

Photo by Cornelia Clarke

Mosquito Eggs.   The eggs of the House Mosquito are laid on the surface of the water in a raftlike mass.   They are blunt at one end and pointed at the other.   Magnified about 50 diameters.

Mosquito. The male shown here feeds on the juices of plants and does not bite or sting.

The name of the Malaria Mosquito is Anopheles. Our common House Mosquito, Culex, does not carry malaria germs. These two types of Mosquitoes can be distinguished at all stages in their life cycles, as eggs, larvae, pupae, and adults. The adult Anopheles holds its body at an angle when it bites, whereas Culex takes a horizontal position. Yellow-Fever Mosquitoes belong to a third type named Aëdes; they have a lyrelike pattern on the back, and white bands on the legs.

The breeding habits of Mosquitoes vary in different species. In general, the eggs are laid in the water in ponds, pools, ditches, cattle tracks, cavities in trees, barrels, tin cans, etc. They hatch usually within a day or two. The larvae, or wrigglers, feed on small particles of organic matter in the water. They come to the surface from time to time to obtain air. In a week or two they change into pupae; these swim about actively for four or five days and then the adults emerge.

Mosquito Larvae. They are hanging with their breathing tubes protruding through the surface of the water.

We may protect ourselves from Mosquitoes by screening our houses or by putting screens over our beds at night when Mosquitoes are active. Smudges will keep Mosquitoes at a distance since they do not like smoke. An ointment, consisting of one ounce of cedar oil, two ounces of citronella, and two ounces of spirits of camphor, rubbed on the hands and face will protect one for several hours. Certain sprays now on the market are also effective. The itching of mosquito bites is allayed by the application of alcohol or ammonia.

Controlling Mosquitoes is usually not difficult. Draining off standing water prevents them from breeding, and is the most effective method. Small fish, especially Top Minnows, are especially fond of wrigglers and are often planted in bodies of water to destroy them. Spraying pools with kerosene or crude oil so as to form a film will prevent breeding. The latest method is to mix Paris green with road dust and scatter it over the surface of the water. This has been done with success with airplanes where large areas need treatment. The larvae of Anopheles swallow the Paris green and are poisoned by it.

Punkies and Sand Flies. Many of the most beautiful mountain areas in this country are rendered practically uninhabitable, especially in the spring and early summer, by various pests. The smallest of

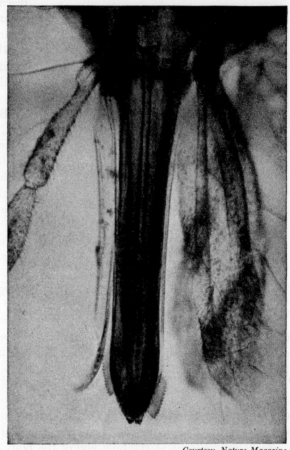

Courtesy, Nature Magazine

Punkie. The beak of this minute fly looks like a group of saw-edged swords when highly magnified.

these, but one that carries a big stick, is the Punkie. Punkies are barely visible to the naked eye, but they make up for their size by their aggressiveness, and by the painful burning sensation of their bites. The Indian name for them is "no-see-um," meaning, of course, that they bite without being seen.

These minute tormenters suck blood with their piercing and sucking mouth parts and inject a poison into the wound that sets up an intolerable itching, which may last for days. The larvae live in pools of water and can be destroyed by drainage much as mosquito larvae are. Smudges and repellents of various sorts

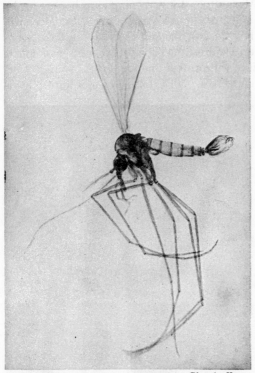

Photo by Hegner

Sand Fly. This fly seems weak but can bite severely. Sand Flies probably carry the germs of the human disease known as Oriental Sore.

help keep Punkies at a distance, but screens are of no value since they are so small they can crawl through the finest meshes.

Closely related to the Punkies are certain Sand Flies that carry disease germs from one human being to another. Three-day fever in the Near and Far East and Oroya fever in the Andes are transmitted by Sand Flies; probably Oriental Sore is, also.

Black Flies. Campers and hunters, and summer residents who migrate to the northern parts of the United States or to Canada too early in the season need not be told what Black Flies are. They are little demons only from $\frac{1}{25}$ to $\frac{1}{5}$ inch long, but with a bite much more painful and enduring than that of a mosquito. Huge swarms of these blood-thirsty pests not only torture both human beings and domestic animals, but may bring about their death. They attack exposed parts of the body principally, but will also bite under loose clothing. Mosquitoes bite mostly at night and can be kept away with screens, but Black Flies are most active when the sun shines.

The body of the Black Fly is stout and black. The thorax is large, giving it a hump-shouldered appearance that has suggested the name Buffalo Gnat for certain species. The larvae live in streams with a swift current. They are attached to rocks by a sucker at the hind end of the body, but can move from place to place. Fan-shaped brushes about the mouth are employed for collecting diatoms and other minute organisms used as food. At times the larvae spin a delicate silken thread one end of which they anchor to a stone. They can then swing about in the current without being swept away. Smudges and repellents may be used to keep the adults away, and a fine-meshed veil over the face and neck, and gloves on the hands furnish adequate protection.

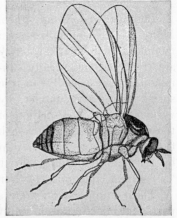

Black Fly. A hump-shouldered little demon, about $\frac{1}{10}$ inch long, whose bite is very painful.

Fruit Flies. To scientists the most important animal in the world at the present time is the Fruit Fly. Not because it is either injurious or beneficial to man, but because it has done more to enable us to solve the mysteries of inheritance than any other organism. Recently the scientist in this country who has studied this subject most thoroughly was given the Nobel Prize for his work.

Fruit Flies are yellowish in color and about $\frac{1}{8}$ inch long. Their eyes are bright red and their mouth parts form a proboscis for lapping up liquid food. Ripe and fermenting fruits have an irresistible attraction for Fruit Flies, not only as food but also as a place to lay their eggs. Scientists rear Fruit Flies in milk bottles, feeding them on banana. Usually only from eight to twelve days are required for a generation, hence a large number of experiments may be carried through in the course of a year.

Hessian Fly. Shortly after the Hessian troops landed on Long Island during the Revolutionary War, the flies now known as Hessian Flies appeared, and soon became our most injurious pest of wheat. The adult is a dark-colored gnat about $\frac{1}{10}$ inch long. The eggs are laid on

Fruit Fly. Scientists have discovered much of importance regarding the mechanism of heredity by studying fruit flies. Size about $\frac{1}{8}$ inch long.

the leaves and the larvae suck juices from the wheat plant. When full-grown they pupate near the base of the plant, remaining in their brown, larval skin which turns brown in color. This is the "flax-seed" stage in their life-cycle. Here they remain during the winter and from them adults emerge the following

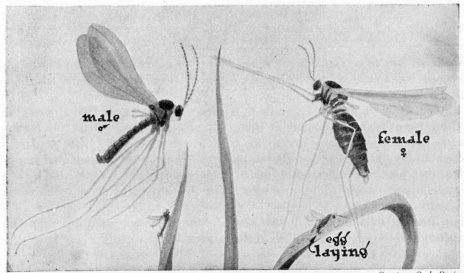

Courtesy, C. J. Drake

Hessian Flies. The female is full of eggs. Both males and females suck the juices from wheat plants and are **very** destructive.

spring. The loss of large quantities of sap so weakens the wheat plants that they do not bear seed.

House Flies. "Swat the fly" is a slogan that is approved by every authority on public health. House Flies are not only a nuisance, but have been found guilty of distributing the germs of various serious diseases, such as typhoid, dysentery, cholera, and anthrax. The germs are carried among the hairs on the legs, or are

Courtesy, American Museum of Natural History

House Fly. The hairs on the body that catch disease germs are well shown in this photograph.

swallowed only to be vomited out again. Food on which soiled House Flies alight becomes contaminated, and persons who eat it may contract some dangerous disease.

About 90 per cent of the flies that are present in houses are true House Flies. Within recent years the number of House Flies has decreased remarkably because of the automobile. This is due to the fact that the flies prefer horse manure in which to lay their eggs, and the automobile has practically eliminated horses. Now they must use any kind of animal or vegetable waste they can find. One female lays about 500 white, oval eggs about $\frac{1}{25}$ inch long. These hatch within 24 hours and the white, legless larvae, or maggots, feed on organic matter. The time from egg to adult is about two weeks. Since there may be a dozen or more generations in a year, House Flies increase exceedingly rapidly where conditions are favorable. The question is often asked, "What becomes of the flies in the winter, and where do flies come from in the spring?" House flies have many enemies, including a fungous plant that kills them in the autumn. A few flies hibernate in crevices and are the spring flies of the next season.

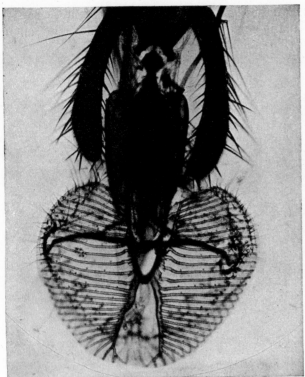

Photo by R. M. Allen.   Courtesy, Nature Magazine

House Fly. The tongue is covered with ridges and used for lapping. Magnified 75 diameters.

The family to which the House Fly belongs includes also the Stable Fly, Horn Fly, and Tsetse Fly. Tsetse Flies are of particular interest, since they are the carriers of the parasites that cause African sleeping sickness, a very important human disease in certain parts of Africa.

Horse Flies. No one can dispute the statement that in the Horse Fly family the female is more deadly than the male, because the female bites viciously and sucks blood, whereas the male contents himself with sweet sap and with the nectar from flowers. Animals are unable to escape from Horse Flies, because they can fly faster than the swiftest horse can run.

Cattle and horses are sometimes driven frantic by the bites of these insects.

One of the larger species of Horse Flies is about an inch long, with body and wings dull black, tinged with blue. The eggs are laid in regular rows on plants in marshes, and the larvae, on hatching, drop into the water and crawl about in the mud on the bottom. Here they feed on aquatic insects, worms, and other small

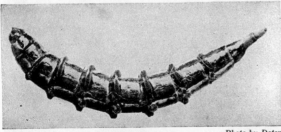

Photo by Doten   *Courtesy U. S. Bureau of Entomology*

Horse Flies. The larva at the left lives in the mud under water. The adult female is a vicious blood sucker; whereas the male lives on sap and nectar.

animals until they are about two inches long. The winter is passed in the earth, but in the spring they pupate and in June the adults emerge. Horse Flies sometimes attack human beings as well as animals.

Photos by Benbrook

Bot Fly Egg. The egg is attached to a hair. The lid that covers the opening through which the larva emerges has been raised. Magnified 37 diameters.

Bot Fly Larva. Anterior end of a Bot showing the hooks used in attaching itself to the stomach of a horse. Magnified 185 diameters.

Bot Flies. Everyone who has examined the stomach of a horse afflicted with Bots is thankful that such loathsome creatures do not infest man. Human beings

Courtesy, U. S. Bureau of Entomology

Bot Fly Larvae. A mass of larvae, or Bots, attached to the lining of a horse's stomach. In the center a number have been removed; the places where they were attached are evident.

may accidentally swallow the larvae of flies and certain species are able to live in the alimentary canal for a while, but this condition, which is called Myiasis, is not serious. Bot Flies are all heavy-bodied insects resembling small bumblebees. Their mouth parts are very weak, and it is probable that no food is eaten by the adults.

The Horse Bot Fly is about ½ inch long and brownish yellow in color. It at-taches its yellowish eggs to the hair on the shoulders, legs, or belly of the horse. These eggs are licked off and swallowed, and the larvae which hatch from them fasten themselves by means of rows of hooklets to the lining of the stomach. When several hundred are present, the horse suffers because of interference with its digestion and from the irritation. The full-grown larvae pass out of the alimentary canal in the excretions and pupate in the ground. The eggs are plainly visible when attached to the hairs of the animal; the hair should be shaved off or moistened with kerosene, which kills the eggs.

Blow Flies. The discovery a few years ago that the maggots of certain Blow Flies were effective in the treatment of a disease of the bones known as chronic osteomyelitis, elevated to respectability these rather unpleasant insects. The maggots de-

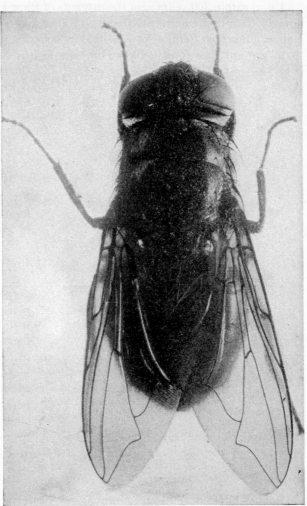

Photo by Cornelia Clarke

Blow Fly. A Blue-Bottle Fly whose larvae are maggots that live in meat, and are now being used to help wounds to heal.

vour the dead and dying cells, thus cleansing the wound and giving the living cells a chance to repair the damage.

Blow Flies are the "Blue-Bottles" and "Green-Bottles" that sometimes buzz loudly about the house displaying their metallic colors. The adults are about the size of house flies.   They lay their eggs in fresh or decaying meat or in the wounds or sores of living animals.   The maggots that hatch from the eggs soon dispose of a dead animal and are valuable scavengers.   Considering the number of eggs laid by a single Blow Fly, about 500 in number, and the voracity of the larvae, it is easy to realize the truth of the statement that "a fly can devour the carcass of a horse more quickly than a lion can."

Up to within 300 years ago, the maggots of Blow Flies were supposed to develop directly from decaying meat, that is, to arise by "spontaneous generation."   An Italian, Francesco Redi, disproved this by covering exposed meat with a screen so as to prevent flies from laying their eggs in it.   No maggots appeared in meat thus protected, and the conclusion reached was that "life arises from life."   This simple experiment had a profound influence on the civilization of the succeeding centuries.

Photo by Hegner

Sheep Tick. A wingless parasite that lives on sheep and sucks their blood. Size, ⅛ inch long.

Sheep Tick, or Sheep Louse Fly. Most parasites are profoundly modified by their habits of life; among insects this often takes the form of the loss of wings. In the case of the Sheep Louse Flies the body has taken on the peculiar shape of a tick, hence the name Sheep Tick, although it is really a fly. Sheep ticks do not lay eggs, but the young are born in an advanced stage. They are glued to the wool of the sheep where they form reddish-brown pupae. About three weeks later the adults emerge; these are reddish-brown in color and about ⅕ inch long. Their mouth parts are adapted for piercing and sucking. Sheep are irritated by them, but usually not seriously injured.

Robber Flies. "A careful observer, when visiting patches of wild flowers such as those found along roadsides and fencerows, may in some years see long, lean, gray flies alighting on stems of plants at the edge of an open space.   These flies rest in this position so as to command a view of any other insects which may fly near. If a wasp or bee comes flying leisurely by, or a young grasshopper jumps into view, the fly darts after it, catches it in mid-air, wraps its long legs about the captive and carries it to some plant upon which to alight.   Piercing a hole just back of the head, where the armor of the thorax is thinner, the robber sucks out the fluids and soft viscera, leaving only the hard outer skin of its victim. Then it drops the empty skin and goes in search of other victims.

"The robber fly is well fitted for its predaceous life. It has a pair of very large, shining eyes and the head is mounted on a narrow neck which can be turned so that the insect can see in any direction. The proboscis is long, sharp, and stiffened by a heavy coat of chitin. The body is an inch in length and lean, but with long, stout legs, and the depth of the thorax shows that it contains very powerful leg and wing muscles. The wings are about three-fourths of an inch long, stoutly built and capable not only of very swift flight but also of carrying the additional weight of the captured prey. The slender, pointed abdomen is marked with a conspicuous black band across the top of each segment. The head, excepting the dark eyes, is covered by a beard of long, blond hairs and most of the body has a sparse covering of short whitish hairs which give to it a general gray color." (Wellhouse.)

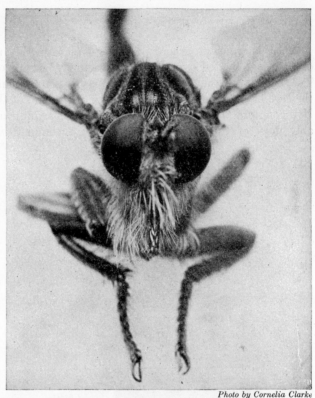

Photo by Cornelia Clarke

Robber Fly. He is a very strong flier, and captures and eats other insects.

The eggs of the Robber Fly are laid in small cavities in the soil; they are whitish and about the size of a pin head. The larvae do their hunting underground, burrowing through the soil in search of earthworms and insects, especially soft-bodied grubs. A hole is eaten into the body of the victim and the soft internal organs are devoured. The larvae of Robber Flies live in the ground for almost three years, whereas the adult lives hardly more than a month.

CHAPTER 16

MEMBRANOUS–WINGED INSECTS, OR HYMENOPTERA

To this group we accord the highest place in the Insect World, partly because of their complicated structure, but principally because of their mental development. The social life of the Ants, Bees, and Wasps is truly remarkable, involving especially the care of the young and provision for the future of the race. In numbers, these Hymenoptera are exceeded only by the Beetles, and Butterflies and Moths. Probably most of them are beneficial, only a comparatively few being destructive.

Photo by Doten

Saw Fly Larvae. Larvae of a species that feeds on leaves. Most of the body is held away from the leaf, and the hinder end is bent downward.

The wings, if present, are four in number and membranous. The fore wings are larger than the hind wings; those on each side are fastened together by means of minute hooks. The mouth parts are typically fitted for chewing, but many modifications have developed for special purposes. The females of many species have the ovipositor transformed into a stinging organ. The larvae may spin a cocoon in which they change into pupae.

Besides the Ants, Bees, and Wasps, with which everyone is familiar, the Hymenoptera include Saw Flies, Ichneumon Flies, Gall Flies, Parasitic Wasps, and many others.

Saw Flies. It is often impossible to determine by its common name where an animal belongs. The Saw Fly is not a True Fly with two wings, but one of the Hymenoptera with four membranous wings. The adult female possesses an egg-laying apparatus, somewhat resembling a saw, with which she saws slits in plants into which she inserts her eggs.

226

The larvae of Saw Flies look like caterpillars, but have one simple eye on each side of the head, in which respect they differ from the caterpillars of butterflies and moths. Saw Fly larvae feed on vegetation, and usually assume the attitude shown in the accompanying photograph, with the hind end of the body curled downward. When disturbed, all of a group of this sort will raise and lower the posterior segments of the body in unison. Some of the Saw Flies are injurious to vegetation, notably the Currant Worm, Pear Slug, and Rose Slug.

Ants. The Ant has always been a symbol for industry and to him the sluggard is advised to go for guidance. No better example of feverish activity is available than that of an ant hill that has been disturbed. Ants are known to nearly every-one, but few probably realize that they are the most numerous of all insects in most localities. The ease with which they can be found and their complex social life have

Photo by Haskins.   Courtesy, Nature Magazine
Ants.   A group of large black ants.   Near the center is a queen with wings.

made them favorite objects for study, and have resulted in the publication of many books devoted to them alone. About 6000 species of Ants are known, and these are widely distributed over the earth. Ants can be distinguished from other insects by the toothlike projection on the upper surface of the segment that forms the slender waist between the thorax and abdomen. Ants will eat almost anything and hence obtain their food with little effort. They build homes largely of earth or in earth and thus have plenty of building material. Other insects are often used by Ants to help them secure food or construct their nests. Seeds, grass, etc. are often stored in underground food chambers. Pieces of leaves may be carried into their nests on which fungi are grown for food.

An Ant colony is usually established by a queen that mated during a nuptial flight and then bit off her wings when she came down to earth.   Her eggs produce

Photo by Doten

sexually undeveloped females, that may become workers or soldiers, males with wings, and other queens. A colony may contain more than one queen. Ants may bring into their colony other Ants that they keep as slaves and plant lice which they "milk" for their honeydew. Parasitic Ants may invade the colony and also other species of insects and various other animals that are more or less unwelcome guests that find the colony for one reason or another a favorable place to live. An Ant colony is certainly a very complex organization.

Ant.   A very characteristic activity for an ant is that of dragging a fly to its nest.

Ants often become very troublesome in houses. The large Black Ants are simply visitors from outside that enter occasionally in search of food. The little Red Ant, however, lives in large nests or colonies in the walls or under the floors. If the nest can be found, it should be destroyed. Otherwise the Ants must be trapped with pieces of meat or with sponges containing sweetened water; the latter can be dropped into boiling water and then "set" again.

Ants may be poisoned by adding sodium arsenate to sweetened water or molasses and placing it in a

Photo by Cornelia Clarke

Ant.   This ant is carrying an aphid, or plant louse, to a place of safety where it can feed on the sweet "honeydew" secreted by the aphid.

dish where they can reach it. An interesting method is used to destroy the Argentine Ant. Pans of slow-acting poison are set out. The Ants feed on this

Courtesy, American Museum of Natural History

Ant. The umbrella ant carries a piece of leaf over its body. The species shown here lives in Bolivia.

and carry it to their young; as a result entire colonies are exterminated.

"The colonies of all our northern ants nest either in the ground or in decaying wood. The nests, or formicaries, may be under stones or logs, and always consist of irregularly excavated, intercommunicating cavities, unlike the regular paper or waxen combs of other social Hymenoptera. Often the nests are surmounted by earthern craters or dome-shaped mounds, or hills. The latter are perforated with cavities which serve as incubators for the young, that is, for the minute eggs, the legless, grublike larvae, and the pupae. The pupae are either naked or enclosed in elliptical cocoons which are spun by the mature larvae." (Wheeler.)

Courtesy, American Museum of Natural History

Ant. Certain ants build "tents" or "sheds" in which they keep aphids, or plant lice, so they can obtain the "honeydew" secreted by them.

Photo by Herms

Yellow Jackets. These stinging wasps have yellow bands on the short, thick abdomen. They build a nest underground.

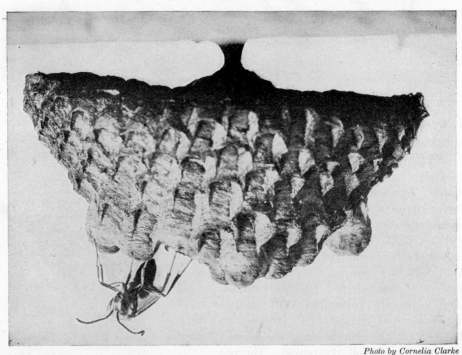

Photo by Cornelia Clarke

Wasp. The nest of the Polistes Wasp is built of "paper" and hangs by a stalk from some support.

Social Wasps and Hornets. Paper is supposed to have been invented by the Chinese, but Wasps and Hornets were building nests of paper long before there were any Chinese. The Social Wasps that are probably most often seen are named Polistes. They collect wood fibers, which they moisten and chew up to form a paste of which they build their grayish-colored nests. These nests consist of a single row of cells and hang down by a stalk from the roof of a shed or porch or similar location. The adults have a long, spindle-shaped abdomen and a slender waist.

Closely related to Polistes Wasps are the Yellow Jackets. These have a short, stout, black body with yellow stripes. Their nests are often built underground and are covered with a coat of paper. These nests may be as large as a bushel basket and contain over 15,000 Hornets.

The Bald-Faced Hornets are somewhat larger, with a black body, and marked with white on the face. They build conical nests covered with paper, which they hang from the limbs of trees, etc.; the entrance is at the lowest point.

Only the queens of Wasps and Hornets live through the winter, hiding in crevices until spring arrives; then they build a small nest and raise a few workers, who thereafter care for the queen and her young.

Photo by Talman

Hornet's Nest. The hornet hangs its paper nest from a tree and fills the inside with cells. The entrance is near the bottom.

The young are fed on flies, caterpillars, and other insects. Wasps sting, but only when annoyed; the sting is painful but not dangerous. Generally there are three castes in a Wasp's nest. The queen is a fertile female that lays all the eggs. The workers are females that do not lay eggs; they are produced throughout the summer. As autumn approaches, young queens appear and also males or drones; the latter develop from eggs that have not been fertilized.

Digger Wasp, or Ammophila. The home life of the Digger Wasp, commonly known as Ammophila, is of great interest to students of animal behavior. The Wasps are of the long, narrow-waisted type an inch in length, mostly black but with an orange-colored band around the front end of the abdomen. They emerge from their winter home in the ground in June and feed on the nectar of flowers, honeydew, and ripe fruit, lapping up the sweetened liquids with the tongue much the way a cat does.

The making and provisioning of the nests keep the female Wasp busy during the summer. Each egg has its own private domicile. The mother digs a shaft in the soil about an inch deep and makes a chamber at the bottom $\frac{3}{4}$ inch in diameter, frequently spending a day in the process. Then she covers the opening with a specially selected lump of earth or stone of the proper size to conceal it. Next she locates a caterpillar, preferably a hairless, green specimen of the cutworm type. "Upon finding a suitable caterpillar, the wasp at once attempts to alight upon it and sting it. Instinctively alert to its danger, the caterpillar repels the attack by rapidly rolling and unrolling its body, with violent contortions, and flinging itself

Photo by Cornelia Clarke

Digger Wasp. The abdomen is very long and slender with a yellow band around it. An egg has just been attached to the side of a paralyzed caterpillar which will later serve as food for the young wasp.

here and there over the ground. The wasp persists in her attempts until she succeeds in straddling her victim near the front end and in grasping its neck firmly with her mandibles. Standing high on her long legs and disregarding the continual struggles of her victim she lifts its front end from the ground, curves the end of her abdomen under its body and jabs the stinger into its lower side between two segments. Instantly there is complete quiet on the part of the caterpillar. The poison from the sting has been injected in the region of the central nerve cord and acts much like the hypodermic injection of an anaesthetic, given by a surgeon to a human patient.

"Limp and helpless, the caterpillar offers no further resistance. For some moments the wasp remains motionless, with her sting inserted into the first point of contact with the victim. Then, withdrawing it, she deliberately plunges the sting into five or six other intersegmental, thin-skinned areas, always choosing the lower surface near the nerve ganglia. She usually injects enough of the anaesthetic to keep the caterpillar's body paralyzed for a week or more before she is satisfied to relax and rest." (Wellhouse.)

The quiescent caterpillar is now grasped by the neck between her jaws and squeezed, probably so as to paralyze the mouth parts. It is then dragged to the nest hole; the cover is removed and the victim drawn down into the nest chamber. The hole is covered again and the mother proceeds to collect a second caterpillar as she did the first. When this is safely stored in the nest chamber, she lays a single egg and attaches it to the side of the second caterpillar. Filling up the nest hole and concealing the entrance is a remarkable performance.

"In filling up her nest she put her head down into it and bit away the loose earth from the sides, letting it fall to the bottom of the burrow, and then, after a quantity had accumulated, jammed it down with her head. Earth was then brought from the outside and pressed in, and then more was bitten from the sides. When, at last, the filling was level with the ground, she brought a quantity of fine grains of dirt to the spot and picking up a small pebble in her mandibles, used it as a hammer in pounding them down with rapid strokes, thus making this spot as hard and firm as the surrounding surface. Before we could recover from our astonishment at this performance she had dropped the stone and was bringing more earth. We then threw ourselves down on the ground that not a motion might be lost, and in a moment we saw her pick up the pebble and again pound the earth into place with it, hammering now here and now there until all was level. Once more the whole process was repeated, and then the little creature, all unconscious of the commotion that she had aroused in our minds, unconscious, indeed, of our very existence and intent only on doing her work and doing it well, gave one final, comprehensive glance around and flew away." (Peckham.)

The egg hatches in two or three days and the larva gnaws a hole in the second caterpillar and devours its contents; this requires about a week. Then the larva attacks and devours the other caterpillar, which is still alive but safely anaesthetized. A pale yellowish, silken cocoon is now spun within which the larva pupates. The Wasp may emerge from the pupa within a few weeks, or if the egg is laid late in the season, it does not emerge until the following spring. Digging a separate nest for each egg and furnishing it with caterpillars renders the Digger Wasp one of the hardest workers of all the insects.

Mud-Dauber and Jug-Building Wasps. Mud Daubers are also of the thread-waisted type. They build nests of mud and attach them under the eaves, or to the walls or rafters inside of buildings, or under stones. Each nest consists of a series of tubes about an inch long arranged in a compact group. Eggs are laid in the tubes and spiders included for the young to feed on. Many of the Wasps we encounter in and about the house or outbuildings, or that we see gathering mud where the soil is moist, are Mud Daubers. These Wasps can be identified by their peculiar habit of nervously jerking their wings from time to time.

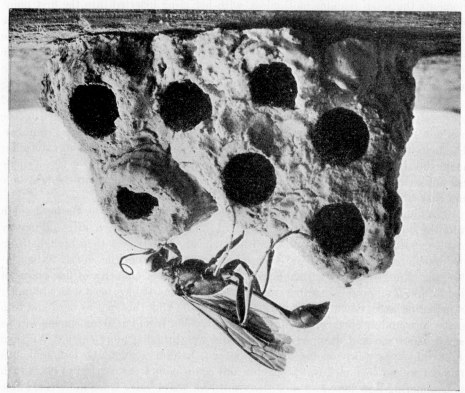

Photo by Cornelia Clarke

Mud Dauber. The waist of this species is a threadlike stalk. The cells are made of mud.

The Jug-Building Wasps are excellent potters, molding mud into jug-shaped nests which are attached usually to the twigs of trees. The egg is fastened at the end of a filament which hangs from the ceiling. A number of small, smooth, paralyzed caterpillars are then stored up in the nest and the opening closed. The mother then seems to lose all interest in her handiwork and her offspring. When the larva hatches it remains for a time on its swinging perch nibbling at its caterpillar food as though afraid of being injured by it, and ever ready to climb quickly out of danger if the victims show too vigorous signs of life. Later the larva descends and lives in the midst of its food supply until full-grown. Those who believe in the mercilessness of Nature can use these Wasps as an argument.

Some species of "Solitary" Wasps show more solicitude for their young. One of them "does not provision its cells with prey amassed in advance, but nourishes its larvae from day to day, with small, entire, paralyzed caterpillars, which are always given to the larva in very small numbers, till its growth is completed. The egg is never walled up in the cell with provisions hastily amassed. The wasp, to judge from what I have been able to observe of her educative procedure, after having laid her egg watches it within the cell till it hatches. As a rule, prey is brought to the egg only at the moment of hatching or a little before, and usually a single caterpillar, rarely two and never three, is found placed at the disposal of the just-hatched larva. Sometimes the larva may be seen fasting in the cell while the mother wasp is away in search of prey." (Roubaud.)

Photo by Cornelia Clarke

Jug-Making Wasp. This little jug-shaped nest of mud is fastened to a leaf.

Bumblebees. Charles Darwin used the Bumblebee to illustrate "how plants and animals, remote in the scale of nature, are bound together by a web of complex relations." Bumblebees, because of their long tongues, are the only bees able to reach the nectar in the flowers of red clover and hence are responsible for fertilization and the production of seeds in this plant. It is impossible to raise red clover in regions where no Bumblebees occur. The number of Bumblebees depends largely on the number of field mice, since these mice destroy their nests. Mice are few in number or abundant according to the number of cats in the neighborhood. Hence where there are many cats, there will be few mice, many Bumblebees and a good crop of clover seed. Huxley suggested that the influence of old maids on the number of cats be added to the story.

Bumblebees resemble wasps somewhat in their home life. The queen is the only member of the colony that lives over winter. She starts a colony in the spring, usually selecting the deserted nest of a field mouse for this purpose. After a few

Courtesy, U. S. Bureau of Entomology

Bumblebee. A stout bee colored yellow and black, feeding on the nectar contained in a flower.

workers have been reared by her, she devotes her time to laying eggs. Late in the summer queens and males develop from some of the eggs. When winter comes, only the queens remain alive; they hibernate in some protected spot until the following spring.

Their large size, noisy hum, or bumble, and conspicuous yellow and black colors, advertise the presence of Bumblebees to all.

Honeybee. So many insects are injurious that we often overlook certain beneficial species such as the Honeybee. Honeybees are domesticated animals, but sometimes return to a wild state and make their home in a hollow "bee tree." The number of bees in a prosperous hive is about 60,000. Most of these are sexually undeveloped females, called workers; a few are males, or drones, and one is the queen. The queen lays all the eggs, the drones fertilize the eggs, and the workers carry on all the activities of the hive.

The wax out of which honeycomb is built is secreted by glands on the under surface of the abdomen of the workers. Wax cells are used for rearing the young and storing honey. Honey is not collected from flowers but is manufactured from the nectar of flowers. Worker bees lap up the nectar with their tongues and suck it into a honey sac within the body, where it is stored until they return to the hive. Then the nectar is disgorged into the wax cells and left until all but 18 to 20 per cent of the water contained in it has evaporated. The cell is then sealed with a cap of wax. The flavor of honey depends upon the kind of flowers visited by the bees. In a single season a hive of bees will produce about thirty pounds of comb honey.

The enormous labor involved in the manufacture of honey is indicated by the fact that about 20,000 trips are necessary for the bees to secure enough nectar to produce a pound of honey. About 250,000 tons of honey are harvested in the United States annually. From this anyone mathematically inclined can determine the number of trips the bees must make each year for our benefit. The wax secreted by bees also reaches a large annual yield, estimated at about 10,000,000 pounds.

Among the other duties of the worker bees, besides those of building honeycomb and manufacturing honey, are the cleaning of the hive, ventilating the hive, guarding the hive, carrying water to the hive for the young in warm weather, feeding the young, and gathering pollen. Pollen grains are the very small fertilizing

Photo by Dodd. Courtesy, Nature Magazine

Honeybee. The two membranous wings on each side are held together by minute hooks. This specimen has no pollen in its pollen baskets.

elements in flowers. Pollen is gathered by the legs of the workers, is stored in wax cells, and furnishes the principal food of the larvae.

Bees swarm in early summer, when the hive is in danger of overcrowding. The workers rear a second queen when the hive becomes crowded, and the old queen then leaves the hive with a few thousand workers and founds a new colony.

The sting of the worker Bee is located at the posterior end of the abdomen. It is left in the wound when a bee stings and the bee dies. The poison may cause swelling, weakness, and labored breathing, especially if injected on the lips or over the eye, etc. Hot compresses and weak ammonia may be used to relieve the pain.

The legs of the worker Honeybee are marvelously adapted to the work they have to do. The first pair of legs are clothed with branched hairs for gathering pollen. At the distal end of the tibia is the pollen brush; on the other side is a flattened movable spine which fits over a curved indentation in the first tarsal joint. This entire structure is the antenna cleaner, and the row of teeth that lines the indentation is the antenna comb. On the front of the metatarsus is a row of spines, the eye brush. The middle legs are provided with a pollen brush, and a spur which is used to pry the pollen out of the pollen baskets and to clean the wings. The last pair of legs possess the pollen baskets, the wax pincers, and the pollen combs. The pollen basket consists of a concavity in the outer surface of the tibia, with rows of curved bristles along the edges. The pollen combs serve to fill the pollen baskets by combing out the pollen that has become entangled in the hairs.

Photo by Cornelia Clarke   Courtesy, American Museum of Natural History

Honeybee. On the way home with her pollen baskets loaded, many pollen grains attached to the hairs on her body, and her tongue extended.
At the right a swarm of a few thousand bees has left a hive and become attached to the branch of a tree.

Parasitic Insects. Have you ever wondered what becomes of the armies of plant lice that infest your rose bushes or the host of pudgy caterpillars that are eating up your vegetable garden? If you will examine them from time to time you will find the plant lice much swollen and perhaps with a circular opening in the top of the abdomen, and in the dying tomato worms you will see from 50 to 100 whitish bodies that look like eggs, but are really miniature cocoons. This is all due to certain wasplike wonder-workers among the insect parasites.

The parasite that destroys our plant lice for us is about $\frac{1}{12}$ inch long. Having selected a plant louse, the female parasite bends her abdomen forward between her

Photo by Cornelia Clarke

Parasitic Insects. This caterpillar of a sphinx moth is covered with the cocoons of a minute insect. The caterpillar is too weak to change into a pupa and will soon die.

legs, jabs her ovipositor rapidly into its body, and lays an egg therein. The larva that hatches from this egg lives on the body juices and tissues of the plant louse; when ready to emerge, the adult cuts a circular opening in the top of the plant louse it has killed, and crawls out.

Every species of insect parasite selects one or a few insects in which to lay its eggs. One of these favors the flour moths. This species is shown in one of the accompanying photographs laying eggs in the body of a flour-moth caterpillar, and, in another, feeding on the juices that have exuded from the puncture. The larvae that hatch from the eggs she lays eventually kill the caterpillar.

Photo by Doten

Parasitic Insect. A caterpillar is being stung by the long, slender spine at the hind end of the body.

The parasites that attack tomato worms lay many eggs under the skin which develop into a devastating battalion of maggots. When full-grown the maggots

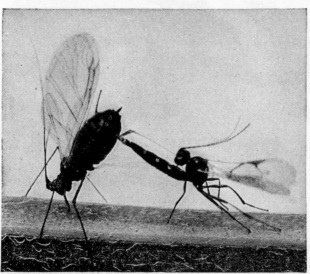

cut holes through the body wall of the worm and spin cocoons; and the worm crawls feebly away to die. About ten days later the adult parasites cut a round cap out of the top of each cocoon and emerge ready for new adventures. Many Plant Bugs are parasitized by Tachnid Flies. These flies glue an egg to the body and the maggot that hatches digs its way inside of the bug where it feeds on fat and other of the less vital tissues. Finally it devours all the organs in the bug, thus killing it.

Photo by Doten

Parasitic Insect. A plant louse, or aphid, at the left, is being stung by a parasitic species. An egg is laid inside of the aphid from which a larva hatches that eventually kills the aphid.

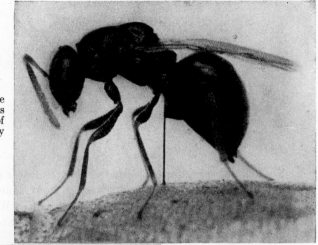

Parasitic Insect. (1) The egg-laying tube, or ovipositor, is being inserted into the pupa of a cabbage butterfly. (Photo by Doten.)

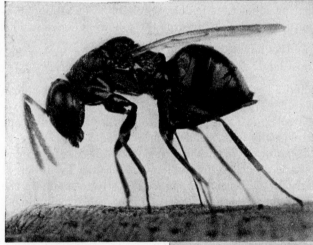

Parasitic Insect. (2) The same insect is here drawing out the ovipositor after laying an egg. (Photo by Doten.)

Parasitic Insect. (3) The same insect is feeding at the puncture made by its ovipositor. (Photo by Doten.)

Chapter 17

FISH

"No human being, however great or powerful, was ever so free as a Fish," says Ruskin. Knowing the number of enemies from which fish must protect themselves, we are unable to agree with this statement. We believe that the amateur fisherman is freer than the Fish he tries to catch, — at least he certainly feels free as, irrespective of age, he starts out to try his luck.

How Fishes live is a fascinating subject. Men have probably been vitally interested in fish life for many centuries. Pericles records the following conversation:

Fisherman. "Master, I marvel how fishes live in the sea."
Master. "Why, as men do a-land: the great ones eat up the little ones."

Fish are aquatic animals and adapted for life in the water. Some of them can exist in both fresh and salt water. Water offers more resistance than air to movement through it, and fish, as a rule, must move rapidly to capture food and escape enemies, hence their bodies are usually long, slender, and pointed.

The tail is the principal locomotor organ; when lashed from side to side it forces the Fish ahead, much as a boat is propelled by sculling or a steamer by its screw. The tail fin aids in swimming, but the other fins are used mostly to maintain the body in an upright position, and for steering purposes. Fishes can remain almost motionless in one place because of the air bladder which decreases their weight until they are exactly as heavy as the amount of water they displace.

Most Fishes are covered with scales arranged in oblique rows overlapping each other; these serve to protect the soft body beneath them. Scales may also produce colors due to reflection and iridescence. Many Fish are brilliantly colored and possess definite color patterns of great beauty; and some of them can change their hues according to the color of the background.

The eyes of Fishes are without lids, since the water keeps the eyeball moist and free from particles. The pupil is large so as to allow as much of the subdued light under water to enter as possible. Fishes probably cannot see in the air. No outer ear is necessary, since sound waves are transmitted by the water directly to the inner ear. Two nostrils are present connected with sacs containing sense cells of smell. Food is not tasted much, since it is usually swallowed whole or in large pieces. The entire skin, but especially that of the lips, is provided with touch cells.

Being truly aquatic animals, Fishes breathe by means of gills, usually four pairs, which are protected from injury by a gill cover. The eggs of Fishes are laid in the water during spawning. Very few of them succeed in producing adult Fish, since they serve as food for other animals, and may be destroyed in various ways. The young Fish live for a time on the yolk stored up in the egg, but soon begin to feed on small crustaceans and insects and later on larger aquatic animals.

For convenience, certain primitive aquatic animals are included here with the Fishes because they seem to be more closely related to them than to any other group. These are the Sea Squirts and Lancelets. Scientists divide the Fishes into four classes, the Lamprey Eels and Hag Fishes, the Sharks and Rays, the True Fishes, and the Lung Fishes.

Most of the Lamprey Eels and Hag Fishes live in the sea. They are slimy creatures without scales, and have a sucker-like mouth devoid of jaws. The mouth is attached to other Fish upon which they live as parasites.

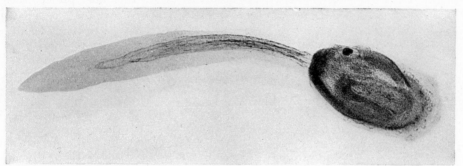

Sea Squirt. This young Sea Squirt looks like a tadpole. Its internal structure proves it to be a near relative of vertebrate animals.

The Sharks and Rays have a skeleton of cartilage, not bone, and are covered with toothlike scales. The mouth is slitlike and located on the lower side of the head. Rays, or Skates, are very much flattened.

The True Fishes include about 15,000 species, of which over 3000 occur in North America. They have a skeleton consisting entirely or partly of bone; are usually covered with scales, and have gills protected by an operculum.

The Lung Fishes, only five species of which have living representatives at the present time, possess air bladders that serve as breathing organs. They are not dependent upon water, but can breathe air. This makes it possible for them to live in marshes and swamps, and in the mud when the water dries up.

Sea Squirts and Lancelets. Sea Squirts and Lancelets play the part of John the Baptist to the Vertebrates to follow. To the visitor at the seashore they don't seem very exciting, but to the scientist they are of the greatest interest, because they are primitive creatures that indicate what the ancestors of the Vertebrates were like. They have on this account been studied in great detail. Zoologists usually include a group of wormlike animals with the Sea Squirts and Lancelets and call them all Primitive Chordates. The scientific name for this group is Hemichordata, a word that means half a cord and that refers to the small size of this structure.

Sea Squirts attach themselves to rocks and to the timbers of wharves, where they are often very abundant.　Their shapes are various, but a typical species resembles a sac with two short, open tubes at the unattached end.　When irritated, water is ejected through these tubes, hence the name Sea Squirt.　The larvae are particularly interesting because they are shaped like a tadpole, swim about with the aid of their tail, and exhibit vertebrate characteristics in their structure.　We should never recognize Sea Squirts as near relatives of Verebrates if it were not for their tadpole-like larvae.　Sea Squirts range from $\frac{1}{100}$ inch to one foot in diameter; some of them are brightly colored.

The Lancelets, named Amphioxus, are semi-transparent, fishlike animals, two or three inches long, that live near shore in various parts of the world.　They lie

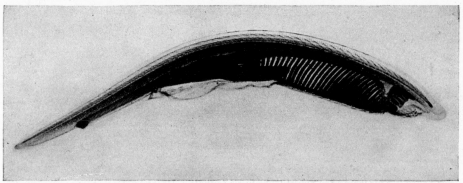

© *General Biological Supply House*

Lancelet. This little fishlike creature is well supplied with gill arches.　It is believed to be much like the ancestors of the vertebrates.

buried in the sand by day, but at night may swim about.　Vertebrate characteristics are exhibited by them, and believers in organic evolution sometimes sing a parody on the war song "Tipperary," ending with the statement, "It's a long, long way from Amphioxus, but we came from there."　In some regions Lancelets are so numerous they constitute an important article of food.　Near Amoy, China, the fishermen for about nine months of the year gather in over a ton of them daily.

Sea Lamprey.　Among the most primitive of the fishlike animals is the Sea Lamprey or Lamper Eel.　It has a long, cylindrical body eel-like in shape, and is probably more interesting because of what it doesn't have than for its peculiar characteristics.　Jaws are absent, but in their place is a large sucker with a piston-like tongue at the bottom and sharp, horny teeth around the sides.　There are no scales, the skin being smooth and somewhat slimy.　There are no paired fins, no ribs, and no bones, the skeleton consisting of cartilage.　The single nostril is located on top of the head.　Lampreys use their mouths to cling to solid objects, hence water for breathing purposes is taken in through seven round gill openings on either side of the neck, and is expelled through the same openings.

Most Lampreys live in the North Atlantic along the American and European Coasts, but many of them occur in lakes in New York State and in Lake Ontario, and those that live in the sea swim up fresh-water streams to lay their eggs. They are vigorous swimmers, moving forward by means of undulations in a horizontal plane. When the current is strong, the sucker-mouth is attached to a rock, then the body is jerked ahead and the sucker-mouth attached again.

The Lamprey's method of obtaining food is far from pleasant. Fish that are not very active or are without scales, such as Catfish and Suckers in fresh water and Cod, Haddock, and Mackerel in the sea, are the usual victims. The sucker-mouth is attached to the living fish and the horny teeth rasp away the skin. The blood and flesh of the fish is gradually consumed, and so tenacious is the sucker-mouth that once it is attached it is very difficult to dislodge.

Lampreys seek small, clear streams in which to breed. They form a circular depression several feet across in a gravelly bottom, moving the stones with their suckers. Then as many as 200,000 or more small, heavy eggs are laid. Spawning occurs only once, after which the adults are carried downstream and sooner or later die. The young are slender and eyeless, with a narrow, toothless mouth. They live for from three to five years embedded in the bottom, feeding on minute animals and plants and organic particles brought to them by the current. Then they move downstream into the sea, where they grow to a length of from two to three feet and a weight of from two to five pounds.

Courtesy, American Museum of Natural History

Sea Lamprey. Primitive, eel-like fish, with seven gill openings back of the eye, are building a nest of pebbles, moving them about with their sucking mouths.

Lampreys were until quite recently a valuable article of food, but are not used much at the present time. The French drown them in wine and then stew them. In the Middle Ages they were considered a great delicacy, and according to history, Henry the First of England died as a result of eating too much Lamprey. Lampreys and their near relatives are known as Cyclostomes, a term meaning " round mouths." About twenty-five species have been described, some living in salt water and others in fresh water.

Sharks. The typical Shark is a long, slender fish with a slitlike mouth on the underside of the head full of sharp teeth, with a row of gill openings on each side back of the head, and with a tail fin that has the upper part much longer than the lower. The body is not covered with scales, but with small bony nodules that are formed like teeth and actually develop into teeth in the mouth. Shark skin is known as shagreen and is used for polishing wood. Several characteristics within the Shark seem worthy of mention; the skeleton consists entirely of cartilage, or gristle, not of bone as in other fish, and no air bladder is present.

The Great White Shark, or Man-Eating Shark, is one of the largest species, reaching a length of over forty feet. It is one of the most voracious of all fish and occasionally attacks human beings, although most of the injuries attributed to Sharks are due to a much smaller, bony fish, the Barracuda. The teeth of the Great White Shark are broad, triangular, and knifelike, with serrated edges. An extinct species, which is known to have had teeth nearly six inches long, must have reached a length of almost 100 feet. The great Swedish scientist, Linnaeus, states that the Great White Shark was the creature that swallowed Jonah. This Shark is met with occasionally in all tropical seas.

The Basking or Elephant Shark is even larger, but is dull and sluggish and without any pep whatever. He loves to float on the surface and wait for food in the

Courtesy, N. Y. Zoological Society

Sand Shark. Here we see the mouth full of teeth beneath the head, the row of gill slits back of the head, and two "shark suckers" hanging on beneath.

form of small marine animals to come to him; for this habit we need not censure him because his teeth are small and weak. Basking Sharks are inhabitants of northern seas.

The Dogfish Shark is a very small species, usually about $2\frac{1}{2}$ feet long, but does the best he can for his size. He has sharp teeth and a greedy disposition; this leads to the destruction of large numbers of herring and other valuable food fishes. Fishermen catch Dogfish Sharks for the oil they can extract from their livers. College students are often given this species as a type for study in their course in Vertebrate Zoology.

The Hammer-Head Shark is the most peculiar of the whole series. The head is shaped like a mallet with an eye near the center of each end. The relation between this strange type of head and the activities of the animal is an unsolved puzzle. Hammer-Heads occur in warm seas. They reach a length of sixteen feet and are of the voracious type.

Among the other species of Sharks are the Frilled Sharks, with their eel-like body and large mouth; the Carpet Sharks, with their carpet-like pattern that con-

Courtesy, American Museum of Natural History

Hammer-Head Shark. It resembles a typical shark except the head, which is shaped like a mallet with an eye at each end.

ceals them as they lie on the bottom; the Blue Sharks, which furnish the sharks' fins that the Chinese like to add to their soup; and the Port Jackson Shark, with its rows of broad, grinding teeth used for crushing the shellfish on which it feeds.

Closely related to the Sharks are the Chimaeras. These are such curious looking creatures that they were named after the fire-breathing monster of Greek mythology whose head and fore legs were those of a lion, whose middle was that of a goat, and whose hind quarters were those of a dragon. The word is now used frequently for any fantastic idea and by architects for grotesque beasts used for decorative purposes. Chimaeras have a long ancestry, being among the first of the Shark Family to appear in the waters on the earth. They have a soft body which tapers gradually backward to a weak, slender tail. The head bears a short, soft conical knob above the mouth. Instead of teeth, the mouth contains flat plates set on edge. The Arctic Chimaera, or Rabbit Fish, has earned the name King of the Herrings because it follows shoals of herrings on which it feeds.

Skates and Rays. The advantage a very flat body appears to give to a fish that lives on the bottom has been developed by the Skates and Rays to the fullest possible extent. The fins on either side have become enormously expanded and the tail correspondingly reduced, serving simply as a rudder while undulations of the side fins propel the body forward. As a rule the underside of the body of Skates and Rays is light colored, but the upper surface is darker, and may be spotted, so that it blends well with the bottom of the sea when viewed from above. The mouth is on the under surface and rather small, hence a Ray "cannot at once seize its prey, and resorts to stealth to secure its dinner — quietly approaching its victim, which may be a crustacean, or small fish, it darts suddenly over it and smothers it with its body." (Norman.)

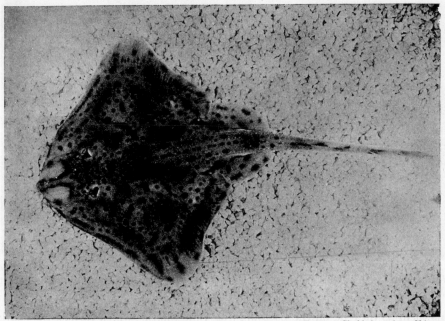

Courtesy, Shedd Aquarium, Chicago

Winter Skate. The body is very flat; the fins much expanded at the side; the tail slender and of little use, and the skin spotted.

Among the better known Skates and Rays are the Torpedo, Sawfish, Sting Ray, and Devil Fish. The Torpedo, or Electric Ray, possesses electric organs near the head which are capable of giving a powerful shock. It reaches a weight of about 100 pounds and may be found off the Atlantic coast of the United States.

Sawfishes are not as broad as the more typical Rays. Their most striking peculiarity is the saw, which is a bony extension at the front end, about five feet in length in a fifteen-foot specimen, that has teeth about $1\frac{1}{2}$ inches long extending out from the sides. Sweeping side strokes with such a weapon render the Sawfish a formidable opponent.

The Sting Ray, or Stingaree, is a rather obnoxious fish, since it lies half-buried in the sand where it is not noticed until someone steps on its tail with his bare foot and is severely injured by one of its spines. Near the base of the tail are one or several spines that may reach a length of a foot or more and are barbed along the sides. Wounds due to these spines are ragged and ugly and often subject the victim to the danger of blood poisoning. In certain localities the "wings" of the Sting Ray are used in preparing a delicacy called "raie au beurre noir."

The largest of the Rays is the Devil Fish, or Sea Bat, which may be over twenty feet broad and weigh over 3000 pounds. One of these enormous creatures when captured is reported to have pulled a motor boat that was going forward at a speed of four or five knots backward at a speed of six knots.

Courtesy, American Museum of Natural History

Sting Ray. Near the base of the tail is a spine that produces an ugly wound if one steps on it with a bare foot.

Common Sturgeon. Sturgeons are among the most primitive of all fish, which means that they resemble ancestors that lived millions of years ago and are known now only from their fossil remains. Some of them live in the sea and others in fresh water. Of the twenty known species, seven occur in the United States. The Common Sturgeon lives both in the sea and in fresh water, ascending rivers to spawn. The Atlantic Ocean from Maine to South Carolina is its home. Common Sturgeons reach a length of twelve feet or more and a weight of over 500 pounds. They have been taken in such numbers that very few large ones still exist and the numbers of smaller specimens are much decreased.

The body of the Sturgeon is protected by five rows of bony plates along the top and sides. The tail has the upper lobe very long, which tends to drive the body down to the bottom. As the Sturgeon swims slowly along the bottom it thrusts its long, sharp snout into the sand or mud to stir up the worms, insect larvae, and other small animals on which it feeds. The mouth is on the under surface and is toothless and sucker-like. In front of the mouth are four filamentous barbels or feelers; these detect the food as the Sturgeon swims along, and the mouth, being some distance behind them, is ready to suck it in without the necessity of stopping the movement of the body for this purpose.

The Common Sturgeon ascends rivers to about the limit of tide water to spawn. As many as two or three million eggs may be laid by a single fish. These are heavy and therefore sink; they soon become sticky and so adhere to the bottom. The eggs or roe of Sturgeons are made into caviar by the addition of salt. Caviar has

Courtesy, N. Y. Zoological Society

Sturgeon. The Sturgeon is shaped like a shark. Note the filamentous barbels under the snout and the rows of bony plates along the side and top of the body. A dogfish shark is in the background.

always been considered a delicacy and food for the rich. Thus Shakespeare has Hamlet remark, "His play . . . pleased not the millions, 'twas caviar to the general."

The best caviar is made in Russia. Russian Sturgeons are said to live for as long as 200 to 300 years. The flesh of the Sturgeon is rather coarse and beefy when fresh but is much improved by smoking. The swim bladder of the Sturgeon is made into isinglass, which is used to clarify wine, and in high-grade glue and court plaster. In England Sturgeons became the property of the king as the result of a decree of Edward II.

The Dogfish Shark and Sturgeon resemble each other very closely in shape, as is shown in our photograph, although their habits are very different.

Long-Nosed Gar. Garpikes are also living relics of the Age of Fishes. They are long, slender fish with a covering of heavy, overlapping plates that effectively protect them from every other animal living in their habitat. The Long-Nosed Gar, or Billfish, is the commonest species in the eastern United States. Other species are the Short-Nosed Gar and the Alligator Gar.

The Long-Nosed Gar has very long, thin jaws armed with long, sharp teeth. It is strong and greedy and very destructive to other fish on which it feeds. The

Courtesy, Shedd Aquarium, Chicago

Long-Nosed Gar. The snout is very long and the body is covered with diamond-shaped plates.

prey is approached stealthily, seized quickly with the alligator-like jaws, and swallowed whole. The young begin to eat fish at an early age; one is on record only two inches long that had eaten sixteen young minnows. Fishermen recognize the Gar as a nuisance and kill all they capture.

The swim bladder of the Gar serves the same purpose as the lung of higher animals, and enables it to breathe without using its gills. Gars often come to the surface of the quiet waters in which they live, give off a bubble of air, and fill their swim bladder with a fresh supply.

The Long-Nosed Gar reaches a length of five or six feet. The scales are extremely hard; Indians have in the past used them for arrow points. The early pioneers found gar skin hard enough to cover their wooden plows, and the Caribbean savages are said to have used the armor of the Gar for a breastplate during their battles with their enemies.

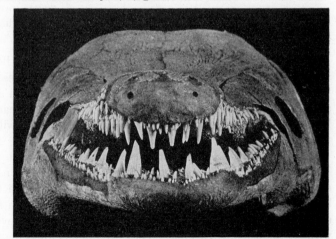

Courtesy, American Museum of Natural History

Alligator Gar. The front view of the skull reveals the many sharp teeth of this species.

Courtesy, American Museum of Natural History

Bowfin, or Fresh-Water Dogfish.   A male is guarding the nest, which is a circular area cleared out among the weeds.

Bowfin, or Fresh-Water Dogfish.   The Bowfin may be added to the Sturgeon and Gar as a "living fossil," being the only existing representation of a large group that lived millions of years ago.   The tail fin is rounded and the dorsal fin is half as long as the body.   The snout is short and the head covered with a hard, bony helmet.   In the male, there is a black spot edged with orange at the base of the tail.

Bowfins reach a length of thirty inches and a weight of about twelve pounds. They have strong jaws and sharp teeth, and their savage nature entitles them to be called the "wolves" of fresh water.   As in the Gars, the swim bladder is used for breathing, and Bowfins rise to the surface to gulp down air occasionally, and are able to live in very foul water, or even in mud, because they can live for long periods without the use of their gills.   They are famous for being tenacious of life.   Their young serve well as bait for pickerel and other carnivorous fish because they will live for hours with a hook thrust through their skull.

Bowfins live in the Eastern and Central States, in lakes and sluggish waters, especially in weedy places. Their habits have given rise to many local names such as Mudfish, Fresh-Water Dogfish, and Grindle. The breeding habits of Bow-fins are peculiar. The males clear away a circular area among the weeds for a nest. The eggs are laid here and become attached to the bottom. The male then guards the eggs, and also the young, until they are about four inches long.

Bowfins are not considered very palatable but are edible when smoked. In Louisiana dried Bowfins are used for making fish balls and jambalaya. Fishing for Bowfins is exciting sport; frogs or minnows serve as bait.

Common Sucker. Some of the most delightful days in the lives of many boys are those during a "run" of Suckers in the early spring, when they ascend the small rivers, creeks, and brooks to spawn. At this time they can be caught with a hook baited with an earthworm, or snared with a wire noose. Enough fish can be caught at such a time to satisfy the most greedy fisherman.

Suckers are so named because the lips are thick, fleshy, and protrusible and used to suck in food from the bottom. The eggs of other fish seem to be considered a special delicacy, since Suckers frequent the spawning beds of Trout and Salmon.

Courtesy, Shedd Aquarium, Chicago

Common Sucker. The scales are large and silvery. At the base of the snout is a sucker-like mouth.

About seventy-five species of Suckers have been described, several in Asia and the rest in North America. They all live in fresh-water lakes and streams.

The Common Sucker is one of the most common and widely distributed fish in the United States. It reaches a length of almost two feet and a weight of five pounds. The flesh is fairly good, but difficult to eat because of the large number of bones. About five million pounds are caught and marketed in this country every year. Some of the other members of the Sucker family are the Stone Roller, Red Horse, Black Sucker, and Buffalo Fish. The Red Horse reaches a weight of five or six pounds and was the largest fish we were able to catch as a boy.

European Carp. When an animal is transferred from one country to another, it is sometimes unable to support itself in its new home, but in many cases it "flourishes like a green bay tree." The European Carp is of the latter type. Asia was its original home and an account of artificially rearing Carp was written by the Chinese as early as the third century. From Asia, Carp were introduced into Europe and in 1877 into the United States by the U. S. Bureau of Fisheries. Soon almost every suitable lake and stream in this country was inhabited by Carp. They are tenacious of life and very prolific and can live in muddy ponds and streams where other fish cannot exist.

Courtesy, N. Y. Zoological Society

European Carp. The carp belongs to the minnow family but may weigh 30 pounds or more. It feeds on aquatic vegetation.

An average-sized Carp weighs from five to ten pounds, but specimens may reach a weight of thirty pounds or more. A four- or five-pound Carp lays from 400,000 to 500,000 eggs. Carp feed on wild celery and grasses that are also eaten by ducks and are accused of the decrease of these birds. Carp also stir up the muddy bottom and make the water murky and unfit for other fish. Their flesh is coarse and of poor flavor, but is used extensively for food, an average of over 25 million pounds being shipped to market from the Central States each year. The United States Bureau of Fisheries distributes every year many millions of young Carp to stock ponds and streams.

Common Bullhead. The long, slender "feelers," or barbels, projecting from the front of the head of the Common Bullhead and "its cousins and its aunts" no doubt suggested the name Catfishes for this family. Over 1000 species of Catfishes have been described, of which about thirty occur in the fresh waters of the United States, although none were present west of the Rockies until introduced there. Some of the larger species are the Blue Catfish, which reaches a weight of 150 pounds, the Channel Catfish, and the Mud Catfish, or Yellow Cat.

The Common Bullhead, or Horned Pout, is a sort of pigmy Catfish reaching a maximum length of only eighteen inches. The skin is naked, the eyes small, and the upper fin which is near the tail is without rays and known as an adipose fin, that is, fatty. The first ray of the dorsal and pectoral fins is a sharp, poisonous spine capable of inflicting a painful wound.

Bullheads are built for life on the muddy bottom of ponds and sluggish streams. Food is found by the sensitive barbels as they are dragged slowly along the bottom.

Anything small, either alive or dead, is engulfed by the capacious mouth without regard to how long it has been dead. Bullheads are ugly and rather repulsive-looking fish, described by Thoreau as "a bloodthirsty and bullying set of rangers, with ever a lance at rest and ready to do battle with their nearest neighbor." They are nocturnal in habit, and live in foul water where other, better fish cannot exist, coming to the surface occasionally to gulp down air into the large air bladder.

That such creatures should show solicitude for their young is rather curious. The father guards the eggs and young, sometimes taking them into his mouth, possibly in order to clean them, although no one knows how many he swallows.

Courtesy, Shedd Aquarium, Chicago

Common Bullhead. Sensitive, filamentous barbels extend out from the head. At the front end of the back and side fins is a sharp, poisonous spine.

Like the Carp, Bullheads are very tenacious of life and will live out of water for a long time if their gills are kept moist. They may be caught with almost any kind of bait and are so greedy they usually swallow the hook. The Catfishes in general are considered favorably as food and are of considerable commercial importance.

Tarpon. The most magnificent and spectacular of the game fishes living in our southern waters is the Tarpon, or Silver King, as he is affectionately called in Florida by the guides. He is famous for his size, his violent struggles, and especially his enormous leaps when hooked. Sportsmen catch specimens with rod and reel up to six feet or more in length. The record seems to be one eight feet two inches long, which was estimated to weigh 350 pounds.

When hooked, the Tarpon will leap out of the water until his snout is twelve feet or more in the air, and after trying to shake out the hook, may fall back again 20 or 30 feet away. If the boat is too close, there is real danger, and instances of severe injuries from blows from a leaping Tarpon are on record. Often several prodigious leaps follow one another in succession, and no fisherman can ever forget the sight when "a mass of molten silver suddenly shoots from an azure sea" into the glorious sunshine of a perfect Florida day.

Fishermen capture the Tarpon for sport since it is not ordinarily considered good to eat. The Indians of Central America, however, seem to find it particularly

delicious.   The scales of the Tarpon are very large and firm, reaching a diameter
of as much as three inches; they are often used as ornaments.   The life history
of the Tarpon is practically unknown.   No one knows where the eggs are laid nor
what they look like when young.   When they are first recognized they are usually
over a foot in length.   They probably lay a large number of eggs, since one specimen
that weighed one hundred and forty-two pounds was estimated to contain about
twelve million of them.

Courtesy, *American Museum of Natural History*

Tarpon.   The mouth is on the upper surface and the back fin ends in a long filament.   Below
is the Menhaden, a member of the Herring family.

Sea Herring.   The Herring family contains about 200 species and billions of
individuals, being the most numerous of all fishes.   It is estimated that ten thousand million are caught annually and that this is only 1 or 2 per cent of all those
in existence.   Besides the Sea Herring, the Menhaden and Shad are well-known
members of this family.

The Sea Herring is usually not over a foot long.   The young fry when three
or four inches long make up part of what is called "whitebait"; these are fried
crisp and eaten without removing head, fins, or entrails.   When the size increases,
the young Herring are canned in the form of Sardines.   Fully grown Herrings
may be eaten fresh, or smoked hard and dry as Red Herring, or lightly salted,
smoked, and canned as Kippered Herring, or large specimens may be lightly smoked
and well salted, becoming Bloaters.

The Sea Herrings are a beautiful deep blue or greenish blue on the back and
silvery on the sides and belly.   When just taken from the water they are iridescent
all over, with different hues of blue, green, and violet, but soon fade.   Sea Herrings
have had a profound influence on history because of their enormous commercial
value.   Amsterdam is said to have been built "on a foundation of Herring heads,"
and the Hanseatic League owed its wealth, and consequently its power, to the
Herring fisheries.

Sea Herrings feed on minute animals that float about in the sea and are collectively known as Plankton.   Water fleas seem especially favored, but as many
as 50,000 of these are necessary for a meal.   It would be impossible for a Herring
to eat this number one by one; they accomplish the "impossible" by swimming

through the water with their mouths open and straining out by means of a sieve-like arrangement all small bodies as the water passes out through the gill slits. The Herring are in turn preyed upon by many larger fish, such as Cod, Mackerel, and Salmon, hence if we do not eat them as Whitebait, Sardines, or Bloaters, we get them in the shape of some other fish. Certain Whales and Squids also feed largely on Herrings.

Sea Herrings live to be as old as twenty years. Their age can be determined because rings appear on the scales, similar to the rings of a tree, representing growth stages during winter and summer. Incidentally, a substance known as guanin, contained in Herring scales, is used in the manufacture of artificial pearls.

Brook Trout. Whitefish, Salmon, and Trout all belong to a family that numbers among its members many of our most important food and game fishes. There are over 70 species in the New and the Old World, mostly living in fresh water. Some of the best known Trout are the Cutthroat, Steelhead, Rainbow, Lake, and Brook.

The Brook or Speckled Trout is very familiar to fishermen; it is considered one of the best fighters of all game fishes. It lives in cold, clear streams, often selecting a deep pool at the foot of a rapids in picturesque surroundings. It reaches a length of eight inches or more and a weight of over a pound.

Courtesy, Shedd Aquarium, Chicago

Brook Trout. The spotted nature of this species is indicated, but its colors must be seen "in the flesh" to be fully appreciated.

Brook Trout capture insects that alight on the surface of the water and hence may be caught by an expert fisherman when they "rise to a fly." They are beautifully colored; the back is a dark-olive, barred or marbled; on the sides are a number of crimson spots edged with brown; some of the fins are bright crimson with a margin of white in front; and the belly is silvery white. Many streams have been fished so much that the Brook Trout have disappeared. The United States Bureau of Fisheries, however, has distributed millions of young fish to restock these streams and others not originally inhabited by Brook Trout. Recently in one year 500,000 eggs, 2,776,469 fry, and 12,755,628 fingerlings were liberated. The young fish are kept in the hatchery during the most dangerous period of their life.

Pacific Salmon.   The Pacific Salmon is the largest and most valuable of all Salmon.   An average specimen weighs twenty pounds, but sixty-pounders are frequently caught, and some may be five feet in length and weigh 100 pounds. They spend most of their existence in the sea, but when they reach maturity migrate up fresh-water streams to spawn.   At this time they are particularly abundant in the Sacramento and Columbia rivers.   They swim up these streams through rapids and over waterfalls and other almost insurmountable obstacles at the rate of from two to four miles per day, finally arriving at the headwaters of the Sacramento about 400 miles from the coast, and of the Columbia nearly a thousand miles inland.   No food is taken during this journey and they arrive at their destination in a rather worn-out condition.

The eggs are laid and fertilized in November and the parents then float downstream, but die before regaining the ocean.   The eggs hatch in about two months,

Photo by the Finleys.   Courtesy, Nature Magazine
Salmon. On their way to the spawning grounds at the headwaters of a river, salmon leap up falls and swim through cataracts.

and when the young are two to three inches long, they travel downstream, eventually reaching the ocean.   Here they remain for several years until they are mature, and then they, in their turn, sacrifice themselves for the good of the race by ascending the rivers to spawn.

The flesh of the salmon is pink or red, as everyone knows. It was first canned in Alaska in 1878; canning salmon has since grown into a vast industry.   The Pacific Salmon has a scientific name worthy of recording here; pronounce it if you can, Oncorhynchus tschawytscha.

Other common names for this species are Chinook, Quinnat, and King Salmon.   Other species are the Atlantic, Humpback, Dog, Silver, and Sockeye Salmon.

The Atlantic Salmon spawns in October and November, swimming up certain rivers from north of Cape Cod to Hudson Bay for this purpose.   Cold streams are preferred.   One female lays from a few thousand to over twenty thousand eggs.   These are heavy and drop to the bottom where they are usually found covered with gravel.   When the young are two years old, they swim down to the sea, where they prey upon small animals such as crustaceans and other fish.   In about four years, they become mature and, like their parents, ascend fresh-water streams to spawn.   They do not necessarily die after spawning as is the case with the Pacific Salmon.

Whitefish. The common Whitefish occurs throughout the Great Lakes region. The mouth is on the underside, and the crustaceans, mollusks, and other animals used as food are picked up from the bottom. During the winter it prefers deep water, but in the spring it migrates to the shallow water to secure insect larvae, which become abundant at that time. It migrates to shallow water again in the autumn to spawn. The eggs are laid over honeycomb rock; and since many of

Courtesy, N. Y. Zoological Society

Whitefish. These inhabitants of the Great Lakes are a favorite article of food in inland cities.

them are covered by sediment or fall prey to mud puppies, yellow perch, crayfishes, and other enemies, very few develop into adult fish. Because of this fact the government each year gathers, rears, and distributes millions of whitefish eggs. Whitefishes are captured in deep water by means of gill nets, which hold the fish just behind the gill covers. The average weight is about four pounds, but they may become as heavy as twenty pounds.

Pike, or Pickerel. Many fish that live in fresh water feed on other animals, but none is quite so fierce and voracious as the Pike, or Pickerel. Powerful and built for speed, it rests quietly among water plants until some small animal approaches, then it darts out with the speed of an arrow, and, like a scaly assassin, seizes its prey in its enormous mouth and swallows it head foremost while still alive. The projecting lower jaw, abundant sharp teeth, low, flat forehead, and evil eyes render it the most dreaded pirate of all fresh-water fish. Frogs, crayfish, young ducks, small mammals, and fish, even of its own kind, are readily attacked.

A fish with such a disposition cannot be expected to live at peace with its neighbors, and consequently we are not surprised to learn that it is solitary in nature, living alone like a hermit except during the spawning season. Pike are excellent game fish, and are also considered by many to be of value as food. They may be caught with a live minnow as bait or with a trolling-spoon, and in winter through a hole in the ice.

The Common Pike is very widely distributed in northern America, Europe, and Asia. The average weight is about five pounds, but some reach a length of four feet and a weight of forty pounds in America; even larger specimens have been recorded from Europe. Other species of Pike are the Chain Pickerel, Red-Fin Pickerel, Grass Pike, and Muskellunge. The Muskellunge occurs in the Great

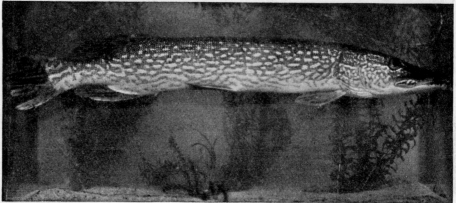

Courtesy, U. S. Bureau of Fisheries

Pike, or Pickerel. The body is built for speed, the lower jaw projects, and the mouth is full of sharp teeth.

Lakes Region and the Upper Mississippi Valley. Specimens over eight feet long and weighing as much as 100 pounds are on record. Such a monster may be considered the greatest prize Nature can bestow on a fresh-water fisherman.

Great Barracuda. The role played by the Muskellunge in fresh water is assumed by the Great Barracuda on the marine stage. This bold, ferocious marauder of the tropical seas is responsible for most of the attacks on bathers that are ordinarily attributed to Sharks. Terrible wounds are sometimes inflicted and not a few people have been killed by them.

Barracudas are built like a Pike, with a long, slender body, and a large mouth filled with powerful teeth of razor-like sharpness. Specimens ten feet long are on record, but the usual size is not over five. Often they seem to kill other fish solely for the joy of killing. They will even leap high out of the water to catch flying fish; leaps up to ten feet in the air have been reported. Their voraciousness sometimes leads to their downfall, however, since they are easily caught on a baited hook. They are good game fish and their flesh is delicate and well flavored. The Northern Barracuda ranges from Panama to Cape Cod; its habits are similar to those of the Great Barracuda, but it is not so dangerous since it rarely reaches a length of more than one foot. The Guaguanche is another small American species.

Photo by Longley

Great Barracuda. A bold, ferocious marauder of the tropical seas hovering over a bed of gorgonian corals. It is usually about five feet long.

Atlantic Flying Fish.   The first vertebrate to become an aviator was the Flying Fish. "Gliding Fish" would be a more suitable name, since the winglike fins are not vibrated after leaving the water, but simply extended like the wings of a glider.   In shape the Flying Fish resembles a modern airplane more closely than does

any other animal. Flying for them is not a sport, but a means of escaping from Dolphins and other enemies.

They swim swiftly to the surface and out into the air, the large lower lobe of the tail fin pushing the body violently upward. Then they glide along several feet above the water, usually for from 50 to 100 feet, although they may sometimes remain in the air for 40 seconds, and travel an eighth of a mile before plunging into the water again. Sometimes they may touch the water with their tail and, after sculling along rapidly, rise again and continue their flight.

The Atlantic Flying Fish travel in large schools. They reach a length of about fifteen

Photo by Davis.   Courtesy, Nature Magazine

Flying Fish.   The broad fins are spread out, sustaining the body in the air after the tail has propelled the fish out of the water.

inches. The young, as well as the adults, are able to fly, and when the iron monster of a steamer approaches, they rise terror-stricken in large numbers, spreading out over the tops of the waves like a flock of silvery insects. About seventy species of Flying Fish are known, mostly in warm seas; twenty-five of these occur in the waters of North and Middle America. Those mentioned by Kipling "On the road to Mandalay, where the Flying Fishes play," were probably in the Bay of Bengal through which boats sail on the way to Burma.

Common Eel. One must examine an Eel rather closely to be certain that he is not dealing with a Snake, since the body is very long and slender; dorsal, caudal, and anal fins form one continuous and inconspicuous fin; and movement is accompanied by undulations of the body. Eels have scales, but they are very small and embedded out of sight in the skin.

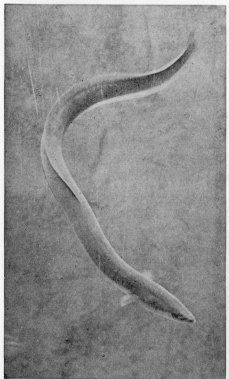

Courtesy, N. Y. Zoological Society

Common Eel. He is slender and "as slippery as an eel." The fins on the back and tail are united into one long fin. He swims by undulations of the body.

For hundreds of years the breeding habits of the Eel were not known. This led to many curious beliefs and fables. The Ancient Greeks called them Neptune's Children. The Greek philosopher, Aristotle, claimed that Eels had no sex and no eggs, and arose from the entrails of the sea. It was not until 1777 that the female Eel was recognized and almost a century later, 1873, before the male was identified. The greatest fisherman of all time, Izaak Walton, wrote in 1653, "Eels are bred of a particular dew falling about May or June on the banks of ponds and rivers."

We now know that the life history of the Eel is even more wonderful than our ancestors imagined. When Eels living in fresh water reach maturity, they change color and are known as Silver Eels. They leave the lakes and rivers and enter the sea. The Common Eels, for some unknown reason, swim to a region southwest of Bermuda to spawn. A single female may lay 10,000,000 or more eggs. The young are very thin and transparent, and are so different in appearance from their parents that they were, until recently, believed to be a separate species of fish. They swim toward the continent, and after about a year, enter the rivers and migrate over all obstacles, sometimes even over land, until they reach inland lakes and streams. Here they live until mature. No other fish is known to live in fresh water and breed in the sea.

Eels may live to a good old age; one is reported to have lived in captivity for 37 years. They are voracious, feeding on all sorts of aquatic animals, including other Eels. They may reach a length of five feet and a weight of over seven pounds. They are caught in traps, eel-pots, and seines and by "bobbing-for-eels." Many people consider them good to eat, but the idea that they should be skinned alive has long been discredited.

Brook Stickleback. The nest-building habits and pugnacious disposition of the Sticklebacks render them of particular interest. The Brook Stickleback lives in the clear, cool brooks of the United States, from western New York to Kansas and northward. It is only two and a half inches long. As the breeding season approaches, the male builds a nest of sticks among the stems of water plants, fastening the sticks together with silklike threads resembling those of a spider's web. These threads arise from glands present only in the male. The nest is made with two openings so that a current of water may flow through. When it is ready, the male drives his spouse into it and then guards it after the eggs are laid and the young hatch.

International News Photo

Stickleback. The builder of the nest is at home guarding the eggs.

Brook Sticklebacks are active and greedy. They feed on other small animals, especially the young (fry) of other fish. Their jaws are bristling with sharp teeth, and on their backs are five strong, pointed spines that are erected at the approach of danger and held in an upright position by a locking mechanism at their base. These teeth and spines, combined with a pugnacious and quarrelsome disposition, make these little fish among the best fighters for their size of all aquatic animals. They will attack larger fish, biting off pieces of their fins, and in the spring the males fight each other, sometimes until one of the combatants is killed.

The Fighting Fish of Siam resemble the Sticklebacks in their fighting ability. They are reared for fighting purposes and kept in glass bowls. When two are placed together in one bowl they attack each other with their spines and teeth until one defeats the other.

Porcupine Fish. What appears to be the best method of defense devised by any fish is that of the Porcupine Fish, or Burrfish. This inhabitant of tropical seas lives in the same waters as sharks and other aquatic bandits. Being only two feet or less in length and a slow swimmer, some effective sort of protection is necessary. This is what happens when one is attacked. The body is covered with sharp, stout spines, each with a broad base so close to the others that a continuous coat of mail results. The body can be inflated either with water or air until it is almost spherical, and in this condition floats at the surface. An inflated ball covered with spines bobbing about in the water is not only almost impossible to grasp, but difficult and disagreeable to swallow, even for a shark.

If a shark is so foolish as to swallow a Porcupine Fish, when the fish reaches the stomach, it is said to secrete what Darwin describes as a "most beautiful carmine-red fibrous matter" supposed to protect the fish from the digestive juices of the

Photo by Hegner

Porcupine Fish. When the body is inflated, it floats at the surface with spines extended, — not a pleasant creature to attack.

shark. Then with its stout cutting teeth, adapted for crushing the coral and shell-fish on which it feeds, the Porcupine Fish gnaws its way out of the Shark's stomach and through the body wall, and finally reaches the freedom of the seas.

Sea Horses. On seeing a Sea Horse for the first time one is apt to get a shock, because, instead of the large animal expected, it turns out to be only about five inches long. The head does resemble that of a horse in appearance and is set at a right angle to the body, but, in general, the Sea Horse looks more like a knight among chessmen or a miniature Chinese dragon. In fact, one species living near Australia is called a Sea Dragon.

The Sea Horse swims with its body upright, but most of the time it lives among eel-grass and seaweed to which it clings with its grasping tail, — the only fish with a prehensile tail. The body is covered with bony plates in the form of rings and the fins are small and fan-shaped. When swimming, the dorsal fin vibrates as though the animal were fanning itself rather than swimming with it. As everyone knows who has watched Sea Horses in an aquarium, their swimming ability is slight and they could hardly escape an enemy by flight. They are protected, however, not only by their bony covering, but also by their resemblence to the seaweeds among which they live, being practically invisible as they cling to a waving seaweed

Courtesy, Shedd Aquarium, Chicago

Sea Horses. They are about five inches long. The mouth is at the end of the tubular snout and the tail is prehensile.

with their tail. The food of the Sea Horse consists of minute animals, which are sucked into the tiny mouth at the end of the tubular snout.

The male Sea Horse plays an important role in bringing up the family. He is provided with a purselike brood pouch located on the lower surface at the base of the tail. Into this the female places the eggs and here the young, which resemble their parents, hatch out. The eggs are thus well protected, which probably accounts for the fact that Sea Horses can rear enough offspring to keep their race from total annihilation.

Sea Horses have been known for centuries. One is painted on a mummy case found in an Egyptian tomb. The Chinese dry them and grind them up **for**

Courtesy, American Museum of Natural History

Australian Sea Horse. An excellent example of camouflage; it resembles the seaweed among which it lives.

medicinal purposes. Dried Sea Horses when coated with silver make beautiful ornaments. In Italy Sea Horses are worn as a charm to avert the "Evil Eye."

One of the most remarkable cases of camouflage among animals is exhibited by the Australian Sea Horse, or Sea Dragon. In this species, long leaf-like appendages, often branched, extend out from the body, both shaped and colored like the surrounding seaweed. Since these Sea Horses are quite defenseless, their concealing shape and color are all that stands between them and extinction.

The group to which the Sea Horses belong also contains a number of other strangely fashioned fish. They are said to be tube-mouthed since the snout is extended to form a long tube at the end of which is the small mouth, usually without teeth. The food is not captured as in ordinary fish but is sucked into the tube with the current of water. The Tube-Mouthed Fishes are abundant in the seas in tropical and temperate regions. Due to their appearance various suggestive names have been applied to them, such as Trumpet Fishes, Cornet Fishes, Snipe Fishes, Shrimp Fishes, and Pipe Fishes. The body of the Shrimp Fishes is flattened and the fins mostly extend out near the posterior end, giving the animal the appearance of a shrimp. They appear to be able to swim while in any position. Pipe Fishes are long and slender and covered with bony rings. Some of them are characteristic inhabitants of coral reefs.

Between the Sea Horses and Perchlike Fishes are placed by ichthyologists (students of fishes) a group of spiny-rayed forms known as Berycoids and Zeoids. One beautifully-colored species that lives in the Atlantic is known in Spain as Alfonsino. Others are called Soldier Fishes because of their formidable spines.

Yellow Perch.   The honor of being called the most perfect example of a fish has fallen to the lot of the Yellow Perch.   In the fish world it is what Miss America represents at Atlantic City.   Its shape, size, structure, and abundance make it a very desirable type for laboratory study, and hundreds of students in high schools and colleges learn about fish from a study of some luckless Perch.

The Yellow Perch lives in lakes and streams, especially the larger rivers in the northern United States west to Iowa and Dakota.   It reaches a length of ten or twelve inches and weighs usually from one-half to two pounds.   Being one of our most abundant species, and easy to catch, it is well known to all fishermen.   What would the youth of our country do during the summer vacation without Perch to catch?   Most anything is satisfactory for bait, since the Perch will bite at grass-hoppers, angleworms, grubs, insects, or pieces of meat.   After one has mastered

Courtesy, Shedd Aquarium, Chicago

Yellow Perch.   The bands on the side of the body are distinctive marks.   Size, about 10 inches long.

the art of catching Sunfish, he is promoted to Perch and may finally graduate with the Black Bass.

The Yellow Perch is dark olive-green in color with six to eight broad bands on its yellowish sides, and a yellow belly.   Its eggs are laid in a single mass which lengthens out into a ribbon sometimes seven or more feet long.   As a pan fish the Yellow Perch is hard to beat.   In some regions it is of considerable commercial importance.

Small-Mouth Black Bass.   To fishermen the Small-Mouth Black Bass is the most desirable of all fresh-water fish.   It occurs in the northern and eastern portion of the United States, frequenting clear, cool lakes and streams, especially swift water.   A large specimen may reach eighteen inches in length and a weight of three pounds, although larger specimens are sometimes caught.   The male builds a nest, when spawning time approaches, choosing a sandy or gravelly bottom and fanning out a depression several inches deep with his tail.   Then he drives the female over the nest and after the eggs are laid keeps guard over them as well as over the young until they are well grown.

The Small-Mouth Black Bass is considered a good food fish, but is more famous as a game fish. "He is plucky, game, brave and unyielding to the last when hooked. He has the arrowy rush of the Trout, the untiring strength and bold leap of the

Courtesy, U. S. Bureau of Fisheries

Small-Mouth Black Bass. A boon to fresh-water fishermen; "inch for inch and pound for pound, the gamest fish that swims."

Salmon, while he has a system of fighting tactics peculiarly his own. I consider him," says Henshall, "inch for inch and pound for pound, the gamest fish that swims."

Courtesy, Shedd Aquarium, Chicago

Sunfish. Fishing for Sunfish is a favorite occupation with American boys.

Basses, Crappies, and Sunfishes all belong to the same family. "The Sunfish is by no means the King of Fishes. But there is no fish which has been oftener sought by the young angler or which has brought more joy to the American boys of every generation. The pumpkin-seed is pre-eminently the small boy's fish, though it is by no means despised by children of larger growth. Never reaching a size that quite satisfies anyone except the boy, yet biting with a vim which makes one regret that it is no larger; for a two or three pound 'Sunny' would surely be a fish to try the skill and delight the heart of any angler." (Jordan and Evermann.)

Mackerel. One of the best and most valuable of our food fishes is the Common Mackerel of the North Atlantic. Its economic importance is largely the result of its abundance. In the spring, "schools" of Mackerel migrate near the surface into shallow water to spawn, and in the autumn swim back into deep water. These schools are sometimes of great extent. One is on record half a mile wide and at least twenty miles long; another was estimated to contain 1,000,000 barrels of fish.

No one knows exactly where the Mackerel go on their migrations, but they are rather erratic and hence fishermen experience good and poor years. During a good year the catch amounts to 50,000,000 barrels, but in a poor year to less than 1,000,000.

Courtesy, American Museum of Natural History

Mackerel. A swift-swimming, beautiful fish of great economic importance. Size, usually about 1 foot long.

Mackerel are built for speed and their streamlined bodies are adapted for moving swiftly through the water. They are usually about one foot long and weigh about one pound each, but may reach a length of thirty inches and a weight of three and one-half pounds. The scales are very small and the skin is therefore velvety to the touch. When freshly caught they are beautifully iridescent.

Mackerel feed on minute crustaceans, especially certain species called by fishermen "red-seeds" or "cayenne," and also on small fish such as herring and anchovy. They fall an easy prey to Sharks, Cod, Porpoises, and Whales. In Hawaii, the natives believe that Mackerel are ruled by a Headfish, which is known as the King of the Mackerels, and disappear if the Headfish is killed. A group of Sharks are called Mackerel Sharks because the tail resembles that of the Mackerel.

Among other members of the Mackerel Family are the Chub Mackerel, the Frigate Mackerel, the Ocean Bonito, an inveterate enemy of Flying Fishes; the Long-Finned Albacore, which reaches a weight of over sixty-five pounds; the Common Bonito; the Spanish Mackerel, which is especially abundant in the Gulf of Mexico; and the Wahoo of the Tropical Atlantic.

Tuna, or Horse Mackerel.   The largest member of the Mackerel family is the Tuna, which is called by the English the Tunny, and on the Atlantic, the Horse Mackerel, or Great Albacore.   The Tuna is shaped like a Mackerel but is more robust, and has a comparatively more slender tail.   In the Mediterranean Sea, and off the coast of California, it reaches a weight of 500 pounds, but in the Atlantic has been caught up to fourteen feet long and weighing 1600 pounds, and specimens of 1000 pounds are not uncommon.

Tunas have been important food fish in Mediterranean countries for centuries, and the ancient Greeks and Romans considered certain portions of flesh from the belly particularly delicious, but it is only recently that we have used them to any considerable extent.   The sardine canneries of California now can about 15,000,000

Courtesy, American Museum of Natural History

Bonito.   The Tuna Fish and Bonito are members of the Mackerel family and look much alike.
Size of Bonito, up to 3 feet long.

pounds of Tuna annually.   The supply does not equal the demand, hence other species are also canned.

The Tuna is famous as a game fish.   "The most sensational fish of these waters (Southern California) is the leaping Tuna, which well compares with the Tarpon — the average large Tuna is a match for two Tarpons of the same size.   The Tuna is the tiger of the California seas, a living meteor which strikes like a whirlwind, and when played with a rod . . . will give the average man the contest of his life." (Holden.)   Flying Fish are used as bait and specimens weighing from 100 to over 200 pounds are caught with rod and reel every year.   A catch is on record of a Tuna off the cost of Nova Scotia that was ten feet four inches long and weighed 710 pounds.

Swordfish and Sailfish.   The Swordfish is also Mackerel-like in shape, but has the upper jaw extended to about one-third the length of the body into a flat, sharp-edged, pointed "sword."   Just back of the head is a sharklike dorsal fin.   The adults are toothless and have no scales.   Specimens sixteen feet long and 300 pounds in weight have been recorded, but they are usually about one-half this size.

Swordfish are fond of moving slowly along the surface of the sea in calm weather and can then be harpooned.   They are game fighters, and, being powerful and

Courtesy, American Museum of Natural History

Sailfish.   The upper jaw is like a sword and the dorsal fin resembles a sail.   When hooked he
leaps far out of the water.   Size, up to more than 10 feet long.

very rapid swimmers, may "sound" at such speed as to drive their swords into the
bottom.   Or they may attack the boat from which they were harpooned, and many
cases are on record in which the sword has been driven through the bottom and
fishermen injured or the boat sunk.   Nets and seines are too weak to hold a Swordfish, but specimens are rarely taken with hook and line.

The sword is supposed to be used for obtaining food as well as for protection.
Large fish may be speared and smaller fish, especially when in schools, are said to be
stunned or killed by side strokes of the sword.   Fish, such as Mackerel, Herring
and Menhaden, and Squids furnish much of the food of the Swordfish.   Only
certain Sharks and Whales are capable of conquering such active, powerful, well-
armed creatures.   Swordfish are often accompanied by Shark Suckers, or Remoras.

Within recent years the flesh of the Swordfish as an article of food has become recognized until now the demand is greater than the supply.   The flesh is firm and white.

Sailfish are nearly related to Swordfish and are similar to them in many respects. The upper jaw is prolonged into a sword and the fin on the back is very long and rises a foot or more from the body like a sail.   Sailfish live in the warm waters of tropical and subtropical seas.   They possess great strength and are rapid swimmers. Sportsmen consider them among the most exciting of all fish to catch.   They are difficult to hook, as they swim along near the surface; when one does get hooked, it will leap many feet above the water in its fight for life.

Sailfish usually weigh from 30 to 100 pounds; a specimen recently taken off the coast of Panama was ten and one-half feet long and weighed 177 pounds.   Several years ago while trolling for Tunas off the Pacific coast of Panama, a Sailfish caught the Tuna we were hauling in and made away not only with our fish but with our hook and most of our line also.   The Sailfish is as good to eat as the Swordfish.

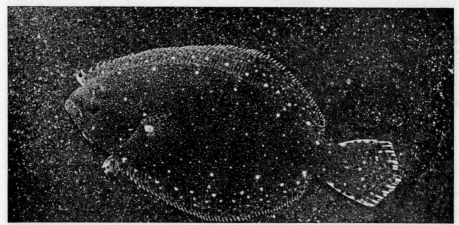

Courtesy, U. S. Bureau of Fisheries

Flounder.   A Flatfish that changes its colors so as to resemble the bottom on which it is resting.

Winter Flounder, or Sole.   The Winter Flounder, Sole, or Mud Dab, is a representative of a large order of Flatfishes of interest to us principally because they are important food fishes, because they become flat in a peculiar manner, and because they are capable of changing their color pattern to a remarkable degree. The Winter Flounder is one of the most abundant Flatfishes along the coast of the North Atlantic and comes next to the Halibut in value as a food fish.   It lives on sandy or muddy bottoms where it lies buried, except for the eyes, ready to dash out quickly whenever a morsel of food appears.   Shrimps and other crustaceans, shell-fish, worms, etc., are eaten, but because of its small mouth only small organisms can be engulfed.

Adult Winter Flounders are about one foot long and weigh about 1½ pounds. Spawning occurs in the winter, from February on.   A large fish lays as many as 1,000,000 eggs; these are heavy and adhesive, collecting on the bottom in large masses. The young are shaped like other fish when they hatch, but as they grow, the left eye moves around toward the right, the entire head becomes twisted to the right and the body becomes "flat as a Flounder." This is the only fish that has both eyes on the same side of the head. The adult swims by undulations of the body, with the aid of the dorsal and anal fins that form a fringe around the outside.

Flounders are light-colored beneath, but darker and changeable above. When on a sandy bottom, the general color becomes light and a fine, speckled pattern is acquired, whereas on a bottom of pebbles the pattern is made up of larger markings. Because of these changes, the Flounder is concealed both from its enemies and from the small animals on which it feeds.

Codfish. Codfish are known to everyone, at least in the salted and dried condition. They are economically the most important fish in the world, both as

Courtesy, Shedd Aquarium, Chicago

Codfish. Note the light-colored lateral line and the filament (barbel) on the chin. Average size, about 25 pounds.

regards the quantity caught and sent to market and their monetary value. Codfish have three dorsal fins, two anal fins, a tail that is nearly square, a light-colored lateral line, and a filament (barbel) on the chin. An average-sized fish weighs 25 pounds; real large specimens reach 75 pounds, and the record is of one over six feet long with a weight of over 211 pounds.

Codfish live in the North Atlantic and migrate extensively in schools. Over a billion pounds are caught annually. They are especially abundant on the Banks of Newfoundland, which was one of the reasons why England established colonies in America. The early settlers owe much to the Cod; it was placed on the colonial seal of Massachusetts and a model was hung in the House of Representatives of that State as a recognition of the debt owed to it. Every Sunday morning brings to the New Englander his "codfish ball."

Cod will eat almost anything.   They travel over the sea bottom in hungry packs searching for crustaceans, shellfish, squid, and anything else that lives, swimming away from the bottom only in pursuit of their prey.   Codfish are very prolific; a 75-pound fish may produce over 9,000,000 eggs in one season.   Only a few of these need to produce young which reach the adult condition in order to maintain the number of Cod.

Codliver oil has been used in the treatment of certain diseases for over 100 years, but we have known why it is of value for only about 20 years.   It contains large quantities of a vitamin, known as fat-soluble A, which prevents certain eye defects, and vitamin D which aids in bone formation, thus preventing the disease of children known as rickets.

Mud Skipper.   Some fish are not satisfied with the food present in the water and go hunting on land.   Of these the Mud Skippers, or Beach-Skipping Gobies, are familiar examples.   These little fish live along the coast of tropical Africa, Asia, and Australia.   When the tide goes out, they may leave the water and go skipping about over the mud flats, and may even invade the region above high-tide mark hunting for food among the roots of mangroves and other plants.   It must give one something of a shock to see a group of little fishes out of water chasing insects.

Courtesy, Shedd Aquarium, Chicago

Mud Skipper.   The front fins serve as crutches for skipping over mud flats; the eyes are elevated above the head.   Size, about 6 inches long.

Mud Skippers can move along more rapidly on land than they can in the water, and can outdistance a man when traveling over a mud flat.   The front fins are very strong and move back and forth like arms.   The eyes are slightly raised on the top of the head so that vision is possible in all directions; they are well adapted for vision in the air.   The respiratory organs are also modified for breathing air and the skin is so thick it prevents evaporation of water.   These features make it possible for Mud Skippers to live out of water for several days.   Why they make their excursions into the air is not known, but at least this relieves some of the competition that exists in the water.

Shark Sucker. It is difficult not to compare lower animals with human beings with similar traits. Thus the Shark Sucker, or Remora, is the lazy hobo of the fish world, a "hitch-hiker" that depends on Sharks and other large aquatic animals for its transportation. On top of its head is a flat, oval sucker of complicated structure that is really a modified fin. With this sucker the Remora attaches itself to the side of a shark, the skull of a sea turtle, or even the side of a ship, thus

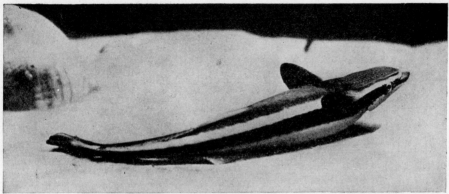

Courtesy, Shedd Aquarium, Chicago

Shark Sucker. The top of the head is modified into a sucker for attachment to sharks, turtles, and even the bottoms of ships, thereby securing free transportation.

getting a free ride. No harm is done to the victim, but the Remora benefits by being carried into fresh ocean pastures, and may even help himself to morsels wasted by the shark when he feeds in a slovenly manner.

Shark Suckers are slender and usually not over two feet long. They are good swimmers, and when smaller fish are encountered, will leave their shark host and catch a few, always returning to their accommodating skipper. Sometimes they attach themselves to ships, a custom that led the ancients to believe that they could stop any ship to which they fastened their sucker.

Shark Suckers are of no particular value to man, but the natives on the east coast of Africa put them to a peculiar use, since they fasten a ring around their tail, attach a line to it, and then send them after sea turtles, to which they become firmly fastened; they are then drawn in with their valuable cargo.

Angler. The living trap of the fish world, operating like a pitfall such as is used to capture wild beasts, is the Angler. Consisting of a mouth a foot wide, with a soft, flabby, sacklike body attached, it represents the glutton of the sea. It is accustomed to hide on the bottom, where it resembles a weed-covered rock. On top of the head is a long, slender, flexible spine with a flashy enlargement at the end which hangs over in front of the wide-open mouth. When this "bait" lures fish and other aquatic animals within reach, a lightning-like snap of the jaws engulfs the luckless prey. It has been suggested that the "bait" acts as a trigger that, when touched by a fish, releases the jaws.

If food does not come to him, the Angler goes hunting in order to satisfy its insatiable appetite.   Aquatic birds are sometimes pulled down as they rest on the surface of the sea.   The teeth of the Angler are attached to the jaw bones so that they bend backward; this prevents the prey that is being swallowed from escaping. The voracity of the Angler is demonstrated by the finding of seven ducks in the stomach of a single specimen.   Its ability to eat an entire goose has given it the

Angler.   A living trap with huge mouth, many long, sharp teeth, and a flexible filament with a "bait" on the end above the mouth.   Size, up to 4 feet long.

name Goosefish.   Among its other 50 or more common names are Fishing-Frog, Monkfish, Allmouth, and Bellows-Fish.

Anglers reach a length of four feet and a weight of 45 pounds or more.   They occur on both coasts of the North Atlantic and are said to be of excellent flavor and much eaten in Europe.   The eggs are laid in a ribbon-like "veil" 20 or 30 feet long and two or three feet wide, consisting of a single layer of eggs, over a million being laid by one fish at one time.

Deep-Sea Fish.   That very little is known about the animals that live in the depths of the ocean is indicated by the results of recent bathysphere descents by Beebe to a depth of half a mile or more.   The descriptions of excursions into the depths of the sea indicate that these vast watery areas which are inhabited by animals both great and small, and both invertebrates and vertebrates, present an almost virgin field for the researches of naturalists.

The physical environment at great depths is peculiar. "The depths of the sea experience a never-ending, starless night, and the intermediate waters enjoy a brief daily bluish twilight." Plants dependent on sunlight cannot live below 3000 feet. The temperature below 600 feet varies only slightly and is about 33° F. from the equator to the poles. The pressure is enormous; at 600 feet it is 270 pounds per square inch and at 6000 feet, over a ton per square inch.

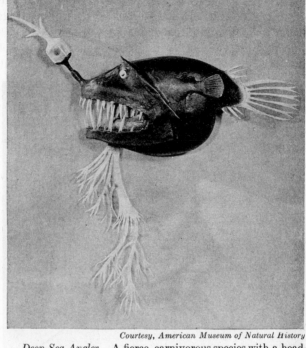

Courtesy, American Museum of Natural History

Deep-Sea Angler. A fierce, carnivorous species with a headlight and luminous "whiskers" possibly used to lure other fish within reach.

Deep-Sea Fish are carnivorous and are supplied with many large, sharp teeth for capturing their prey. Their mouths are extraordinarily large, probably so as to accommodate such an array of teeth. Some species can swallow other fishes much larger than themselves and store them in their distensible stomach.

Courtesy, American Museum of Natural History

Deep-Sea Fish. Captured near Sumatra at a depth of about 3000 feet. Luminous organs form a row along the side, and a peculiar appendage hangs down from the chin.

The eyes of Deep-Sea Fish are modified in two directions; they are either very large, so as to gather in as much as possible of the subdued light, or are very small or absent, as though the fish had given up the struggle of trying to see anything under such adverse circumstances.

The bodies of Deep-Sea Fish are generally very soft and the tissues are loose in texture. Dark and silvery shades predominate, but red fins or filaments occur rarely. Luminous organs are present in many Deep-Sea Fish. They appear like "brightly glistening jewels set in the skin" and are arranged usually in several rows along the sides and under surface. Some of these light organs are located on filamentous appendages extending up from the top of the head or hanging down from the chin. Beebe states that "the first animal lights were seen at 680 feet, and there appeared to be a slow but appreciable increase in number to the deepest depth, and in relative size to 2500 feet. The most apparent fact was an increase in the number of large fish from 2300 feet down to 3000." At 2500 feet "there were hardly any seconds without lights or definite organisms com-

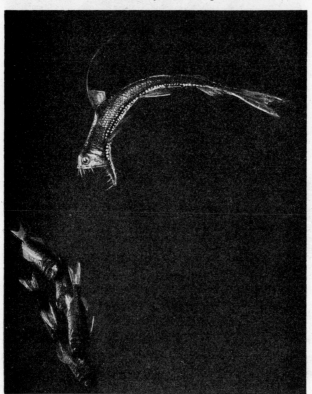

Courtesy, American Museum of Natural History

Deep-Sea Fish. A luminous Viper Fish about one foot long is chasing a group of Big Heads. Note the width of the mouth and length of the teeth.

ing into view. In one period, chosen at random, I counted 46 lights, 10 of which were of unusual size, most of them pale yellow but a few bluish." Along the sides of the body of one fish "were five unbelievably beautiful lines of light, one equatorial, with two curved ones above and two below. Each line was composed of a series of large pale-yellow lights, and every one of these was surrounded by a semicircle of very small but intensely purple photophores."

Coral-Reef Fish. Coral reefs have long been famous for the brilliantly colored fishes that use their caves and crevices as hiding places. Dr. W. H. Longley, who has spent many hours on the sea bottom studying the behavior of these fishes, writes about his experiences as follows:

Photo by Longley

Coral Reef Fish. Underwater photograph of Yellow Goat Fish (in center) and Yellow Grunts
(below). Living, massive coral at the sides, and plantlike gorgonian coral above.

" Fishes by hundreds are often here within a few paces of my position, swimming
above me or peering out from their hiding places; fishes by thousands are within
the radius of my hundred-foot hose. I can at any time find specimens here of
any one of fifty species I choose, but in many respects I enjoy the tiny ones most.
Perhaps it is because I see, or think I see, more of their world and understand
their relation to it better than I do that of the larger, stronger ones.

"One lurks under the sharp-spined black sea urchin, and a safer place could
scarcely be discovered. Another lives by preference under the overhanging margin
of living coral, above such dead faces as surround me in this cleft. It moves about,
upside down, under the coral caves as easily as the fly walks on the ceiling. Just
how it does this I have not yet made out.

"Its fins are under its throat and it often stands upon them with its trunk parallel
with the rock face, but not touching it. Sometimes it stands so and swings its
tail from side to side. Two, even — perhaps by chance only — facing one another
did the same, giving an absurd and probably false picture of swelling anger.

"At noon the timorous squirrel fishes, whose great eyes and conspicuous shyness
prove them creatures of night, are hugging their shelters close, except when the
sucking ground swell, tugging them alternately this way and that, for comfort
drives them from hiding.

Coral-Reef Fish. Underwater photograph of Gray Snappers among plantlike, gorgonian coral at the left and "pepper coral" at the right.

Coral-Reef Fish. A Red Parrot Fish among plantlike gorgonian corals.

"They are night feeders, whose behavior changes subtly as the light fails. As the hour of their release approaches, their apparent air of expectancy increases as imperceptibly, but as obviously, as lengthening shadows. They seem to ask, 'Is it time? Is it time?' They venture out more and more from the gloom and first pass freely to the open in the twilight.

"Other species creep away into holes in the reef. I see them narrowing their excursions from it as the

Courtesy, Shedd Aquarium, Chicago

Coral-Reef Fish. The Lion Fish is noted for the peculiar development of the fins and the zebra-like color pattern.

light fails, and see them peeping from it at night. Some, too, when night finds them, fling themselves down beside some boss upon the bottom that protects at least the side toward it. So I often see parrot fishes in their bottom-matching patterns."

Lung Fish. The evolution of a gill-breathing, aquatic fish into an air-breathing terrestrial animal like a salamander is not difficult to imagine when one has learned about the structure and activities of Lung Fishes. These peculiar fish are survivors of a group that was well represented on earth millions of years ago. Now only five species remain alive; one species lives in the rivers of Queensland, Australia; a second, in the Amazon River and its tributaries, and three species inhabit the rivers and swamps of Central Africa.

The African Lung Fish, or Mud Fish, has an elongated, eel-like body. The paired fins are whiplike

Photo by Longley

Coral-Reef Fish. Underwater photograph of Pork fishes swimming above long-spined sea urchins and at the side of a mass of coral (at the right).

filaments of no use in swimming, but possibly of creeping value, since they are moved back and forth alternately on the two sides of the body.   Scales are present but completely embedded in the skin.   Besides gills for breathing under water as in other fish, the air bladder has developed into a double lung with which the fish can breathe air.   By coming to the surface at frequent intervals for fresh air, the Lung Fish can live in foul water, where fish with gills only could not exist, and can live through periods of drought.

During the summer when the marshes are dry, the Lung Fishes are safely estivating in the mud.   They burrow down to a depth of about eighteen inches, where they coil up in a flask-shaped chamber, with a hole in the cover through which they obtain air.   The sides of their sleeping chamber are covered with hardened mucus, and a constant supply of mucus is secreted to keep the skin moist.   As in hibernating animals, the fish live on fat stored up in the kidneys and other organs during the four or five months they remain underground.   When the rainy season returns, they wriggle out of their underground cells and breathe with gills again.   Specimens of Lung Fishes in their "cocoons" have been shipped successfully to various parts of the world where they revived and became active as soon as released in the water.

Courtesy, American Museum of Natural History

African Lung Fish.   A fish that can breathe under water or in the air and hibernates in the mud; it reaches a length of 6 feet.

The nest of the African Lung Fish is a hole in the bottom of the marsh about a foot deep.   The eggs are laid on the muddy bottom of this hole and the male stands guard; he also keeps the eggs clean and provides fresh water by lashing his tail back and forth over them.   The young have a sucker just back of the mouth on the under surface of the head much like that of a newly hatched frog tadpole.   They also have four pairs of tadpole-like, plumose gills.   These disappear about a month after they leave the nest and breathing is then accomplished with internal gills and the lunglike air bladder.   The adults reach a length of six feet.   They are relished as food by the negroes of West Africa, who dig them out of the mud.

CHAPTER 18

AMPHIBIA

In many respects the Amphibia, such as Frogs and Salamanders, lead an enviable and carefree existence. The Greeks gave them the name Amphibia, which means "double life," but this double life has nothing to condemn it, since it simply refers to the habit of spending part of the time on land and the rest of the time in the water. In fact, a sort of summer vacation on a river or lake or at the seashore, delightfully extended throughout the year, with a swim whenever desired and sun baths galore.

Some Amphibia never enter the water even to bathe, others very seldom leave the water. Those that live on land may have a rough, dry skin, but most species have a smooth, moist skin through which they soak up water instead of drinking it as we do. These species must keep the skin from drying, and hence are to be found in the water or in damp places, such as underneath stones and in burrows in the earth.

The United States is well supplied with Amphibia, as everyone knows who has lived near a Frog pond during the breeding season, when the chorus of voices is in full blast, or has recognized as such the sweet trill of the Garden Toad that enters our open windows in the early spring evenings. Frogs and Toads are particularly abundant in the tropics, but Salamanders are more numerous in temperate regions.

Amphibia cannot be considered large animals and neither are they small. They probably believe they are about the right size. Frogs and Toads are comparatively short, being only a few inches long. Salamanders are rather long and slender; some are very small but others reach a length of several feet. Most Amphibia have two pairs of limbs, but some have only a single pair and a few none at all. Tails, when present, are round in those that live on land or flattened for swimming purposes in those that live in the water. Frogs and Toads seem to get along perfectly well without a tail.

The feet of aquatic Amphibia have the toes connected by skin and are said to be webbed. When the toes are spread out, a large fanlike area is formed which is pushed backward against the water like the blade of an oar. Amphibia have enormously large mouths, often cleft beyond the eye, and many of them have a large number of small, sharp teeth. As a rule they do not bite, scratch, or sting, but rely on concealment or flight when confronted by an enemy. The skin is highly glandular; some of the glands secrete a creamy poison which may be very potent. In parts of South America the Indians use the secretion from a certain

283

species of Frog for poisoning their arrows. Other glands in the skin secrete mucus which may be so abundant that the body is always slimy.

Amphibia breed usually once a year, and for this purpose most of them migrate to water in the spring to lay their eggs. The young are commonly known as tadpoles or pollywogs. Tadpoles and certain Salamanders exhibit the peculiar ability to replace lost parts, known as regeneration. If a leg or tail is bitten off by a bird or fish, a new one soon grows out to replace the one lost. The young of Amphibia are often vegetarians, but the adults live on other animals, usually insects, spiders, and worms.

Amphibia are divided into three groups: (1) legless Caecilians, (2) Salamanders and Newts, and (3) Frogs and Toads. About 2000 species are known; of these about 134 occur in North America.

NEWTS AND SALAMANDERS

All Amphibia with tails are either Newts or Salamanders. Often small species are called Newts and the larger species, Salamanders. They have long, more or less slender bodies, and usually two pairs of legs that are weak, but strong enough

Photo by Spencer

Salamanders. The head of the larval Salamander is large, and behind the head on either side are three tufts of gills for breathing under water.

for walking on the bottom of the pond or stream in which most of them live. The eyes are small and the ears are entirely internal, having no external eardrum as in the Frogs and Toads.

Salamander eggs are generally laid in the water, where they give rise to larvae with three pairs of external gills at the sides of the neck. Most Salamander larvae lose their gills, but some of them retain them throughout life.

Salamanders and Newts are timid, harmless creatures with a smooth, slimy skin, free from scales. This cold, slimy skin gave rise to the belief in medieval times that Salamanders live in and are not injured by fire. From this arose the imaginary being in human form living in fire and called a Salamander. In like manner, the term Salamander has been applied to various inanimate objects used in connection with fire, such as a poker or fire-proof safe. Nearly 200 species of Salamanders are known; they live mostly in the temperate regions of the Northern Hemisphere. About 70 species inhabit the United States.

Mud Puppy. The names Mud Puppy and Water Dog are well known to fishermen, who find this amphibian attached to their hook instead of the hoped-for fish. It is not a very pleasant-looking creature, with its flat, rectangular head and mean little eyes, but is quite harmless. Some fishermen consider it poisonous, and it

Courtesy, Shedd Aquarium, Chicago

Mud Puppy. A Salamander that retains its bushy red gills throughout life; it may reach a length of 2 feet.

does secrete poison from glands in the skin, but this poison is not injurious to man; it probably serves to protect the animal from enemies in the water that find it distasteful.

Mud Puppies spend their entire lives in the water and are well adapted to an aquatic existence. The tail is flattened laterally, which makes it an efficient swimming organ. The four legs are short and rather weak, — strong enough for crawling about on the bottom, but held against the body as useless appendages while swimming. Adult Mud Puppies are from one to two feet long, and dark brown in color, mottled and spotted with darker brown or black. Just behind the head on either side are three tufts of bushy, velvety-red gills for breathing under water. Anyone who tries to hold a living Mud Puppy finds this a feat more difficult than catching a greased pig, because of the thick slime covering the body.

Mud Puppies live in rivers and lakes, especially in the tributaries of the Great Lakes, the Mississippi River System, the Upper Hudson River, and the rivers of North and South Carolina, Georgia, and Alabama. They are rather slow, sluggish animals but sometimes bite with vigor. During the day they usually hide under a stone or partly buried in the mud, but as evening approaches, they move about in search of worms, insect larvae, crayfishes, fish eggs, and other aquatic delicacies.

The eggs are laid in May or June, each attached by a gelatinous stalk to the underside of a stone or log in water up to five feet or more in depth. Usually 60 or 70 eggs are laid together in a "nest." The young are $\frac{3}{4}$ inch long when they hatch, and resemble their parents in general appearance. They are still attached to a yolk sac from which they derive nourishment until they are about double their original size, and have had time enough to learn how to obtain their own food.

Mud Puppies are usually considered a nuisance, but are really good to eat. They are said to be "fine in quality and very white" and to "rival frog legs in flavor." Furthermore a large Mud Puppy furnishes as much meat as a dozen frogs. Finally the value of Mud Puppies for educational purposes should be noted, since teachers find them excellent for dissection work in courses in vertebrate anatomy. One firm in Chicago sells as many as 2000 of them in a year for educational purposes. A "dwarf" Mud Puppy lives in the Neuse River in North Carolina, and a large species in North and South Carolina, especially in rice-field ditches. A close relative, the Olm, inhabits underground streams in caves in the mountains east of the Adriatic Sea; it is colorless and blind.

Congo Snake. Slightly above the Mud Puppy in the scale of life is the Congo Snake, Congo Eel, Conger, or Blind Eel, as it is variously called. This amphibian does not have external gills, and the internal gills are rudimentary. There is a gill opening on either side of the neck, but breathing is carried on principally by lungs. The Congo Snake, as its name implies, is long, slender, and snakelike in form and reaches a length of over three feet. The body is cylindrical, the head small with

Courtesy, N. Y. Zoological Society

Congo Snake. A snakelike Salamander with small, weak legs.

an elongated snout, the eyes very small, and the tail short and flattened laterally. The two pairs of legs are small and weak and provided with only two toes each. They can be of very little use to their owner.

Congo Snakes live in bayous, sluggish streams, and swamps in the southeastern United States. Some natives consider them poisonous snakes. The eggs, about 150 in number, are laid on land in two strings that are twisted together. The female coils her body about them as a protection from enemies. The young hatch out in late summer.   They are about three inches long and provided with external gills which they later lose.   The Congo Snake has only one near relative, which also lives in the southeastern United States.   It is somewhat larger and has three toes on each foot.

Hellbender and Giant Japanese Salamander.   In general appearance the Hellbender, or "Mountain Alligator," resembles the Mud Puppy, except for the absence of fluffy gills and the presence of a prominent fold of skin on either side of the body.   The Hellbender has gills inside, the water that bathes them passing through two openings on either side of the neck.   Hellbenders are dark brown in color,

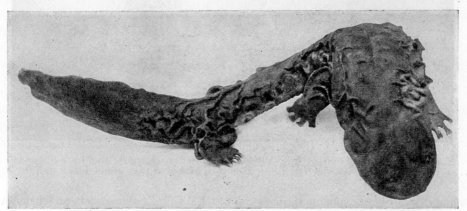

Courtesy, American Museum of Natural History

Hellbender.   The skin of this Salamander is conspicuously folded, the head is flat, and the eyes mean-looking; it may be over 2 feet long.

have a flat head and body and a flattened tail for swimming.   They are stout and reach a length of two feet or more, and hence are worthy of a place in the family of Giant Salamanders.

Hellbenders prefer rocky bottoms, where they hide during the day under stones, coming out at night to capture worms, insects, crayfish, etc., and to be captured by turtles and fish.   Fishermen often catch them on their hooks and are afraid of the hideous creatures, although they are perfectly harmless.   Eggs are laid in August and September, to the number of about 400, in a long, tangled string, usually under a rock.   They hatch in about six weeks.   The father stays with the eggs so as to prevent the mother from eating them.   He himself is known to devour many of them as a reward for his parental care, but enough are left to prevent the race from dying out.

The skin of the Hellbender is shed frequently and eaten by the owner.   Hellbender flesh is said to be very palatable but is very seldom eaten.   One may expect to find Hellbenders in the rivers and lakes of the eastern United States from the Great Lakes to Georgia and Louisiana; they are abundant in rivers that flow from the Allegheny highlands.   Probably because of its ugliness, many people believe that the Hellbender is poisonous.   While this is not the case, the belief no doubt saves many specimens from attack.

The largest of all Salamanders lives in China and Japan and reaches a length of over five feet. It resembles the Hellbender in appearance, with its large flat head, minute eyes, laterally flattened tail, and fold of skin along either side which

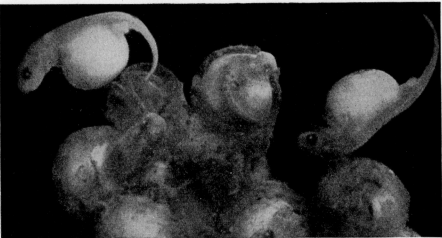

Courtesy, American Museum of Natural History

Salamander Eggs and Young.   One is hatching and two have emerged; they have gills and a prominent yolk sac which furnishes them with food until they can find their own.

undulates during movement through the water.   Giant Salamanders prefer mountain streams where they lie concealed under rocks waiting for insects, fish, worms, and other luckless aquatic animals to wander within their reach.   When captured

Courtesy, American Museum of Natural History

Crimson-Spotted Newt.   A common Salamander as it appears when floating in the water; it has a row of crimson spots on each side.

they secrete a slimy substance, with an odor like that of the leaves of Japanese pepper, which soon hardens into a gelatinous mass.

The Japanese esteem these Salamanders as an article of food, and catch them with line and hook baited with worms. The eggs are about the size of small grapes, yellow in color, and laid in a string. The male protects the eggs as in the case of the Hellbender. Giant Salamanders probably live to a good old age.

One lived in an aquarium in Amsterdam for 52 years. The Hellbender and Giant Salamander belong to the same family and have no nearer relatives than the fossilized Great Salamander that lived about 250 million years ago and was described by its discoverer as a fossil man.

Crimson-Spotted Newt. One of the most common salamanders in certain parts of the eastern and central United States is the little Crimson-Spotted Newt. Newts are to be found in ponds and streams where there is plenty of aquatic vegetation. They are three or four inches long, olive or yellowish-green in color, with black spots on the under surface and a row of black-bordered crimson spots on either side. Their food consists of snails and other small aquatic animals, especially insects. They creep up on their prey with slow, deliberate movements and catch it with a sudden snap of the jaws.

Courtesy, American Museum of Natural History

Tiger Salamander. Yellow bars on a dark-brown background give this species its name; length, from 6 to 10 inches.

The life history of the Crimson-Spotted Newt is very peculiar indeed. The courtship is complicated. The eggs are laid singly and attached by their sticky covering to water weeds. When the larvae escape from the eggs, they have gills, but these are lost when they are about one inch long, and the juvenile animals leave the water and spend several years on land, living in the woods under stones and logs where it is damp. Their color at this time is bright coral red, which suggested the name Red Eft for them during this period. Then they return to the water, where they remain the rest of their lives, changing in color to the adult condition described above. In many localities this Newt has trypanosome parasites in its blood that can be observed easily under a microscope (see page 17).

Tiger Salamander. So familiar to everyone are the yellow stripes of the Tiger that the term has been used for descriptive purposes for butterflies, salamanders, and other animals. The Tiger Salamander is made conspicuous with many yellow spots or bars on a dark-brown background. The body is rather stout and six to ten inches long, and the skin is smooth and shiny.

These Salamanders are active at night, and during the day hide in burrows in the ground or under stones and logs. The eggs, up to 75 in number, are laid in ponds and streams, early in the spring, in clusters about three or four inches across, attached to weeds or sticks. The larvae lose their gills in about three months.

The Tiger Salamander is very widely distributed, ranging from New York to California and southward to Central Mexico. Perhaps the most interesting thing

Courtesy, American Museum of Natural History

Spotted Salamander. This species is shining black, spotted with yellow, and about 6 inches long.

about this species is the fact that in certain regions in the western United States, and in the lakes near Mexico City, the larval condition is retained throughout life. The larval form, which is known as an Axolotl, was even given a separate specific name until 1865, when species that were being kept in the Zoological Gardens at Paris, France, lost their three pairs of fluffy, feathery gills and the crest on their tails, developed eyelids, and changed color, becoming thereby Tiger Salamanders. The Axolotl was thus shown to be a "permanent larva" of this species.

About a dozen species of Salamanders closely related to the Tiger Salamander occur in the United States, including the Mole Salamander and the Marbled Salamander. One species has been reported from Siam.

Spotted Salamander. To see Spotted Salamanders one must visit a pond with a flashlight during March or April when they are breeding, or look for them under stones and logs in fields or woodlands where it is moist. By day, they remain quietly in seclusion. The body is stout and broad, about six inches long, and shining black, with a few scattered round, yellow spots.

The eggs of the Spotted Salamander are laid in spring-fed ponds and streams, forming a jelly-covered mass. Besides this, each egg has its own envelope of jelly. These eggs are larger than frogs' eggs, and their development into tadpoles can be observed easily in an aquarium. The larvae are about half an inch long; their heads are flattened and their gills well-formed. Spotted Salamanders occur in various parts of the eastern and central United States.

Siren, or Mud Eel. This slender, elongated, eel-shaped amphibian lives in shallow ponds, swamps, ditches, and other muddy places. It is really a permanent larva with certain adult characteristics. The larval features include three pairs of gills and very small eyes without lids. There are no hind legs. The shape of the Mud Eel fits it for wriggling through the dense vegetation in the habitat where it lives. The skin is smooth and dark gray in color. The head is

Courtesy, N. Y. Zoological Society

Siren or Mud Eel. An eel-like Salamander with permanent gills, but without hind legs; the length averages over 2 feet.

flat and the jaws are toothless but covered with a horny sheath. An average-sized specimen measures about 2½ feet long. Mud Eels occur in the South Atlantic and Gulf states.

FROGS AND TOADS

Among the first of the vertebrate animals to venture forth on land were the Frogs and Toads, the "sirens of the ditch." They apparently liked it so well that some of them not only spend all their lives on land, but even in burrows in the ground. Certain species live in trees, from which they may glide to the ground like a bird. There is no definite method of distinguishing between a Frog and a Toad. As a rule Frogs are slender and have a smooth, moist skin; whereas Toads are squatty and covered with tubercles and warts.

The body of Frogs and Toads is usually short and compact. The young of most species live in water and have gills and tails, but the adults breathe by means of lungs, and are deprived of the joy of wagging their tails, since this expressive appendage is absent. The neck is short. The front legs are also short, just long

A pond community with a Bullfrog on the lily pads at the right, a Water Snake just beyond the Bullfrog, a Leopard Frog resting at the surface at the left, and several other frogs spending a pleasant afternoon together.

enough to hold up the shoulders and head, but the hind legs are very long and muscular and adapted for leaping.

The head is very large and provided with huge, protruding eyes that are in position to see everything that goes on around them, but are particularly adapted to see *moving* objects. They can be withdrawn into sockets in the head so that they are in no danger of being knocked off by an accident. The eyes are well supplied with eyelids. Behind the eye is the circular tympanic membrane of the ear, often very conspicuous.

The mouth is enormous, but Nature has done only half of her duty, since she failed to supply the lower jaw with teeth. Connected with the mouth cavity, especially in the male, are vocal sacs that supply the power for the well-known Grand Opera furnished by Frogs and Toads in the spring of the year.

One of the most remarkable features of these amphibians is the tongue, which is fastened to the front of the mouth instead of to the back as ours is. For this, as the advertisement states, "there's a reason," since the tongue is actually thrown out of the mouth full length at any moving insect, spider, or worm that chances to come too close, or rather, from the Frogs' point of view, close enough. The tongue is sticky and the luckless prey adhere to it long enough to be drawn into

Photo by Cornelia Clarke

Frog Tadpoles. The small tadpole hatches from the egg and grows very large; hind legs appear, then front legs; the tail becomes shorter and shorter as it is absorbed; and finally the adult appearance is attained.

the mouth. All food is swallowed whole and without any respect for table manners, since, if the victim is large, the front feet are used to push it into the mouth, there being no other "pusher" available, such as we supply for our babies. Swallowing is accompanied by ludicrous convulsive movements, and by the withdrawal of the eyes into their sockets, evidence of either pleasure or pain, but of which your guess is as good as ours. The insects captured by Frogs and Toads annually, if placed end to end, would reach around the world. Most of these are destructive to vegetation and hence injurious to agriculture. It is to our advantage, therefore, to see that Frogs and Toads are well protected.

Frogs and Toads are modified in various ways for their mode of life. Aquatic species have fully-webbed feet for swimming; tree-living forms have adhesive disks on their toes for clinging to leaves and branches; and many species resemble their surroundings so closely in color that their enemies have difficulty in finding them. During the winter, Frogs and Toads cease their activities and hibernate under a stone or in the mud. In the spring they awake and migrate to water, where they lay their eggs. The tadpoles, or pollywogs, that hatch from the eggs possess fluffy gills; later lungs and legs develop, and the froglets are then ready to take their place in the sun, and help populate the earth with their species.

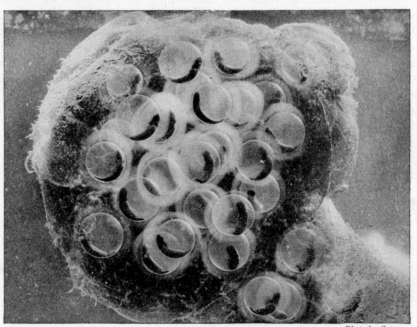

Photo by Spencer

Frog's Eggs. The eggs are laid in masses and within each spherical egg a little tadpole develops.

Frogs and Toads are not "ugly and venomous," but of considerable economic importance. They devour vast numbers of insects that would otherwise destroy flowering and food plants in our gardens and fields, and their hind legs when properly prepared are among God's greatest gifts to food-loving Man.

Leopard Frog. This, the most common Frog in the United States east of the Sierra Nevada, deserves first place among the Frogs and Toads. It is a spotted Frog, the spots being elongate or round, and dark with yellow or white margins; they are so arranged on back, flanks, and legs against a greenish-gray background as to suggest a leopard-like appearance. Leopard Frogs are to be found in almost every pond, stream, marsh, and meadow. often far from water, and are so abundant and easy to capture that they are used more than any other vertebrate for the study of anatomy and physiology. In almost every high school and college the Leopard Frog is the type used for the study of vertebrate anatomy, and in spite of its lowly station and queer habits, it is remarkably like the human body in structure. Its use for physiological experiments is so widespread that it appears to have been created solely for this purpose.

Photo by Hegner

When at rest the hind legs of the Leopard Frog are folded up ready to spring should danger approach. Then a sudden extension propels the body through the air in a leap of two or three feet or more. When swimming, the toes

Leopard Frog. One of our commonest species; the spots and bars give it a leopard-like appearance.

of the hind legs are spread apart and the webbed feet are then pushed backward against the water, thus forcing the body violently forward; the front legs are held against the body. Frogs may float at the surface with lungs full of air, legs hanging down, and just the tip of the nose exposed for breathing. From this position they can dive down out of danger very quickly. This is a great advantage since frogs are often attacked as they rest near the surface.

Photo by Hegner

Leopard Frog. A hypnotized specimen; he was held on his back and gently stroked, after which he held this position for many minutes.

The croak of the Leopard Frog is a sort of *au-au-au-au-auk*, louder in the male than in the female, and most commonly heard during the breeding season in the spring. Croaking is just as easy under water as in the air, since air is forced from the lungs into the mouth past the vocal cords and back again during the process and not out or in through the nostrils. When seized by their arch enemy, the snake, Frogs emit a screaming sound. When grasped with the hand, they will inflate the body with air, which makes them more difficult to hold, and eject a flood of liquid from the bladder. By remaining perfectly quiet Frogs often escape notice and hence avoid capture.

The breeding season is in the early spring and depends largely on the temperature. The eggs, up to 6000 or more in number, are laid in masses two to six inches in diameter, usually attached to vegetation in the water. The tadpoles at first cling to vegetation by means of a sucker at the front end. Their food consists of vegetation, which they scrape from pond weeds with their fine teeth. In the fall Leopard Frogs bury themselves in the mud under water where they are safe from frost. They can withstand a very low temperature, and can even be frozen in a

Courtesy, American Museum of Natural History

Wood Frog. A land frog with distinctive markings, namely, a dark-brown streak through the eye, a light line along the upper jaw, and a ridge of skin on either size; size, about 2½ inches long.

block of ice and live, if gradually thawed out, but will die if their tissues are entirely frozen. Frogs can easily be hypnotized by anyone. Grasp one firmly, place it on its back, and rub its belly gently. It will soon cease struggling and when the hand is slowly removed, will often remain in a ludicrous position for several minutes or more without moving.

Wood Frog. The common names of animals usually suggest one of their conspicuous characteristics, hence we are not surprised to learn that Wood Frogs live in wooded areas. They migrate to ponds and pools in the spring to lay their eggs, but spend the rest of the year in the woods, hibernating during the winter, not in the water, but under stones and logs or in crevices in stumps and tree trunks. Their appearance is quite characteristic. The general color is reddish-brown. On each side of the head is a dark-brown streak, and along the upper jaw is a prominent light line. The body is about two and one-half inches long; the head rather pointed and the legs long.

Wood Frogs utter short, snappy *clacks*, from two to six in rapid succession, which suggest the quacking of ducks. The eggs are laid during March or April in a mass about two and one-half inches in diameter, containing from 2000 to 3000. The tadpoles that hatch from them transform into young frogs in about two months. Wood Frogs range from Quebec to South Carolina and westward to the Great Plains. The Wood Frog "looks much more intelligent than other frogs. It jumps farther than most of the others, and has the habit of turning during the movement, so that when it strikes the ground it is facing the enemy. It is much more alert in getting food, resembling the toad in this respect." (Dickerson.)

Green Frog. The brilliant green color of the head and shoulders of this frog is responsible for its name. The posterior part of the body is of a brownish-olive hue. The males and females differ in the coloration of the throat, that of the male being a bright orange-yellow, and that of the female, white with dark spots. The most conspicuous feature that may be used to distinguish this species from Bullfrogs and other frogs is the ridge of skin running from the eye along the back on either side. The ear (tympanum) is about the same size as the eye in the female, but much larger in the male.

Green Frogs belong to the "aquatic" type of frogs, since they spend most of their time in the water. They prefer ponds, permanent pools, and small streams, on the banks of which they rest, plunging into the water when disturbed. Since almost every pond is inhabited by one or more Green Frogs, the name Pond Frog is often used for this species. Young Green Frogs when frightened are said to leap high into the air, dropping into the water with a short, high-pitched cry resembling a scream. On this account, the name "Screaming Frog" was formerly given to it.

Green Frogs are about four inches long, and their hind legs are large enough to be of some value as an article of food. The call note of the adult Green

Courtesy, American Museum of Natural History

Green Frog. A large aquatic frog with green-colored head and shoulders; a ridge of skin runs back from the eye on either side.

Frog is a low-pitched, rather musical, short croak. It has been represented by the letters *k-tun-n-ng*, or *chu-n-ng*, and compared to the sound made by plucking the string of a cello. It is delivered explosively and usually repeated several times in succession.

The eggs of the Green Frog, up to 4000 in number, are laid in separate packets, usually among water plants; these merge to form a disklike, filmy mass of a single layer of eggs that floats on the surface and covers an area of less than one square foot. The tadpoles are vegetarians. They do not change into frogs until the year after they hatch, passing the winter under the ice. The adults hibernate under water in the mud or under a submerged stone or dead leaves.

Bullfrog. The features that make the Bullfrog one of the best-known species in the United States are its large size, the use of its legs for food, and the character of its voice. The Bullfrog is the largest frog in this country, reaching a length of eight inches or more. The hind legs may be ten inches long, the toes are fully webbed, and the muscles are large and strong. This enables their possessor to swim with great speed and to leap a distance of five or six feet while on land. However, the Bullfrog is perhaps the most aquatic of our frogs, seldom leaving the water. The hind legs of this species provide most of the frogs' legs of commerce, about 250,000 pounds of which are sold in this country per year.

Courtesy, American Museum of Natural History

Bullfrog. Our largest frog; reaching a length of over eight inches; an aquatic species with a bull-like voice; a ridge of skin passes from the eye around the ear to the front leg.

The voice of the Bullfrog has been compared to the bellow of a distant bull. It is a sonorous bass with wonderful carrying power. It is first heard in the spring, several weeks after the frogs emerge from the mud in which they hibernate during the winter. By the first of July when many are present their voices reach the "chorus" stage. The males croak more loudly than the females, mostly at night, aided by two resonating vocal sacs inside the throat. Attempts have been made to represent their voice by words such as *jug-o'-rum*, *blood n' 'ouns*, and *knee deep*.

Bullfrogs occur throughout North America east of the Rocky Mountains. They are mostly greenish-brown in color. The ear (tympanic membrane) is as large as the eye in the female, and larger in the male. A fold of skin extends from behind the eye around the ear and to the front leg, a characteristic that may be used to distinguish it from the Green Frog. Bullfrogs live in mill-ponds, lakes, bayous, and less often in streams. They are very voracious, often sitting half-immersed in the water waiting for their prey. This consists of insects, crayfish, snails, fish, other frogs, and other aquatic animals.   Bullfrogs in their turn are preyed upon by snakes, turtles, alligators, and birds, such as herons, hawks, and owls.   This accounts for some of the Bullfrog's characteristics.   "Independent, self-composed, silent, he may sit for hours with no slightest movement to tell that he is alive.   But he is fully alert to every disturbance of the water and to every shifting shadow." (Dickerson.)

The breeding season of Bullfrogs is in full swing by July 1.   A single female may lay up to 20,000 eggs, usually among brush ; these eggs spread out in a disk form over an area of from three to five square feet.   The tadpoles do not change into young frogs during the first season, but remain in this stage for two or three years.

Photo by Overton.   Courtesy, American Museum of Natural History

Bullfrog.   Sitting in the water at the edge of a pond waiting for an insect or some other small animal to pass by with which he can satisfy his appetite.

During this period they become very large, reaching a length of six or seven inches. Like their parents, they are very voracious and will eat almost anything without regard to hygienic principles, which makes them excellent scavengers.   Young Bullfrogs that have grown legs and absorbed their tail measure about two inches long.

Tree Frog.   This beautiful little acrobat is quiet during the day, and resembles its surroundings so closely that it is not often seen.   The Common Tree Frog of eastern North America has a rather warty skin and may be colored with many shades of brown, gray, and green depending on the color of the background.   When the latter is changed, the color of the frog changes also, a process that requires about half an hour.   This helps to conceal the frog from its enemies.   Regardless of its general color, there is always a white mark beneath the eye ; it is about two inches in length.

Tree Frog.   Hs is singing a love song, during which his throat is distended into a large sac.

Tree Frogs, or Tree "Toads," as they are often erroneously called, live among the branches of orchard and forest trees, in shrubbery, and on fences, etc. They are most active at dusk, leaping from branch to branch and catching insects with their sticky tongues. Disks on the tips of fingers and toes enable them to stick to smooth vertical surfaces, even of glass, without difficulty.

Tree Frogs sing especially during damp weather or before a rain and have quite a reputation as weather prophets.   Their song is a melodious trill aided by a fully inflated vocal sac.   The eggs are laid in ponds in the spring, singly or in small

Tree Frog.   Noted for his color changes, brown, gray, or green according to the color of the background; note the sucking disk at the end of each toe: size, about 2 inches long.

lots, and attached to vegetation. They hatch in two or three days, and the tadpoles are graceful swimmers. The Tree Frog family contains about 200 species, of which 18 species occur in the United States.

Common Toad. To one who has not studied the habits of the Toad it appears to be the "most deformed and hideous of all animals" and "its general appearance is such as to strike one with disgust and horror." The beauty of the Toad's eye, however, has long been recognized, for Shakespeare refers to it in the following well-known lines:

> *Sweet are the uses of adversity,*
> *Which like the toad, ugly and venomous,*
> *Wears yet a precious jewel in his head.*

The pupil of the eye is black, oval in form, horizontal in position, and surrounded by a broad border of gold. This "jewel" was considered in ancient times to be a

Courtesy, Nature Magazine

Common Toad. He may be warty but is really quite handsome, especially his eye, which lies like a "precious jewel in his head."

precious stone that served as a talisman to protect the wearer from evil. Toads are generally considered loathsome creatures that give warts to anyone that handles them; and are accused of various evil deeds. Actually they are perfectly harmless, and even very beneficial, because of the harmful insects they capture for food. They are grotesque in appearance but self-effacing, dignified in their movements, and among the most interesting of all animals to watch.

Toads sleep by day in a cool, moist place under a stone or board, but become active at dusk. The tongue, as in other frogs and toads, is sticky and fastened at the front of the mouth so it can be thrown out at any moving insect within reach and then drawn back with its prey firmly fastened by the gluelike secretion.   The skin

is shed five or six times each year, and promptly swallowed.

Toads are among the longest-lived of the lower animals; one specimen is known to have reached the age of 36 years. That toads can live for hundreds of years embedded in rocks or trees is certainly a fable, since this is physiologically impossible.   Those who report the discovery of these ancient toads believe what they say, but are unfortunately not critical, scientific observers.

Toads are commonly considered to be poisonous. They do secrete a milky

Courtesy, Natural History Society of Maryland
Common Toad. His song is one of the sweetest sounds in nature; his throat is fully extended as he trills his roundelay.

substance from glands in the skin that is poisonous, but not to the human skin. In China, toad skin is used as a medicine, and not without reason, since some of the glands contain adrenalin, which increases the blood pressure and the amount of

sugar in the blood when injected into a human being.

Toads leave the gardens and fields in the spring, and migrate to the nearest pond to lay their eggs; these form a long, gelatinous string containing from 4000 to 12,000 in a single row.   It never "rains" Toads, but when thousands of the tadpoles change into minute Toads, and leave the ponds to find a home, especially during a rain storm, they seem to have rained down. Unfortunately most of them meet an early death.

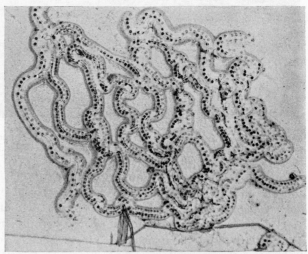

Courtesy, American Museum of Natural History
Toad's Eggs. They are laid in a string of jelly, from 4000 to 12,000 in a single row.

The song of the Toad is a sweet trill and one of the most beautiful sounds in nature. Only the male sings, distending his throat into a large light-colored sac during his vocalizing. When held in the hand with hind legs hanging free, the Toad will utter a low note similar to that of a baby chicken but much sweeter. He may also trill for you if you are patient. About 100 species of Toads have been described, 16 of which occur in the United States.

Photo by Chace. Courtesy, Nature Magazine

Common Toad. Bow-legged but determined to be dignified as he rests beneath the toadstools.

Spadefoot Toad. The spur that develops on the heel of this species, and that suggested its name Spadefoot Toad, enables it to dig burrows in the ground, sinking backward into the burrow as it digs. Only one specimen lives in a burrow, and because of this solitary habit, the name Hermit Spadefoot is sometimes applied to it. It certainly lives a hermit's life, remaining in its burrow all day, and coming out only at night in search of food, or for a few days in the spring, long enough to travel to a near-by pond to lay eggs.

The Spadefoot Toad is about two and one-half inches long, brownish, yellowish, or greenish in color, with smooth skin, and eyes with a vertical pupil. Although it occurs throughout the Eastern and Gulf states, it is seldom seen because of its solitary and nocturnal habits. During the breeding season the males make a noise that is very loud, considering their size, and that has been described as "a deafening, agonizing roar, hoarse and woeful." About 70 species of Spadefoot Toads are known, three of which live in the United States.

© General Biological Supply House

Spadefoot Toad. A burrowing type that digs himself backward into the ground with the help of a spur on each hind leg.

Midwife Toad. Many strange breeding habits occur among Frogs and Toads. One of the most famous of these is that of the Midwife or Obstetrical Toad. In this species the father brings up the family. The eggs are laid in two strings containing, in all, from 20 to 60. The father pushes his hind feet through the convoluted strings, and carries them with him wound around his hind legs, hiding his "shame" under a stone, or in a burrow in the ground.

Courtesy, American Museum of Natural History

Midwife Toad. The husband carries the egg-string draped around his hind legs; habitat, Europe; size, about 2 inches long.

If it becomes too dry, he ventures forth after dark, as though not wishing to be seen in his humiliating condition, and bathes the eggs in dew or in a pool of water. In about three weeks, when the eggs are ready to hatch, he enters the water. The tadpoles that emerge are in an advanced stage of development.

The Midwife Toad occurs in western Europe, but is rarely seen, because it is nocturnal and rather small, being only two inches long. The species name Obstetricans, everyone must admit, is appropriate for a Toad with habits like these.

Surinam Toad. The way the Surinam Toad raises its family is even more remarkable than that of the Midwife Toad. The skin on the back of the mother becomes thick and spongy during the breeding season. The eggs are spread over it by the parents in a single layer. They adhere to the surface and gradually sink into the skin until each is enclosed in a cup-shaped cavity. Each cavity then becomes covered over by a horny lid. Here the eggs develop and pass through the tadpole stage. Eventually the lids pop open and fully-formed froglets emerge.

Surinam Toads are curious-looking creatures. The body is extremely flat, and the head triangular in shape. There is a fleshy flap at the angles of the mouth and one or two short tentacles in front of each small eye. The fingers are long and slender and not webbed; each finger has a star-shaped disk at the end that forms a delicate organ

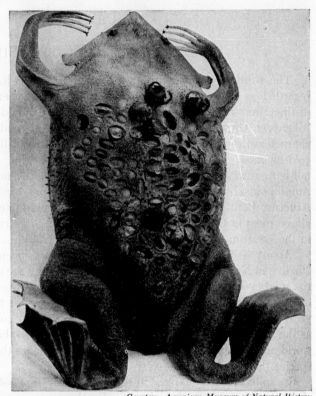

Courtesy, American Museum of Natural History

Surinam Toad. A native of northern South America with a very flat body and peculiar feet; the eggs develop in cavities in the back of the mother and the young emerge as minute toads as shown here.

of touch. These Toads must live without tongue or teeth; they succeed in doing so, although we are sure no one envies them. They are aquatic in habit. The skin is rough, being covered with small tubercles, and dark-brown in color. The name Surinam is a term formerly used for Dutch Guiana, where these Toads were first found. They are now known to inhabit Trinidad and Amazonian-Brazil as well as the Guianas. Several species have been described from this region.

CHAPTER 19

DINOSAURS AND CROCODILIANS

The word Reptile means "an animal that crawls," and Reptiles are usually regarded as rather low in the scale of life. To scientists, Reptiles belong to a distinct and rather advanced division of the Animal Kingdom. If we examine Alligators, Crocodiles, Lizards, Snakes, and Turtles, all of which are Reptiles, the characteristics in which they resemble each other will be revealed. They are all cold-blooded. Most of them are covered with scales. The skin is dry, hence it is not correct to speak of a "slimy" Reptile. Gills are not present as in the Fish and Amphibians, but Reptiles, both young and adults, breathe by means of lungs. In structure Reptiles resemble very closely the Amphibians below them and the Birds above them in the scale of life. The differences in structure are largely variations in the skeleton, which cannot be seen unless the animals are killed and dissected.

About 4000 different species of Reptiles have been described; of these about 300 live in North America. The Reptiles of today are mere pigmies compared with the mighty monsters that roamed the earth in bygone times, and are now known only from their fossilized remains. At one time in the past, about 150 million years ago, Reptiles dominated the earth and on that account that period is known as the Age of Reptiles. Most of the living Reptiles inhabit the warmer parts of the world and become more numerous as one approaches the equator, where the largest species thrive in the low, moist, hot forests.

In spite of their bad reputation, very few Reptiles are poisonous and most of them do more good than harm. Furthermore, many species are as brilliantly colored as birds or butterflies, and vary so much in their modes of life that they serve as fascinating objects for study. Some are slow and awkward; others scamper about with great agility; some spend their lives in the sea, coming to land only to lay their eggs; and a few can even "fly." Most Reptiles lay eggs, always on land. Usually they are kept warm by the sun, and the young must shift for themselves when they hatch. Although Reptiles grow slowly, they do not stop growing at a certain age, as we do, but continue to increase in size throughout life. Some of the great-grandfather Reptiles reach what to us seems like a good old age, that is, 100 years or more.

The food of Reptiles consists of both animals and plants. Frogs and fish are favorite articles on the daily menu. Most of the smaller species of Reptiles feed upon worms and insects. In general, it may be stated that Reptiles do very little damage in destroying animals and plants for food, but that they are often of considerable benefit, since they kill large numbers of obnoxious insects and other forms of life.

Dinosaurs. No more suitable group of animals could be selected to lead the reptilian division of our parade than the Dinosaurs, or Terrible Lizards. Some of them were among the largest and most terrible monsters that ever lived, and their fossil remains are very abundant in our western states. Here about 150 million years ago during the Age of Reptiles, lakes, rivers, and marshes supported a luxurious vegetation amid which the Dinosaurs held sway. Only their fossil remains are known now, but these are so numerous that a very good idea of their size, shape, and habits has been acquired. Because of the extensive deposits of fossil remains an area of 80 acres in Uintah County, Utah, was set aside October 4, 1915, as a reservation and named the Dinosaur National Monument. When we visited this Monument in 1934, the bones were covered by a landslide, but were being dug out again.

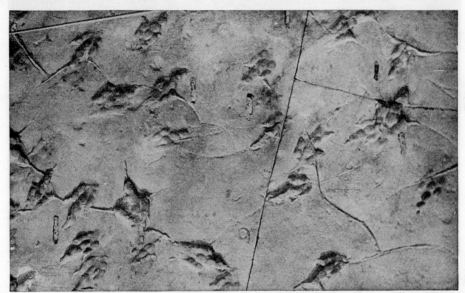

Courtesy, American Museum of Natural History

Dinosaur Tracks. These footprints were made by two different kinds of dinosaurs. They were found in a slab of "brown stone" in the Connecticut River Valley near Middletown.

Some of the Dinosaurs were no larger than certain of our lizards of today such as the Iguana (page 318), but the most interesting species are those enormous creatures in contrast to which the elephant, mammoth, and mastodon pale into insignificance. Not only did the Dinosaurs leave fossilized bones behind them, but also the impressions of their feet (tracks), and of their skin, and within the past few years their eggs have been discovered. The most famous Dinosaur tracks are those of the Connecticut Valley found in 1802 and popularly known as the tracks of Noah's Raven. Some of these three-toed tracks are shown in the photograph in a slab of brown stone quarried near Middletown in 1778. Two species of Dinosaurs have left the impressions of their feet here. Dinosaur eggs have been found in France and Mongolia; those shown in the photograph are about eight inches long.

Dinosaurs were of various shapes, but most of them had a long tail, strong limbs for the support of the body, a skin, either naked or covered with scales, or bony armor, teeth that were very sharp in the meat-eating species and blunt for grinding up vegetation in the herbivorous species, a skull very small in comparison with the body, and a diminutive brain.   Emerson's saying that, "Everything in nature is engaged in writing its own history," is certainly true of the Dinosaurs, which have left us so much interesting information about themselves.   Little did these large animals dream that their footprints would be examined by tourists in automobiles or their eggs placed on view in the American Museum of Natural History.

Courtesy, American Museum of Natural History

Dinosaur's Nest.   Thirteen fossil dinosaur eggs in a nest found in Mongolia.   Each egg was about eight inches long.

The Thunder Lizard.   Among the largest of the Dinosaurs was the Thunder Lizard, called Brontosaurus, a monster whose size it is difficult to imagine.   It was over 75 feet long and 15 feet high and must have weighed 30 or 35 tons.   A large Indian elephant that weighs five tons would look like a mouse playing with a lion alongside such a monster.   An elephant of five tons eats about 1000 pounds of green fodder and 20 pounds of grain each day.   The Thunder Lizard must have eaten five or six times this amount.   This was a real feat because its head was absurdly small compared with the size of its body, and its teeth were very weak.   It is believed that the Thunder Lizard spent most of its time in the water feeding on aquatic plants.   Its long neck enabled it to reach out in all directions for food without moving its enormous body.

Is it not fortunate for us who love to attend the ceremonial dances of our southwestern Indians that these monsters perished when they did!   When reading of Jack the Giant Killer, we try to picture the activities of huge creatures; but

Thunder Lizard. A painting to show what thunder lizards probably looked like and where they lived. Size, over 60 feet long and 30 tons in weight.

these animals which walked up Broadway in the past ages were really too large to imagine.

The King of the Tyrant Reptiles. This Dinosaur was not as long as the Thunder Lizard, and probably did not weigh as much, but it lived on land and preyed on other animals. It was probably the most terrible creature that ever lived on the earth. It grew to a length of at least 47 feet and stood 20 feet high. Its head was over four feet long and its mouth, which had a gape a yard wide, was filled with double-edged teeth from three to six inches long.

The King of the Tyrant Reptiles walked on its hind legs, with its front legs high in the air. Its claws were long and sharp and well fitted for grasping its prey while it was torn to pieces by its terrible teeth. The plant-eating animals that existed at that period must have been an easy prey for such a fearful monster. A human being would have a poor chance for his life against such a creature even with the most powerful gun that he could carry. Why did such formidable animals disappear from the earth? Perhaps the Tyrant Reptiles multiplied so that their food supply gave out, since they no doubt could exist only on other animals; then they began to eat each other until none were left alive to perpetuate the species.

Courtesy, American Museum of Natural History

King of the Tyrant Reptiles. Fossil bones dug up and fastened together. The head was over 4 feet long and teeth from 3 to 6 inches long.

Courtesy, Smithsonian Institution

Plated Lizard. A model showing how this monster probably looked when alive. Length, 35 feet. The plates are over 2 feet high.

The Plated Lizard. Not as large as the Thunder Lizard and the King of the Tyrant Reptiles, but nevertheless an enormous creature, was the Plated Lizard, Stegosaurus. Its fossilized bones were discovered in the Rocky Mountains and fitted together with great care. The result is an amazing Reptile thirty feet long and ten feet high with hind legs seven feet long, a double row of enormous plates along the back, long spines near the end of the tail, and a ludicrously small head. The plates, which suggested its name, were arranged on edge in two alternate rows. They are over two feet high and two feet long, but only about an inch thick, and were covered with horn when the animal was alive. Near the end of the tail were four pairs of spines about two feet long. The swing of such a deadly weapon as this tail must have swept everything from its path. Protective devices of this kind were necessary, however, to protect a plant-eating animal like the Plated Lizard from such meat-eating monsters as the King of the Tyrant Reptiles.

Not the least interesting characteristic of the Plated Lizard is its small head, in which was what was probably the smallest brain compared with the size of the owner of any vertebrate living on land. This brain weighed about ten pounds. A human being similarly constructed could boast of only one tenth of a pound of brain instead of the two pounds which have given him dominance over all other life on earth. The Plated Lizard was, however, provided with a second "brain" in the region of the hip bones, which was an enlargement of the spinal cord and must have weighed about 200 pounds. This "brain" was needed to control the enormous hind legs and tail. This condition inspired the following flight of fancy on the part of the late Bert L. Taylor, a columnist on the staff of the *Chicago Tribune*:

> *Behold the mighty dinosaur, Famous in prehistoric lore,*
> *Not only for his power and strength, But for his intellectual length.*
> *You will observe by these remains, The creature had two sets of brains —*
> *One in his head (the usual place), The other at his spinal base.*
> *Thus he could reason a priori, As well as a posteriori.*
> *No problem bothered him a bit; He made both head and tail of it.*
> *If something slipped his forward mind, 'Twas rescued by the one behind.*
> *And if in error he was caught, He had a saving afterthought.*
> *Thus he could think without congestion, Upon both sides of every question.*
> *Oh, gaze upon this model beast, Defunct ten million years at least.*

The Winged Lizard — Pteranodon. Long before birds appeared on the earth a group of Reptiles, the Pterosauria (G. *pteron* = wing + *sauros* = lizard) developed the art of flying. They were birdlike in shape, with a long neck, light, hollow bones, a breastbone with a ridge for the attachment of the wing muscles, and fore limbs with a diminutive thumb, three fingers with claws, and a leathery, smooth membrane extending between the very long little fingers and the sides of the body, which constituted the wings.

Some of these Dragons of the Air were no longer than sparrows, but Pteranodon was the largest flying animal that ever lived. It had a spread of wing of about twenty feet, whereas the Albatross, one of our largest flying birds, has a wing spread of only about ten feet.   Pteranodon had a long crest on its head of unknown use. From the tip of this crest to the end of the beak was almost four feet.   The remains of this peculiar prehistoric Reptile were found in the rocks of Kansas.

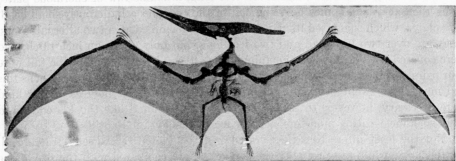

Courtesy, American Museum of Natural History

Winged Lizard — Pteranodon.   The fossil bones of a Dragon of the Air with wings indicated. Distance across wings about 20 feet; from end of crest to tip of beak, about 4 feet.

CROCODILIANS

To this group belong the Alligators, Crocodiles, Caimans, and Gavials.   These are the largest of the survivors of the Age of Reptiles, and although small when compared with some of the Dinosaurs, are really the giants among living Reptiles. They are semi-aquatic monsters, reaching a length of over 30 feet.   The Salt-Water Crocodile is said to be 33 feet long, whereas a species lives in South America that is never more than four feet long.

The hind feet are usually webbed and sometimes the front feet also.   The tail is compressed from side to side, which fits it for swimming purposes and also for knocking down an enemy.   The feet are held against the body and not used in swimming.   The eyes are elevated on top of the head, and the nostrils are also raised, so that the beasts can float at the surface with only the eyes and nostrils above water.   The nostrils can be closed by a valve.   The tongue and roof of the mouth are provided each with a fold which fit together so as to separate the mouth cavity from the windpipe.   This enables the creatures to grasp their prey with their jaws and draw it under water without getting water into their lungs.   The body is covered with scales and plates.   The jaws are very powerful and provided with many sharp, conical teeth set in cavities in the jaw bones.   Behind each eye is an ear opening protected by a flap of skin.

Two species of Alligators and about 25 other species of Crocodilians have been described.   Two of these occur in the southern United States, and the others in streams, ponds, and swamps in tropical countries.   All of them live on other animals, and several species are notorious man-eaters, especially the Salt-Water Crocodile and the Nile Crocodile.   During the cool part of the year, or the dry season, most species hibernate in the mud for several months.   Alligators and Crocodiles can remain under water for five or six hours without drowning.

All Crocodilians lay eggs. The young have an "egg-tooth" on the end of the snout with which they break through the egg shell at the time of hatching; the tooth is then lost.

The African or Nile Crocodile is an abundant species in Africa and Madagascar. "None among the legions of wild brutes of the Dark Continent has caused greater loss of human life than the present terrible creature. And it is consequently no wonder this ponderous, vicious reptile has been notorious from ancient times down to the present." In Egypt the Nile Crocodile, while lying in the sun with its mouth open, may be visited by a species of plover which feeds on the parasites that lodge among the crocodile's teeth.

Two species of Crocodilians are known as Gavials. The Indian Gavial occurs in northern India in the Ganges and Brahmaputra rivers and their tributaries, and the Malayan Gavial in Borneo and Sumatra. "Like many of the crocodilians,

Courtesy, N. Y. Zoological Society

Nile Crocodile.   A vicious reptile notorious in Egypt as a man-eater.

the Gavial is a timid animal, dashing into the silty, opaque water at the sight of man, to show, some time later, merely a pair of greenish, catlike eyes and the extreme, lumpy tip of the snout. Again alarmed, there is no commotion. The creature sinks noiselessly, when a few viscid bubbles break on the brown current. Judging from the massive structure of a big specimen, one might be led to believe it would literally wallow for the water when frightened. Conditions are quite the reverse. The great body is raised well from the ground when the creature runs for the sheltering, muddy current. From the agility displayed by even the most gigantic individuals, man must consider himself fortunate that this mammoth reptile is seldom or never hostile to him. Its prey consists largely of fish." (Ditmars.)

American Crocodile. The salt marshes of southern Florida are inhabited by a species of Crocodile that probably swam over from Mexico. The West Indies and mainland as far south as Ecuador are also the habitat of this species. The

American Crocodile can be distinguished very easily from the Alligator by the shape of the head, which is triangular with a pointed snout, whereas the Alligator has a broad head and wide snout. Also the fourth tooth on either side of the lower jaw of the American Crocodile fits into a notch on the outer side of the upper jaw, whereas that of the Alligator rests in a pit when the jaws are closed.

The Crocodile does not range as far north as the Alligator because it is more easily affected by cold weather and becomes practically helpless when the temperature reaches 45°F. The color of the Crocodile is olive-green or gray, whereas the

Courtesy, N. Y. Zoological Society

Gavial. A type of Crocodilian that lives in the Far East. The snout is very narrow.

Alligator is black. The Crocodile is an active beast, vicious and treacherous, and hence must not be approached too closely. It may not wait until one gets within reach of its powerful tail, but may actually move to attack.

Certain Crocodilians of Central and South America are known as Caimans. Among South American Crocodiles are the Orinoco Crocodile, the Brazilian Jacaré Tinga, and the Jacaré Assu. The Mugger, or Marsh Crocodile, lives in India. The Crocodile was one of the "sacred animals" of the ancient Egyptians and at one time the Ombites and Tentyrites waged war against each other because one town had killed a Crocodile venerated by the other town.

Formerly in certain parts of India the natives in times of sickness or distress sacrificed children to some deity by throwing them into the river to be devoured by Crocodiles. At Saugor near the mouth of the Ganges 23 cases of this kind took place in 1801 in the course of one month. (Allen.) The practice has long been discontinued.

Certain old travelers are accused of the fiction that Crocodiles shed tears over those they devour, hence the common expression "Crocodile tears."

American Alligator. Of the two species of Alligators known to exist at the present time, one inhabits the southeastern United States and the other the Yangtze Kiang Kiver in China. The body of the American Alligator is thick, and dark-brown or black in color. The larger specimens have all been killed for their hides, hence the maximum length of those living today is not sixteen feet as formerly, but twelve feet or less. They favor fresh-water rivers, ponds, and marshes, where they may be found basking in the sun on the bank or on top of a log. They dig caves for themselves in the ground in or near water, where they may conceal themselves. They recognize man as an enemy, and will hide or swim away if possible. Unlike Crocodiles, they are not vicious, although just as powerful.

Photo by Hegner

American Alligators. Part of a group on an Alligator farm. The snout is broad, and the teeth of several well displayed.

During the breeding season, the male Alligators give vent to loud noises resembling a roar or bellow, which can be heard for a mile or more, and secrete musk from their chin glands. The female makes a nest on land, from five to eight feet in diameter, in which she lays from 20 to 40 eggs, and covers them over with vegetation which ferments, thus producing heat. The eggs hatch in about two months. The young are eight inches long when they hatch, and are black in color with yellow cross bars. Many of them are sold to tourists, but do not live long in captivity, because they are not ordinarily properly cared for. They grow more rapidly than usually supposed, reaching a length of one and one-half feet the first year, and six feet in five years, and a weight of over 70 pounds.

CHAPTER 20

LIZARDS

Lizards look somewhat like miniature crocodiles although some of them are very large, reaching a length of about 10 feet. The body and tail are usually long and slender, and most species possess four legs. The eyes are small and provided with upper and lower eyelids and an additional membrane that can be drawn over them from the side. The skin is covered with scales and is shed from time to time. Lizards that live on land have the body flattened vertically; those that live in the water are flattened from side to side; and those that burrow in the ground are usually cylindrical and snakelike.

Courtesy, American Museum of Natural History

Lizard. The body is long and slender and covered with scales. This species is a tree climber.

Many lizards escape if grasped by the tail because the tail breaks off very easily, not at a joint, but in the center of a vertebra. The enemy is left with a wriggling tail and the lizard grows a new tail. Many lizards are brightly colored and are able to change their colors rather rapidly. Most of the 2000 or more species of lizards live in the warmer regions of the world. Over 100 species live in the United States, including the Gila Monster, one of the only two poisonous lizards known.

Tuatera. The Tuatera looks like a lizard, but is a representative of a group of Reptiles that flourished during the Age of Reptiles. Its ancestors played with Dinosaurs, but unlike the Dinosaurs it became a "living fossil" instead of a National Monument. It is limited to the islands of Cook Strait, New Zealand. The Maori natives named it Tuatera, which means "having spines."

Externally there is little to distinguish it from lizards but internally are revealed many fundamental differences. Of especial interest is a third eye, located on top of the head and known as the pineal eye. This structure is present in a degenerate form in lizards, but lies within the skull in mammals, being known as the pineal organ or epiphysis,—a ductless gland which secretes into the blood a substance (hormone) that probably influences the growth and development of the body.

Courtesy, American Museum of Natural History

Tuatera. A "living fossil" from New Zealand. It has a third eye on top of the head.

The Tuatera lives in a hole in the ground about five inches in diameter and three feet long. The end is enlarged into a small chamber which it shares with a Petrel, the Tuatera usually occupying the right side and the Petrel the left. A large specimen reaches a length of two and one-half feet. Tuateras are becoming quite scarce.

Gecko. Geckos are among the few lizards that make sounds other than hissing. The calls of the Gecko sound like the word *gecko*, hence its name. The White-Spotted Gecko shown in the photograph has a short, thick body about six inches long, and a stubby tail. It has no eyelids, but the eyes are covered by a transparent, glasslike membrane. The pupil of the eye is elliptical like that of a cat. If a Gecko is held up to the light, it appears to have a window in its head, since there is no obstruction, such as bone, between the ears.

Geckos sleep during the day, but become active at dusk, hunting insects, spiders, etc., as they creep up and down trees and the walls of houses. The sucking disks on their toes enable them to creep along the ceiling also without falling. We have spent many hours in the Philippines watching Geckos capture flies on the ceiling. They do not seem to be able to locate their prey unless it is moving. How often we wished there was a Gecko language that we could use to tell them where they could locate the next victim. However, in course of time they always "got their man."

Their prey is caught with the thick, sticky tongue. Geckos are not poisonous, but on the contrary are decidedly beneficial because of the noxious insects they destroy. Six of the 300 species of Geckos live in North America, the others inhabit various tropical countries.

Photo by Ditmars, Reptiles of the World

Gecko. A lizard with sucking disks on its toes which enable it to walk on the ceiling.

Iguana. A traveler in the American tropics becomes familiar with this large, but harmless, lizard that looks as though it had been resurrected from a bygone age. Although it reaches a length of six feet and a weight of thirty pounds, it climbs trees with ease, and loves to lie along a branch over the water, into which it plunges at the approach of danger. The greenish color and brownish bands tend to conceal it amid the branches. Along the middle of the back is a crest of

Courtesy, N. Y. Zoological Society

Iguana. A tropical lizard highly ornamented with soft spines and a dewlap. It climbs trees and eats leaves and fruit.

soft, leathery spines, and under the chin is a dewlap that adds to its fierce appearance.

The food of the Iguana consists largely of leaves and fruit, although insects, birds, and other small animals are accepted, when available, to vary the diet. In many localities the flesh of the Iguana is regularly eaten. It is white and delicate and tastes somewhat like chicken. Iguanas are brought to market tied up with the tendons of their own toes.

Photo by Hegner

Galapagos Iguana. A fierce-looking marine species that lives in huge colonies and feeds on seaweed.

An interesting relative of the common Iguana is the Marine Iguana. Thousands of these antediluvian-looking creatures congregate on the shores of the Galapagos Islands, where they swim about in the sea and feed on seaweeds.

Chameleons. The Chameleon is a delicate, slender little lizard that grows to a length of about six inches. Its body is colored a golden green above and white below. Under the chin is a dewlap of vermilion that adds to its beauty. It is an inhabitant of trees, and not only runs swiftly along the branches, but leaps from leaf to leaf like a tree frog. It is quite an acrobat, and apparently can cling to the side of a wall as easily as to a branch. Its food consists of insects, which it creeps up on and then captures suddenly with its sticky tongue.

Chameleons make interesting pets, but must be kept in a warm, sunny place, fed on flies and meal worms, and sprinkled occasionally, since they drink dew drops in nature and lap up drops of water when in captivity.   Chameleons are famous for their rapid changes in color, which may range from green to yellow or gray. The home of the Old World Chameleon is in the region of North Africa, Syria, and Asia Minor.   Here it frequents trees, where it clings to twigs with its feet and prehensile tail.   Its toes are arranged in two opposed groups which adapt it admirably to its clinging mode of life.   Its movements are very slow. Its eyes do not move together, but one may be directed forward or down, while the other peers backward and up.   Its food consists of insects which it captures with great ease.   "Approaching an insect with an air of perfect deliberation a chameleon regards it calmly for a second or two with one bulging eye, while the other may indifferently examine various objects.   A sudden flash of the tongue follows to a possible distance of six or seven inches and the morsel is snapped back to the jaws, where it is well masticated by sharp teeth before it is swallowed."   (Ditmars.)

The Chameleon is especially famous for its color changes. These are due to changes in light, temperature, and the emotions of the animal.   A lowering of the temperature changes the color from grayish-green to dull gray; a rise in temperature, to green; anger increases the density of the lighter areas; fright induces lighter shades; sunlight gives a dull black appearance; and darkness, a cream color.   Not only the color, but also the yellow spots and brown patches on the sides of the body, may change in size and color.

Coutesy, National Zoological Park

Chameleon. A large species that lives in Cuba and Jamaica and may reach a length of 16 inches.

Common Swift, or Fence Lizard. Because Lizards may remain motionless in one place for a long time does not mean that they are slow. We remember our first attempt to catch a Swift; by the time our hand had traveled the three feet to where he was, he had almost vanished in the distance, so rapidly did he scamper away over the ground. Swifts are especially abundant in Mexico and Central America, but the Common Swift may be found from New York to Florida. It is grayish in color with dark wavy bands, and about five inches long.

"Old fences are much frequented by this species. The lizards scamper along the stiles, or, if approached, dodge over on the side opposite to the observer. In the dry pinelands of the southeastern portion of the United States, there is a swift or two for every fallen tree trunk. To catch a specimen one must exercise con-

Photo by Ditmars. Courtesy, American Museum of Natural History
Common Swift, or Fence Lizard. One has just captured a cockroach, and another is displaying the colors on the undersurface.

siderable ingenuity, as a rush at the creature would cause it to scurry under the tree trunk, there to wriggle its way into the debris, or jump from the log, run to the nearest tree and ascend to a perfectly safe distance to peer saucily downward. As the collector approaches a log on which a swift is basking, the lizard generally dodges over the side, away from view. The spot whence the specimen has disap-peared should be noted; for it will usually be found that the lizard has simply danced round the horizontal trunk. Bringing the hand slowly over the log, but keeping the body out of sight as much as possible, the collector should take an instant's glance to locate his specimen, then slap the hand down over the reptile. In two instances out of three the rough little body squirms under the hand. Not so unless the motion of securing the prize is lightning quick. How many times has the writer gazed ruefully upon a lizard's spasmodically wriggling tail, realizing that as the hand descended the reptile started, yet not quick enough to get away with all its possessions. Swifts may be hunted around saw mills, especially if a number of old logs are lying about, for on these the reptiles find such food as the fat-bodied grubs of the wood-boring beetles." (Ditmars.)

Skinks. Skinks are rather distinctive-looking Lizards, the one shown in our photograph being typical of the group. The scales are large, rounded, and glossy. All variations occur among Skinks with respect to the character of the legs. Some are limbless; a few have a small pair of hind legs only; others have two pairs of weak legs; and a number of them possess well-developed legs with which they can scurry over the ground at great speed.

A common species is the Five-Lined Skink which ranges from New England to Florida and west to Texas. The young of this species have five longitudinal yellow stripes on a black background, and a tail of brilliant blue. After three or four years the adult condition is attained. The color of the females is then brownish and the stripes are obscure. The male loses the stripes entirely but acquires a fiery-red head; he was at one time considered a separate species and called the Red-Headed Lizard, or Scorpion. The females reach a length of about seven inches and the males ten inches.

"This handsome skink is difficult to capture. When basking it keeps a convenient hiding place in mind to which it instantly darts if frightened. The old

Courtesy, American Museum of Natural History

Skink. A lizard with large, rounded, glossy scales. The head is pointed and the neck thick.

males are very shy and cunning, living on pine trees, with always a snug retreat in the shape of a deep cavity, near by. Into this they rush as an intruder draws near, but from it is soon poked a fiery red head with wide, swollen temples and pointed snout, this member looking quite as formidable as the head of some deadly snake."

"After fruitlessly trying to noose these lizards by fastening a piece of fine copper wire on a slender pole, the writer adopted new tactics. He was in the South Carolina pine-lands and skinks were everywhere abundant. By tearing away the bark of the trees we found the skinks in hiding. As it was disclosed, a reptile would be momentarily dazed; in that instant it had to be grabbed or it would recover its wits and dart away." (Ditmars.)

Horned Toad. The Horned Toad is not really a toad but a lizard. If it were 40 feet long, it might pass for a modern Dinosaur (see page 310). Fortunately for us, it is only about five inches long, but no doubt to the ants and other insects on which it preys, it looks like a terrible monster. Horned Toads are true sun lovers and will die in captivity unless they are given plenty of warmth and sunlight. They are able to live in dry places without dying of thirst, because they drink dew in the early mornings from the leaves of plants.

During the winter, Horned Toads sleep in burrows underground, but when spring comes, they crawl out into the sun and put on their Easter costume by simply

Photo by Murray. Courtesy, Nature Magazine

Horned Toad. Not a real toad but a lizard with many spines that lives in dry regions.

shedding their skin. At this time if they are handled roughly they may "spit" blood from their eyes. In some regions the country folk believe their bite at this time is deadly, but this is not true. When irritated the Horned Toad may wag its tail like an angry cat. Its tail differs from that of many other lizards, since it does not break off easily, therefore the easiest way to catch a specimen is to grasp it by the tail.

Anyone who wants to try his skill at hypnotism will find the Horned Toad an easy subject, since a few gentle strokes between the eyes will put him to sleep, and he will then remain quiet for a long time. The Horned Toad depends upon his armor for protection from enemies, and will puff himself out and lower his head so as to present his sharp horns like a barrier of bayonets. Sometime during the months of April to July the female digs a hole about six inches deep in which she lays usually 24 yellowish-white eggs with tough, leathery shells which are a little over $\frac{1}{2}$ inch long and a little less than $\frac{1}{2}$ inch wide.

Horned Toads live only in North America, most of them in the desert regions of the southwestern United States and in Mexico.

Collared Lizard.   Why Lizards so frequently select desert-like regions for their homes is a difficult question to answer, but anyone who lives for any length of time in a dry and barren part of the country, such as certain areas in our southwestern states, is thankful that they do.   Some of these lizards are very beautiful indeed.   The Collared Lizard "exhibits a striking coloration, particularly during the breeding season.   Then the male is rich green, profusely dotted with pale yellow spots; on the neck is a double sooty black collar; as completing touches to the gay coloration, the throat is of a deep orange hue, while there are numerous rusty red spots scattered over the hind legs.   Not to be outdone, the female as well takes on especially gay colors during the early summer.   She is normally a slaty gray, with a much narrower collar than the male.   Before the eggs are laid, however, her sides assume the brightest of brick-red hues, dots of the same color appearing on the limbs and sides of the tail.   Notwithstanding its stoutness of body, the

Courtesy, American Museum of Natural History

Collared Lizard.   A beautifully colored species that lives in dry country and can run very swiftly on its hind legs.

Collared Lizard runs at great speed — generally upon the hind legs.   These lizards are also able to hop and jump like a frog, owing to the long hind legs; such tactics are adopted in traversing rocky places."   (Ditmars.)

Gila Monster.   This brightly colored Reptile is famous because it is the only poisonous lizard living in the United States and one of the two poisonous lizards in the world.   It inhabits Arizona, especially in the region of the Gila River.

from which it derives its name. It is a clumsy, heavily-built lizard with a thick tail which serves as a reservoir of nourishment on which it could keep itself alive for months without food.

The body is covered with beadlike tubercles that are brightly colored with orange or pink, and black or brown resembling Indian beadwork. These bright colors make it conspicuous and are supposed to warn other animals of its poisonous

Photo by Hegner

Gila Monsters. The only poisonous lizard in the United States; an inhabitant of Arizona near the Gila River.

nature. The poison is secreted by glands in the lower jaw and flows out between the gums and teeth and along grooves in the teeth. The venom is not injected into the prey as is that of the rattlesnake, but must flow in, hence, it is said, this repulsive creature must turn over on its back before biting, to allow the force of gravity to carry the venom into the wound.

Usually the Gila Monster sleeps in concealment by day and crawls about sluggishly in the evening in search of the eggs of birds, other reptiles, ants, and other small animals on which it feeds. If angry it will strike like lightning and hang on like a bulldog. One observer states that it may froth at the mouth and blow the poisonous spray toward an enemy. The eggs are soft-shelled, $2\frac{1}{2}$ inches long and $1\frac{1}{2}$ inches wide. Each female lays about a dozen in a hole in the sand from three to five inches deep and covers them over with sand. The young lizards, which hatch in about a month and are four inches long, are left to shift for themselves. The death of human beings has been reported due to the bite of a Gila Monster, but this is certainly a very rare occurrence. Apparently Gila Monsters will not bite unless they have been well warmed in the sun. However, the effects of the poison are so deadly we do not advise anyone to play with them at any time.

Flying Dragon.   The Flying Dragon is an Oriental Lizard that should be large and terrifying to live up to its name, but is in reality a slender creature with a body about five inches long and a thin, nonbreakable tail of equal length.   On each side is a large winglike membrane that is ordinarily folded against the side, but may be held out by half a dozen elongated ribs.   These wings are a brilliant orange color with black markings, and when spread, produce a butterfly-like appearance.

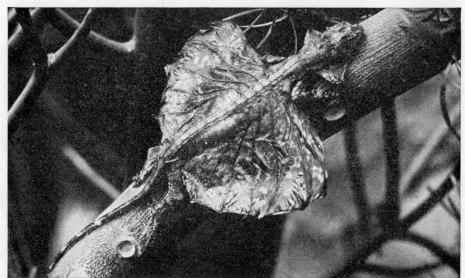

Photo by Ditmars.   Courtesy, American Museum of Natural History
Flying Dragon.   The wings are used to glide with and are not flapped like the wings of a bird.
Size, about 5 inches long.

They are used like a parachute, enabling their owner to glide gracefully from the top of one tree to the bottom of another.   Ants are a favorite article of food.   Over twenty species of these Flying Dragons inhabit the Indo-Malayan countries.

Mole Lizard.   An animal cannot live underground unless it is adapted to that kind of existence, hence it is not strange that burrowing lizards should differ from the species that live on the surface or in trees.   The mole lizard is a curiously grotesque reptile.   The hind limbs have been lost, and the fore limbs are short and broad with five toes that are molelike in form and well fitted for digging.

The body is long, slender, and cylindrical and the tail is short and blunt.   The head is no thicker than the body.   The eyes are rudimentary and the mouth small.   The surface of the body has circular indentations that divide it into rings much like the segments of an earthworm.   These rings are divided into small square areas.   Reptiles of this type are sometimes called Two-Footed Worm Lizards, or Two-Handed Blind "Snakes."   They occur in Lower California. The near relatives of the Mole Lizard are equally degraded, living underground like a worm and sporting rings instead of the conventional scales.   One of them is the Florida Worm Lizard that is often brought to light when fields are plowed.

Glass "Snake." Even more degenerate than the Mole Lizard is the Glass "Snake," or Joint "Snake," a legless lizard that moves like a snake by undulations from side to side, and is covered with scales that are as highly polished as glass. This rigid armor renders its movements stiff and clumsy. The tail is very brittle and breaks off when grasped. It wriggles for some time after separation from the owner, but is never fastened on again as some people believe. The Glass "Snake" is

Photo by Ditmars. Courtesy, American Museum of Natural History
Mole Lizard. He would be mistaken for a worm if he didn't possess two front legs to dig with.

blackish or olive in color with greenish or yellow spots or stripes along the body. It occurs in the southern United States. In the Old World similar species are known as the Blind Worm or Slow Worm.

Dragon Lizard of Komodo. The largest of all the Lizards is one of the most recently discovered species. It lives on the small islands of Komodo, Rintja, and

Photo by Ortenburger. Courtesy, Nature Magazine
Glass "Snake." Not a snake but an elongated, legless lizard. The tail is very brittle and breaks off easily.

Flores in the Dutch East Indies. The natives in this region claimed that Dragons existed on these islands, but not until 1914 were these "Dragons" discovered to be lizards. They are heavily built, powerful reptiles reaching a length of about 9 feet and a weight of over 250 pounds. They are very active and ferocious, capturing wild pigs and other animals on which they feed. The other Monitor Lizards that are known live also in the Old World. They are all covered with small scales, are more slender, have long, whiplike tails, and a long snakelike tongue.

Photo by Hegner

Dragon Lizard of Komodo. The largest living lizard. It may reach a length of over 12 feet and a weight of over 250 pounds.

Courtesy, American Museum of Natural History

Dragon Lizard of Komodo. No wonder the natives on the island of Komodo in the Dutch East Indies considered it a dragon. One is lurking among the roots of the tree at the right.

Chapter 21

SNAKES

Snakes are very highly specialized Reptiles that have lost their legs, and even most of the bones and muscles inside of the body to which the legs are attached in other types of Reptiles. The number of vertebrae in the backbone of snakes has been increased to almost 300 in some species, and there is a correspondingly large number of ribs. The 2000 or more species of snakes known may be grouped into Ground Snakes, that live above ground, Sand Snakes, that live on loose sand, Burrowing Snakes, that live chiefly underground, Tree Snakes, that spend most of their lives in trees and bushes, and Water Snakes, that frequent the water, some of them being exclusively aquatic.

Snakes have no eyelids and hence their eyes are always open; they are covered by a transparent cap. The pupil is vertical or round; it expands or contracts as in human beings, according to the intensity of the light. The tongue of Snakes is long and slender and forked at the end; it is not poisonous, but serves for detecting odors and vibrations in the air. Snake's teeth are numerous, conical, and curved backward. In some of the poisonous Snakes certain teeth are hollow fangs and serve, like hypodermic needles, for carrying poison into their prey. Teeth that are lost are quickly renewed; this includes the fangs, hence a Snake from which the fangs have been removed soon becomes dangerous again.

It is the general impression that Snakes move rapidly, but this is a mental delusion, due probably to fright, since actual measurements have shown that one of our swiftest species, the Blue Racer, never travels over $2\frac{1}{2}$ miles an hour. The internal machinery of ribs, backbone, and muscles is extremely complicated and enables Snakes to wriggle and bend in any direction. Horizontal undulatory movements are responsible for rapid movement, sidewinding or rolling is characteristic of certain species, and caterpillar traction with the aid of scales on the belly results in a gliding movement with the body fully stretched out. There is no Snake that takes its tail in its mouth and rolls along in the form of a hoop. All Snakes can swim and some of them can remain under water for several hours without drowning.

Snakes shed their skin as a whole, beginning at the lips and turning it backward and inside out. Snakes all live on other animals, the character of the food depending somewhat on the habits of the species. Common articles of food are worms, insects, frogs, lizards, bird's eggs, fish, birds, and other Snakes. They catch their prey in their mouths and swallow it at once alive, or may crush it first in their coils, or they poison their prey with their fangs and swallow it after it is dead.

329

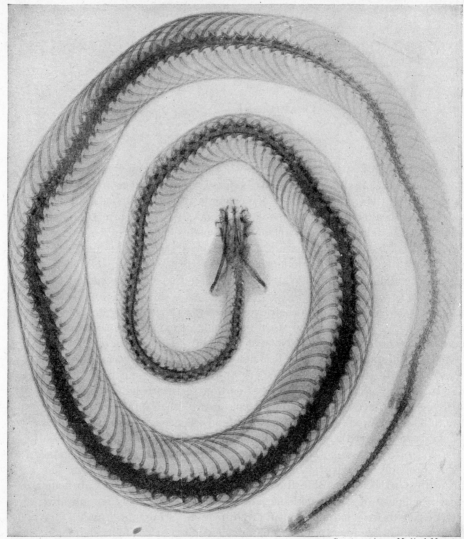

Courtesy, Army Medical Museum

Rattlesnake. An X-ray photograph showing the many ribs and several rattles at the end of the tail.

Snakes do not chew their food but swallow it whole. Animals several times as thick as the Snake can be swallowed because the bones of the jaws are loosely connected with elastic ligaments.

When a Snake swallows, the backward-curved teeth on the jaws on one side hold the prey while those on the jaw on the other side are thrust forward into a new hold. By this method of alternately advancing the teeth on one side and then on the other, the prey is gradually forced down the throat. A python can swallow a calf, and a garter snake can swallow a frog with ease. Snakes do not need to take food very often. For example, an Anaconda in the Paris Zoological Garden was fed only 36 times in seven years. Snakes do not lick their prey in order to cover it with slime before swallowing it, neither do they swallow their young to protect them from danger, although certain Snakes eat other Snakes.

Most Snakes lay eggs, but only a few care for them. Others bring forth their young alive. Of the 2000 or more different species of Snakes known, about 150 live in North America. There are many more Snakes in any locality than most people think, since they naturally hide from man and other enemies, such as birds of prey, skunks, pigs, etc. Very few persons are killed in this country by poisonous Snakes, but in India as many as 20,000 lose their lives every year from Snake bites. Snakes do not chase people nor deliberately attack them but will run away, if possible. They do not fascinate nor hypnotize people or other animals, although animals may be frightened to a standstill. Poisonous Snakes are not injured by their own bites or the bites of other Snakes of the same species, but are poisoned by the venom of other species.

Snakes have been separated into a number of families and subfamilies. One family contains burrowing species with small eyes covered with scales. The family Boidae includes the largest of all snakes, such as the Pythons and Boas. Garter Snakes, Water Snakes, King Snakes, and Hog-Nosed Snakes are harmless; whereas, Sea Snakes, Cobras, Coral Snakes, and Vipers are poisonous.

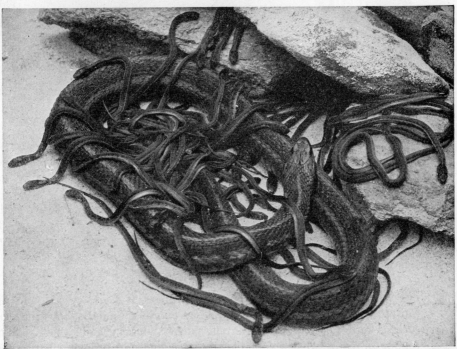

Photo by Ditmars. Courtesy, American Museum of Natural History

Garter Snake. The young are brought forth alive and are about 6 inches long. More than 30 may be born at one time.

Common Garter Snake. Garter Snakes are the commonest Snakes in North America; there are about twenty species of them. They seem to prefer moist meadows and the borders of streams into which they may plunge for safety if disturbed. When captured they often escape by pouring out a foul-smelling fluid from glands near the base of the tail. The Common Garter Snake reaches a length of over three feet and a diameter of an inch. The usual color is dark

Photo by Kennedy

Garter Snake. A favorite attitude for this species; it is watching a frog.

brown with three longitudinal yellow stripes; between these are rows of dark spots. This color pattern is responsible for the name Ribbon Snake sometimes applied to this species. Before we knew its correct name we called it a Grass Snake.

Garter Snakes feed on earthworms, toads, frogs, and other cold-blooded animals. They bring forth their young alive, sometimes over thirty in number. These are about six inches long at the time of birth. When in danger, they do not creep into their mother's mouth for safety.

Bull Snake. One of the most valuable serpents in this country is the Bull Snake of the wheat belt in the Central States. It is a powerful constrictor that captures, crushes to death, and swallows enormous numbers of injurious rodents such as rats, mice, ground squirrels, pocket gophers, and rabbits. Farmers are coming to realize what a valuable ally he is, and now protect where formerly they destroyed. The Bull Snake may reach a length of almost nine feet, and is one of the four largest snakes in North America.

The Bull Snake is yellowish-brown above with a row of large rectangular, reddish-brown or black blotches on the back and smaller blotches on the sides. The head is pointed. It is a powerful hisser and may be heard at a distance of over fifty feet.

The eggs are creamy white and over a dozen may be laid by one female. Bull Snakes are fond of eggs. "When the egg has passed about a foot down the throat the reptile presses its body firmly against the ground, contracts the muscles in advance and posteriorly to the egg and breaks it. The action is quite deliberate and consumes a full ten seconds. The egg collapses with an externally discernible crunch and the fragments of shell are swallowed." (Ditmars.)

Photo by Hegner

Banded Water Snake. This harmless Reptile is sometimes called "Water Moccasin." It reaches a length of 3 or 4 feet.

Black Snake, or Blue Racer. This is one of the most lively of our snakes; not only does it move rapidly over the ground, but is an excellent tree climber, especially if the tree contains a bird's nest it wishes to rob of its young. Birds are said to be "charmed" by Black Snakes, but all who have made careful studies of them

Photo by Hegner

Blue Racer. A long, slender snake with a bad temper but perfectly harmless to man. It can move over the ground with great speed, and climb trees.

declare this to be untrue. The surface of the back is black and satiny, not shiny, and the chin and throat bear a patch of white. The young differ in color from the adults, being light gray with brownish blotches.

The Black Snake inhabits the eastern United States. In the Central States lives a variety that is bluish-green in color and known as the Blue Racer. One of these is shown in the accompanying photograph that was taken in Iowa. Another variety occurs in the Pacific States. Black Snakes exhibit bad temper when disturbed, and will attack with great ferocity. Fortunately their bite is harmless. When angry they vibrate their tail rapidly, and when this occurs among dry leaves, a sound results resembling that produced by a Rattlesnake. Black Snakes grow to a length of six feet. They are partial to shady, shrubby patches near water, where they are most apt to find the birds, frogs, small mammals, and young snakes on which they feed.

Photo from Ditmars, Reptiles of the World

Hog-Nosed Snake, or Puff Adder. The point on the snout is used for digging; the body back of the head can be spread out wide; loud hissing is another accomplishment of this species.

Hog-Nosed Snake, or Puff Adder. The snout of this snake is turned up and ends in a strong, triangular shield that fits it for burrowing in the dry, sandy soil in its habitat. Several common names have been applied to it because of its peculiar habits. The terms Spreading Adder and Puff Adder refer to its habit of spreading the anterior part of the body when irritated. This is possible because some of the ribs near the head are elongated; they usually lie along the body but may be extended so as to present a terrifying appearance like that of a Cobra. The habit of hissing loudly has suggested the name Blow Adder. It seems needless to remark that no poison is blown from the mouth.

Spreading the neck, hissing, and striking viciously at the annoyer with *mouth closed* are of course meant to frighten away the enemy. "These actions are impelled by pure bravado, and this is of short duration. If the snake is further annoyed, it appears to be attacked with convulsions. The head is twisted to one side, the body kinks, the mouth gapes helplessly open and the tongue lolls from it. There is further kinking and twisting and the reptile rolls upon its back. It is a fine piece of acting, in simulating death agonies, then complete demise. Everything is perfect but the snake's insistence on remaining upon its back. If rolled over on its crawling surface with a stick, it will dextrously turn upon its back again." (Ditmars.) In spite of their "poisonous" and viperish appearance, Hog-Nosed Snakes do not bite if captured.

Hog-Nosed Snakes attain a length of three and one-half feet. They have a stout body and a stumpy tail and exhibit great variations in color. In general, they are gray or brownish with irregular dark blotches on the back. Four species occur in the United States; the Common Hog-Nosed Snake in the eastern states, and the others in the central states, southeastern states, and southern Florida.

Courtesy, National Zoölogical Park

King Snake, or Chain Snake. Called "King" because he captures and kills other snakes, including poisonous species. A large specimen is 6 feet long.

King Snake, or Chain Snake. The Common King Snake, or Chain Snake, lives in the eastern United States and frequents moist, shady localities, but does not enjoy swimming or climbing trees. The name is appropriate since King Snakes do not hesitate to attack and kill other snakes larger than themselves, including poisonous species, such as rattlesnakes, moccasins, and copperheads. A large King Snake six feet long is a match for practically any snake that lives in North America. Besides other snakes, birds, rats, mice, lizards, and various species of small animals are captured, and squeezed to death before being swallowed. The venom of the poisonous snakes it captures does not injure it.

"King Snakes are surprisingly gentle in their attitude toward man, making beautiful and interesting pets. They are hardy, not at all particular as to the character of their food — eating dead animals or strips of raw beef — and live for years in confinement." (Ditmars.)

The colors of King Snakes vary according to the part of the country in which they live. A common color is black, with narrow white or yellowish cross-bands.

One of the King Snakes is called the Milk Snake because of the belief that it steals milk from cows.   This is really a myth; the snakes are often found near cow sheds because of the mice that they find there.

King Snake.   The eggs have a rough, white parchment-like shell.   The young look much like their parents.

Boa Constrictor.   Many different kinds of snakes are called Boa Constrictors, but the one that really deserves the name is known to scientists as *Constrictor constrictor* and lives in tropical America.   It is a beautiful large reptile, but not the largest by any means.   A large specimen reaches a length of from ten to fifteen feet.   The Boa is pale brown above with from 15 to 20 cross-bars of brown.   On the tail the colors become brick-red, black, and yellow.   That the ancestors of the Boa had legs is indicated by the presence of degenerate hind legs in the Boa, in the shape of a clawlike spur on each side of the vent.

Boa Constrictors are good tree climbers, but they do not wind their tail about a limb for support while they lunge down upon the unwary traveler, crush him in their coils, and lift him up into the tree for a quiet feast.   Birds and small mammals, however, may be captured in this way.   The story is told of how a Boa became an involuntary cannibal.   Two Boas began to swallow a bird at the same time.   When they reached the middle of the bird's body neither could back away because the teeth are curved backward.   Finally one Boa succeeded in cramming into its mouth not only the entire bird, but also the head of the other Boa and continued to swallow until he had engulfed his entire companion. Boas are savage when caught, and may hiss like a leaky steam radiator, but become quite tame in captivity and, therefore, are favorable reptiles for display in Zoological Gardens.

Photo from Ditmars, Snakes of the World

Anaconda, or Water Boa. A Constrictor that spends much of his time in the water; length, 25 feet or more; weight, as much as 250 pounds.

Not all Boas are large; some of them are small and burrow in the ground. Many people seem to think that all snakes live in holes in the ground and to them any small, round hole in the earth is a snake's hole. On the contrary, the burrowing habit is so unusual that we feel it worth while to mention it when it occurs.

Photo from Ditmars, Snakes of the World

Boa Constrictor. A native of tropical America that squeezes its prey to death; it is not poisonous; length, from 10 to 15 feet.

Anaconda, or Water Boa. This is the Water Boa of Central, Tropical, and South America and represents the longest snake living in America and the heaviest snake in the world. Certain Pythons are longer, but the Anaconda is bulkier. Anacondas over 30 feet long have been reported, but the longest specimen that had scientific verification was 25 feet from the tip of the snout to the end of the tail. A specimen in the New York Zoological Park 19 feet long was 36 inches around and weighed 236 pounds.

The Anaconda has a leopard-like color pattern with cross-bars of black on a greenish-yellow background. As the name Water Boa implies, it is very fond of water, often lying in the rivers of the Amazon Basin with only the head above the surface waiting for a luckless bird or small mammal to pass that way. Like the

Courtesy, National Zoological Park

Python. The longest living snake, reaching a length of 33 feet; it lives in the Far East and constricts its prey to death.

Boa Constrictor it crushes its prey in its coils before swallowing it. The lifeless body is swallowed under water.

The Anaconda is dreaded by the natives, but very rarely, if ever, attacks human beings. Boas and Anacondas bring forth their young alive, from eggs that hatch in the mother's body. A specimen 17 feet long is reported to have given birth to a family of 34 young, each 27 inches long and one inch thick, and all "the living image" of their parent.

Pythons. The Regal or Reticulated Python is the longest living snake, reaching a length of 33 feet. Like the Boa Constrictor and Anaconda, it is a constrictor and crushes its prey to death in its coils. It lives in Burma, Indo-China, the Malay Peninsula, and the Philippines. The colors of this snake are very beautiful, light yellowish-brown with large bluish-black spots. Healthy specimens give off beautiful iridescent tints.

Pythons are excellent swimmers and tree climbers, a favorite perch being a limb of a tree near water. Birds and small mammals are captured for food. About 100 eggs, oval in shape and covered with a leathery shell, are laid. The mother coils about them and appears to keep them warm. When captured, Pythons are quite savage and often go on a hunger strike which can only be conquered by forcible feeding. The body of a rabbit or other animal is forced down the snake's throat while it is held out straight by a group of men. Well-known species of Pythons are the Indian Python, the Rock Python of Africa, the West African Python, and the Australian Carpet Snake.

Banded Rattlesnake*. Rattlesnakes identify themselves by their rattle, but descriptions of the various species are necessary in order to distinguish one from another. A species that is widely distributed and well known is the Banded or Timber Rattlesnake of the East and Middle West. We frequently encountered them in northeastern Iowa and could find one or more of them almost any day

Photo by Hegner

Banded Rattlesnake. A beautifully colored specimen with seven rattles; usually about three or four feet long.

during the spring and summer on a certain hillside where the layers of rock projected so as to form small ledges with plenty of crevices. Here they made their home, lying in the shade, well protected from the hot sun.

The Banded Rattlesnake varies in color. The paler-colored specimens are sulphur-yellow with wide, irregular cross-bands of dark brown or black. The average length of this species is three or four feet, but one specimen over six feet long and nearly three inches in diameter is on record. Banded Rattlers feed on mice, rats, shrews, rabbits, squirrels, and occasionally on birds, and are, therefore, mostly beneficial to man. In the winter they congregate in a "den," often a fissure in the rocks, where they can hibernate without being disturbed by other animals or injured by the cold.

The rattle is made up of a series of hollow rings of dry skin. Every time the skin is shed, the ring at the end of the tail is also shed, but is not lost since it is held loosely to the "button" at the end of the tail. The age of a snake cannot be determined by the number of rattles because the skin may be shed two or three times in a single season, and rattles may be lost. Usually about a dozen rattles are present.

About fifteen species of Rattlesnakes live in the United States. The southwestern states are inhabited by at least 10 species, including the Pacific, Tiger, Horned, Green, and White Rattlesnakes. The Diamond-Back Rattlesnake lives in the southeastern United States; the Massasauga and Prairie Rattlesnakes, in the central United States; and the Texas Rattlesnakes occur from Texas to

Photo from Ditmars, Snakes of the World

Copperhead. A poisonous pit viper but seldom fatal to man; the top of the head is copper-colored; length, 3 or 4 feet.

California. The Mexican and Upland Rattlesnakes live in Mexico; the Gray Rattlesnake in Central America, and the South American Rattlesnake in Mexico and South America. It is thus evident that almost every part of the New World is infested with one or more species of Rattlesnakes.

We are often asked what to do when bitten by a poisonous snake. Very few people are killed by Rattlesnakes, although a Banded Rattler may inject a large amount of poison, capable of causing death in a short time if it enters directly into a vein or within ten or twelve hours otherwise. The fangs are like two hypodermic needles. A ligature should be located at once between the two punctures and the heart. Then an incision about $\frac{3}{8}$ inch deep should be cut across the wounds and the blood sucked out. The injured region swells up and thus delays the passage of the poison into the circulation, so that sucking the wounds is very important. This involves no danger unless there are cuts or sores on the lips. The best type of ligature is rubber. This should be loosened about every ten minutes and the wound should be sucked at frequent intervals for several hours. Snake serum, if it can be obtained, should be injected to neutralize the poison — the sooner after the bite the better. A weak solution of potassium permanganate applied to the incision destroys any venom that it comes in contact with.

Copperhead. Copperheads may be found in swampy places, but appear to prefer rocky hillsides, stone fences, and plantations. For this reason, they are often known as Upland Moccasins. Other common names are Pilot Snake and Chunk Head. Certain species of harmless Snakes are sometimes called Copperheads, especially the Water Snake, Hog-Nosed Snake, and Milk Snake. Being a pit viper, the Copperhead has a pit between the eye and the nostril, which is absent from harmless Snakes; also the pupil of the eye is elliptical.

Copperheads occur in the eastern and part of the central United States. They are more abundant than generally supposed, because their habits are secretive and their activities are greatest after dark. They are more brightly colored than Water Moccasins. The general tone is pale brown, with about fifteen crossbars of darker brown which are larger on the sides. The top of the head is coppercolored, hence the name Copperhead. It is smaller than the Water Moccasin, reaching a length of three or four feet, and its bite is less dangerous. There are very few records of death resulting from its bite. As a rule it bites only when stepped on. It will fight if necessary, but glides away from danger if allowed to do so. Before striking, the tail is vibrated rapidly, producing a sound, in dry leaves, like a rattle.

The food of this Snake seems to vary with the season, consisting largely of frogs in the spring and fall, birds in the late spring, and mice in the summer. From three to nine young are born at one time. Their tails are sulphur-yellow in color, and are said to move like a grub so as to lure small animals within reach.

Courtesy, National Zoological Park

Water Moccasin. A poisonous snake with a thick, clumsy body and a whitish mouth; it lives in or near water; length, from 4 to 6 feet.

Water Moccasin. One of the snakes of the southeastern United States most dreaded by the natives is the Water Moccasin, Water Viper, or Cotton-Mouth Snake. It is one of a group of ten species that has representatives in both the Old and the New World. The Copperhead is a very close relative. As the common name implies, Water Moccasins live in or near water, especially in damp, swampy localities, or in trees or bushes overhanging the water, into which they plunge when disturbed. The other pit vipers of the United States are less fond of water.

The Water Moccasin reaches a length of from four to six feet, but has a thick, clumsy body and is therefore very heavy. Its general color is olive-brown, with 20 to 30 darker cross-bars. Favorite items in its bill of fare are fish, frogs, other snakes, birds, and small mammals. Most poisonous Snakes bite only when stepped on or handled, but the Water Moccasin will raise its head and open its whitish mouth wide, a habit that gives it the common name Cotton-Mouth Snake, and, after several seconds' delay, will strike at any animal within reach. Its venom is not as virulent as that of certain other snakes, and very few deaths from its bite are on record. In captivity the Water Moccasin becomes very tame and gentle toward its attendants.

Coral Snake. Brilliant colors have provided this snake with at least three common names, Coral Snake, Harlequin Snake, and Bead Snake. The scales are smooth and glossy, and the body is covered with rings of crimson, black, and yellow. Coral Snakes are poisonous, but are comparatively small and have short

Courtesy, National Zoological Park

Coral Snake. A slender species colored with crimson, black, and yellow rings; poisonous but not very dangerous; length, about 3 feet.

fangs, and hence are not very destructive, although the death of human beings as a result of their bites has been recorded. They do not strike, as other poisonous snakes do, but when stepped on or handled, will bite and even chew their annoyer, and will hang on tenaciously. The venom acts on the nerve centers rather than on the blood as does that of certain other poisonous snakes.

The Coral Snake lives in the southeastern United States and southward. It spends its time on the ground, often in damp localities, and loves to burrow, frequently being exposed when fields are plowed up. The young of other snakes, lizards, and other small creatures serve as food. A large specimen measures three feet long and $\frac{3}{4}$ inch in diameter. Other species of Coral Snakes live in tropical Mexico, Central and South America.

Coral Snakes "appear stupefied by captivity. The prevailing idea is to avoid the light and observation, and this they do, if there are any facilities for burrowing or coiling beneath some object. Once secreted, all ideas of food seem to vanish among the majority of specimens." (Ditmars.)

Bushmaster and Fer-de-Lance.   The Bushmaster deserves a prominent place in the reptilian division because it is the largest of all Vipers, reaching a length of twelve feet.   It inhabits tropical Central and South America, especially damp, steamy forests, where it frequents holes in the ground made by Armadillos and other animals.   In color, it is reddish-yellow with dark cross-bars; a black stripe extends from the angle of the jaw to the eye.   The Bushmaster is a bold snake, behaving as though it were well aware of its power.   Because of its long fangs and large amount of poison, it is extremely dangerous.   Dr. Ditmars found the fangs of a specimen to be 1⅜ inches long and records the death of a man only ten minutes after being bitten.   Most vipers bring forth their young alive, but the Bushmaster lays eggs.

Another famous tropical American snake, a near relative of the Bushmaster, is the Fer-de-Lance, so called because its head is lance-shaped.   This species reaches a length of only five or six feet, but is poisonous, and a dangerous species to encounter in the jungle.   Several years ago in Panama, while night-hunting, one of our party was about to grasp the head of a Fer-de-Lance, thinking it was a frog, when our guide shot the head off, thereby no doubt saving his life.

Photo by Vestby.   Courtesy, Nature Magazine

Fer-de-Lance.   A very poisonous, dangerous, tropical American species with a lance-shaped head; length, 5 or 6 feet.

The Fer-de-Lance is especially dangerous at night, since at that time he does his hunting, and his poison glands are well filled after a long day of rest.   During the day he remains quietly in hiding, and his bite is not so effective, because most of his poison was used up in capturing small animals the preceding night.

Photo from Ditmars, Snakes of the World

Bushmaster. The fangs are long and hollow; a virulent poison is forced through them when the snake bites; length of body, up to 12 feet.

Cobra-de-Capello. The spreading of the neck of the Cobra into a sort of hood suggested the above name, which was given to it by the Portuguese, and means "hooded snake." The markings on the hood resemble somewhat a pair of spectacles, hence its other name, Spectacled Cobra. Ten species of Cobras are known. Several of them, including the Cobra-de-Capello, live in India, southern China, and the Malay Archipelago. One lives in the Philippines and a number in Africa.

The Cobra is probably the most notorious of all Snakes. When disturbed it erects the forward one third of its body, and spreads the skin of the neck by means of its long ribs. Then follows a hiss and a strike. The fangs are short, and thick clothing is sufficient to prevent injury, but in India the natives go about with bare feet and legs, which accounts for the several thousand deaths each year due to Cobra bites.

The Cobra does not insert the fangs and withdraw them at once, leaving two pinprick-like wounds, as does the Rattlesnake, but grasps and attempts to chew the victim, producing a number of wounds. The venom acts directly on the nervous system and works rapidly. "Snake stones" are of no value as a cure for Cobra poison. Anti-venom is effective, but this must be injected soon after the bite with a hypodermic syringe to be of any value. Cobras may "spit" venom six feet or more. The poison glands are compressed, as the Cobra throws its body forward, and two jets of venom shoot out from the ends of the fangs, aided probably by the expulsion of air from the lungs. If this venom reaches a wound in the skin, it may prove fatal, or if it gets into the eyes, it may blind a person temporarily or permanently.

In India the Cobra is held in a sort of superstitious reverence and is not molested. It feeds on frogs, birds' eggs, and especially on mice, which it searches for in houses. A Cobra in the house is in some localities considered an omen of prosperity. The Cobra-de-Capello is not one of the largest poisonous snakes, although it reaches a length of six and one-half feet, but it is one of the most deadly.

Photo from Ditmars, Snakes of the World

Cobra-de-Capello. The neck can be spread into a sort of hood on the back of which are markings resembling spectacles; a very poisonous species that kills several thousand persons annually.

Curiously enough it falls before the attack of one of the small mammals, the Mongoose. A fight between a Cobra and a Mongoose usually ends with the teeth of the latter deeply sunk in the Cobra's neck and the spinal cord severed. Cobra poison is deadly to the Mongoose, but by moving quickly it succeeds in escaping the Cobra's bite. The Egyptian Cobra, or Asp, is considered by some to be the species used by Cleopatra when she put an end to her life on August 20, 30 B.C., by applying an Asp to her bosom.

Sea Snakes. The real Sea Serpents are not the imaginary monsters reported from time to time by deluded or unreliable persons, but are a family of extremely poisonous Snakes that have become adapted to life in the sea. Most of the Sea Snakes live in the Indian Ocean and the western tropical Pacific, but one species, the Yellow-Bellied Sea Snake, reaches the tropical waters off the western coast of the New World from Lower California to northern South America.

This species is eel-like in shape and usually less than three feet long. The tail is flattened laterally and forms an effective paddle-like swimming organ. The upper surface is black or brown in color and the belly bright yellow, the two colors being sharply separated. The sides of the tail are yellow with vertical black bars. Locomotion out of water is clumsy and ineffective. The Snake has no gills but must come to the surface from time to time to obtain fresh air. The fangs of Sea Snakes are short and permanently erect; the venom, like that of the Cobra, affects the nerve centers of the animal bitten.

Courtesy, American Museum of Natural History

Sea Snake. The real "sea serpent" that lives in the ocean; it is poisonous and dangerous; length, usually less than 3 feet.

CHAPTER 22

TURTLES

No definite distinction exists between Turtles, Tortoises, and Terrapins, but the members of this group are easily distinguished from all other animals by the presence of an oval, and more or less highly arched, shell. Many naturalists use the term Turtle for those that live in the water most of the time, Tortoise for those that live on land, and Terrapin for the hard-shelled, fresh-water species that are used for food.

The most striking characteristic of Turtles is the shell. This consists of an arched upper "shield," called the carapace, and a flat lower shield, the plastron. These two shields are connected on either side by a bridge, leaving spaces in front and behind for the legs, head and neck, and tail to protrude. In many species these can be drawn inside the shell for protection. The shields are covered by horny plates, which may show concentric "lines of growth," due to the alternation of a period of growth during the summer with a period of rest when the Turtle hibernates during the cold season of the year. The skin is tough and leathery, and that of the head, neck, and legs is usually covered with scales. The head is flat and triangular in shape and very solid and compact. The neck is long and flexible and serves to extend the head in any direction, like a flash. The tail is short and stout. The feet of aquatic Turtles are more or less webbed, and those of the marine species have developed into flippers.

Most Turtles are at least partially aquatic, but all of them lay their eggs on land. Many of them can remain under water for long periods, during which they use the air dissolved in the water. The water is drawn in and forced out of the mouth, or the hind part of the intestine is enlarged to form two large sacs supplied with many blood vessels; water passes in and out of these sacs through the vent. Land Turtles feed largely on vegetables and small animals, aquatic Turtles capture animals, such as frogs, fish, and water birds, which they tear to pieces and devour under water. The eggs are ovate or round, with a tough skin or brittle shell. During the breeding season, usually late in the spring or early in the summer, the male Turtles may become noisy and utter hoarse bellowing sounds.

The Turtles of today number about 275 species, of which about 65 live in North America. These are the survivors of a much more numerous group that lived during the Age of Reptiles.

347

Mud Turtle. The common Mud Turtle is probably more widely known to the inhabitants of the eastern and central United States than any other species of turtle, because it frequents muddy ponds, streams, and ditches where boys and girls love to go in wading or fishing. It is a small species with a shell only about four inches long and two and one-half inches wide. The general color is dark brown, and the head is speckled with yellow. When handled, a strong, musky odor is given out, but this is not as strong as that produced by a near relative, the Musk Turtle, which is also called a Mud Turtle by some people. The lower shell is broad, and when the head, legs, and tail are drawn in, can be moved so as to close the shell almost completely.

Musk or Mud Turtle. A small species with shell about 4 inches long; it emits a strong, musky odor.

The Mud Turtle is a water-loving animal, and prowls about on the muddy bottom in search of fish, tadpoles, and insects. Fishermen frequently catch them on baited hooks, much to their disgust, and no doubt the turtle's surprise. When danger approaches, these turtles live up to their name and dive into the bottom, throwing up a "smoke" screen of muddy water that conceals them from view.

The Mud and Musk Turtles comprise a family that inhabit the New World only. They are all rather small and look very much alike. The three species of Musk Turtles are the Common Musk Turtle, Southern Musk Turtle and Keeled Musk Turtle. Mud Turtles comprise eleven species that live in various parts of the United States and Central America.

Snapping Turtle. The Snapping Turtles are among the most ferocious of all turtles. When they "snap," the head darts out like a flash and the sharp jaws meet with such force that they can easily bite off a finger, and those of the large Alligator Snapper can amputate a hand or foot. The Common Snapping Turtle is a small species, although it may reach a length of three feet and a weight of forty pounds. It occurs throughout the United States east of the Rockies in rivers and the larger bodies of water, being aquatic in habit. The head is very large, the shell rough and dull in color, and the feet fully webbed. It loves to float on the surface with the tip of the snout sticking out like that of an alligator, or to lie buried in the mud at the bottom, where it awaits any luckless fish that

Courtesy, Natural History Society of Maryland

Snapping Turtle. A vicious reptile with strong, sharp jaws; the shell and skin are rough and the feet webbed; length, up to 3 feet.

chances to swim that way. It is said that pale pink filaments may be extended from the tip of the tongue which serve as bait. Frogs are captured on the banks and ducks may be drawn down from below and torn to pieces.

Although Snapping Turtles are sinister-looking beasts, their flesh is considered a delicacy by many people, and large numbers are brought to market, often by fishermen who catch them with hook and line. The females wander a considerable distance from the water to lay their eggs, walking awkwardly and slowly along with the body held high above the ground and the head and tail fully extended. The eggs are spherical and covered with a thin, brittle shell. They are buried under debris and left to be hatched by the sun. The Florida Snapper lives in central and southern Florida and the Alligator Snapper, the giant among American fresh-water turtles, in the southern United States. The Alligator Snapper has "a head as large as that of a bull-terrier and jaws that can chop up an ordinary broom handle," and a bad temper as well.

Snapping Turtle. Eggs and recently hatched young.

Soft-Shelled Turtle.　　The shell of this turtle is soft and pliable and free from horny shields; it is oval and very flat.　The shell of the adult is about one foot long.　The head is long and narrow, and the snout is tubular.　Fish, frogs, and other aquatic animals that serve as food are captured by quick movements of the neck.　Muddy rivers are preferred as a place to live, and this aquatic habitat is correlated with the development of fully webbed feet.　The body is olive-brown in color, and in the young, is provided with round, dark spots with black margins. Soft-shelled Turtles are often captured by hook and line, cleaned through a hole in the shell, covered with corn meal and fried.　This custom has given them the name Flap-Jack Terrapin in some regions.　The family contains about 30 species, of which four occur in the United States.

Soft-Shelled Turtles look rather helpless but are fully able to protect themselves in time of danger.　"Hidden by the lips, are a pair of mandibles remarkably keen and strong; on many specimens the mandibles form the outer border of powerful crushing processes — the alveolar surfaces of the jaws; examples thus provided feed largely on mollusks.　Taken at a disadvantage, out of the water, the soft-shelled turtles are savage fighters.　The head darts at an offending object like that of a snake.　Large turtles are dangerous: for they can amputate a man's finger — possibly his hand."　(Ditmars.)

Diamond-Back Terrapin.　This is the most famous of all the turtles as an article of food.　It has been said that no champagne dinner is complete without

Photo by Ditmars.   Courtesy, American Museum of Natural History

Soft-Shelled Turtle.   A young specimen showing dark spots on the shell; the body is flat and the snout tubular; length of shell in adult, about 1 foot.

it.   And it competes favorably in price with champagne, since a fully-grown specimen seven inches long and weighing four pounds costs about six dollars.   The plates on the back of the shell have concentric rings on them shaped somewhat like a diamond, hence the name.

These turtles live in the salt marshes along our eastern coast.   In winter they hibernate in the mud, where they are found and dug up.   So many have been captured that comparatively few remain.   Attempts to raise them on farms have been more or less successful. Often the so-called Slider Terrapins are substituted for Diamond-Backs.

Courtesy, Shedd Aquarium, Chicago

Diamond-Back Terrapin.   The shell has diamond-shaped ridges on the back; the most famous of all turtles as an article of food.

Painted Turtle. The shell of this turtle, or terrapin, is so highly colored that it seems as though it must be painted. When the animal is removed from it, and varnish has been applied, it makes an ornament that used to be highly prized in the nineties, and probably is even yet in some localities. The back is smooth and dark olive in color. The shields are edged with yellow. On the shields around the edge are blotches of crimson. Three yellow bands run lengthwise down the neck. The lower shell is yellow with a central patch of black.

Photo from Ditmars, Reptiles of the World

Painted Turtle. An inhabitant of rivers and ponds, fond of basking in the sun on a log.

The Painted Turtle lives in the eastern United States, but has a near relative, which looks almost like a twin, that is very common in the central and western states. Painted Turtles frequent rivers and ponds, where they may be found in considerable numbers basking in the sun on the top of a stone or log. They are very timid, and at the approach of danger, slide off into the water and dive to the bottom. Before climbing up into the sun again, they rise to the surface with only the eyes and snout above water, and look around carefully to make certain that the coast is clear. These turtles make beautiful pets, especially when young, but will bite viciously until they learn to know their master. They should be fed on insects and small pieces of meat.

Box Turtle. The ventral part of the shell of this turtle is divided crosswise, and the two parts fastened together by a hinge of cartilage. When an enemy appears, strong muscles draw the movable shell together so that the body is encased in a sort of box that is tightly closed and very difficult to pry open. The Box Turtle lives on land and possesses short, webless fingers. It prefers dry woods

Courtesy, N. Y. Zoological Society

Box Turtle. The under part of the shell is hinged and encloses the animal as though in a box.

for a home and flourishes in warm weather, seeking shelter under a log on cool nights. As winter approaches, it digs a burrow in the ground about fifteen inches deep in which it sleeps until spring.

The accompanying photograph gives a good idea of the shape of the shell. It is colored black and yellow or orange-brown and is about five and one-half inches long and three inches high. The eyes of the male are red and those of the female brown. When in search of its food, which consists largely of insects, earthworms, and berries, it holds its shell high above the ground and extends its head on its long neck, — a truly ludicrous sight. The eggs are laid in June or July and hatch

Photo by Hegner

Giant Tortoise. A land turtle that reaches a weight of 500 pounds and may live over a hundred years.

in about three months. They are oval in shape, and the shell is very thin and brittle. Vast numbers of Box Turtles are killed every year by automobiles as they wander leisurely along the road. There are five species of Box Turtles in the United States; two live in Florida, one in the Middle West, and one in the Gulf States.

Giant Tortoise. Although almost exterminated now, Giant Tortoises were present several hundred years ago in enormous numbers on certain islands in the Pacific and Indian oceans in tropical latitudes. Some of them still exist on the Galapagos Islands, about 500 miles west of northern South America, islands that received their name from the Spanish word *galapago*, which means "tortoise." Other Giant Tortoises inhabit the Aldebra and Mauritius-Rodriguez islands.

Thousands of these tortoises were captured for use as food by ships, others were killed by pigs liberated on certain of the islands, and many have been captured and carried away to exhibit in zoological gardens.

The Giant Tortoise lives on land and feeds on leaves and berries. It may reach a weight of 500 pounds and an age of 100 years or more. The head is comparatively small and the neck is long and slender. In captivity these tortoises are gentle and easy to handle. The love-making of the male has been described as follows: "He stalks about the female in a circle, frequently stopping in a position facing the side of her shell. Here he raises as high as his stubby limbs will permit and batters his shell against her, repeating the operation a dozen times or more. This is supposed to be courtship, but the resounding thumps are like the blows of a heavy mallet or sledge and look far more ludicrous than romantic. At such times the males utter deep, trumpeting calls." (Ditmars.)

Hawksbill or Tortoise-Shell Turtle. The long, beaklike snout of this sea turtle is responsible for one of its names, and the beautiful horny shields on its back suggested its other name, that of Tortoise-Shell Turtle. There are thirteen large shields on the back that overlap like shingles on a roof. These are beautifully marbled with yellow on a rich dark-brown background and are one eighth of an inch or less thick. Those from a single turtle weigh from five to ten pounds. To obtain these shields, the turtles are captured and sometimes suspended, while still

Courtesy, Shedd Aquarium, Chicago

Hawksbill or Tortoise-Shell Turtle. A marine species with a beaklike snout and beautiful horny shields on the back that furnish the tortoise shell of commerce.

alive, over a fire to loosen them. After they are removed, the turtle is set free and is supposed to grow a new set of shields, but, as a matter of fact, they do not. Another method of removing the shields is to kill the turtle by a blow on the head and immerse it in boiling water. The shields can then be stripped off easily.

Tortoise-shell combs and other articles are made of shields that are boiled until soft and then welded together with hot irons. Imitations, which are now

very common, can be detected because they lack the fine lines which show where
the real shields are fastened together. Like the Green Turtle, the Tortoise-Shell
Turtle is adapted to life in the water. Its legs are flippers, which make it a strong
swimmer. The shell of a large specimen is two and one-half feet long. Fish and
shellfish serve as food, the shells being easily crunched between the powerful,
horny jaws.

Green Turtle. Many species of turtles are edible, but this one is often called
the Edible Turtle. The green color of its fat gives it its other name. The body
of the Green Turtle is adapted to life in the water. Its legs are paddle-shaped for
swimming. The shell is smooth and polished, olive or brown in color, marbled
with yellow. Specimens may be over three feet long and weigh over 400 pounds,
but those usually sold in markets are less than half this size.

When they come to land to lay their eggs, they may be captured easily and
turned over on their backs. They are unable to turn over again, hence cannot

Courtesy, American Museum of Natural History

Green Turtle. A marine species often used as food; its fat is green in color; the legs are flippers
for use in swimming; length, 3 feet or more; weight, 400 pounds or more.

wander away. A single female may lay several hundred eggs in a hole in the
sand above high tide. She leaves them to be hatched by the heat of the sun and
returns to the sea again. She seems to realize that the nest can be traced by her
tracks and therefore takes a roundabout way back to the water. Egg-hunters
stick poles in the sand to locate the nests. Green Turtles feed largely on seaweed and are on this account usually found near the shore. They are said to be
fond of floating at the surface asleep in the sun. Nets or harpoons are used in
their capture. The natives dive for them.

The shell on the under surface of the Green Turtle is not as firm as in turtles
that live on land or in fresh water, but is rather pliable. Obviously, since they
are buoyed up by the water, they seldom rest on a solid object and do not need
a hard shell for this purpose.

Leathery Turtle. So called because the shell is covered with tough, leathery skin instead of horny shields, the Leathery Turtle takes its place as the largest of all living turtles.   It lives in tropical seas, but may be carried in the Gulf Stream as far north as Long Island.   Specimens have been recorded that measured eight feet in length from the end of the snout to the tip of the tail and weighed 1500 pounds.   The paddle-shaped flippers make it possible for this species to remain at sea at all times, except when the eggs are laid.   The general color is dark brown with yellow spots.   These turtles feed on seaweeds and shellfish, but are not considered edible.   Specimens are rare everywhere.

Courtesy, American Museum of Natural History

Leathery Turtle.   A marine species with a leathery skin; the body reaches a length of 8 feet and a weight of 1500 pounds.

CHAPTER 23

TOOTHED BIRDS AND FLIGHTLESS BIRDS

To most people Birds are the most interesting of all animals. We hear their serenade when we awake in the morning and their vespers in the evening at dusk. They give animation to the landscape and some of them are usually within sight, even from our fourth-story window near the middle of Baltimore. Their beauty of form, pleasing colors and color patterns, and marvelous evolutions in the air attract the favorable attention of almost everyone.

Birds are distinguished from all other animals by their feathers. These serve various purposes. They protect the body from mechanical injury. They are admirably constructed so as to prevent the escape of heat from the body, since they form innumerable small air spaces, which are non-conductors of heat. Without them, flight would be impossible. Beneath the large outer feathers are the smaller down feathers. Molting occurs in the autumn and new plumage is acquired at that time. Many species molt again in the spring; the males, especially, become clothed then with fresh feathers and nuptial plumes.

The body of the bird is built for flight. It is spindle-shaped, offering a minimum of resistance to movement through the air. The bones of the skeleton are closely united, giving the rigidity required by a body supported only by air. The breastbone bears a projection to which the enormous wing muscles that form the breast are attached. Many of the bones are hollow, which decreases the weight of the body considerably. The wing feathers are spread out during flight, thus offering a large surface against the air. The tail serves principally as a rudder, steering the body in the desired direction. The power of flight has enabled birds to distribute themselves throughout all the inhabitable parts of the world.

Birds use their feet for many purposes. In birds that ordinarily perch on limbs the feet are strong and fitted for grasping. Swimming birds have their toes entirely or partially connected by webs. Wading birds have long legs and long, slender toes, which prevent them from sinking into the mud. The toes of the birds of prey are very strong and bear sharp, curved claws for capturing small animals. Birds that spend most of their time in flight, like the swift, possess weak feet. Usually there is one toe behind and three toes in front. An examination of the bones in a bird's foot shows at once that birds walk on their toes.

When at rest, birds often maintain themselves for hours perched on a limb, with the toes holding the body upright. This would soon tire the muscles if it were not for a special mechanism which automatically causes the toes to grasp the perch. The tendon which bends the toes passes over the back of the ankle

357

joint.   The weight of the body bends this joint, draws the toes around the perch, and automatically holds the bird firmly in place.

Birds, like turtles, are toothless; and the jaws are covered by horny sheaths, which constitute the beak.   The beak of the bird performs many of the functions of human hands; it is used to obtain food, build nests, preen the feathers, care for the young, etc.   Birds must be able to move their heads freely if the beak is

Photo by Finley and Bohlman.   Courtesy, Nature Magazine

Terns in Flight.   Note how closely the birds about to alight resemble a modern airplane with landing gear lowered.   Photographed on Little Klamath Lake in California.

to succeed in accomplishing all these duties; they are able to do this because the neck is comparatively long and the vertebrae in it move easily upon one another.

Just as the feet differ in different birds according to the habits of the species, so the beaks are much modified for particular purposes.   Birds preen themselves by pressing a drop of oil from the oil gland, which lies just above the tail, and spreading it over their feathers.   Besides this general function, beaks are used in many different ways; that of the woodpecker is chisel-shaped and fitted for digging into the wood of trees; the beak of the sparrow, which eats seeds, is short and thick for crushing its food; insect-eating birds, like the thrush, possess beaks that are longer and not so strong; birds, like the swift, that catch insects in the air, have small beaks but a wide mouth opening bordered with bristles; and birds of prey are provided with strong, curved beaks for tearing flesh.   These are but a few of the many different forms and uses that might be mentioned.

The songs and call notes of birds are produced by a modification of the windpipe, called the syrinx.   This enlargement of the windpipe contains a valve which vibrates when air is forced out of the lungs and which can be tightened by muscles, thus regulating the number of vibrations and consequently the pitch of the sound produced.

Call notes form the principal language of birds, since anxiety, fear, and other emotions can be expressed by them. Songs, on the other hand, are heard most frequently during the nesting season. Usually only the males are able to sing. The importance of learning the call notes and songs of birds cannot be too strongly emphasized, since they are among the most beautiful sounds in nature; moreover, birds are so effectively concealed most of the time by the foliage of the trees that we hear many more than we are able to see.

One of the most remarkable activities characteristic of birds is their migration from cold northern climates southward in the autumn and back again the following spring. Not all birds do this, however. Those that remain in one locality throughout the year we call permanent residents; those that pass through on their way south in the autumn and on their way north in the spring, like most of the warblers, we call migrants; and those that leave in the autumn and return the following spring, remaining with us to nest, we call summer residents.

Formerly birds were supposed to hibernate during the winter in caves, hollow trees, or, in the case of swallows, in the mud at the bottom of lakes and ponds. This is now known to be incorrect.

Photo by Gross.   Courtesy, Nature Magazine

Osprey. The Osprey has a head covered with white feathers with a dark band on the side across the eye. The sharp, curved beak is characteristic of Birds of Prey.

Most birds migrate on clear nights at an altitude sometimes of a mile or more. Each species has a more or less definite time of migration, and one can predict with some degree of accuracy the date when it will arrive in a given locality. The speed of migration is, as a rule, rather slow; a daily rate of twenty-five miles is about the average.

Many theories have been advanced to account for the migration of birds, such as the temperature and condition of the food supply. Other theories attempt to explain how birds find their way during migration. The best of these seems to be the "follow-the-leader" theory. According to this, birds that have once been over the course find their way by means of landmarks, and the inexperienced birds follow these leaders.

Most birds mate every spring and separate again in the autumn, although a few species remain mated throughout life. Nests are built soon after mating; those of one species resemble each other but differ from the nests of other species, hence one familiar with birds' nests can tell the kind of bird that built any particular nest. A few birds lay their eggs directly on the ground, or on the earth

Courtesy, American Museum of Natural History

Canada Geese in Migration. They form a wedge-shaped figure and "follow the leader.'

in a burrow in the ground. Others build a nest in bushes and trees. Some nests are flimsy affairs, but others are strongly constructed and are able to withstand the winds and storms of several seasons.

The eggs of birds are covered by a hard shell of calcium carbonate. The shell is either pure white, as in the case of woodpeckers and kingfishers that lay eggs in dark places, or variously colored and covered with specks, spots, and lines of different hues. The number of eggs laid in a single nest, called a "clutch" or "set," is usually the same for individuals of one species but differs in different species. They range from one to twenty or more, but four or five is the usual number. The eggs must be kept warm, or incubated, in order to develop; this is accomplished by the bird's sitting on them. Sometimes the female alone performs this duty; sometimes both birds take turns; and in a few instances, like that of the ostrich, the male alone incubates the eggs. The period of incubation lasts from ten or twelve days among the smaller birds to over a month in the case of the largest species.

When the young hatch, they may have a covering of down (precocial birds) or be practically naked (altricial birds). The young of precocial birds are able to run about like young chickens soon after they are hatched. The eggs of these birds must be correspondingly large in order to contain food material (yolk and white) enough to enable the young to reach such an advanced stage in development. The killdeer, nighthawks, bob-whites, and ducks are common precocial birds. The young of altricial birds, on

Nest of the Prairie Horned Lark. A substantial nest is built in a slight hollow in the ground. The two eggs covered with coarse spots were laid in the nest by a cowbird.

the other hand, hatch in a very immature condition and must remain in the nest a long time, until their feathers are grown and they become strong enough to walk or fly. Most of our common birds are of this sort.

Birds are principally beneficial to mankind. They are largely responsible for the destruction of insect pests and other obnoxious animals, and destroy countless numbers of weed seeds. With the exception of the domesticated species, birds are now of very little commercial value. Game birds have been and still are in certain localities a common article of food. Most species, however, have been so persistently hunted by sportsmen and market men that very few are left; some species have actually been exterminated. The hunting and transportation of game birds are now regulated by law in most localities.

Nest (?) of Nighthawk. The grayish-colored eggs are laid on a bare hillside with no effort to build a nest. Except for their regularity in shape, they look much like the small stones surrounding them.

The use of birds' skins and feathers as ornaments was for many years a source of income for hunters, middlemen, and milliners.

Laws and public sentiment, however, have slowly overcome the barbarous custom of killing birds for their plumes. Ostriches are now commonly reared for their feathers, and there is no more objection to the use of their plumes for ornament than there is to the use of hens' eggs for food, since they are now procured almost entirely from domesticated birds.

A curious product of great value to man is guano, which is used as fertilizer. It consists mainly of the excrement of sea birds that live in large colonies and feed on fish. Guano accumulates only in dry regions where it is not washed away before it has a chance to harden.   The most valuable deposits are on small islands near the coast of Peru.   The birds produce a layer about four inches deep, or 750 tons on an acre per year.   A layer 100 feet thick was found in certain localities, and 500,000 tons were carried off annually for a number of years.   This gradually depleted the supply until the amount mined had to be limited.

Photo by Hegner

Young Rail. This little "precocial" baby has just emerged from the egg but can stand alone and swim with "the greatest of ease."

Birds are of great importance as destroyers of injurious animals and plants. Within the past two decades detailed investigations have been carried on by the United States Department of Agriculture, state governments, and private parties in order to learn the relations of birds to man with regard to the destruction of injurious animals. The results of these researches may be found in government publications or in books.

A very large proportion of the food of birds consists of insects. Practically all of these are injurious to plants or animals and consequently harmful to man. Another large element in the food of birds consists of small mammals, such as field mice, ground squirrels, and rabbits. For many years hawks, owls, and other birds of prey have been killed whenever possible, because they were supposed to be injurious on account of the poultry and game birds they captured. Careful investigations have shown, however, that at least six species are entirely beneficial; that the majority (over thirty species) are chiefly beneficial; that seven species are as beneficial as they are harmful; and that only the gyrfalcons, duck hawk, sharp-shinned hawk, Cooper's hawk, and goshawk are harmful.

Certain birds are of importance because they act as scavengers. This is particularly true in our southern states and in tropical countries in general. Black vultures, or carrion crows, and turkey vultures, or buzzards, quickly dispose of the carcass of any animal they find. So many of these scavengers occur in the tropics that no landscape is complete without a few sitting quietly on the limb of a dead tree or on the roof of a building, waiting patiently for an animal to die or a choice bit of garbage to be thrown out. No one pays any attention to them.

Birds have for many centuries been under the control of man and have produced for him hundreds of millions of dollars' worth of food and feathers every year. The common hen was probably derived from the red jungle fowl of northeastern and central India. The varieties of chickens that have been derived from this species are almost infinite. Domestic pigeons are descendants of the wild, blue rock pigeon, which ranges from Europe through the Mediterranean countries to Central Asia and China. Geese are supposed to be derived from the gray-leg goose, which at the present time nests in the northern British Isles. Most of our domestic breeds of ducks have sprung from the mallard. The common peacock of the Indian peninsula, Ceylon, and Assam has been domesticated at least from the time of Solomon. The mute swan of Central Europe and Central Asia is a common domesticated species. The guinea fowl is a native of West Africa. The turkey is a domesticated bird that has been brought under control within the past four centuries. Our domestic turkeys are descendants of the Mexican wild turkey.

A fairly good idea of the numerical distribution of birds in various regions and on different types of land has been obtained by making bird censuses. In the region north of Maryland and the Ohio River and east of the Great Plains about 130 pairs of birds have been found to nest, on the average, on 100 acres of land immediately surrounding buildings, including lawns and orchards, and about 112

Photo by Hegner

Altricial Birds. Young blue jays are born in a naked condition and must live in the nest for a number of days while feathers grow out.

pairs on 100 acres of an entire farm. The robin is the most abundant bird and the English sparrow next, there being about 9 pairs of robins and 8 pairs of English sparrows to 100 acres. Small patches of woodland are well populated, with an average of 182 pairs to 100 acres, whereas deeper woods have only 68 pairs to 100 acres.

The number of birds varies from time to time, due largely to favorable or unfavorable weather conditions, to changes in the use of the land, and to variations in the food supply. Draining marshes drives away large numbers of them. A suburban residence surrounded by trees and plenty of shrubbery appears to have great attractions.

It is usually an easy matter to attract wild birds to the vicinity of one's home. First of all, birds need food before they can carry on any of their nesting activities. The food consists largely of insects, seeds, and berries. Insects are present almost everywhere, and as a rule seeds are abundant; consequently, trees or shrubs that bear berries eaten by birds should be planted. In winter the permanent residents or winter visitors sometimes have difficulty in finding enough food to keep them warm and will welcome any help from human friends. Grain scattered about on the snow or on a food shelf or food house will attract tree sparrows, juncos, and others. Pieces of pork rind or of suet tied to a limb of a tree will tempt the appetites of woodpeckers, nuthatches, and chickadees.

Courtesy, American Museum of Natural History

Guano Birds. The cormorants shown here are on a Chincha Island off the coast of Peru; their excrement, known as guano, is commercially important as fertilizer.

Water is needed by birds both to drink and for bathing, of which they are very fond. This is especially true during the hotter days of summer. If there is a water tap on the lawn, a very good bird bath can be constructed by making an indentation a few inches deep and three feet long and lining this with round stones set in clay. In such a place as this, many different kinds of birds make their toilets on warm summer days.

Many birds make their homes in hollows in trees, fence posts, and similar places. Where no nesting sites of this kind occur, houses should be made and put up to attract those birds that otherwise would seek homes elsewhere. A section of the hollow limb of a tree makes a home most nearly like that which the bird naturally uses. When a hollow limb is not obtainable, a limb may be bored out. House wrens, chickadees, bluebirds, martins, and screech owls are the species that are usually attracted by bird houses.

Fourteen thousand or more different kinds of living birds are known at the present time; of these about 850 occur in North America. A single State may be inhabited by over 300 species. The number in any particular locality depends largely upon the amount of water, swamps, and forests in that vicinity; an average number is about 200.

Birds are divided by scientists (ornithologists) into groups, called Orders, of which about twenty-five are usually recognized. The Orders are subdivided into Families; these into Genera, and the Genera into Species. For convenience, the orders and families are considered here under fourteen headings as follows:

1. *Toothed Birds.* Three orders of birds with teeth in their jaws; known only from fossil remains.

2. *Flightless Birds.* Four orders of terrestrial birds with wings too weak for flight. Examples: ostrich, rhea, emu, cassowary, kiwi, moa, elephant bird.

3. *Diving Birds.* Birds with webbed feet and body adapted for movement under water. Examples: loon, grebe, auk, puffin, murre, penguin.

4. *Swimming Birds.* Birds adapted to swimming; many with long pointed wings and powerful in flight. Examples: albatross, petrel, gull, tern, pelican, cormorant, booby.

Photo by Hegner

House Wren. The natural home of the House Wren is a cavity in a tree, from which this bird is emerging, but Wrens will nest in bird houses if these are provided for them.

5. *Storklike Birds.* Mostly wading birds with long necks and long legs.

6. *Water Fowl.* Aquatic birds with webbed feet and, usually, long, flat beak. Examples: ducks, geese, swans.

7. *Marsh Dwellers.* Mostly wading birds. Examples: crane, rail, gallinule.

8. *Shore Birds.* Frequenters of shores where they probe for food in the mud. Examples: killdeer, woodcock.

9. *Birds of Prey.* Carnivorous birds with curved, hooked beak, and strong, sharp claws. Examples: eagle, hawk, owl, vulture.

10. *Game Birds.* Terrestrial birds sought for food. Examples: turkey, pheasant, grouse, quail.

11. *Pigeons and Doves.* Examples: mourning dove, passenger pigeon.

12. *Parrots, etc.* A group containing a curious aggregation of diverse types. Examples: parrot, kingfisher, nighthawk, hummingbird, cuckoo, swift.

13. *Woodpeckers.* Birds adapted for climbing trees and digging in wood.

14. *Perching Birds.* Most of our common birds belong in this group, comprising about 25 families and nearly 15,000 species.

Archaeopteryx, a Toothed Bird. Fossil remains showing claws on the wings, and long tail with feathers on each side. The jaws had teeth in them.

A Toothed Bird — Archaeopteryx. Although the expression "as scarce as hen's teeth" is based on fact, since hens have no teeth, certain birds that lived millions of years ago not only had teeth, but must have used them effectively to catch fish and other animals on which they preyed. Teeth may have been of great value to these birds, but nevertheless all Toothed Birds became extinct many aeons ago, and are known now only by their fossilized remains. The most famous of all Toothed Birds is the Lizard-Tailed Bird, whose scientific name is Archaeopteryx. In 1861 a single feather of this bird was discovered in a limestone quarry at Solenhofen,

Bavaria, in Germany. Later in the same year parts of a skeleton were uncovered in the same quarry and are now in the British Museum; and in 1877, a skeleton that is almost perfect was found near by and is now in the Berlin Museum.

Archaeopteryx was about the size of a Crow, but had a tail that was longer than its body. It looked like a bird, but combined in its structure many of the characteristics of Reptiles. The body was long and narrow; the head was small; the tail had a central axis of vertebrae, each of which bore a pair of stiff feathers; the feet were adapted for perching and walking; and the wings were provided with three long, slender fingers, each with a hooked, sharp-edged claw at the end, no doubt used to climb about among the branches of trees, as young Hoactzins do now (see page 445).

The teeth of Archaeopteryx were all of one type, conical in shape, sharp at the tip, and fastened in sockets. They were probably shed and new ones acquired at frequent intervals. Why such a bird as Archaeopteryx became extinct in spite of its many superior features is a scientific problem that seems insoluble.

Western Toothed Bird. Europe did not have a monopoly on Toothed Birds, since many of them have been found in the United States. The Western Toothed Bird, with the scientific name Hesperornis, was discovered in the chalk beds of western Kansas in 1870. It must have seemed like a terrible monster to the fishes

Courtesy, American Museum of Natural History

The Western Toothed Bird, Hesperornis. Restoration showing teeth, wingless condition, and powerful legs at the sides of the body for swimming and diving.

in those ancient seas, since its shape and structure prove that it was a magnificent diver, measuring about four feet in length. Its body was narrow, neck long and slender, and toes probably webbed.

The wings were undeveloped, and swimming and diving were accomplished by the legs alone; these powerful organs of locomotion were not attached to the body as in modern birds, but extended out on either side like a pair of oars. The sharp, backward-pointed teeth, that occupied a groove in the long slender jaws, were very effective in catching and holding fish and other aquatic animals on which Hesperornis preyed.

Many different species of Toothed Birds have been discovered in the form of fossils. They varied in size and in habits, some being much smaller than Hesperornis and adapted for flying. Bird study might not be such a delightful and harmless pastime if the earth were now populated only with birds "with teeth in them."

FLIGHTLESS BIRDS

Flight is an accomplishment that has enabled birds to distribute themselves practically all over the world, and to wander far and wide at will, but birds belonging to at least six families are unable to fly. Such birds are not as successful in escaping their enemies, especially man, as are the birds that are able to fly, and, as a result, two of the families have become exterminated within recent times, and the other families have come to occupy a rather minor place in the bird universe.

Photo by Hegner

Ostriches. The bird on the right bears some of the white plumes for which ostriches are famous. Photographed on an ostrich farm near Los Angeles in California.

Many Flightless birds are said to be "wingless," but some of these possess wings too small to raise the body from the ground, or else only the rudiments of wings are present, concealed beneath the feathers of the body. The Moas and

Elephant Birds, or Rocs, are all extinct; the Emus, Cassowaries, Rheas, Ostriches, and Kiwis are still among the living.

Ostriches. The Ostrich is the most powerful and largest of all living birds, a veritable giant, reaching a height of over eight feet and a weight of 300 pounds. A large part of its height consists of the long neck, which has given it the name Camel Bird. Its wings are small for its size, but are really quite large, and are said to be used as sails when running.

Male and female Ostriches differ widely in coloration. The feathers on the body of the male are glossy black with the exception of the magnificent white plumes of the wings and tail. The feathers of the female are dull, grayish-brown. This is really of advantage to her since she is rather inconspicuous as she sits on the eggs during the day and thus escapes observation.

What the Ostrich lacks in wings it makes up for in legs. Twenty-five feet at a stride has been recorded and "What time she lifteth up her wings on high she scorneth the horse and his rider" (Job), although her speed of about 25 miles per hour doesn't seem so great now, when compared with automobiles and airplanes, as it did in the days of the Prophet. The Ostrich also uses its legs to defend itself, and can kick viciously. Only two toes are present, and one of these, the third, does all the work, the other, or fourth toe, being very small.

Ostriches live on dry, sandy, waste land; they may lie flat on the ground to conceal themselves, but never bury their heads in the sand to escape observation, as often stated. They are very restless and nervous, going about in groups of a few to a dozen or more. The male is polygamous and his three or four wives lay their eggs all together in a hollow scratched in the sand. The male sits on the nest at night and a female during part of the day. The eggs weigh about three pounds each and will hold the contents of about 18 hen's eggs. The young run about as soon as hatched.

There are in South Africa several hundred thousand tame ostriches, and most of our ostrich feathers come from them. The income varies, of course, with changes in fashions. At one time about $10,000,000 annually was derived from the plumes of these birds. Ostrich farming is now successfully carried on in California, Arizona, Arkansas, North Carolina, and Florida. The feathers are clipped without pain to the birds; those from a single adult weigh about one pound. Ostriches belong to four or more species; they occur in certain desert regions in Africa, Arabia, and southern Palestine.

Rhea, or South American Ostrich. Rheas resemble Ostriches in certain respects and differ from them in others. They are smaller, have three instead of only two toes, and have feathers on the head and neck; they lack white plumes on the wings, and are without a tail. In habits, they resemble Ostriches quite closely. Their family life would satisfy the most ardent feminist. The husband stays home and sits on the eggs or watches the young with pathetic concentration, while his several wives disport themselves over the neighboring pampas. One female lays about a dozen eggs, but since several of them use the same depression in the ground as a nest, the male may have 50 or more eggs to hatch.

Like the Ostrich, the Rhea can run very rapidly. "Their speed and endurance are so great that, with a fair start, it is almost impossible for the hunter to overtake them, however well mounted. When running the wings hang down like those of a wounded bird, or one wing is raised and held up like a great sail, for what reason it is impossible to say." (Hudson.) They roam about usually in flocks of about half a dozen except after the breeding season when bands of 25 are common, consisting of males, females, and young. The natives of South America hunt Rheas with bolas, which they try to wind about their legs.

When persecuted, Rheas become very wary and run away from the least sign of danger with the speed of a race horse, but when treated kindly, are friendly and without fear. The specimen shown in the accompanying photograph was wandering about freely in the Zoological Garden in Buenos Aires where we encountered him.

Photo by Hegner

Rhea, or South American Ostrich. Tailless as well as flightless; an excellent runner with great endurance. Photographed at Buenos Aires in Argentina.

Cassowary. The Cassowary resembles the Ostriches and Rheas in general structure and habits. It is a forest-loving bird, living in Australia, New Guinea, Ceram, and Aru, and feeding on fruit, insects, and other small animals. The head bears a conspicuous horny helmet, or casque, and this, as well as the rest of the naked head and neck, is brilliantly colored. The wings are rudimentary, consisting of five or six long, black, shining spines.

Only one female Cassowary lays in each nest, and the male takes entire charge of incubating the eggs and caring for the young. He is very quarrelsome, and the nail of his inner toe may inflict a nasty wound when he kicks. Both male and female have rather unpleasant reputations. "Their temper is generally sullen and treacherous, and they are extremely pugnacious, even the different sexes often fighting at other seasons than the breeding season." (Rothschild.)

Cassowaries have done fairly well in spite of their inability to fly, since about twenty species are living at the present time. To the same family belong two species of flightless birds that live in Australia and are known as Emus.

Kiwi, or Apteryx. Among the most interesting of the flightless birds is the Kiwi of New Zealand, known to scientists as Apteryx. It is comparatively small in size, being no larger than a domestic fowl. As it walks about the Zoo, its curiously humped body reminds one of a little old man. In its native haunts it spends the daylight hours in a hole, but comes out at dusk and glides about stealthily, like a rat, in search of food.

Photo by Hegner

Cassowary. A flightless bird with five or six long, black spines in place of wing feathers, and with a brilliantly colored helmet, or casque, on the head. A native of Australia photographed at Buenos Aires in Argentina.

The bill of the Kiwi is long, slender, and slightly curved, and at the end are slitlike, sensitive nostrils with which it smells its prey in the dark. It is said to stamp on the ground with its powerful feet, which induces worms to come to the surface deluded into thinking that rain is falling.

The Kiwi nests in a hole in a bank, at the end of which is a chamber upholstered with grass. The one or two eggs are enormously large for the size of the bird and may weigh as much as a pound each. The male bird utters "a somewhat hoarse, shrill whistle, often distinctly like Ki-i-wi," which has given the bird its name. The

Courtesy, Nature Magazine

Kiwi, or Apteryx. A flightless bird of New Zealand with a hunchback and a long slender bill.

Maoris consider Kiwis very good for food, which will probably, in time, lead to their extinction.

Moa. Another flightless bird that once inhabited New Zealand is the Moa, known now only from the bones and egg shells that have been found scattered about on the ground, buried in river banks, or hidden in caves.   No one knows when the Moas became extinct, but the last one was killed and eaten by the natives of New Zealand probably about 300 years ago. Some of the Moas were feathered giants at least nine feet tall, but others were no larger than turkeys.

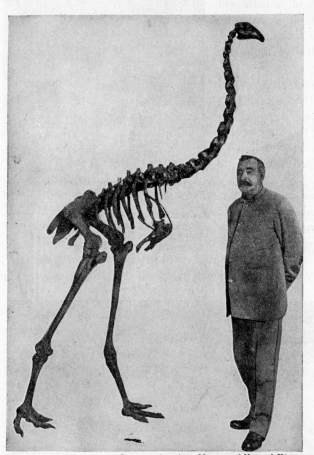

We are so accustomed to see birds in flight that we are apt to wonder how any of them can get along without wings, but we must remember that the dominant animals now on the earth (human beings) have no wings, and have only recently learned to fly. In the region where the Moas lived, they were probably the dominant animals until Man appeared, from whom they were unable to escape by running, and, as a result, became extinct.

Courtesy, American Museum of Natural History
Moa.   The bones of a large species about 9 feet high.   Moas probably became extinct about 300 years ago.

Elephant Bird, or Roc. And finally the last of the flightless extinct birds, and probably the largest, is the Elephant Bird of Madagascar.   Marco Polo states that the giant bird of Arabian folk tales, the Roc, lived in Madagascar, and the Elephant Bird was at one time supposed to represent the Roc.   Like the Moa, this species has probably been extinct for about 300 years. Its eggs were first discovered on the seacoast, and are remarkable for their size, being over a foot long and nearly a foot broad, and having a capacity of over two gallons.   The natives used the eggs for water jars.

Elephant Birds apparently lived inland, and the many bones that have been found indicate that over a dozen species once existed, the largest being nine or ten feet tall. The bones of the legs were especially massive, some of them being eighteen inches in circumference at the upper end. Such a bird must have been able to kick like a mule, but, as scientists appear to have proved, over-specialization of this type is apt to lead to extinction.

Courtesy, American Museum of Natural History

Eggs of Feathered Giants.   From left to right, Elephant Bird or Roc, Ostrich, Moa, and below at left, a hen's egg.

CHAPTER 24

DIVING BIRDS AND SWIMMING BIRDS

DIVING BIRDS

The Divers are more thoroughly adapted for life in the water than any other of our birds. Divers must be able to live in cool or cold water without losing their body warmth, to escape from their enemies by diving or swimming, and to capture food consisting largely of fish and other animals that live in the water. Both in structure and in habits the Divers answer these requirements.

The body is more or less boat-shaped, and is covered with dense plumage that water does not penetrate; a layer of fat beneath the skin helps to keep the heat of the body from escaping. The feet are, of course, adapted for swimming, and the toes are, therefore, either webbed or lobed. The wings are used very little during daily life and are very short. The legs are placed far back on the body where they can propel the bird forward with the greatest ease, but on this account Divers are

Courtesy, American Museum of Natural History

Loon. The distribution of white and black feathers is interesting as well as the long, sharp beak. The bird is represented as about to sit on its two eggs.

374

very awkward on land, and must rest in a peculiar, almost upright, position. Among the Divers are the Loons, Grebes, Auks, Puffins, and Murres.   The Penguin is included here with the Divers for convenience.

Loon.   Probably the most expert of all diving birds is the Loon, or Great Northern Diver.   No lake in the northern part of our country is complete without the presence of one or two pairs of Loons.   Their loud and far-reaching cries, uttered often at night or early in the morning, leave a lasting impression.   They resemble the howls of a lone wolf or the wild laughter of an insane person, and make one feel as though he had finally reached the wild, primeval wilderness.   However, anyone who is "as crazy as a Loon," is really a very sane person, since Loons are able to battle very successfully in the struggle for existence.

Courtesy, Natural History Society of Maryland

Grebe.   How easily she rests on the water.   Her webbed feet are located far back where they can propel the body most effectively.

They reach a length of three feet and are about the size of a goose.   When diving they may use their legs or their wings or both together.   Fish and frogs have very little chance to escape, because they can swim under water with the speed of a motor boat and can dive down to a depth of 50 feet or more.   The body is flat and heavy, and may be submerged with only the head and neck remaining above the surface.   The bill is long and sharp and forms a most efficient weapon.   Loons cannot be approached very easily, being very wide awake and suspicious.   They dive at the flash of a gun and are below the surface before the shot reaches them, usually coming to the surface again at some unexpected spot.   The nest is built in a hollow in the ground near water; it consists of sticks, moss, and grasses, and usually two dark greenish-brown eggs are laid.   The young can swim as soon as they become dry after hatching; they are often allowed to mount their mother's back as a special treat. The four species of Loons live in the northern half of the Northern Hemisphere.

Pied-Billed Grebe. The best chance to observe this small cousin of the Loon is to explore the rushes at the edge of a fresh-water lake. It is less than half the length of the Loon, but resembles the latter both in structure and habits. As a diver, it excels the ducks and almost equals the Loon, having well earned the name Hell Diver. The toes are provided at the sides with lobes which aid in swimming on or under water and as a rudder when the Grebe reluctantly takes to the air. The bill is whitish with a black band around it, hence the name "Pied-Billed."

The nest is a remarkable structure of weeds collected from under water and massed together on top of other weeds so as to form a sort of floating raft. In it are laid from six to nine eggs. When the parent gets tired of sitting on the eggs, she covers them over with water-soaked vegetation and then takes a vacation. Young Grebes do not need to be taught to swim. "When out of the shell, the young has not far to walk; he looks for a few moments over the edge of his water-drenched cradle and down he goes with the expertness of an old diver." Grebes feed on fish, crayfish, and other aquatic animals. They appear to be harmless. About 25 species of Grebes are known, of which six occur in North America. Holboell's Grebe, the Horned Grebe, the Eared Grebe, and the Western Grebe are familiar species. The Western Grebe has a long, swanlike neck covered with black and white feathers with a satiny finish. Hundreds of them may nest together in a colony.

Photo by Hegner

Pied-Billed Grebe. The nest is built on the muck among the reeds in a swamp. At the left the eggs are covered as left by the mother; at the right the decaying vegetation is removed so as to reveal the eggs.

Photo by Finley.   Courtesy, Nature Magazine

Western Grebe.   The nest on which the bird is sitting is built of decaying weeds.   The neck
is long and graceful and the bill long and slender.

Auks. The Auks are diving birds that constitute a large element in the bird life of the Arctic seas.   They are adapted for life in the water much as are the Loons and Grebes.   The Razor-Billed Auk frequents the coasts and islands of the North Atlantic.   It feeds largely on fish, which it captures under water, swimming with

Courtesy, American Museum of Natural History

Great Auk. Mounted specimen of a species that became extinct about 1850. The wings were too small for flight and hence the birds were easily killed for meat and feathers.

both wings and feet. During most of the year it spends a large part of its time at sea, but as the breeding season approaches, large numbers congregate on cliffs above the ocean. No nest is made; each female lays a single egg on the bare rock, and the parents are very careful not to leave it uncovered for an instant. The bill of the Razor-Billed Auk is flatly compressed, and black crossed by a white line.

The Great Auk, or Garefowl, is of particular interest because it has become extinct within less than 100 years. In length it measured about 30 inches, or twice that of the Razor-Billed Auk. Unfortunately it was unable to fly and hence was easily captured. Large numbers nested on the coasts and islands of the North Atlantic, where sailors collected them by the thousand when they needed fresh meat. Their eggs were also used for food, and their feathers for pillows and feather beds. The last record of a living specimen was one captured near Iceland in 1844. All that remains of this species are about 70 eggs and 80 mounted birds in museums. Man alone is responsible for its extermination.

Tufted Puffin. One of the most interesting of the diving sea birds of the northern Pacific Ocean is the Tufted Puffin. The body, which is about fifteen inches long, is topped by a sturdy neck which bears a grotesque head of large proportions. The sides of the head are white, and extending backward from each eye is a tuft of straw-yellow feathers about four inches long. The bill is very large and masklike, vermilion in color, narrow, and with ridges on the sides; all of which gives the bird the expression of a wistful little dog. The name Sea Parrot is applied to the Puffin on this account, and the puffed-out beak is said to have suggested the name Puffin.

Why such an absurd bill should ornament the Puffin is an unsolved problem. Anyone who has put his hand down the nest hole when mother Puffin was at home knows that it is an unpleasant weapon, but other sea birds catch fish as effectively with more reasonably sized beaks. In some places Puffins lay their single egg in a hole or crevice among the rocks, but in others they dig a burrow in the earth, sometimes three or four feet deep, in which to raise their offspring. "The young one is a real Puffin, as it is covered with down like a powder puff, but as it sits at the

Courtesy, Nature Magazine

Tufted Puffin. Head-on view of a Sea Parrot; the bill does not look as clumsy as it does from the side.

mouth of the burrow it looks, at a distance, like a little rat peeping out of its hole."

Courtesy, American Museum of Natural History

Sea Birds. This group includes a Horned Puffin (at the left), three Pacific Kittiwakes (above), and two Tufted Puffins (below, at the right).

Photo by *Finley & Bohlman*.   *Courtesy, Nature Magazine*

California Murres.   Part of a colony on the rocky coast of the Pacific ocean.

California Murre.   Another diver that lives in the North Pacific is the California Murre.   Apparently never happy when alone, these Murres congregate in large numbers on the rocky shores.   They are about 18 inches long, with a snow-white breast and sooty-brown back.   The bill is black and sharply pointed, well fitted to catch fish.

Murres swim under water with great speed, using their wings as oars and their feet as propellers.   The single egg is laid on the bare rock, and as is the case with many birds, is large at one end and pointed at the other, hence if it starts to roll, it circles around the pointed end instead of rolling off into the sea.   There seems to be no good reason why Murres should crowd so closely together at their breeding places, but they evidently enjoy the continuous tea party that this habit provides.

Photo by Hegner

Penguins. They stand upright; the wings are flippers covered with scalelike feathers. These two are in conference.

Penguins.   Thanks to Antarctic explorers and their moving pictures, we are privileged to watch the amusing antics of Penguins, which we would otherwise never witness, because Penguins all live below the equator, and many of them inhabit the bleakest and most inaccessible regions of Antarctica.   Penguins may be seen in the flesh in the larger zoological gardens, but only the "movies" can give an adequate idea of the tens of thousands that nest together in their huge rookeries, or of the behavior of the breeding birds.

Penguins and Sea Elephants. A photograph taken in the Antarctic region demonstrating the abundance and fearlessness of the penguins.

Penguins have no flight feathers and are unable to fly. Their fore limbs are paddle-like flippers that have become rigid; movement is possible only at the shoulder. Swimming is accomplished with the wings alone, which are used like oars as the birds move about flat on the surface, or dive for food underneath. The feathers are very broad and scalelike. The legs are short and stout and serve very well for walking about. When on land Penguins ordinarily assume an upright position.

The food of Penguins consists largely of fish and crustaceans. The eggs, one or two in number, are laid in a slight hollow in the ground, lined with pebbles or shells. The female does the incubating while the male stands by or goes fishing for himself and his spouse. Young Penguins are covered with down, are quite helpless, and must remain in the nursery for a long time.

About seventeen species of Penguins are known. The largest is the Emperor Penguin, which reaches a height of over three feet and a weight of over eighty pounds. The smallest is the Blue Penguin of South Australia and New Zealand, which measures about seventeen inches high.

SWIMMING BIRDS

Diving birds swim and swimming birds dive, otherwise they would have a difficult time making a living as Water Birds. For the sake of convenience, we are considering in one group certain representatives of a dozen or more families of birds that occur in various parts of the world, are conspicuous along seacoasts and lake shores, and possess webbed feet. These we call Swimming Birds, although many of them seem to spend more time in the air than in the water. Their wings are usually long and pointed, which is characteristic of many birds that fly continuously, and their bills are strong, and in many species, hooked at the end, and thus adapted for capturing and holding fish, which make up a large part of their food.

Most of the Swimming Birds are comparatively large, and some, such as the Albatrosses, have an enormous spread of wings. Only one or two or three eggs are laid, and the young are helpless when hatched and must be cared for by their parents for a considerable period before they can shift for themselves. Those of us who live inland almost never see these Swimming Birds, but no vacation to lake shore or seacoast is complete without the shrill, harsh noise of their cries and the amazing agility of their aerial gyrations. Among the Swimming Birds are the Albatrosses, Shearwaters, Fulmars, Jeagers, Skuas, Petrels, Gulls, Terns, Kittiwakes, Skimmers, Pelicans, Cormorants, Darters, Gannets, and Frigate Birds.

The Albatrosses, Fulmars, Shearwaters, and Petrels are called Tube-Nosed Swimmers because their nostrils are tubular. The Pelicans, Gannets, Cormorants, Tropic Birds, Darters, and Man-o'-War Birds are classed as Totipalmate Swimmers since the toes are fully webbed. The Gulls, Terns, Jaegers, Skuas, and Skimmers are water birds with long wings. The Gull and Tern families comprise about 100 species and are distributed throughout the world. About 40 species occur in North America. Skimmers are peculiar because they fly along with the lower part of the bill beneath the water, skimming the surface for food; the lower mandible is actually longer than the upper mandible.

Laysan Albatross.   The Albatross is famous for the enormous spread of its long, narrow wings and marvelous powers of flight. "With outstretched motionless wings he sails over the surface of the sea, now rising high in the air, now with a bold sweep, and wings inclined at an angle with the horizon, descending until the tip of the lower one all but touches the crests of the waves as he skims over them.   Suddenly he sees something floating on the water and prepares to alight; but how changed he now is from the noble bird, but a moment before all grace and symmetry. He raises his wings, his head goes back and his back goes in; down drop two enormous webbed feet straddled out to their full extent, and with a hoarse croak, between the cry of a raven and that of a sheep, he falls 'souse' into the water. Here he is at home again, breasting the waves like a cork.   Presently he stretches out his neck, and with a great exertion of his wings runs along the top of the water

Photo by Pollock.   Courtesy, Nature Magazine

Black-Browed Albatross, or Mollymawk.   The wings are very long and narrow; they sustain the bird hour after hour without apparent fatigue.

for seventy or eighty yards until, at last, having got sufficient impetus, he tucks up his legs, and is once more fairly launched in the air."   (Hutton.)

Albatrosses are much larger than Gulls or Terns, reaching a length of three feet or more.   No wonder the Ancient Mariner complained when "instead of the cross an Albatross around my neck was hung."   Even in Coleridge's day sailors considered it unlucky to kill an Albatross.   Like Gulls, the Albatross will follow a steamer hour after hour and apparently day after day, although there is some doubt as to this point.

Laysan Island, which is about 700 miles west by north of Honolulu, has been the breeding place of enormous numbers of Laysan Albatrosses, and here hundreds of thousands of birds have been deprived of their eggs by hunters, or killed for their feathers. Now this island is part of the Hawaiian Island Reservation for Birds and the slaughter of the Albatrosses has ceased.

The courting antics and peculiar dances of these Albatrosses have been described as follows: "The old birds . . . spend much time in a curious dance, or perhaps more appropriately a 'cake-walk.' . . . At first two birds approach each other, bowing profoundly and stepping heavily. They swagger about each other, curt-seying solemnly, then suddenly begin to fence a little, crossing bills and whetting them together, sometimes with a whistling sound, meanwhile pecking and dropping stiff little bows. All at once one lifts its closed wing and nibbles at the feathers beneath, or rarely, if in a hurry, quickly turns its head. The partner during this short performance assumes a statuesque pose, and either looks mechanically from side to side, or snaps its bill loudly a few times. Then, the first bird bows once, and pointing its head and beak straight upward, rises on its toes, puffs out its breast, and utters a prolonged nasal *Ah-h-h*, with a rapidly rising inflection and bovine quality. . . . Often both birds raise their heads in the air and favor the appreciative audience with that ridiculous and indescribably bovine groan. . . . Occasionally while 'cake-walking' one will lightly pick up a straw or twig, and present it to the other, who does not accept the gift, however, but thereupon returns the compliment, when straws

Courtesy, Nature Magazine

Laysan Albatrosses. Two dancing birds raising their heads and uttering their "ridiculous and indescribably bovine groan."

are promptly dropped, and all hands begin bowing and walking about as if their very lives depended upon it." (Fisher.)

Herring Gull. To many people any sea bird is a Sea Gull, and as a matter of fact the Herring or Sea Gull is the most widespread and commonest Gull in the Northern Hemisphere. Visitors at the seashore are certain to be entertained by their aerial feats and hoarse cries, and "those who go down to the sea in ships" may watch them for hours as they follow in the wake, eagerly descending upon any little morsel that may be thrown overboard.

The Herring Gull is a master of the air. "It can fly forward or backward, veer gracefully in any direction, soar with stiffened pinions or shoot downward like an arrow, sail on steady wing against the wind and perform numberless evolutions with grace and ease."

Gulls feed largely on fish and are not particular whether the fish are fresh, in fact they are quite useful as scavengers. On rocky shores Gulls may be seen cracking clam shells by carrying them to a height of 40 or 50 feet and dropping them; if they

Photo by Pettingill.   Courtesy, Nature Magazine

Herring Gulls.   Sea Gulls are a common sight along our seacoast.   They are trim-looking birds and masters of the air.

Courtesy, Nature Magazine

Herring Gull.   The cry of the Herring Gull is a familiar sound at the seashore; it has more volume than beauty.

do not break sufficiently at the first trial they are dropped again and again until the juicy meat within can be extracted.   The Mormons have a special affection for Sea Gulls, because in the early days, when their precious crops were threatened by hordes of crickets, thousands of Gulls appeared as though heaven-sent and devoured them.   A statue in Salt Lake City now commemorates this event.   Herring Gulls nest in large colonies on rocky shores and islands.   The young are able to run about soon after they hatch.   Of about 50 species of Gulls, 23 have been reported from North America.   Among these are the Laughing Gull, whose call notes remind one of maniacal laughter;   the Atlantic Kittiwake, whose cries resemble the syllables *kitti-aa, kitti-aa;*   the Ivory Gull with its pure white plumage;   and Franklin's Gull, which is seldom seen near the seashore but prefers to live in the interior of the country where it feeds largely on grasshoppers.

Photo by Hastings.   Courtesy, Mich. Dept. Conservation

Common Tern.   How gracefully this Sea Swallow alights by its nest!   Size, about 15 inches long.

Common Tern.   Terns are in general much smaller than Gulls but quite similar in shape and in flight.   The Common Tern is white with a mantle of pale pearl-gray and a crown of lustrous greenish-black.   Although classed among the Swimmers, it spends much of its time in the air, where its agility has won it the name Sea Swallow.   Terns are excellent fishermen.   Often large fish, such as mackerel and bluefish, pursue smaller fish, which leap out of the water in their efforts to escape. The Terns are on the lookout for such a commotion and gather from all directions in such numbers that it almost seems to rain Terns as the birds dive like plummets into the waves after their finny prey.   Fishermen are sometimes guided to good fishing in this way.   Other aquatic animals, such as shrimp, as well as various kinds of insects, also serve as food for the birds.

Terns are sociable birds and breed in large colonies. The nest is generally a hollow in the sand in which three eggs are laid. The eggs are very large for the size of the bird. Both eggs and young resemble their surroundings very closely, that is, are "concealed" by their colors.

The Common Tern is widely distributed in the Northern Hemisphere. One species of Tern, the Arctic Tern, is renowned because it performs the most extensive migration of all birds. It nests within 8° of the North Pole, spends the northern winter in the Antarctic, and probably passes about eight months of the year in continuous daylight.

Photo by Hegner

Black Tern. The nest was made of weeds on the ground in a marshy region near Madison, Wisconsin. The three eggs were brownish, heavily blotched with blackish-brown.

We have encountered the graceful Black Terns in the Middle West. The head and under parts are black, the back, wings, and tail are slate-colored and the under tail coverts white. The nests of grass and reeds are built on the ground in marshes. The two or three eggs are olive-brown and very heavily blotched with blackish-brown.

Cormorant. This living submarine is not a beautiful creature but warrants our admiration because of its ability to swim and dive, sometimes to a depth of over 100 feet, as it pursues and captures fish, using both wings and feet as propellers. As in other birds that are expert divers, the hind legs are so far back that an upright position is assumed when on land, with the strong, stiff tail serving as a third leg.

The Shag, which is another name for the Cormorant, is three feet long, and black in color. It may be seen along seacoasts and in the mouths of large rivers, and nesting on the ground among rocks. The three or four eggs are laid in the midst of a mass of sticks, moss, and seaweed. The young thrust their bills far down into the throat of the parent for the fish brought to them from the briny deep.

Cormorants are proverbially voracious, and the term *cormorant* has in the past been aptly applied to gluttonous, miserly, or avaricious persons. The awkward movements of Cormorants on land, their grotesque actions when feeding their young, and the harsh croaks, which are their substitute for a voice, bring forth involuntary laughter in the observer. Strange as it may seem, Cormorants can be

Courtesy, Nature Magazine

Cormorant. She protects her apparently indifferent babies with vigor, especially from other Cormorants near by.

trained to fish for Man. When taken from the nest they are easily tamed. In olden times in England one of the officers of the royal household was the Master of Cormorants. At the present time Cormorants are used for fishing in China and Japan. We saw them several years ago near Soochow, China, perched on the edge of their owner's boat ready to do his bidding. A strap is fastened around the bird's throat to prevent it from swallowing the fish it catches. Then it is released into the water, where it swims about under the surface searching for its prey.   When its capacious throat contains a load, it returns to its owner, and after disgorging, is rewarded with a portion of its catch.

Among the most important of the guano birds are Cormorants (see page 362). Recently the Peruvian government has issued an edict prohibiting airplanes from flying within a radius of 3000 feet of the guano islands near their coast and also prohibiting steamers from blowing sirens or whistles in the vicinity. Fear is expressed that the birds may migrate to some other more isolated islands where they will be undisturbed.   The average production of guano during the past ten years is reported as 135,000 tons per year, on which there is a government tax which nets Peru a good and very welcome income.

Courtesy, Nature Magazine

Cormorant. This bird has selected a nesting site which combines a wonderful sea view with splendid isolation.

Pelican. The Pelican is especially noteworthy because of the enormous pouch that hangs from its lower bill, which may be as much as eighteen inches long and six inches deep.   This pouch serves as a scoop-net for capturing and storing fish.   Pelicans are very large birds measuring up to five feet or more in length, and with a spread of wings of as much as nine feet. When in flight, they usually flap their wings and sail alternately, keeping so close to the water that one expects to see them splash in at any moment.   And seldom is one seen flying alone, since Pelicans like company and live together, often in large numbers, especially during the breeding season.

The White Pelican nests in parts of the western United States, particularly in southern Oregon and northern California.   The nest is built on the ground of weeds and sticks.   The best-known colony of Brown Pelicans is on Pelican Island in Indian River, Florida, although Louisiana is known as the Pelican State.   This species builds its nest either on the ground or in mangrove trees.   The young are ludicrously helpless infants, but when mealtime arrives, they know how to thrust their beaks into their parent's pouch for a quart of delicious fish soup.   Fish are captured by diving and menhaden are usually the victims.   Often the birds travel as far as fifty miles away from their nests in order to obtain food for their young.

Brown Pelicans.   A group on Pelican Island in Indian River, Florida.   The babes in the foreground are having a meal of fish soup.

Stormy Petrel.   Although only about seven inches long and one of the smallest of all sea birds, being no larger than a Swallow, the Stormy Petrel, or Mother Carey's Chicken, succeeds in living out the most severe storms at sea.   It is supposed to appear only in stormy weather and hence is not greatly loved by sailors.   Petrels, however, are restless wanderers over the ocean in calm as well as in stormy weather, and are usually seen many miles from shore, fluttering over the waves with ceaseless

activity, sometimes using their feet to run or skip along the surface; hence the name Petrel, which means Little Peter, and refers to the Apostle Peter, who tried to walk on the waves.

The Stormy Petrel is a summer tourist in the North Atlantic, and was long a bird of mystery, since its winter haunts were not known.   We have learned, however, that it nests on the islands of the Antarctic, where a single white egg is laid in a crevice or burrow. Petrels obtain their food from the surface of the sea while in flight.   Fish oil is especially fancied by them, and when captured they are apt to eject a quantity of rancid oil from the stom-ach through the mouth. Oil is sometimes collected

Courtesy, American Museum of Natural History

Petrel.   The petrel lays its single white egg in a crevice among the rocks.

by capturing the birds and then setting them free after they have disgorged. During the breeding season they lose all fear and may be taken from the nest.

Gannets, or Boobies.   When a bird fails to show fear in the presence of a human being it may appropriately be called a Booby, for which we should feel very much ashamed.   Gannets, however, are also simple and foolish-looking birds and probably deserve to be considered Boobies.   They are large birds almost three feet long and have long, pointed wings.   Many of them are white with dark wings and tail; others are brownish in color.   They live much at sea, where they feed on fish. "Their prey is almost invariably captured by plunging upon it from a height and a company of Gannets fishing presents a curious and interesting spectacle.   Flying in single file, each bird, when it comes over the shoal, closes its wings and dashes perpendicularly and with a velocity that must be seen to be appreciated, into the waves, whence it emerges after a few seconds, and shaking the water from its feathers, mounts in a wide curve, orderly takes its place in the rear of the string,

to repeat its headlong plunge as soon as it again finds itself above its prey." (Newton.)

Gannets nest in large colonies on rocks at the seashore, for which reason these rocks are ordinarily known as Bird Rocks. A famous breeding place is Bass Rock at the entrance to the Firth of Forth in Scotland. "Upon reaching the Bass a few Gannets may be seen sailing dreamily about, but you have no idea of the immense

Courtesy, American Museum of Natural History

Gannets, or Boobies. These birds breed in colonies. Their eyes are near the base of the bill and appear to be absent.

numbers until you have climbed the rugged hill. But when the summit of the cliff is reached the scene that bursts upon one's gaze is one that wellnigh baffles all description. Thousands upon thousands of Gannets fill the air, just like heavy snowflakes, and on every side their loud, harsh cries of 'carra-carra-carra,' echo and

Photo by Cleaves. Courtesy, Nature Magazine

Booby. Certainly a silly-looking bird; it is sitting on a nest in a shrub on Tower Island in the Galapagos group.

reëcho among the rocks. The Gannets take very little notice of our approach, many birds allowing themselves to be actually pushed from their nests. Others utter harsh notes, and with flapping wings offer some show of resistance, only taking wing when absolutely compelled to do so, and disgorging one or two half-digested fish as they fall lightly over the cliffs into the air. On all sides facing the sea Gannets may be seen. Some are standing on the short grass on the edge of the cliffs, fast asleep, with their heads buried under their dorsal plumage; others are preening their feathers; whilst many are quarreling and fighting over standing-room on the rocks." (Dixon.)

The Bird Rocks in the Gulf of St. Lawrence were once the breeding grounds of vast numbers of Gannets and "were as full of birds as any meadow is of grass." An ornithologist who visited these Bird Rocks in 1860 estimated the number of birds at about 150,000. Since then they have been killed off in large numbers and by 1898 only about 1500 were left. The efforts of ornithologists within the past 30 years to conserve bird life will probably prevent the extinction of this species for many years to come.

Frigate Bird, or Man-o'-War Bird. This is an ocean bird of the "first water" and equally a bird of the air since most of its life is spent flying about over the sea. It resembles somewhat a giant Barn Swallow with its extremely long wings, long, forked tail, and short legs. "Throughout the hours of daylight they remain in the air, floating over the water of their island home without the slightest effort on motionless wing, plunging down to the surface of the sea to pick up some floating object, or pursuing other sea-birds to make them disgorge their booty. At dusk they retire in companies to some favourite clump of trees near the coast to roost. In some of the Pacific Islands Frigate-birds are domesticated and used like Pigeons for sending messages from one island to another." (Alexander.)

The Frigate Bird is about forty inches long, of which the tail occupies sixteen inches; the bill is five inches long and the wings have a spread of seven feet. The plumage is mostly black with a blue-green sheen on the head and a green gloss on the back. The female has a white breast and a light-colored bill. The male bears a bright red pouch on the chin which is inflated during the mating season, apparently to attract the female.

The food of the Frigate Bird consists of fish, jellyfish, and other aquatic animals that it is able to pick up from the surface with its bill while in flight, or of fish that it forces other sea birds to disgorge while in the air and catches before it drops into the water.

The Great Frigate Bird, which is one of five recognized species, lives over the warmer parts of the Indian and Pacific and South Atlantic oceans. It breeds in colonies on tropical islands, building nests of sticks in bushes and trees. One white egg is laid. "During the breeding season one or other of the parents is almost always at the nest, for, if it is left unguarded, neighbouring Frigate-birds will at once begin to steal the sticks of which it is composed. After the chick is hatched the parent's vigilance becomes even more necessary, as the neighbouring birds do not hesitate to appropriate it for a meal if opportunity offers." (Alexander.)

Related to the Frigate Birds are the Darters, also known as Snakebirds or Water Turkeys. There are only four species of them but they are widely distributed — one species each in Africa, Asia, Australia, and America. "They are silent birds, generally living in pairs or colonies on bodies of fresh water with wooded shores. They select a perch over the water, and when alarmed sometimes drop into the element below and disappear beneath its surface, or fly upward to a considerable height and circle about like sailing Hawks. They swim well, and when approached too closely, sink quietly backward, frequently leaving the long, thin neck and narrow, pointed head above the surface, when one at once observes the origin of the name 'Snakebird.' They obtain their food by pursuing it under water, and their finely serrated bill assists them in retaining their hold upon it." (Chapman.)

Courtesy, Nature Magazine

Frigate Bird, or Man-o'-War Bird. One white egg is laid in a nest of sticks built in a low tree. The bird looks awkward when perching but when on the wing resembles an enormous, forktailed swallow.

CHAPTER 25

STORKLIKE BIRDS AND WATER FOWL

STORKLIKE BIRDS

The circumstance that burdened the Stork with the duty of bringing babies into the world has made him one of our best-known birds, yet there are no Storks in America except those imported and exhibited in zoological parks. Herons, on the other hand, are common and in many ways resemble Storks. We are often asked what the difference between them really is. The answer is not simple. Both types of birds have long legs and long necks. Storks are stouter and have a thicker neck and a larger bill; they have no voice, but snap their beaks when they wish to make a sound; the hind toe is short and set above the level of the front toes, whereas in Herons the hind toe is long and on a level with the front toes;

Photo by Naether.   Courtesy, Nature Magazine

White Stork.   Father Stork is alighting on a nest on the top of a house.

the inner edge of the middle claw is not comblike as in Herons; there are no patches of "powder-downs" on the breast as in Herons; and Storks fly with the neck outstretched, whereas Herons fly with the neck bent backward so that the head rests between the shoulders.

The group of Storklike Birds includes also the Bitterns, which belong to the Heron family, the Ibises, Spoonbills, and Flamingos.

396

White Stork. In Holland, Germany, and Denmark it is considered lucky to have a pair of White Storks nesting on the roof of the house. As an aid in attracting this good fortune, a platform or an old cart wheel is put in place on which the nest can be built. The nest consists largely of sticks and, since it is added to year after year, becomes very large. A very characteristic scene in these countries is a White Stork standing motionless on one leg on top of a house. The parents feed their young by regurgitation and exhibit great affection for them.

White Storks are not entirely white. Their bill and legs are bright red and the quill feathers are black. They are about three feet in height. Their food consists largely of frogs, insects, and other small animals. In the autumn they migrate to Africa in large flocks and at a great height. Every child is familiar with Storks, due to the old fables and fairy tales in which these birds play a prominent role.

Adjutant. The pompous gait of the Adjutant is responsible for its military title. Its long legs, huge beak, combined with stately movements give it a ludicrous appearance. "There is something rather disreputable about the appearance of these birds, for the head and neck are bare, save for an untidy straggling mass of hairlike feathers, while from the throat hangs a loose fold of pinkish, scurf-covered skin, which, at will, can be suddenly inflated to form a pendulous bag of considerable length, and as suddenly the air will be expelled." (Pycraft.)

Photo by Hegner

Adjutant. A rather wise-looking bird with an overgrown beak. The "marabout" feathers under the tail are highly valued for millinery purposes.

Adjutants occur in Africa and in India. They are giants among the Storks, reaching a height of five feet. Although awkward on land, they are marvelous flyers, soaring about high in the sky after the fashion of vultures. Like vultures also is their taste for food, since, besides small birds, frogs, and fish, they are so fond of carrion as to be protected in some regions because of their service as scavengers.

Adjutants are sociable birds, congregating in large flocks during their ordinary activities and breeding together in colonies. Their nests are made of sticks and placed on the ledge of a cliff or in a tree.   The under tail feathers of the Adjutant, the "marabout" feathers, are eagerly sought by milliners.

Great Blue Heron.   No vacation at the river side is complete without the presence of a Great Blue Heron.   Although about four feet long, it weighs only from six to eight pounds, since it consists mostly of legs and neck and a slender body that looks emaciated no matter how many fish, frogs, or mice the bird eats. When flying it looks enormous, with a wing spread of five or six feet and legs trailing along behind.   Its bill is shaped like a stiletto. is about six inches long, and is a weapon to keep away from.

Photo by Finley and Bohlman.   Courtesy, Nature Magazine
Great Blue Heron.   Long legs, long neck, slender body, and stiletto-like bill are characteristics of this species; the eye is bright and the crest on top of the head is black.

The Great Blue Heron lives by his "wild lone" except during the breeding season.   It is so keen of sight and acute of hearing that one can seldom get very close to a specimen. While fishing it stands upright and as still as a statue waiting for its prey to come near enough, then a flash downward too quick to be followed by the human eye and the fish or frog is transfixed and soon on its way to satisfy an appetite that seems insatiable. Colonies of Great Blue Herons nest in trees along the river bank.   The nests are bulky structures, built of sticks and twigs and lined with dry grass.   The young are ugly-looking caricatures such as only a mother could love.   Not all of this species is blue. The throat and the center of the crown are white. On top of the head is a distinct crest of long feathers, which, together with the large, staring eyes and yellow beak, give the bird a fierce appearance.   Two of the feathers of the crest are extra long and filamentous during the breeding season.   At the bend of the wings the feathers are chestnut-rufous in color.

Green Heron. The Green Heron is one of the smaller members of the family, being only about seventeen inches long. When we were young, many of them nested along the Upper Iowa River, and one grove of small trees could usually be depended on to furnish half a dozen sets of eggs for our collections. The nest is a flimsy platform of small sticks. From three to six pale, greenish-blue eggs are laid. "When startled" the Green Heron "springs into the air with a frightened *skeow* or explosive whistle, and, alighting at a safe distance on a tree or on some elevated perch, with upstretched neck watches the intruder." (Chapman.)

Courtesy, Natural History Society of Maryland

Green Heron. Herons are not handsome when they are babies; this young Green Heron looks as though he would like to know what it is all about.

The young, like all young Herons, are not things of beauty and we are probably doing their mother an injustice by publishing the photograph of one of them.

Black-Crowned Night Heron. The Night Heron selects the most enjoyable time of day for his various activities. He is not really a night bird but spends the evening hours in search of food, when he joins the "voices of the night" with his loud and raucous *quawks*. He is not as dignified as the Great Blue Heron and does not wait for his prey to come to him, but wanders about diligent*l*y in search of fish, frogs, and other aquatic animals.

According to an old story the Night Heron emits a light from its breast which attracts small fish as it shines on the water, but no reputable observer has ever seen this phenomenon. A wooded swamp is preferred as a nesting place. Here up to several hundred pairs may nest at one time, usually in trees or bushes, the nests being large masses of sticks. From three to six pale, sea-green eggs are laid.

Photo by Squire.   Courtesy, Nature Magazine

Black-Crowned Night Heron. The crown is black, the forehead white, and two or three white plumes about 8 inches long arise at the back of the head.

Egret. The word Regret might better be used as the name for this bird, because no nature lover can but regret the inhuman manner in which the Egrets of America have been destroyed so that their plumes might be used to furnish topknots for ladies' hats. These long white plumes, that look like spun glass and are known as aigrettes, grow out from the back of the bird during the nesting season. They can be obtained only by shooting the birds, and since the adults usually have nestlings, the young are left to starve. The gregarious habits of the birds made it easy for hunters to kill them by the thousands, and the enormous rookeries that existed in

Courtesy, American Museum of Natural History

White Heron, or Egret. The "aigrettes" arise from the back of the adult bird. The nest is built in a tree in a swamp.

Florida and other southern states were soon depleted. Only laws prohibiting further killing of Egrets have prevented their extinction. Egrets are entirely white except for the yellow bill and black legs and feet.

A remarkable change has taken place in the attitude of the public toward bird life during the past 30 years. Formerly birds of many types were destroyed by the hundreds of thousands so that milliners might have ornaments for their hats. Efficient laws have done away with this slaughter and in its place bird refuges have been established. The situation that existed 30 years ago with regard to Egrets is indicated by an account written at that time. "Twenty-five years ago these beautiful birds were abundant in some southern states; stragglers occasionally came north as far as New England. Nesting time was the plume hunter's opportunity. There was little difficulty, then, in securing the birds by shooting them when they were sitting on the nests or hovering over their helpless young. So the old birds were shot, the plumes stripped from their backs, and the young left to starve in the nests or to become the prey of Hawks, Crows, or Vultures. When I was in Florida, in 1878, great flights of these birds were seen along the lakes and rivers of the southern counties. One heronry was estimated to contain three million birds. Ten years later they were rare everywhere, and now they are practically extirpated." (Forbush.)

Shoe-Billed Heron. Just as in the navy, when a new and more efficient type of armament is perfected, a more powerful gun is invented to destroy it, so among animals, when a hard-shelled body-covering is built up, enemies develop methods of breaking through the barrier. The enormous bill of the Shoe-Billed Heron, or Whale-Headed Heron, probably evolved in this way, since it feeds largely on the bichir fish of the White Nile, which are covered with a coat of thick, dense scales that only a powerful beak could crush.

The Shoe-Bill looks like an ordinary heron from its long-toed feet to the upper end of its long neck. Then we encounter one of the most amazing transformations in all nature. The long, slender beak of the heron becomes modified into a broad, heavy weapon with a formidable hook on the end. This grotesque beak with two staring eyes at the base transforms the Shoe-Bill from "just another heron" into a bird that not only affords us considerable amusement, but also furnishes scientists with a puzzling problem, that is, how such a monstrous beak evolved, — a problem still to be solved.

Photo by Hegner

Shoe-Billed Heron. The enormous bill is used to crush the hard scales of a fish that lives in the Nile River.

Least Bittern. The Least Bittern is our smallest Heron. It lives in weedy marshes in company with Rails, Marsh Wrens, Gallinules, and Red-Winged Blackbirds. Like the Rails, they are very difficult to see as they skulk about among the reeds, and when approached closely, they seem to freeze into position with neck, head, and bill pointed to the sky and the streaks along the throat simulating the surrounding reeds. The eyes are yellow and stare at one with a malignant intensity.

As a rule, Least Bitterns are shy birds and are seen only by those willing to don rubber boots and become covered with muck. They have the habit of rising

Photo by Hegner

Least Bittern.   The nest is built of reeds among the reeds a foot or two above the water in a marsh.

abruptly at one's feet with a startled *qua*, and, after a short flight, of dropping into the marsh again as though too exhausted to continue.   In the evening and early morning they wander about with greater freedom.   The nest is a platform of reeds built a foot or more above the water on a foundation of decaying vegetation. From three to six bluish-white eggs are laid.

White-Faced Glossy Ibis.   The southwestern United States is favored by the presence of a Storklike bird that is well described by its name.   The small patch of white feathers at the base of the bill gives it a white face, and its rich green and purple plumage of metallic luster, augmented with iridescent violet on the head, give it a very glossy appearance.   It is about two feet in length, and possesses a long, slender bill that is curved downward.   Like many other Herons it wades about over the low, water-soaked fields near lakes and rivers in search of frogs, crayfish, and insects.   The nest is built of dead reeds woven together and fastened to upright living reeds, and is about a foot in diameter.

Photo by Finley.   Courtesy, Nature Magazine

White-Faced Glossy Ibis.   The feathers have a glossy appearance in the living bird; the feathers at the base of the long, curved bill are white; the length is about 2 feet.

This species is a relative of the Sacred Ibis of Ancient Egypt, which was considered to be the secretary of Osiris, and served to transcribe and recount the deeds of the dead.   The Sacred Ibis was carved on the monuments of the ancient Egyptians and its mummified remains were carefully preserved in the temples.   Since the Ibis was once abundant in Egypt and fed on animals destructive to agriculture where the life of the people depended so directly on the success of the crops, it is not strange that the Ibis was selected for veneration.

Ibises live in vast colonies.   When a gun is fired near them, they rise in the air by "hundreds of acres," furnishing a most amazing spectacle.   They and their relatives are partial to the warmer parts of the world.   Of the thirty or more species known, only four occur in North America; these are the Glossy Ibis, White Ibis, Scarlet Ibis, and White-Faced Glossy Ibis.   The Roseate Spoonbill belongs to the Ibis family; its bili is flattened, and shaped like the bowl of a spoon.

Flamingo. Flamingos are known to most of us only as museum specimens or as denizens of zoological gardens, since their haunts are in the American tropics and their nests are built on inaccessible islands. They are among the most gorgeous of birds, with scarlet or pink plumage and with vermilion-colored feathers in the wings. The bill is very heavy and sharply curved, black on the end, orange in the middle, and yellow at the base; it is used to strain out snails and other animals from the mud of mud flats and shallow lagoons.

Flamingos nest in large colonies. A conical pile of mud about 18 inches in diameter at the base and a foot at the top, and usually about a foot in height, is scraped up with the bill, so that the egg that is laid in a hollow in the top may be secure from rising waters. How the birds disposed of their legs was long an unsolved problem. They were usually pictured astride their curious chimney pot nests. We now know that their legs are doubled under them as are those of other Storklike birds when sitting on their nests.

A careful observer who built a hiding place, or blind, near a colony of Flamingos gives the following account of the actions of the birds after he had concealed himself in the blind. "Without further delay, the birds returned to their homes. They came on foot, a great red cohort marching steadily toward me. I felt like a spy in an enemy's camp. Might not at least one pair

Photo by Hegner

Flamingos. Storklike birds with peculiarly curved beaks; the plumage is pink or scarlet. Photographed at Buenos Aires in Argentina.

of the nearly four thousand eyes detect something unnatural in the newly grown bush almost within their city gates? No sign of alarm, however, was shown; without confusion, and as if trained to the evolution, the birds advanced with stately tread to their nests. There was a bowing of a forest of slender necks as each bird lightly touched its egg or nest with its bill; then, all talking loudly they stood up on their nests; the black wings were waved for a moment and bird after bird dropped forward on its egg. After a vigorous wriggling motion, designed evi-

Courtesy, American Museum of Natural History

Flamingos.   The nests of mud are about 1 foot high; the birds sit on the nest with the legs doubled under them.

dently to bring the egg into close contact with the skin, the body was still, but the long neck and head were for a time in constant motion, preening, picking material at the base of the nest, dabbling in a nearby puddle, or perhaps drinking from it.   Occasionally a bird sparred with one of the three or four neighbors which were within reach, when bill grasping bill, there ensued a brief and harmless test of strength."   (Chapman.)

Six species of Flamingos are recognized by ornithologists.   Four of these occur in America, ranging from the Bahama Islands to southern Chile.

Water Fowl

Ducks, Geese, Swans, and Mergansers are usually classed as Water Fowl. About 200 species are known, of which about 50 occur in North America. They are adapted for life on the surface of the water. The body is broad and flat and is lightened by means of air sacs, hollow bones, air spaces between the feathers, and a layer of fat beneath the skin. The plumage includes a great quantity of down feathers over which the more rigid contour feathers fit; these are kept well oiled, or preened, by the bird so as to prevent water from reaching the skin. One peculiarity of Water Fowl is the loss of their wing-quills all at the same time after the breeding season, which leaves them helpless and forces them to depend on swimming.

The feet are webbed and moved by powerful leg muscles. The neck is long enabling the owner to reach the bottom easily, where food is obtained. The beak in most species is broad and flat with grooves at the side forming an effective strainer. The center of gravity of the body lies forward so that no effort is necessary to tip up as the sensitive beak searches for food at the bottom. Among the species that may be encountered in North America are the Whistling and Trumpeter Swans; the Canada, Blue, and Brant Geese; the Mallard, Black, Baldpate, Pintail, Teal, and Wood Ducks; the Redhead, Canvasback, Scaup, Golden-Eye, Bufflehead, Eider, and Scoter Ducks; and the Hooded, American, and Red-Breasted Mergansers.

Courtesy, National Zoological Park

Swans. These birds have worn a path up the bank between the water and the nest.

Swans. The sounds made by Swans can hardly be considered songs, yet poets have invented a "Swan Song" in the form of a dirge which the birds chant at the time of their death. The voice of the Trumpeter Swan is very deep and trumpet-like, due to the exceedingly long windpipe, hence part of it is coiled up within its breast bone. The Mute Swan, which is most often used as an ornament in parks, has no voice, but compensates for this by raising its wings gracefully over its back when it swims.

The Whistling Swan is a North American species that utters high notes that might be compared to a whistle if one's imagination is stretched far enough; it usually sticks to bass notes, however. It is about four and a half feet long, and pure white except for a black bill with a yellow spot at the base, black feet, and eyes with a brown iris. The nest is built on the ground near water and is often an enormous structure of sticks, weeds, moss, etc., two feet or more high and six feet across. The eggs are laid on a bed of down. The young cygnets are covered with grayish-brown down which later changes to white.

Swans are all white except a species living in Australia which is black and another species which has a black neck. They do not dive for food as ducks do, hence the neck must be long in order to reach the bottom of ponds where they obtain their food. The beautifully arched neck is, therefore, not developed for our enjoyment, but for a useful purpose.

Photo by Hegner

Canada Goose. Our largest wild goose, a harbinger of spring and a forerunner of winter; size, about 3 feet long.

Canada Goose. The largest of our wild geese is the Canada Goose. As a harbinger of spring and a forerunner of winter it is unexcelled. Its trumpet-like honk invariably attracts our attention to the flying wedge as with slow, measured wing strokes the flock follows their leader in their sweep across the sky.

Canada Geese breed in the northern part of the United States and in Canada. They mate for life, and if one loses its mate, it may remain single for many years. The male is a model of domestic faithfulness, guarding the female as she sits on her nest and threatening the intruder away with hisses and upraised wings. They are easily domesticated, but when time for migration arrives, they will join the flocks as they fly over unless their wings are clipped. They love to congregate in grain fields, where they feed on scattered grain, weeds, grasses, etc., and are known to post sentinels to warn the flock of approaching danger. Sand is swallowed to aid in grinding up the hard particles of food.

Mallard Duck. One of our commonest and best-known ducks is the Mallard. This species is of especial interest because most of our domesticated ducks have been derived from it. Its success is largely due to its adaptability, since it can live happily in a lake or in a mud puddle and can be content with a menu consisting of grain, seeds, or plant food, or of insects and other small animals.

The male and female, as is the case with the many other species of birds, differ so markedly in color that they would never be considered of the same species if they were not known to be the offspring of the same parents. The male is a large, handsome bird about two feet long, with head and neck

Mallard Ducks. Two pairs, the males with head and neck of glossy green and the females with plumage streaked with brown.

of glossy green, a white ring around the neck, a grayish-brown back, a purplish-chestnut breast, and central tail feathers curved upward. The female is more quietly colored, the feathers being streaked with various shades of brown.

Canvas-Back Ducks. The males have a red head, a black band around the neck, and a canvas-colored back; the female (at left) is mostly brownish or grayish-brown.

Economically the Mallard is of great value, having supplied us with immense quantities of food and feathers. Its nest is built of grass, leaves, and reeds among concealing vegetation on the ground and comfortably lined with down. From six to ten pale olive or buffy-green eggs are laid.

Canvas-Back Duck. The king of the Water Fowl, so called because of the flavor of its flesh, is the Canvas-Back. Its delectable flavor is due to the eel-grass, known as wild celery, that it eats. Other ducks might gain as high a reputation with epicures if they adopted the wild-celery habit. They might also be killed off more rapidly, as the Canvas-Back has been. The Canvas-Backs of Chesapeake Bay are especially famous and Baltimore became the "gastronomic capital" of America largely because of their abundance. However, Canvas-Back must be eaten in moderation to be properly appreciated. For example, an old contract between two slave owners of Virginia stipulates that the one who hired certain slaves from the other should not feed them Canvas-Back Duck more than five times per week.

Canvas-Backs are about the size of Mallards. The males have a red head, a broad black band around the neck and fore part of the body, and a grayish-white, "canvas"-colored back. The bill is very long and forms an almost straight line with the forehead and crown.

Eider Duck. Most of us cannot expect to study Eider Ducks in their native haunts, because they spend a large part of their time at sea, and nest on the Labrador coast and the less accessible regions around Hudson Bay. However, we may have used their feathers in pillows or coverlets, since eiderdown has become a famous article of commerce.

Eiderdown is plucked by the female from her own breast and used to line her nest. In certain regions, especially in Iceland and Norway, the birds are carefully

Photo by Cleaves.   Courtesy, Nature Magazine

Eider Duck.   Famous for the down which the mother plucks from her breast and uses to make a soft blanket for the eggs.   Photographed in Labrador.

protected, the nests are visited regularly, and the down gathered. Each nest yields about $\frac{1}{6}$ pound of down, and if most of the eggs are removed, the female will reline the nest and lay another clutch of eggs ; if most of these are removed, a third clutch will be laid, down for which is said to be furnished by the male. The males, at this time, congregate together and the females and young form separate flocks. Near relatives of the Eider are the Spectacled Eider and King Eider.

CHAPTER 26

MARSH DWELLERS AND SHORE BIRDS

MARSH DWELLERS

A real treat is in store for every bird lover who, for the first time, visits a marsh at the right season of the year. Here he will see many birds that had hitherto been merely names. Many years ago we had this experience within the city limits of Chicago. A large area on the south side of this large city was occupied by a marsh, and the Marsh Dwellers were using it as a summer home in spite of the encroachment of human habitations.

The Rails, Gallinules, and Coots are Marsh Dwellers that are exceedingly shy and not often seen; ten species of a family of about 225 occur in North America. The Cranes are so large that they cannot conceal themselves easily. They resemble Herons in appearance, but differ from them in certain respects; for example, they fly with the neck extended whereas herons bend their necks when in flight. The range in size of the Marsh Dwellers is extensive, from a length of five inches in the smallest Rail to over four feet in the Cranes.

Some of the more common Marsh Dwellers of the United States are the Whooping and Sandhill Cranes, the King, Clapper, Virginia, and Sora Rails, the Purple and Florida Gallinules, and the American Coot.

Sandhill Crane. Cranes, like Herons and Storks, are large birds with long legs and a long neck. They usually live near marshes or bodies of water, but do not wade as Herons and Storks do. Their nests are built on the ground and they themselves are ground-inhabiting birds.

The Sandhill Crane seems to prefer dry land more than marshes, and may be found on sandy hills and in fields. It is about four feet long, and deep slaty-gray in color. Grain, acorns, seeds, roots, and small animals constitute its food. The nest is made of reeds and grass, and located either in a marsh or on dry land. Two eggs are laid.

"During courting and the early breeding season their actions and antics at times are ludicrous in the extreme, bowing and leaping high in the air, hopping, skipping, and circling about with drooping wings and croaking whoop, an almost indescribable dance and din, in which the females (an exception to the rule) join, all working themselves up into a fever of excitement only equaled by an Indian war-dance, and, like the same, it stops only when the last one is exhausted." (Goss.)

Sandhill Cranes often unite in large flocks and fly along the water courses. "Such ponderous bodies, moving with slow-beating wings, give a great idea of momentum from mere weight — of force of motion without swiftness; for they

411

Courtesy, American Museum of Natural History

Sandhill Cranes.   The nest of reeds and grass is built in a marsh; the birds are slaty-gray in color and about 4 feet long.

plod along heavily, seeming to need every inch of their ample wings to sustain themselves.   One would think they must soon alight fatigued with such exertion, but the raucous cries continue, and the birds fly on for miles along the tortuous stream, in Indian file, under some trusty leader, who croaks his hoarse orders, implicitly obeyed.''

The Crane is by nature a wary bird.   "His vigilance is rarely relaxed even when he is feeding, where less thoughtful birds feel perfectly secure.   After almost every bending of his long neck to the ground, he rises erect again, and at full length and glances keenly on every side.   He may resume his repast, but should so much as a speck he cannot account for appear to view, he stands motionless, all attention. Now let the least sound or movement betray an unwelcome visitor — he bends his muscular thighs, spreads his ample wings, and springs heavily into the air, croaking dismally in warning to all his kind within the far-reaching sound of his voice." (Cowes.)

King Rail. One of our common Marsh Dwellers is the King Rail, a bird that is more often heard than seen, his voice being a harsh, henlike clattering. Marsh Hen and Mud Hen are well-deserved local names for him. He is a very retiring bird, skulking through the reeds in a timid, self-effacing manner, flying up from time to time and fluttering through the air for a few yards with legs dangling, and then dropping into the water again as though too exhausted to continue. This is just a pose, however, since he is known to migrate for long distances.

King Rails are inhabitants of eastern North America. They build a nest of dead reeds and grass in which from six to twelve eggs are laid. The parents are not easy to see amid the surrounding vegetation, but are solicitous enough to approach within a few feet while their nest is being photographed.

The Virginia Rail and Sora are much smaller than the King Rail. They likewise live in fresh-water marshes where there are plenty of long grasses and reeds.

Photo by Squire.   Courtesy, Nature Magazine

King Rail. A nest of reeds and grass is built in a swamp and from six to twelve eggs are laid; the eggs are buffy white spotted with rufous brown.

Florida Gallinule.   In the same marsh in which we observed the King Rail, we found another "Mud Hen," the Florida Gallinule, nesting.   The word *gallinule* means "little hen" and was applied to this species because of its henlike movements and squawks.   It walks about with rapid upward jerks of its tail, but can also swim and dive like a duck.   The scarlet head shield and bill distinguish it from other marsh birds.   A near European relative is the Moor Hen of England.

Photo by Hegner

Florida Gallinule.   The stalks of flat marsh weeds are used by the Gallinule in building the nest; some of the stalks form a platform down which the sitting bird can slide into the water.

The nest consists of a raft of weeds floating on the water and, as the photograph shows, may have a toboggan of flat rushes in front of the door down which the sitting bird may slide into the water with very little effort.   Young Gallinules have a small spur on the bend of the wing which they use in creeping among the reeds.   Another species, the Purple Gallinule, is distributed throughout tropical and subtropical America.   "This is a common species on ponds densely grown with yellow pond lilies (in Florida known as 'bonnets') and other aquatic plants, where it may be seen walking daintily and conspicuously over the leaves or swimming when occasion requires." (Chapman.)

Coot.   Still another "Mud Hen," which is also called locally a Marsh Hen or Sea Crow, is the Coot.   Although closely related to the Rails, the Coot differs in several respects.   Its toes have lobes along the side which enable it to swim and dive much like a Duck or Grebe.   As it swims about, its head bobs in time to the strokes of its feet, and when it takes flight it patters along the surface with its toes until it gains momentum enough to rise into the air.   The bill of the Coot is white, which distinguishes it from the Gallinules.

The "haunts of Coot and Hern" are among the reeds or rushes bordering freshwater ponds.   Coots are more frequently heard than seen, and may be very noisy indeed, calling loudly and almost screaming, as they gabble and chatter like a bevy of excited women at a crowded tea party, doing their best to make themselves heard.   During the early morning and evening hours they feed sociably in the shallow water near the edge of the pond, catching insect larvae, worms, and other small aquatic animals.   Coots are inedible and hence not favorites with sportsmen. The silly look on the face of the Coot has given rise to the expression "silly as a Coot," applied to certain people.

Photo by Finley.   Courtesy, Nature Magazine

Coots.   A group of Coots posing before the camera and trying to look pleasant; the white bill is very conspicuous.

SHORE BIRDS

Shore Birds spend much of their time probing for small animals in the sand or mud on shore, or wading about in shallow water for the same purpose.   Often small groups will fly up as one approaches and settle down again a hundred yards away.   Open fields and marshy localities are also favorite haunts of Shore Birds.   Their legs are long and adapted for wading, and their necks are correspondingly long so that they can reach the ground with their bills.   The bills are long and slender and fitted for extracting food from under the surface of the ground.

The nests of Shore Birds are mere hollows in the ground, usually lined with small pebbles or a few pieces of dry vegetation.   Their eggs are very large, blunt at one end, and pointed at the other.   They are usually four in number and laid with the pointed end toward the center of the nest.

Some of the Shore Birds migrate great distances from their breeding grounds to their winter home and return.   For example, the Golden Plovers arrive in the "barren grounds" above the Arctic Circle the first week in June.   In August, after the nesting season is over, they fly to Labrador, where they feast on the crowberry and become very fat.   After a few weeks they reach the coast of Nova Scotia and then set out for South America over 2400 miles of ocean.   They may or may not visit the Bermuda Islands and the West Indies.   After a rest of three or four weeks in the West Indies or northern South America, the birds depart and are next heard from on their arrival in southern Brazil and Argentine.   Here they spend the summer, from September to March, and then disappear.   Apparently they fly over northern South America and Central America and over the central

Photo by Hegner

Killdeer.   The parent is about to sit on the eggs; the nest is a slight hollow among the rocks lined with a few weed stalks; the four large, darkly spotted eggs are laid with the pointed end toward the center.

portion of North America, reaching their breeding grounds beyond the Arctic Circle the first week in June.   The elliptical course they follow is approximately 20,000 miles in length, and this remarkable journey is undertaken every year for

Photo by Hegner

Killdeer.   Four recently hatched young, beautifully colored and able to run about.

the sake of spending ten weeks in the bleak, treeless, frozen wastes of the Arctic region.

We can describe only a few of the many species of Shore Birds; but the names of other members of this group may be of interest.   These are the Oyster Catchers, Turnstones, Surf Birds, Snipe, Sandpipers, Curlews, Yellow-Legs, Godwits, Dowitchers, Willets, Knots, Ruffs, Avocets, Stilts, Phalaropes, and Jacanas.   The Jacanas are especially interesting because their exceedingly long toes and claws enable them to walk about on floating lily pads without sinking.

Killdeer. The Killdeer, or Killdee, is well named, since its oft-repeated, piercing cries sound like its common name; its scientific name Vociferus is also deserved. Killdeer Plovers are usually encountered along the beds of streams, but may live in fields half a mile or more from water. Their cries are often heard as they fly swiftly, but more or less erratically, over town and countryside.

The eggs are laid in a slight hollow scratched in the ground, and the four heavily spotted eggs are laid with the pointed ends toward the center. The sitting bird does not flush directly from the nest but when approached too closely "runs like a Killdeer" for some distance and then begins to scream and flutter along the ground, as though in terrible agony, in an effort to entice the intruder away from the nest. The nest is not difficult to find, provided one has plenty of time, since the birds remain in its vicinity and will be seen to sneak back to it when everything is quiet again. The young can run about as soon as they escape from the egg; those in the photograph were kept within bounds by a stone wall which we built around the nest several days before the eggs hatched.

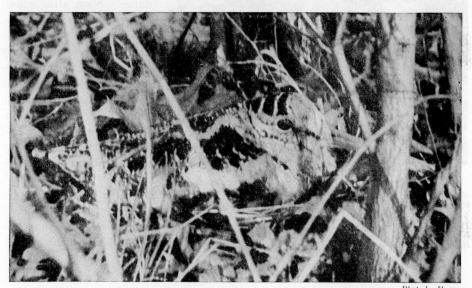

Photo by Hegner

Woodcock. The parent sitting on the nest resembles her surroundings very closely; she did not leave the nest although the camera was placed only 2 feet from her.

Woodcock. In marked contrast to the Killdeer, the Woodcock is so quiet that its presence usually passes unnoticed. By day it remains hidden in the scrubby land along water courses, but in the evening it becomes active. Its long bill is one of its most remarkable characteristics, since the upper tip is flexible and can be moved independently like a finger, thus serving as a forceps in grasping worms that it detects while probing in the mud.

Woodcocks are curious-looking birds, with a short, thick neck, eyes located far back and high in their heads, and short tail and legs. The outer wing feathers make a whistling sound or "winnowing" as they move through the air, very characteristic of this species.   Concealing coloration is exhibited to a marked degree by these birds.   Their brown colors blend so well with their surroundings that the parent on the nest can be seen only with difficulty even when one is near by.   The birds seem to know that they are protected by their colors, since they will remain on the nest even while a camera is put in place, focused and snapped within two or three feet of them.

Photo by Hegner

"At courting time, and all through the period of incubation, the male indulges in a curious aërial dance. Soon after sunset he whirls up in spirals, chirping and twittering, to a height of fifty or sixty feet, then circles horizontally and descends, giving voice to his ecstasy in a continuous 'cheeping' until he reaches the ground where he struts like a tiny turkey-gobbler, with drooping wings and upright tail, changing his notes to a series of rather hard *paiks*."

Woodcock.   The eggs on which the bird in the accompanying photograph was sitting; a few leaves make up the nest; the eggs are buffy colored and spotted with rufous.

(Brasher.)   The parents take good care of their young and in case of danger the mother is said to carry them one by one between her legs to a place of safety.

Chapter 27

BIRDS OF PREY

The Birds of Prey are adapted for capturing and devouring animals. They are powerful, and often fierce and savage, with a strongly hooked beak and usually stout legs, sturdy toes, and sharp, curved talons. They work in two shifts, so that no matter at what time of day other animals are active, there are always Birds of Prey to keep them from getting too carefree. The Hawks, Eagles, Kites, Ospreys, Falcons, Caracaras, Gyrfalcons, Vultures, and Condors are active by day, and the Owls come forth on their foraging expeditions at nightfall.

Wherever there are ground squirrels, rabbits, and other small mammals, or birds, there will be found one or more species of these rapacious Birds of Prey. It has been for many years the custom of farmers, ranchmen, and others to shoot a Hawk or Owl on sight, either for "sport" (?) or with the idea of ridding the world of an injurious animal. As a matter of fact, very few Birds of Prey are harmful and most of them are decidedly beneficial, because they destroy vast numbers of field mice, ground squirrels, insects, and other animals that cause enormous injury to field crops, fruit trees, and all sorts of vegetation.

The Owls are notoriously misunderstood. Because they are active at night and their silky-soft, loose plumage renders their flight silent and ghostlike, they have for centuries been considered birds of ill-omen and foreboders of misfortune. Shakespeare included Owl's wings in the deadly brew in the witches' caldron. In Spain Owls are supposed to desecrate the shrines of saints by drinking the oil in the lamps suspended before them. On the other hand, the ancient Greeks employed the Owl as a symbol of wisdom and the expression "as wise as an Owl" is still in use.

Bald Eagle. It is fitting that we should select the Bald Eagle for our National Emblem, since he is the leader of the mighty Birds of Prey. Bald he is in name only, since his head is covered with white feathers, also his neck and tail. Many Bald Eagles are not even "bald" in this sense, since the young are Black Eagles during the first year, Gray Eagles during the second year, and only acquire their white headdress after several years.

The Bald Eagle is a majestic bird, about three feet long, and with a wing spread of six feet or more. We should like to state that he has no faults, but this is not possible, since his food habits cannot be condoned. He preys on other animals, but is inclined to attack wounded birds that cannot escape easily, and, although very fond of fish, he often allows the Osprey to catch them for him and then swoops

419

Photo by Hegner

Bald Eagle.   The head is not bald but covered with white feathers; the neck and tail are also white.

down from above so that the Osprey drops its catch, which is then deftly grasped by the Eagle before it reaches the water.   Dead animals are also accepted as food. These habits induced Audubon to deplore the choice of the Bald Eagle as our National Emblem, and led Benjamin Franklin to write, "For my part, I wish the Bald Eagle had not been chosen as the representative of our country.   He is a bird of bad moral character and does not make his living honestly."   But we all have our faults.

The Bald Eagle nests in tall trees or on cliffs, building an enormous structure of sticks which is added to year after year.   Stories of children being carried away to its nest appear to be gross exaggerations.   In flight, the Bald Eagle is particularly majestic.   "He draws great lines across the sky; he sees the forests like a carpet beneath him; he sees the hills and valleys as folds and wrinkles in a many colored tapestry; he sees the river as a silver belt connecting remote horizons.   We climb mountain peaks to get a glimpse of the spectacle that is hourly spread out before him.   Dignity, elevation, repose, are his.   I would have my thoughts take as wide a

Photo by Finley and Bohlman.   Courtesy, Nature Magazine

Golden Eagle.   Even when young the Golden Eagle looks fierce and courageous and has strong,
sharp talons.

sweep.   I would be as far removed from the petty cares and turmoils of this noisy and blustering world."   (Burroughs.)

Golden Eagle.   The character of the Golden Eagle is that of an "Eagle" and without those flaws that lead us to criticize the Bald Eagle.   He lives in mountainous regions in North America, Europe, and Northern Asia, and is a fierce, courageous bird, master of all he surveys.   He is "a clean, trim-looking, handsome bird, keen-sighted, rather shy and wary at all times, even in thinly settled parts of the country, swift of flight, strong and powerful of body, and more than a match for any animal of similar size."   It is not surprising that the Eagle has been adopted as an emblem and its feathers used as a headdress by our Indians.   His food consists almost entirely of birds and mammals that he captures himself, including rabbits, ground squirrels, prairie dogs, grouse, and water fowl.   He is seldom destructive.

The Golden Eagle selects a large tree or inaccessible cliff as a nesting place. Here he gathers together a mass of sticks to which he adds year after year until an enormous, conspicuous eyrie evolves.   He is said to live to a good old age, perhaps a century.

> *He clasps the crag with hooked hands; Close to the sun, in lonely lands,*
> *Ringed with the azure world he stands, The wrinkled sea beneath him crawls :*
> *He watches from his mountain walls, And like a thunderbolt he falls.*

> (Tennyson.)

The capture of a jack rabbit by a pair of Golden Eagles has been described as follows : "The Eagles circled about him at a height of about thirty feet ; first one would swoop down on the rabbit and then the other, but the result was always the same, for the rabbit was quick enough to dodge just as the birds struck at him. The chase was nearing the fence, and it seemed if the rabbit could succeed in reaching it, he could, by dodging around among the trees, baffle his pursuers.   The Eagles seemed to know this also, for when within fifty yards of the fence, the larger one of the two swooped down at the rabbit, and when he dodged, the Eagle pursued him, flying at a height of about three feet above the ground.   The rabbit redoubled his speed and made straight for the fence, the Eagle following and both doing their best.   This unequal race was kept up until the fence was reached, the Eagle having gained until she was but two or three feet behind the rabbit.   When the rabbit passed through the fence, I expected to see the Eagle give up the pursuit, but she had no intention of doing so, for without slacking her speed she raised herself just enough to clear the fence, and, dropping down behind the rabbit, continued as before. Instead of dodging around among the trees he was so crazed with fear that he ran in a straight line down the orchard.   The velocity with which the Eagle flew at this stage of the chase was something wonderful.   Fast as the rabbit ran, the 'great black shadow' behind him drew nearer and nearer, until, poising an instant over its victim, the Eagle pounced upon him.   A short struggle, a cry or two from the rabbit, and all was still."   (Atkinson.)

Harpy Eagle. The Harpy Eagle is well named. To the monkeys, sloths, fawns, and foxes that it preys on, it is a fierce and ravenous monster. A full-grown bird is about four feet long, which puts it in the "giant" class. Its talons, as our photograph well shows, are exceedingly strong, and its beak is well fitted for tearing large animals into pieces small enough to swallow. The Spanish-Americans call it the Lobo Volante or "Flying Wolf."

Harpy Eagles live in the forest. The wings are short and rounded and the tail fan-shaped. The feathers are soft, resembling in this respect those of the owl. Perhaps their most conspicuous feature is the crest on top of the head.

The Harpy Eagle can fly through the trees very swiftly and "can overtake the swiftest birds of the tropical woods, and in spite of its size steers its way through the labyrinth of forest trees and hanging vines, and rarely fails to rise with a 'Pheasant,' a Woodcock, or a small mammal in its claws, after plunging like a meteor from the clouds into the leafy maze of the *tierra caliente*." (Oswald.)

Nearly related to the Harpy Eagles are the Hawk Eagles. One of these that inhabits the Philippines is known as the Great Monkey-Eating Eagle on account of its large size and fondness for monkeys. Another beautiful species is the African Crowned Eagle.

Courtesy, National Zoological Park

Harpy Eagle. A "Flying Wolf" with strong talons, a sharp, curved beak, and a fierce disposition; it lives in the jungles of tropical America.

Red-Tailed Hawk.   The Red-Tailed Hawk, Hen Hawk, or Chicken Hawk, is a childhood friend without whose inspiration the Parade of the Animal Kingdom might never have been written.   Its majestic circling flight is marvelous enough to inspire anyone, as on motionless wings a keen watch is kept on the meadows below from a height that renders the bird a mere speck in the firmament.   "One Hawk was watched in the air, without once alighting, from seven in the morning till four in the afternoon."   Occasionally a long-drawn, squealing whistle, somewhat resembling steam escaping from an engine, announces its presence.

Although called a Chicken Hawk, it is almost guiltless of catching chickens or any other species of bird.   When hunting seriously, it usually perches on a tree near a field where there are field mice and ground squirrels.   When the prey is located, a flashing streak descends like a bolt of lightning and the farmer is relieved of one more of his enemies.

Eastern North America is the home of the Red-Tail.   The nest is built high up in a tree, often at the edge of a field.   Preference for birches and pines is evident. The bulky nest of sticks is used year after year and may usually be seen for a long distance.   Two to four heavily blotched eggs are laid.   We once made a large collection of eggs of this species, usually finding two in a nest, more rarely one, three, or four.

Photo by Hegner

Red-Tailed Hawk.   This bird is taking its own picture by sitting on a string that snapped a camera fastened in a near-by tree; the nest was in a birch tree about 40 feet from the ground.

Photo by Hegner

Red-Tailed Hawks. These youngsters still have patches of baby clothes mixed in with their grown-up feathers. They are exhibiting the expectant attitude of other young birds when their mother arrives with a load of provisions for the "inner bird."

Cooper's Hawk. The real "Chicken" Hawk is Cooper's Hawk, a villain whose misdeeds are usually laid at the door of the Red-Tailed Hawk or Red-Shouldered Hawk. He lives in small forests or woodlots adjoining fields, building his nest of sticks in the crotch of a tree some distance away from the edge of the grove. So quick and active is his flight that he seems to dash about in a continual hurry.

All sorts of birds, but especially pigeons, are selected as prey by this fierce and destructive bird, even birds larger than himself, such as grouse and ducks. Rabbits, squirrels, and other small mammals are also captured. When in pursuit of his prey he seems practically fearless, darting

Photo by Hegner

Cooper's Hawk. The real "Chicken Hawk" builds a nest of sticks in a small tree in a grove, usually including a few pieces of bark as a lining; the eggs are bluish-white.

into the barnyard after a pigeon or chicken in spite of the presence of the owner. His voice sounds like that of a real "wild" creature, resembling the syllables *cac cac cac* often repeated, as he flies through the woods just out of gunshot. Cooper's Hawks are among the few birds that are more harmful than beneficial.

Scientists determine the character of a bird's food by killing a few specimens and examining the stomach contents. In the case of Cooper's Hawk, of "133 stomachs examined, 34 contained poultry or game birds; 52, other birds, 11 mammals; 1 frog; 3 lizards; 2 insects; and 39 were empty." (Fisher.)

Courtesy, Nature Magazine

Osprey. The Fish Hawk is a handsome bird colored dark brown and white; the nest is very bulky, — quantity seems to count more than quality.

Osprey. The master fisherman among the Birds of Prey is the Osprey, well named the Fish Hawk. He circles about high above the water until he locates his prey, then with closed wings he drops like an arrow, striking the water with a resounding splash which often entirely conceals him as he drives his sharp talons into his finny prey. He holds his captive head foremost and if it is small enough eats it on the wing; otherwise he flies in triumph to a favorite perch, where he has his supper without further effort. This is the course of events provided no Bald Eagle is near by to take the fish away from him. If the Osprey uses bad judgment and attacks a fish too large for him, according to some observers, he may be drawn under water and drowned.

The Osprey is a conspicuous bird about two feet long. The upper parts are dark brown and the head, neck, and under parts white, except for a broad brownish-black stripe extending from the bill along the side of the head to the neck. His roughly scaled feet with their long, sharp, curved claws are traps from which no fish can escape. Like many other Birds of Prey, Ospreys seem to develop a real affection for one locality, to which they return year after year. Their nests, which are built in a tree or on the ground, become very

Courtesy, N. Y. Zoological Society

Gyrfalcon. A fierce Bird of Prey of the Far North; it preys largely on other birds and is sometimes used in falconry.

bulky as they are added to year after year. In the side of such a nest a pair of Purple Grackles sometimes find a favorable hole in which to raise their family in safety.

Gyrfalcon. The Falcons are among the most active of the Birds of Prey. They form a large group, that has representatives almost everywhere in the world. In North America occur the Duck Hawk, Pigeon Hawk, Sparrow Hawk, and Gyrfalcon; and in Europe, the Peregrin Falcon, Merlin, and Kestrel. These Falcons fly so swiftly that they have very little difficulty in capturing other birds, which make up a large part of their menu, although mice, insects, and reptiles may be added.

The White Gyrfalcon is circumpolar in its distribution, living within the Arctic Circle when food is abundant there, and moving southward when winter comes. It is a large species about twenty-two inches long, with whitish plumage and dusky bars. Bird neighbors live in terror of the Gyrfalcon, whose food consists largely of water fowl, ptarmigan, and other birds. The three or four eggs are usually laid on a ledge of a cliff. In the Middle Ages Gyrfalcons were used for hawking purposes. This custom dates as far back as 200 B.C. in China, and has been practiced in various countries since that time, including India, Africa, and Europe. The Peregrin Falcon appears to have been the most-favored species. The Falcon is taken out hunting with a hood on to keep it quiet. When a bird is seen, the Falcon is released and after a short dash usually captures its quarry, which is then taken charge of by the master, and other birds located. Even today falconry is actively pursued in both England and the United States.

Sparrow Hawk. Our smallest Falcon is the Sparrow Hawk, a bird that has an amiable disposition and is quite harmless when compared with some of the other members of the Falcon family. The Sparrow Hawk is rufous color above and whitish below, with two distinctive, vertical black bars on each side of the head. It inhabits all of temperate North America. Its favorite hunting grounds are in a field where a good lookout can be maintained from the top of a dead tree. When a grasshopper or field mouse is located, the bird flies out, hovers over it a few moments, and then plunges down and captures it with its sharp, curved claws.

Photo by Hegner

Sparrow Hawk. This Falcon is mild tempered and feeds largely on grasshoppers; it has two upright black bars on each side of the head.

Sparrow Hawks usually nest in a hole in a tree, often that dug in a previous year by a woodpecker. They live in harmony with other birds and may nest in the same tree with a flicker or a bluebird. When a human being approaches the nest tree, the birds become much alarmed and sound their call notes, *killy, killy, killy, killy*, rapidly and repeatedly. They are not as destructive as the larger Falcons as indicated by the presence of fewer birds and more mice in their stomachs.

Secretary Bird. The Secretary Bird is a native of South Africa. He looks more like a Crane or Heron than like a Bird of Prey because his legs and neck are long.

These convert him into a "Vulture on stilts" about four feet in height.   The plumage in general is bluish-gray.   The skin around the eyes is bare, and orange in color, giving the bird a decidedly wicked stare.   On the head are long feathers that can be erected when the bird is excited; they are said to have given the bird his name

Photo by Hegner

Secretary Bird. A long-legged, snake-killing Bird of Prey that lives in South Africa, or in a zoological park; the long feathers on the head are supposed to look like the quills held behind the ears of a secretary.

because of their resemblance to quill pens lodged behind a secretary's ears.   He is an imposing bird, and as pompous as are some executive secretaries we have known.

Secretary Birds are famous snake killers and for this reason enjoy the protection of mankind.   They circle about their victim until a good opening occurs; then, with powerful strokes of their wings and sledgelike blows with their hammer-like feet, they soon deprive the snake of life, and proceed to swallow it head first.   The nest is a huge, slovenly mass of sticks gathered together in a bush.   The male brings food to the female while she incubates the two or three eggs.   The young are confined to the nest for five or six months.   Cape Sparrows sometimes build their nests under that of the Secretary Bird.   The Sparrows, for some strange reason, are not molested by the Secretary Birds, but are actually protected by them.

California Condors. These birds are now rare; the plumage is sooty black, the bare head is orange, and the iris of the eye is red.

Condors. Our largest Bird of Prey, the California Condor, or Vulture, is also one of our rarest birds.   So rare is he that when several were located recently (July, 1934) the fact was conspicuously noted in California newspapers.   He is about four feet long and has a spread of wing of from nine to eleven feet.   His food consists of dead animals; poisoned meat scattered about by stockmen for the purpose of destroying wolves, coyotes, bears, and other predaceous animals is largely responsible for the decrease in the numbers of Condors.   The general color of the plumage is sooty black, the bare part of the head is orange, and the iris of the eye red.   The nest is built usually in a cave or crevice several hundred feet from the bottom of an inaccessible cliff.

The Condor of the Andes of South America is even larger, reaching a length of over four feet and a wing expanse of ten feet or more.   He is one of the largest living birds capable of flight, but is now relatively rare.   The male has a ruff of white, downy feathers at the base of the neck.   These Condors are very fond of sunning themselves, with wings spread and back presented to the rays of light.   An interesting method of capturing Condors that is practiced by the natives of South America is to dig a pit and place a dead animal in the bottom.   The Condor enters the pit, but is unable to fly out again, and hence is easily caught.

Vultures. Distance certainly lends enchantment to the Vultures, or Buzzards, since they are most attractive when in flight high in the air, sailing gracefully in ever-changing circles without any apparent effort.   A close view reveals an exceedingly hideous creature, that we would consider repulsive even if we were unacquainted with its habits.   The head of the Vulture is naked, giving an unpleasant appearance to the whole bird.   The claws are blunt and not adapted for grasping as in other Birds of Prey.

The gruesome feeding habits of Vultures are perhaps their most marked characteristics.   Dead and often partially decomposed animals fall to their lot. "When they find a dead animal they will not leave it until all but the bones and other hard parts have been consumed, and if it be a large one, or if it have a tough skin, they will often remain near it for days, resting by night in the trees near by.   After they have eaten — and sometimes they will gorge themselves until the food

Photo by Gross. Courtesy, Nature Magazine
Black Vulture.   The naked head is blackish and the plumage is glossy black; the bill is not as much hooked nor as strong as that of the eagles, hawks, falcons, and owls.

will run out of their mouths when they move — they will, if they are not too full to fly, roost in the nearest trees until their meal is partly digested, and then commence eating again." (Ralph.) Sometimes when disturbed they will vomit the foul contents of their stomachs, — a habit that seems offensive to us but that is welcomed by the young, since they are fed by regurgitation.

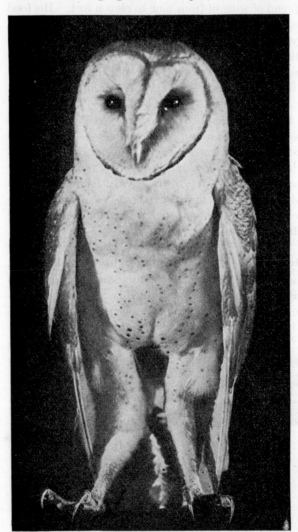

Whether Vultures find their food by sight or by smell has been a problem studied by many scientists and the subject of voluminous discussion. Darwin decided, as the result of his experiments, that smell is of no importance and that sight leads the birds to food. "From an altitude of one thousand feet or more, a hungry bird will survey the country, and, finding a body, at once descends; another, a mile or so off, noting its action, swiftly hurries after it. And so, for miles round, each bird noting the action of his nearest neighbour receives his summons to the feast. Thus, in an incredibly short space of time a host assembles, where an hour before not one was to be seen." (Pycraft.)

The two eggs of the Turkey and Black Vultures are laid on the ground among rocks, or under a log, or in a hollow stump, or even in the crotch of a large tree. They are beautifully spotted and blotched with various shades of reddish-

Courtesy, American Museum of Natural History

Barn Owl. A knock-kneed "flying cat" and a wonderful mouser; he lives in hollow trees or in barns where mice are plentiful.

brown and lavender. The Turkey Vulture ranges over most of temperate and tropical America. The Black Vulture likes warmer weather and does not occur in the more northern States. It seems to have a preference for the seashore and for towns and cities. The Old World Vultures belong to a separate family which includes the Bearded Vulture, the Griffon, and the Egyptian Vulture.

Barn Owl. The Barn Owl, or Monkey-Faced Owl, is a "flying cat" and one of our most useful birds because of the large number of mice it catches. "The face looks like that of a toothless, hook-nosed old woman, shrouded in a closely fitting hood, and has a half-simple, half-sly expression that gives it a mysterious air." The natural home of the Barn Owl is in a hollow tree, but barns and other buildings are often favored, and the presence of these birds in old deserted buildings has probably given rise to belief in certain haunted houses.

The number of mice devoured by Barn Owls is almost beyond belief. "A case is on record where a half-grown Barn Owl was given all the mice it could eat. It swallowed eight, one after another, and the ninth followed, all but the tail, which for a long time hung out of the bird's mouth. In three hours, this same bird was ready for a second meal and swallowed four more mice." The voice of the Barn Owl is a sort of querulous quavering cry. The eggs, five to seven in number, are dull white and laid in various curious places. Both parents help incubate them, and the male is known to feed the female while she sits on the eggs. Barn Owls are permanent residents throughout most of the United States.

Great Horned Owl. Conspicuous ear tufts of feathers two inches long are responsible for the name of this species. Its well-known cry, which is a deep-toned *to-who-hoo-hoo* repeated many times, has earned for it the title of Hoot Owl. This is a large, fierce "tiger of the air" that may well be called bloodthirsty. Most of the damage attributed to Owls in general is the dirty work of the Great Horned Owl. His menu regularly includes chickens, ducks, geese, turkeys, pigeons, bob-white, grouse, song birds, rats, mice, squirrels, rabbits, and even skunks. There is no escape

Photo by Cornelia Clarke

Great Horned Owl. His ear tufts, or "horns," are laid back and he looks as though he had had a wild night.

from his mighty talons, and no warning of his approach, as he glides as silent as a shadow over the fields and through the woods. He is a ruthless savage, solitary and unsociable, that kills more than he can eat.

During the day the Great Horned Owl remains concealed in the woods, but no one, we believe, has ever seen one that was not looking at him, although he

is not supposed to be able to see well in daylight. His eyes by day are mere slits; they are located side by side in the front of the head, hence he must turn his head in order to keep a moving person within his vision. Sometimes he seems to twist his head all the way around, but this is an illusion, since a quick revolution in the opposite direction brings his eyes almost straight behind him on the reverse side.

Great Horned Owls lay their eggs very early in the spring, in February or March, usually while there is still snow on the ground. We used to hunt for their nests each spring on skis. A hollow tree, crevices among the rocks in a cliff, or the last year's nest of a hawk or crow serves the purpose of a home.

Photo by Hegner

Great Horned Owl. The young bird is covered with down and no signs of "horns" are evident, nevertheless he looks like an owl.

Except in the extreme north this Owl is a permanent resident.

A Great Horned Owl makes a very poor pet. "In disposition it is fierce and untamable, and in point of strength and courage is inferior to none of our rapacious birds. It is so savage and seemingly so devoid of the confidence usually shown by birds of prey kept in confinement that it is with the greatest difficulty that it can be tamed even when taken young from the nest. It is morose and sullen, lacks affection for its keepers, and will often fly viciously at any one who attempts to handle it or enter the apartment in which it is confined." (Fisher.)

The amount of food required to rear a family of Owls may be judged from the contents of a nest containing two young birds. The larder consisted of a "mouse, a young muskrat, two eels, four bullheads, a woodchuck, four ruffed grouse, one rabbit, and eleven rats, in all weighing about eighteen pounds."

Photo by Hegner

Great Horned Owl. The eggs are often laid in the last year's nest of a hawk or crow.

The Screech Owl. Screech Owls are among the smallest of the nocturnal Birds of Prey. They possess conspicuous ear tufts of feathers and are sometimes called Little Horned Owls on this account. An interesting peculiarity of Screech Owls is the color difference between different individuals, some being grayish and others rufous red in general appearance. Males and females may be of either color, and some of the young in a single nest may be gray and others red. The eggs, usually four or five in number, are white and are laid on the leaves or chips at the bottom of a hole in a tree, often dug by a woodpecker a year or two before. The young are covered with white down.

During the day, Screech Owls hide in a hole in a tree, or among dense foliage, but they become active as darkness approaches. Then, on noiseless wings, they set about capturing insects, mice, and other small animals on which they feed, or, if socially inclined, seek the companionship of others, making known their presence by means of the peculiar call notes that have given them their name. The "screech" is delivered in a quavering tremolo, and this eerie, wailing whistle,

Photo by Hegner

Screech Owl. This "Little Horned Owl" is famous for his weird nocturnal cries. He is not as fierce as he looks, except to the mice he captures.

when heard in the middle of the night, is apt to make the listener's blood curdle. No doubt these weird sounds are as sweet to the lady owl as a Spanish serenade is to a beautiful senorita. After a bird lover becomes accustomed to them they even seem not unpleasant to the human ear.

"The Screech Owl frequently makes its home near our dwellings, and sometimes selects a convenient nook in them in which to lay its eggs. But its favorite retreat is an old apple orchard, where the hollow limbs offer it a secure refuge from the mobs of small birds which are ever ready to attack it. A search in the trees of an orchard of this kind rarely fails to result in the discovery of one or more of these feathered inhabitants who may have resided there for years. They attempt to escape capture by a show of resistance and a castanet-like cracking of the bill, but when brought from their hiding-place sit quietly, dazzled for a moment by the sudden light." (Chapman.)

Burrowing Owl. No one interested in nature can travel over the plains of the western United States without encountering Prairie Dogs and Burrowing Owls. The Owls can see about as well as other birds in daylight, and are active during the day, although their real play time awaits the setting of the sun. The old story about Prairie Dogs, Rattlesnakes, and Burrowing Owls occupying the same burrow in peace and harmony has no foundation in fact. Burrowing Owls live in or on the outskirts of Prairie Dog "towns" because they are fond of young Prairie Dogs. They are also able to deal with Rattlesnakes, although the latter no doubt succeed occasionally in making a meal of Owl's eggs.

Photo by Hegner

Burrowing Owl. He is not a "Night Owl" but is often active by day. He lives in a hole in the ground which he usually allows a prairie dog to dig for him.

Lizards, insects, and other small animals also serve as food for the Owls. Certainly there are plenty of ground squirrels available, judging from the number that scamper across the road as one drives along in a motor car, and the number that do not succeed in getting across but leave their poor remains on the highway.

Burrowing Owls have long legs adapted to life on the ground, a comparatively small head, and a square tail. They usually nest in the abandoned burrows of prairie dogs, foxes, or badgers, but may dig a burrow for themselves. They are permanent residents and remain mated for life.

CHAPTER 28

GAME BIRDS, PIGEONS, AND DOVES

GAME BIRDS

Many types of birds, including Water Fowl, Shore Birds, and Doves, may be considered Game Birds, but this term is usually applied to certain families of ground dwellers that are fowl-like in form. They are the Pheasants, Turkeys, Partridges, Quails, Grouse, Ptarmigan, Peacocks, Curassows, Mound Builders, etc. They are adapted for life on the ground, where they obtain their food largely by scratching for it. The body is heavy; the beak short, stout, and convex; the legs strong; and the wings short.

Game Birds lay a large number of eggs in a nest built on the ground. The young are covered with down when they leave the egg, and are able to run about soon after they hatch, like young chickens. The flesh of most of the Game Birds is edible and much sought after. Game Birds occur throughout the world and are well represented in the United States.

Photo by U. S. Forest Service

Wild Turkey. Our largest Game Bird, reaching a length of 4 feet and a weight of over 30 pounds. He is now rare in nature.

Wild Turkey. The largest of all Game Birds is the Turkey. He reaches a length of four feet and a weight of thirty pounds or more. The domestic Turkey is a descendant of the Mexican Turkey that was introduced into Europe in the sixteenth century and then returned to this country. The Wild Turkey was once widely spread, but has been hunted so persistently that it is now not far from extinction, and is restricted to mountains far from civilization and to swampy bottomlands. It is a permanent resident, moving about in flocks except during the breeding season, when the polygamous male takes charge of as many females as he can control.

He then displays all his charms before the female, approaching her with "his widely spread tail, his dewlap and warty neck charged with bright-red blood, and drooping his wings as he struts before her, he sucks air into his windbag, only to discharge it with a pulmonic puff, that he evidently considers irresistibly fascinating. Dandified, overwhelmingly conceited, ruffled up with self-importance, he struts and puffs, until suddenly an infuriated rival rushing at him gives battle at once; spurs, claws, beaks make blood and feathers fly, and the vanquished sultan retires discomfited, leaving the foe in possession of the harem." (Blanchan.) During the mating season the male can be called within gunshot by imitating the plaintive notes of the female.

Ring-Necked Pheasant. If our game birds had been properly protected, there would be no excuse for the many attempts that have been made to introduce foreign species to take their place. However, in certain parts of our country the Ring-Necked Pheasant has been more or less successfully transplanted from its native home in eastern Asia.

Photo by U. S. Forest Service

Ring-Necked Pheasant. A species imported from Eastern Asia; it has a black head, a white collar, and narrow black bars on the tail.

The male Pheasants are brilliantly colored enough to decorate any landscape. They are shaped like other pheasants and have a very long tail. The head appears to be black, the collar white, the breast bronzy, the yellow sides spotted with black, and the tail with narrow black bars. The female wears the "conventional" brown.

Ring-Necked Pheasants prefer moist thickets, where they live in flocks, the males in one flock and the females in another. Usually they roost on the ground at night, and hence are exposed to the attacks of predatory "vermin," such as

foxes and coyotes.   The nest consists of leaves and grass gathered together on the
ground in a field or patch of weeds.   From seven to fifteen eggs are laid.   Insects
and seeds make up most of their food.

Ruffed Grouse.   The Pheasant of the South, called Partridge in the North, is
a woodland bird that has made himself famous as a drummer.   Scientists for
many years were uncertain how this drumming was effected but the problem now
seems to have been solved.   "The Grouse frequently comes to his log on moonlight nights, or at least before dawn, even in the rain, and he frequently drums
every five minutes for several hours.   When getting ready to drum, the bird

Photo by Sherwood.   Courtesy, Nature Magazine

Ruffed Grouse.   The male beats his wings against the air, producing a drumming sound characteristic of this species.

selects the same spot on the log and faces in the same direction each time.   He
does not beat the log with his wings nor do his wings strike his breast or each
other behind his back, as has frequently been asserted.   The sound is produced
entirely by fanning the air.   The bird stands stiffly erect with his tail down and
begins with a few deliberate strokes of his wings.   The first two are short and
produce no sound, the third produces a dull thump as do the next twenty, gradually increasing in rapidity until one can no longer count them and the thumps
blend into a whir.   The first strokes are directed forward and downward but the
later ones forward and upward, forcing the bird backward until his tail is pressed
so tightly against the log that when the drumming ceases, it springs upward as

Photo by Hegner

Ruffed Grouse.   The eggs are laid on a bed of leaves in the woods, often at the base of a tree or beside a log.

if in recoil. The sound produced is of such a nature that it seems no louder at a distance of 20 feet than it does at 200 yards."

"During the mating season, the male Ruffed Grouse displays his charms before the female; both wings are drooped to the ground and the fan-like tail is lifted as with the more gorgeous peacock. The iridescent black ruff feathers which normally lie almost concealed on the sides of the neck are then lifted until they make a perfect circlet like a large Elizabethan ruff, into which the head fits. The cock bird struts beside the hen until the spirit moves him to enter into the final stage. He then begins to peck at the ground and to shake his head from side to side, uttering short, hissing sounds with each twist. Finally, with a short, quick run, he gets in front of the female, and, shaking his head so rapidly that the ruff is but one continuous iridescent blur, he turns quickly, stiffening his legs and turning his tail laterally so that she will get the full benefit of the climax of his effort. At the same time, his short notes that have kept time with the shaking of his head grow into one loud prolonged hiss." (Allen.) The nest is frequently located at the base of a tree, where the eggs are laid in a hollow on a bed of leaves. Sometimes the eggs are covered over with leaves when the parent leaves the nest. The young resemble closely the leaves among which they live, and when danger nears, cower motionless, apparently realizing that they become thus invisible.

Flushing a Ruffed Grouse is an experience never to be forgotten. The bird springs suddenly into the air at one's feet with a rushing noise, and dashes through the trees with terrific speed, skillfully avoiding the branches, and alighting again several hundred yards away. The Ruffed Grouse is a permanent resident; in the winter the feathers on his legs grow long, and horny, comblike fringes grow out from the sides of his toes, turning his feet into snowshoes.

Bobwhite. The Quail of the North and the Partridge of the South named himself for all by his call of *Bob-white! Ah, bob-white, bob-bob white.* This joyous whistle uttered from the top of a fence post, like that of a happy urchin calling for his chum to join him for a few hours of adventure, has great carrying power and is certainly one of the most cheerful sounds in nature. The Bobwhite is a plump little brown bird that trusts for protection to his concealing coloration. He is a sociable bird and lives throughout the winter with others of his kind in coveys. By day he hunts for weed seed, waste grain, grasshoppers, plant lice, and other insects, especially potato beetles, being one of the few birds that will eat this species of insect. At night the covey roost together in shrubbery or under an evergreen tree in a close circle with their heads facing out.

Photo by Bundy.   Courtesy, Nature Magazine

Bobwhite. The young have hatched from the white eggs and are being brooded in the nest.

When disturbed, Bobwhites spring from underfoot like feathered bombshells, but after a short but speedy flight drop again into cover. They have many enemies, such as cats, crows, Cooper's hawks, great horned owls, and snakes. They are among our favorite game birds and would soon be annihilated if they were not protected.   They are said to be able to withhold their odor so that dogs cannot find them by their scent.   Bobwhites are permanent residents.   They lay from 10 to 18 white eggs in a nest on the ground, and both parents take part in incubation.

Heath Hen and Prairie Chicken.   The Heath Hen and Prairie Chicken are geographical races of the same species.   The early colonists found the Heath Hen abundant in New England and were glad to welcome it as an article of food. Hunting and the cultivation of its natural haunts brought about such a decrease in numbers that by 1870 no Heath Hens existed except on Martha's Vineyard Island.   In 1890 about 200 birds were still alive there; these increased to about 2000 by 1916 as a result of strict protective measures; then a series of calamities befell them; a fire in 1916 was followed by a hard winter and an unprecedented flight of predatory Goshawks, and in 1920 a disease killed many of them.   In 1927 thirteen birds were counted, only two of which were females; only one remained in 1930 and this one disappeared during the fall of 1931.   In this case we know most of the facts that have led to the extermination of a bird esthetically desirable and economically valuable.

The Prairie Chicken has not been quite so unfortunate, but has been exterminated over a large part of its former range.   The mating behavior of this species

Photo by Gross.   Courtesy, Nature Magazine

Heath Hen.   The last of the race; when this bird died, the Heath Hen became extinct.

offers an entertaining spectacle. "At short range the bird's note suggested the mellow, resonant tone of a kettledrum, and when bird after bird, all still unseen, uttered its truly startling call, the very earth echoed with a continuous roar. As a rule, each bird had its own stand separated by about ten yards from that of its neighbor. The boom is apparently a challenge. It is preceded by a little dance in which the bird's feet pat the ground so rapidly as to produce a rolling sound. This cannot be heard for a greater distance than 30 yards. It is immediately followed by the inflation of the great orange air sacs at the side of the neck, which puff out as quickly as a child's toy balloon whistle; the tail is erect and widely spread, the wings drooped, the neck tufts are raised straight upward, giving the bird a singularly devilish look, then with a convulsive movement of the lowered head, the boom is jerked out, and at its conclusion the air sacs have become deflated.

"One might imagine after so violent a performance the bird would feel a certain sense of exhaustion or at least quiescent relief, but his excess of vitality seeks still

Courtesy, Nature Magazine

Heath Hen. The male is displaying all his charms in the act of strutting.

other outlets; uttering hen-like calls and cacks he suddenly springs a foot or more straight into the air, whirling about as though he were suffering from a combined attack of epilepsy and St. Vitus dance. But all this activity is only a prelude to the grand finale of actual combat. Like a strutting turkey cock, the neighboring birds go towards each other by short, little runs, head down, the orange eye-brow expanded and evident pouch inflated, neck tufts, and tail straight up, and looking like headless birds with two tails. Their meeting is followed by no make-believe duel but an actual clash of wings. Uttering a low, whining note they fight as viciously as game cocks; and the number of feathers left on the ground testifies to effective use of bill and claws." (Chapman.)

Sage Hen. The largest of the American Grouse is the Sage Hen, or Cock of the Plains. "This remarkable bird inhabits the sterile sage-bush plains of the West; an abundant and characteristic species of those forbidding regions. Its center of abundance is the artemisia tracts of Colorado, Wyoming, Utah, Nevada, Idaho,

Eastern California, and Oregon. It straggles through the sage-bush, but I have seen packs of hundreds in the fall. In the breeding season its sonorous hullaballoo resounds on every hand where the birds are numerous. The flesh is edible or not, 'as you like it.' The behavior towards man varies with circumstances; sometimes the birds may almost be knocked over with a stick, at others it is difficult to get a shot. In walking, the tail is somewhat elevated, and swings sideways with each step. The flight is extremely vigorous, and is accomplished with a succession of quick energetic wing-beats, alternating with sailing with stiffly motionless wings until the impulse is spent." (Coues.) Another western species is the Prairie Sharp-Tailed Grouse. "When 'dancing' the male inflates a pink sac, utters a bubbling crow, rattles its tail quills, etc."

Willow Ptarmigan. The fame of the Willow Ptarmigan, or Snow Grouse, rests in part on its food value, but largely on its remarkable changes of color according to the season of the year. It lives in the far north where snow covers the ground about eight months of the year. In winter the feathers are entirely white, except for certain tail feathers, which are black but mostly concealed. When resting against a snowy background, such a bird escapes the notice of foxes, birds of prey, and other enemies.

In the spring, the white feathers fall out and black, brown, or buff feathers grow in to take their place. The birds thus assume a plumage that blends well with their surroundings during the summer. As winter approaches, white feathers again take the place of the colored plumage.

The winter coat is thicker than that worn during the summer. Also, in winter hairlike feathers clothe the feet and keep them warm; these are worn away as summer approaches. The long toe-nails that serve as ice creepers during the winter likewise are cast off in summer.

Courtesy, U. S. Bureau of Biological Survey

Willow Ptarmigan. In the winter the plumage is white and blends with the snow.

The nest of the Willow Ptarmigan is built in the moss. The eggs number about a dozen. The young are covered with down and like their parents are effectively concealed from sight by their colors, which blend into the background.

Hoactzin. The Amazon Valley in South America is the home of one of our most peculiar birds. The Hoactzin differs so much from other birds that its kinship is still doubtful, but it probably is most closely related to the Game Birds. Although provided with wings, Hoactzins prefer to creep among the branches of the trees in which they live rather than fly. Their

Photo by Rose. Courtesy, U. S. Forest Service

Willow Ptarmigan. In the spring the white feathers of winter are replaced by black, brown, or buff plumage.

flight from tree to tree is slow and laborious. The young are very active climbers. The thumb and second finger each bear a claw, resembling the claws of the Toothed Bird, Archaeopteryx (see page 366). The terminal wing feathers do not grow out as early as in most birds, and hence do not prevent the use of the claws. At the base of the claws is a pad which helps the claws in grasping limbs. These claws are absorbed and disappear as the young grow into the adult condition.

The adult Hoactzin is about the size of a Mourning Dove. The color is dark olive with white streaks above and rufous streaks below. The crest on top of the

Photo by Beebe

Hoactzin. The wings of this young South American bird are provided with claws which help it climb about among the branches.

head is held erect at all times. The tail is long and broad, the legs short, and the feet very large. The food of the Hoactzin consists of the fruit and leaves of certain tropical trees that grow along the river banks, often in the water. The food is ground up in a muscular crop, and not in the gizzard as in other birds. The flesh of the Hoactzin gives off a peculiarly disagreeable odor, resembling that of raw hides, — a characteristic that has led the natives to give it a name which means, when translated into English, "stinking pheasant."

Pigeons and Doves

The family to which the Pigeons and Doves belong contains about 600 species and subspecies, twelve of which occur in North America. Pigeons and Doves have a plump, full-breasted body, pointed wings that make a whistling sound during flight, a small head, a bill horny at the tip and with a tumid swelling at the base, short legs, and toes adapted for life both in trees and on the ground. The voice is a *coo* that is often plaintive and in certain species extraordinarily powerful considering the size of the bird. When drinking, Pigeons immerse the bill to the nostrils and suck in water continuously, not, as in other birds, in small gulps which are swallowed with the aid of gravity. Turtle Doves are symbols of conjugal fidelity.

Mourning Dove. The *coo-ah, coo, coo, coo* of the Mourning Dove certainly sounds mournful but to other Mourning Doves it is no doubt as cheerful and expressive as the song of the Robin. It is a low-pitched, moaning dirge that can be heard for a long distance. The first note is long and the other three short; the plaintive, sad cooing, lasting three or four seconds, is repeated again and again. One often sees Mourning Doves dusting themselves in the road, or visiting fields where grain can be found among the stubble, or searching for fine pebbles that they

Courtesy, Natural History Society of Maryland

Mourning Dove. The parent has come to feed the two young lying in the flimsy nest of sticks.

can swallow to help the muscular gizzard grind up their hard food. Doves are devoted to each other; apparently the mated birds remain together throughout the year. Thus the Mourning Dove lives up to the long-established reputation of Turtle Doves.

Mourning Doves, although considered rather shy, are not only numerous but are frequently seen as one wanders over the countryside. We encountered large numbers of them in driving across the United States during the past summer; in fact, they constituted probably the most abundant type of animal life seen on the trip.

The nest of the Mourning Dove is a flimsy affair consisting of a platform of a few twigs usually laid on a horizontal

Photo by Hegner

Mourning Dove. A young bird tries his wings, but comes to rest on a branch of an evergreen tree.

branch. The two white eggs can often be seen through it. The male brings the twigs and the female arranges them; the male incubates by day and the female by night. Both birds feed the young, at first, by regurgitation; the young thrust their beak into the throat of the parent and the latter pumps "pigeon milk" into their mouths. After two weeks, the young begin to feed on seeds and insects. Mourning Doves perform a very interesting soaring flight. They rise to a height of about 100 feet, and then on motionless wings, glide downward in sweeping circles, resembling somewhat the flight of the Sparrow Hawk.

Photo by Hegner

Passenger Pigeon. One of the last of the millions that once lived in this country.

Passenger Pigeon. The Passenger Pigeon is one of our "inexhaustible resources" that has totally disappeared. Passenger Pigeons were accustomed to live together in enormous flocks. Alexander Wilson in 1808 saw a flock near Frankfort, Kentucky, which contained over two billion birds. Audubon writes of flocks that darkened the sky like the approach of a tornado. Coming to roost "the noise which they made, though yet distant, reminded me of a hard gale at sea, passing through the rigging of a close-reefed vessel. . . . The pigeons, arriving by thousands, alighted everywhere, one above another, until solid masses were formed on the branches all round. Here and there the perches gave way under the weight with a crash, and, falling to the ground, destroyed hundreds of birds beneath, forcing down the dense group with which every stick was loaded." (Audubon, 1840.) These vast flocks of birds are no more.

Various ideas have been expressed to account for the extermination of Passenger Pigeons, including disease epidemics, forest fires, and storms, but it seems probable that their ruthless, wholesale destruction by man is alone responsible. From one nesting ground in Michigan, which covered an area twenty-eight miles long and three or four miles wide, over a million birds were sent to market in a single year. The last Passenger Pigeon died of old age in the zoological park in Cincinnati in September, 1914. The one shown in the accompanying photograph was one of the last survivors; it was in the collection of Professor Whitman of the University of Chicago.

Dodo. Dodo is a word often applied to someone who is stupid or out of date. It actually means "simpleton" in Portuguese, so called because sailors of that nation who encountered it on the island of Mauritius found it to be sluggish, without fear of man, and with no apparent desire to escape. Being flightless, they were easy to capture and in course of time became extinct. They were first reported by a Dutch admiral in 1598 and were last observed alive about 1681.

Although as large as a turkey, the Dodo belonged to the Dove tribe. His body was covered with curly, gray feathers above and whitish feathers on the breast and tail. He had an enormous beak ending in a hook, and his legs were short. All together a clumsy cartoon of a bird that no doubt deserved extinction, although we should like very much to have a few living specimens to satisfy our curiosity and that of posterity. Several were brought to Europe alive, but only a few remains are left to prove that such a duncelike, simple bird once existed.

Courtesy, American Museum of Natural History

Dodo. A member of the Dove tribe but as large as a turkey; the beak is very large and ends in a hook, and the legs are short and stout; it became extinct shortly after 1681.

CHAPTER 29

PARROTS, KINGFISHERS, NIGHTHAWKS, HUMMINGBIRDS, ETC., AND WOODPECKERS

The study of anatomy frequently reveals to us many strange bedfellows. Two birds may not look much alike when examined superficially, but may prove to be closely related when their anatomical structure is revealed. The strangely diverse assemblage of birds considered together here have been shown to be more closely related to one another than to other groups of birds. Only a few of their names are given in the above head-line; some of the others are as follows: Macaw, Cockatoo, Kea, Cuckoo, Road Runner, Horn Bill, Chimney Swift, Trogon, Hoopoe, Jacamar, and Wryneck.

Macaws, Cockatoos, and Love Birds. The Parrot family is noted for brilliant colors and discordant voices. One of the largest and most brightly colored of the group is the Red and Blue Macaw. This gorgeous bird is colored scarlet-red both above and below with here and there some pale blue and a touch of chrome-yellow for good measure. Macaws live in Tropical America. They may be seen flying over the jungle in pairs or in groups of pairs, usually "talking" sociably to each other. Their true colors are not evident when seen against the sky, but a specimen that was winged and brought into camp proved to be the most gaudily colored bird we had ever seen. The enormous beak of the Macaw is used to crack hard-shelled nuts.

The Cockatoo is a near relative of the Macaw. It is restricted to the Australian region and the Philippines. It is the only Parrot with a crest on the front of the head. The color is often white, there being none of the Parrot-green so common in this family. The Great Black Cockatoo "feeds on fruits and seeds of various kinds, but especially on the kernel of the Kanary-nut, the shell of which is so hard as to need a heavy hammer to crack it. But this bird accomplishes the feat with ease by means of its massive beak. Taking the nut, smooth and triangular in shape, end-ways in its beak, and keeping it steady by means of an unusually slender and fleshy tongue, red in color and tipped with a black, horny plate, it cuts a transverse notch in the shell by a sawing motion of the chisel-like edge of the tip of the lower jaw. This done, the nut is seized with the foot, and, biting off a piece of a leaf, it uses this to prevent the smooth shell from slipping, and fixes the tip of the lower jaw in the newly made notch, when by a powerful nip it breaks off a piece of the shell. Again transferring the nut to the foot, it inserts the long, sharp-pointed tip of the upper jaw into the hole, and picks out the coveted kernel with the long extensible tongue." (Pycraft.)

Macaws. Gorgeously colored Parrots with plumage of scarlet-red, blue, and chrome-yellow; residents of tropical America.

Among the smallest of the Parrots are the Love Birds, which are only about six inches long. They are natives of the Ethiopian region. Mates are very affectionate with each other, sitting side by side with their heads together, evidently very much in love.

Kea. One member of the Parrot family has become notorious due to a change in habits of a totally unpredictable nature. The Kea, or Mountain Nestor, of South Island, New Zealand, lives in the mountains during the summer and in the lowlands during the winter, where its food consists largely of insects. Since sheep have been introduced, however, their habits have become modified. "Parties of them now go a-hunting; worry a sheep till exhausted, and then dig down through the back, and so wound the intestine that death results." The death of all Keas will be the final result if this bad habit continues. How the birds formed such a peculiar habit is a problem that awaits solution.

Keas are not brilliantly colored as are so many parrots. The general color pattern is olive-green marked with black. The bill is rather slender and crossed at the tip.

Photo by Hegner

Kea. A Parrot that inhabits New Zealand; its beak is sharply hooked and sometimes used to tear open the back of living sheep.

Belted Kingfisher. This bird wears a bluish-gray belt and is a King among fishermen. He lives along a water course, a certain section of which he pre-empts as his demesne. Any other Kingfisher that trespasses is immediately attacked and the fierce fight that ensues may have a tragic result. The bird shown in the accompanying photograph looks like a triumphant warrior, but he was conquered by another Kingfisher, and in the battle sustained a broken wing which may be seen hanging down on the further side.

When fishing, the Kingfisher may sit on a limb overhanging the water and wait for his prey to swim within reach, or may fly up and down the stream in search of fish, uttering occasionally his loud, harsh, rattling cry. When a fish is located, he hovers over it briefly to take aim and then dives like an arrow into the water, grasping or spearing his prey with his long, powerful bill. If the captive is small, he is swallowed head first, forthwith; if large, he is taken to a perch and killed before being swallowed.   Once while fishing for bass with a spoon hook, we were amazed to see a Kingfisher mistake it for a fish and, diving down, become hooked.   He was probably more surprised than we were, and beat an ignominious retreat when we released him.

One of the scientific names of the Kingfisher is Halcyon.   Alcyone, the daughter of Aeolus, threw herself into the sea and was changed into a Kingfisher, called Halcyon by ancient Latin-speaking people.   According to Pliny, "Halcyons lay and sit about midwinter when daies be shortest; and the times while they are broodie is called the halcyon daies; for during that season the sea is calm and navigable."

The Belted Kingfisher does not build a nest but digs one.   The nest hole is usually excavated in the bank of a stream and extends horizontally for a distance of about six feet.   At the end a chamber is dug out and from five to eight white eggs laid

Photo by Hegner

Belted Kingfisher.   He looks like a conqueror but his wing was broken in a fight with another Kingfisher and now hangs down on the other side of the body.

on the bare earth.   The birds make two grooves in the bottom of the nest hole as they waddle in and out; the presence of these grooves indicates that the hole is in use.

Nighthawk.   The Nighthawk is not a member of the Hawk family, but has received its name because it "hawks" its food while flying about in the air.   Since it captures mosquitoes, it might appropriately be called a Mosquito Hawk.   In the South it is known as a "Bull Bat."   Most of the day is spent quietly resting on the ground, on the limb of a tree, or on the top of a building.   As in most birds

Photo by Hegner

Nighthawk.   A parent sitting on two eggs; she resembles very closely in appearance the rocky
hillside where she lives.

that spend a large part of their time in flight, its feet are very weak and cannot be used to grasp twigs the way perching birds do.   It must, therefore, rest lengthwise on top of a larger branch when in a tree.

Nighthawks feed in the evening and early morning, when beetles, flies, and especially moths are on the wing in large numbers.   The mouth opens very widely, which is an aid in capturing flying insects.   When there are young to feed, the parents fill their throats with their insect prey before returning to their young; then they bring it back into their mouths and pass it into the throats of their offspring, a process known as regurgitation.

Nighthawks do not build a nest, but lay their two eggs on the ground in a field or on a barren hillside, or on the flat gravel roof of a city building.   The eggs are elliptical in shape and speckled gray, thus resembling in appearance the ground on which they are laid.   The young are likewise practically invisible because their grayish covering of down resembles their surroundings.   The parent as she sits on her eggs is also seen to be protectively colored.

Nighthawks, as in certain other birds, have the habit of fluttering along the ground as if with a broken wing in order to entice away anyone who approaches their young.   An interesting activity of the male during the mating season is his habit of diving down rapidly through the air and then swooping upward again, thereby producing a roaring sound as a result of the passage of air through the wing feathers.   In certain localities large numbers of Nighthawks gather together in the fall and migrate southward in huge flocks.

Whip-Poor-Will.   Although very similar to the Nighthawk in appearance, the Whip-Poor-Will exhibits widely different habits.   It is a forest bird that is rarely seen because it is active only after dark; however, it is well known because of its voice.   Its call notes sound like the words *whip-poor-will*, and if one is close enough, he will hear a cluck before each call.   The number of calls uttered without pause is tremendous.   One bird "actually laid upon the back of poor Will 1088 blows, with only a barely perceptible pause here and there, as if to catch its breath.

Photo by Hegner

Whip-Poor-Will.   The two eggs are laid on the leaves in the woods; they are beautifully marked with lilac.

Then it stopped about half a minute and began again, uttering this time 390 calls, when it paused, flew a little further away, took up the tale once more and continued till I fell asleep." (Burroughs.)   The eggs of the Whip-Poor-Will are two in number, beautifully marked with delicate lilac blotching.   They are laid usually on a bed of leaves, and resemble their background so closely that they can be located only when the sitting bird is flushed.

Hummingbirds.   The smallest bird living in the eastern United States is the Ruby-Throated Hummingbird.   In the western states about 20 different species of "feathered-gems" occur, and about 500 other species inhabit tropical America. Hummingbirds, as everyone who has seen one knows, are remarkable fliers and make a humming noise with their wings as they dart through the air like shooting stars.   Their extraordinary powers of flight are correlated with enormously developed breast muscles.   The birds must have rest, however, and are often to be seen sitting quietly on the limb of a tree or a telephone wire.

Hummingbirds collect nectar and small insects from flowers while in flight, and in so doing, unconsciously distribute pollen, much as bees do.   The bill is long and slender, and the tongue is also long, and can be extended so as to reach the nectar at the base of honeysuckle and trumpet blossoms.   The nest of the Ruby-Throated Hummingbird is one of the most delicate and beautiful of all bird's nests.   It is built by the female, usually on top of the branch of a tree, and covered with lichens so that it resembles the bark of the tree very closely. Two tiny, white eggs about the size of beans are laid.   The mother incubates the eggs; she feeds the young by regurgitation.

The quickness and agility of Hummingbirds enable them to escape enemies, and their freedom from attack seems to have made them fearless of other animals, regardless of size, hence they have developed a pugnacious disposition and a tend-

Hummingbird. A typical view; the nest is built on top of a limb; the outside of the nest is covered with lichens; note the long, slender bill and the long wings and tail.

Broad-Tailed Hummingbird. The young are fed by regurgitation; they are about ready to leave the nest; photographed in Colorado.

ency to fight on the least provocation. They are fond of bathing in the rain or in spray, and also in dew which they gather by flying among leaves in the early morning.

Cuckoo. Cuckoos are abundantly referred to in literature, including the Bible and the writings of Aristotle, Pliny, and the poets. This is due largely to their voice and the character of their home life. Most of the references to Cuckoos are to European birds; these, like our Cowbirds, lay their eggs in the nests of other birds, which incubate them and raise the young birds as carefully as they do their own. The Cuckoos of the United States are ethically on a much higher plane; they build a nest and raise their own family. The nest is a flimsy platform of sticks built on the lower limb of a tree or in a bush, but it serves its purpose satisfactorily. However, one wonders what keeps the eggs from rolling out or how the young prevent the wind from blowing them away during a storm.

The voice of the Cuckoo has made it famous, and the invention of the cuckoo clock has spread this fame throughout the world. The common Yellow-Billed and Black-Billed Cuckoos of the United States begin their call notes with *tut-tuts* or *cl-ucks* and complete them with a series of *cow, cow, cows*. Their voices have certain of the qualities of a ventriloquist, and the birds are so retiring, sly, and furtive, as they glide silently from tree to tree, that usually they are not seen, a phenomenon that led Wordsworth to write

O Cuckoo! Shall I call thee bird,
Or but a wandering voice?

"In his manner the Cuckoo gives the impression of being deeply preoccupied and quite absent-minded. He slips in and out of trees like a ghost. Upon first alighting, he looks about him as if he were dazed, but almost immediately recovers himself and proceeds to search for his preferred fare of tent caterpillars of which he destroys great numbers, thereby placing himself in the category of highly useful birds." (Gladden.)

Courtesy, American Museum of Natural History
Yellow-Billed Cuckoo. The body is slender and the tail long; the lower part of the bill is yellowish; the nest contains several eggs.

Cuckoos are long, slender birds, rather dovelike in shape. They are highly beneficial because they devour large numbers of injurious insects, especially hairy caterpillars that are shunned by other birds. Certain farmers and others believe that they predict rain when they call, and from this the name of "Rain Crow" has arisen.

Road Runner. Closely related to the Cuckoo is the Road Runner, or Ground Cuckoo, also known as the Chaparral Cock, or Snake Bird. He is a familiar figure in the desert tracts of the southwestern United States, where he lives among the cacti, mesquite, and sagebrush near the river valleys. He is a long, slender,

Photo by the Finleys.   Courtesy, Nature Magazine

Road Runner.   A long, slender bird and an excellent runner; his specialty is catching lizards and snakes; he loves our dry Southwest.

brownish bird with strong legs and weak wings. We have encountered many of them running along the road in front of our motor car and others perched on fence posts from which they volplane to the ground with wings held out like those of an airplane. They attempt to escape by running and could distance a horse-drawn vehicle, but are no match for a motor car.

The small animals of the desert provide food for the Road Runner, especially lizards and snakes. Even the young are fed on lizards, often too long to swallow all at once, leaving the tail hanging from the mouth. The nest is built in the low vegetation among which it lives; it consists of sticks and is lined with grass, feathers, snake skins, etc. The eggs appear to be laid at long intervals since fresh eggs and large young may occupy a nest at the same time. The story is told of how the Road Runner surrounds the sleeping rattlesnake with a ring of cactus; when the snake awakes, it attempts to escape, only to be filled with cactus spines and eventually to be killed and eaten.

Chimney Swift. A "Swift" should be able to fly rapidly, hence the Chimney Swift is well named, because he probably flies at times at a speed of 200 miles per hour, and is said to travel as much as a thousand miles in a single day, while busily engaged in providing for his family. Originally Chimney Swifts nested and rested in hollow trees, and still do so in some localities, but are now quite

Photo by Hegner

Chimney Swift. The mother courageously sits on the nest while a camera is lowered into the chimney and this photograph is taken.

civilized and usually nest in chimneys. While outside of the chimney, they are continuously on the wing and never stop to rest. They fly about with quivering wings and shrill twitterings, catching insects on the wing, or breaking off dead twigs from the branches of trees, with their feet or bills, with which to build their nests.

The wings of the Swift are very long and adapted for sustained flight. The tail is short and the feathers end in sharp spines which are used to brace the body against the side of the chimney. The feet are weak, but the toes terminate in sharp, curved claws capable of clinging firmly to a vertical surface. Weak feet are characteristic of birds that spend most of their time in the air.

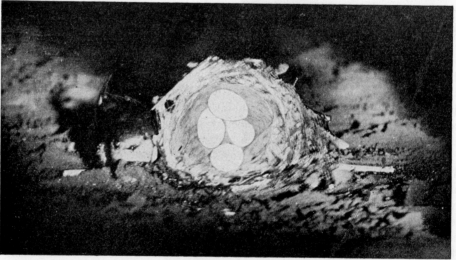

Photo by Hegner

Chimney Swift. The mother is clinging beside her nest facing upward; the nest is of twigs and contains four white eggs.

The nest is a semicircular bracket fastened to the inside wall of the chimney with a gelatinous "glue" secreted by the salivary glands; the twigs of the nest are also stuck together with this glue. The young are ugly, naked, and blind and the less said about them the better. The nests of Chimney Swifts are often overrun with bugs, but these are not bedbugs, but a similar species that cannot live away from the Swifts. Swifts are devoted parents, in spite of the reptile-like appearance of the young, and reports, apparently authentic, exist of birds that entered the chimney of a burning house and perished with their young.

Late in the summer the Swifts for miles around congregate in a hollow tree or large chimney. We have seen hundreds of them at sundown swirling around above a tall chimney in a funnel-shaped flock and

Photo by Hegner

Chimney Swift. The young are naked and blind; no wonder their parents hide them away in a dark chimney.

one by one, as they reached the point of the funnel, raising their wings and dropping in for the night.

Certain species of Swifts build their nests entirely of pure saliva; these "white" nests are the edible birds' nests so highly prized by the Chinese. The birds' nest soup we were served in Chinese homes in Soochow and in Manila was certainly delicious. A cave containing dozens of nesting Swifts that we visited on the island of Luzon in the Philippines, was not in a very sanitary condition, but the nests were practically free from grass and feathers, and hence suitable for use as food.

Toucans. Although we are accustomed to see bizarre-looking animals in zoological parks, when we see a Toucan for the first time, or even the second time, we are apt to wonder whether our eyes are deceiving us. The Toucan and the Hornbill enjoy the distinction of having the largest bill for the size of the body of any of the birds. The bill of the Toucan, however, is somewhat deceptive, since it is not really massive. The horny sheath is only about $\frac{1}{30}$ to $\frac{1}{50}$ inch thick, and the inside is filled with air and a delicate filigree of bone.

Why such an enormous Roman nose developed is difficult to explain. The beak is used to pick fruit from trees and to capture insects. Soft fruit is cut up by means of the serrated edges of the bill, and the "smaller morsels are held by the tip of the beak, dexterously tossed into the air, and caught in the mouth, to be swallowed at a gulp."

About sixty species of Toucans are known. They live principally in forested regions from northern Argentine to southern Mexico. In many of them both the plumage and the bill are brilliantly colored. One species utters a call that resembles the Brazilian word *tucano*, hence the name Toucan. One peculiar characteristic of these birds is the presence of a ball-and-socket joint that hinges the tail to the body so that the tail can be bent up over the back.

Nearly related to the Toucans are the Trogons. "These are all birds of great splendour, and the 'hall-mark' of the tribe seems to be a crimson abdomen, but in some the whole breast is thus coloured. Many have the upper parts of a glorious bronze-green, simulating burnished metal. The most famous of all is the superbly beautiful Quezal of Mexico. Of a brilliant iridescent green above, tinged with blue on the tail, and of a gorgeous crimson below, the plumage of this bird gains added splendour by the fact that the upper tail-coverts are produced into long streamers, the middle pair being the longest, three and a half feet long." (Pycraft.)

Photo by Hegner

Toucan. Just an ordinary bird except for the beak with its sawlike edges; the beak is hollow and its sheath is very thin and light; he lives in tropical America.

Hornbills. The home life of the Hornbills would guarantee them a place in the sun even if their enormous, grotesque bills did not. "Incubation and the brooding of the young is performed entirely by the female, who, directly she begins to sit, is made a close prisoner. The male closes up the entrance to the hole in the tree-trunk containing the nest with clay hardened by secretions from his salivary glands. But a slit large enough to permit the passage of the beak is left open, and through this she is fed. And here again is a remarkable thing. The male does not bring food in its natural state, but such as he has recently swallowed, which is regurgitated, enclosed within a bag formed by the lining of his stomach, which has to be renewed before he can feed her again. No wonder that by the time she emerges with her youngster, the male is worn to a mere skeleton and sometimes dies from exhaustion." (Pycraft.)

The bill of the Hornbill is not as heavy as it looks. Like that of the Toucan, it consists of a thin, horny, outer shell and is a mere air chamber filled with a delicate meshwork of bone. Hornbills feed on fruit and small animals. They are large birds, many of them reaching a length of over four feet, and only a few of them being less than two feet long. They live in Africa and in the Indo-Malayan region, but mounted specimens may be seen in most of our natural history museums.

WOODPECKERS

The carpenters of the woods are distributed throughout the forested parts of the world, except Madagascar and the Australian region. About 700 species are known. Sixty-four species and subspecies live in North America.

Woodpeckers are adapted for climbing trees, digging in wood, and extracting insects therefrom. The four toes are arranged in two pairs so as to suspend the body in front and support it behind. The claws are curved and sharply pointed so that they can cling to any crevice in the bark. The tail terminates in stiff-pointed feathers which are pressed against ridges in the bark and support the body like the third leg of a tripod. Progress up the tree is made in a series of hops.

The beak is hard and chisel-shaped; the neck is short and stout; and the head large and heavy, consisting of strong bones. The result is an effective apparatus for digging in wood. The tongue is highly modified for penetrating small holes and bringing forth grubs. It is long, slender, and very flexible, and the end is pointed and barbed, being used to pierce insect prey. Woodpeckers dig holes in trees and lay their white, glossy eggs on the chips in the bottom. The young are among the noisiest of all infant birds. Among the more common North American species are the Flicker, Red-Headed

Photo by Cowles. Courtesy, Nature Magazine

Hornbill. His bill rivals that of the toucan; in the tip of the bill is a morsel of food; his spouse is sealed up in a hollow in the tree while she hatches the eggs.

Woodpecker, Downy Woodpecker and Yellow-Bellied Sapsucker. The Hairy Woodpecker is a sort of enlarged edition of the Downy. Several very large species are the Pileated and Ivory-Billed Woodpeckers of the southeastern States.

Flicker. The Flicker has a wavy, galloping flight during which a white spot on the back at the base of the tail is alternately exposed and covered, hence his name is very appropriate. However, over 100 other names have been applied to this species, the most common being Yellow Hammer, Wake Up, High Hole, and Golden-Winged Woodpecker. He is the largest of our common Woodpeckers, reaching a length of almost a foot, enjoys the society of human beings, and is very noisy. His drumming on a resonant limb or the roof over our heads in the early morning is rather exasperating, but his loud calls of *whick-ah*, *whick-ah* are so cheerful as to disarm criticism.

Photo by Hegner

Flicker. The mother has a throat full of ants she is about to distribute among the youngsters in the hole in the tree.

Flickers are often seen on the ground searching for ants, and as much as half of their food may consist of these insects, 5000 ants have been reported from the stomach of a single bird. Flickers may dig a nest-hole or lay their eggs in a natural cavity in a tree, or even in a nest-box. Ordinarily the birds lay five to nine glossy white eggs, but if all but one are taken, they will continue to lay eggs and will lay one a day for several weeks if one is left as a nest egg; one bird is reported to have laid 71 eggs in 73 days. Young flickers are even more noisy than their parents; their incessant cries no doubt encourage their parents to hunt more diligently for food.

Red-Headed Woodpecker. The Flicker and the Red-Headed Woodpecker nest more often close to human habitations than do other Woodpeckers. This made it difficult in our nest-robbing days to add eggs of these species to our collections. On this account, when a promising nest was located, we waited until after dark, then hastily climbed the tree and began with a sharp knife to dig out the nest-hole so that we could slip a hand in to get the eggs. This proved to be satisfactory except on one occasion when the nest chanced to be located in a tree near the front porch of a young lady who came home with a young man as escort, and decided the hammock was a good place to spend the evening. The lovenaking of others ceases to be amusing after an hour or two, especially when one is perched on an uncomfortable limb of a tree, but there is an end to everything and the young man finally went home.

The Red-Headed Woodpecker is a brilliantly colored bird with head and neck bright crimson; back black and underparts white. He is a Woodpecker, but stores up nuts for the winter like a Jay and catches insects on the wing like a Flycatcher. He is often seen in the open, using a telegraph pole as a drumming station or as a perch from which to fly out after passing insects. He digs into wood for his supper less frequently than the Downy Woodpecker, but much of his food consists of scales, weevils, cicadas, and other harmful insects. He is a noisy fellow, his *tchm-tchm* reminding one somewhat of the call of the tree frog. He is "a great genius, no less brilliant and versatile in character than in plumage — very accomplished, of endless resources, with tricks and manners enough to fill the rest of this volume with good reading matter!"

Photo by Bond. Courtesy, Nature Magazine

Red-Headed Woodpecker. The head and neck are bright crimson; the back is black, and the underparts white; the bill is chisel-shaped.

Downy Woodpecker. One of the best-beloved but smallest North American Woodpeckers is the Downy. He is sometimes called a Sapsucker, but this is a great injustice, since he does not suck sap. On the contrary he eats the eggs of wood-boring beetles and of leaf-eating moths, and the larvae and adults of all sorts of destructive insects. He is the natural protector of our fruit trees and does a very good job of it. He starts at the bottom of a tree and works up; then he dives down to the foot of another tree and repeats the performance. He is a model of patient industry and perseverance, has a happy and buoyant disposition, and is always genial and friendly. Often a number of Downies are encountered hunting through the woods in company with Chickadees.

The Downy digs a hole, usually in the under side of a decayed limb, just large enough to enter. "The nesting cavity is wrought out with happy labor. The entrance is just large enough to admit the owner by tight squeezing, and the interior is trimmed into graceful curves, rounding at the bottom into a receptacle for the snowy eggs. The birds sometimes carry the chips away, but are often careless of concealment, and let them fall about the foot of the tree." (Forbush.) Four or five eggs are laid. The young are always hungry and their vociferous twittering can be heard for some distance. Downy Woodpeckers are black and white and resemble Hairy Woodpeckers, with which they might become confused. The Hairies are much larger and the two outside tail feathers on either side are entirely white, whereas in the Downies they are white with two broad, black bars.

"Downy is a bird of the old orchard in summer. He prefers to inhabit trees that are neglected by their owners, and assumes the self-appointed guardianship of such trees in the happiest frame of mind imaginable. He does this for the reason that these neglected orchards harbor a host of insects and vermin, in the destruction of which he revels. Under those scales of bark there lurk in early spring the larvae of the codling moth, which pass the winter in their loosely spun cocoons. Downy knows just where to find them. He circles the trunk and limbs, climbs up or comes down backward, and ever and anon he taps and sounds the bark, until the tell-tale vibration given back by the scale above the cocoon corroborates the evidence of his eyes. Every stroke with which he knocks on the door of an insect's retreat sounds the crack of doom. He pierces the bark with his beak, then with his barbed tongue drags forth the insect, and moves on to tap the last summons on the door of the next in line. Now and then an intelligent bird carries the warfare against the apple worm still farther, and pecks the fruit upon the tree; but, so far as my experience goes, he attacks only wormy fruit, and when he has the worm, he leaves the apple." (Forbush.)

Photo by Hegner

Downy Woodpecker. She has a bill full of wriggling insects for her young in the hole in the tree; note how she braces herself with her tail.

Yellow-Bellied Sapsucker. The old respectable Woodpecker family contains one feathered drunkard. He is the only really destructive Woodpecker in eastern North America. As the name Yellow-Bellied Sapsucker implies, he sucks the sap that flows into shallow holes that he digs in the bark of trees. He also eats the inner bark, or cambium. The holes are dug in a horizontal row around the tree and often two or more series may be made one above the other. Trees are often weakened as a result, and sometimes are killed. Even if the trees are not killed they are often so badly injured as to be rendered unfit for lumber. Other Woodpeckers are unjustly accused of causing the damage and pay for the Sapsucker's misdeeds with their lives.

Sapsuckers are beautiful birds; they can be distinguished by the red color which extends from the base of the bill to the top of the head, and by the black patch on the breast. The tongue is not as long as in other Woodpeckers, but ends in a brushlike tip which serves to gather in the sap.

Sapsuckers are shy birds and the holes they make are better known than the birds. Many species of trees are attacked but especially basswood, hickory, cypress, and oak. Freshly dug holes are visited as fast as they fill up with sap, much as a collector of maple sap visits his buckets, and one bird may remain for many hours on a single tree. Sapsuckers, like Flickers, are fond of ants and about one third of their food consists of these noxious insects, so that, as usual, there is some good in the worst of us.

Western parts of the United States are inhabited by the Red-Naped Sapsucker, which has the bad habits of the Yellow-Belly but is differently colored. The nape of the

Photo by Blickensderfer. Courtesy, Nature Magazine
Red-Naped Sapsucker. This master carpenter has chiseled a nesting cavity out of a live, quaking aspen; he injures trees by digging holes in them to obtain sap.

neck is scarlet instead of white. It prefers live aspens as a place to dig a nest hole probably because the wood is softer than in other trees.

CHAPTER 30

PERCHING BIRDS — FLYCATCHERS, HORNED LARKS,
AND SWALLOWS

Although the Perching Birds constitute only one of the twenty-one orders of Birds, this single order includes about one half of all the species known. Such an order, containing nearly 15,000 species, is difficult to characterize. Their hind toe is well developed and their feet adapted for grasping. They live usually in trees and bushes and are not generally aquatic. Their young are hatched in a weak and naked condition and remain in the nest for a long time.

Perching Birds live a strenuous life. They are very active, breathe rapidly, and consume comparatively large quantities of food. Two suborders are recognized on the basis of the structure of their vocal apparatus, the syrinx. In one suborder are placed the songless perching birds and in the other the song birds. All of the North American Perching Birds are "song" birds except one family, the Flycatchers. Inclusion among the singing birds doesn't necessarily mean that the bird can sing; it signifies only that the syrinx is of the song-bird type.

The twenty-one families of Perching Birds may be listed by their common names as follows: Flycatchers; Larks; Swallows; Crows, Jays, etc.; Titmice; Nuthatches; Creepers; Wrens; Thrashers, Mockingbirds, etc.; Thrushes, Bluebirds, etc.; Kinglets and Gnatcatchers; Wagtails and Pipits; Waxwings; Shrikes; Starlings; Vireos; Wood Warblers; Weaver Finches; Meadowlarks, Blackbirds, etc.; Tanagers; Grosbeaks, Sparrows, etc.

Kingbird. The Kingbird is a King among birds, not because of his size and strength, but because of an inner force which drives him to attack other birds larger than himself in defense of his own home and those of other small birds. With snapping bill he mounts above any hawk or crow that approaches his home, and like an avalanche, hurls himself down upon the back of his opponent, picking and screaming. There is no large bird that will not hasten away from the field of battle as rapidly as possible when this eight-inch savage and courageous warrier attacks him from above.

The scientific name of the Kingbird means "tyrant flycatcher." In common with other Flycatchers, his bill is broad and flat, with a hook at the tip; his mouth opens very wide; and there are flaring bristles at the angles of his jaws. Thus he is fitted for capturing insects while on the wing. His favorite pastime is sitting on a perch, such as the limb of a tree, a telephone post, or a telephone wire, from which he dashes out to capture insects that may pass by, returning again to the perch after each foray. He has been accused of capturing bees in large numbers and

466

Photo by Merwin.   Courtesy, Nature Magazine

Kingbird. While she sits on her nest she keeps a sharp lookout for possible invaders.

consequently is known as the Bee Bird, or Bee Martin; but the bees he devours are drones, which he probably selects because they have no sting.

The Kingbird is not conspicuously colored. The upper parts are black and gray and the underparts white. On the crown is a large orange-red patch which appears only when the feathers are erected on top of the head. The nest is built in trees, of twigs, weeds, rootlets, etc., and lined with wool, horsehair, and feathers. Three or four eggs are laid.

Phoebe. The call note of the Phoebe sounds like *Febe*, but every bird that says *Febe* is not a Phoebe, since the chickadee also includes this note in its repertoire. However, one who has listened to both can easily distinguish between them. Where Phoebes live their voices are among the first to be heard in the morning, often before daylight. The Phoebe resembles in general shape and color the Kingbird, but is somewhat smaller. His disposition is radically different; no more gentle and confiding bird could be imagined.

Phoebes usually build their nests near water, and their original nesting site was on a cliff. Human civilization has changed their habits, and now one finds them nesting under bridges or about buildings; for example, above the window molding under a porch as in our photograph. The nest is made of mud, grass, and vegetable fibers, lined with horsehair and feathers, and often covered with moss.

The birds may return to the same nest year after year or build other nests near by. We know a cliff where a nest was being used and three other old nests in

Phoebes. The father brings food to the brooding mother, who passes it over to the young; the nest is built over a window beneath a porch and sunlight was reflected upon it with a mirror so that a snapshot could be taken.

various stages of disintegration were visible within six feet, all apparently the product of one pair of birds in successive years. The nests are often infested with red mites and lice. The eggs are white and usually five in number. The parents, like the Kingbird, are accustomed to fly out from a perch to catch insects for themselves and their young.

Wood Pewee. The Wood Pewee is a Flycatcher somewhat smaller than the Phoebe. It is common in the deep woods of eastern North America. The voice of the Wood Pewee is a sad, plaintive "human sigh" exactly duplicating its name, and its *pee-wee*, or *pee-a-wee*, may be heard at any time of the day. Like the Mourning Dove, its dreamy, sorrowful notes emanate from a happy little bird that is really enjoying life among the woodland trees.

The nest is usually saddled on a dead limb not far from the ground, and is a beautiful cup of grass, rootlets, and moss, so thickly covered with lichens as to look like a part of the tree. The eggs are three or four in number, white with a wreath of umber-colored markings around the larger end.

The Wood Pewee satisfies its appetite very largely with flying insects that it captures on the wing, "but it often flutters about the foliage, picking off caterpillars and plant lice. Daily in the early morning and in the dusk of evening, even in the uncertain gloom of the deep woods, this bird pursues its prey unerringly."

Wood Pewee. The dainty nest is saddled on a limb and covered outside with lichens; the eggs have a wreath of umber-colored markings around the larger end.

Prairie Horned Lark. The word *lark* has been applied to various species of birds in this country, but the true Larks are mostly inhabitants of the Old World, where the Skylark is the most distinguished representative. One species, with over a dozen subspecies, is distributed over North America, especially on the plains and deserts. They can be distinguished by the tufts of dark feathers (horns) above and behind the eyes, and the black mark across the breast. The hind toe is provided with a long, straight claw, the "lark-spur."

Prairie Horned Larks nest very early, often before the snow has all disappeared. A softened spot of ground is selected where a slight depression is dug. This is lined with fine grass and feathers. The mother flies directly from the nest when one is still a considerable distance away, but returns to the nest with mouselike movements along the ground. We once attempted to find out whether the mother bird

Photo by Hegner

Prairie Horned Lark. The male has two tufts of feathers, or "horns," on top of the head; he is a devoted father.

or father bird or both parents protected the young at night. A camera and flashlight were placed by the nest before dark and set off at 10 P.M. The result shows the mother bird at home. No one knows where father Lark spends his evenings. During the mating season the tips of the winter feathers are worn away, bringing to the surface the brighter colors that were concealed beneath.

The song flight of the male may be witnessed at this time. "A little bird sits on her sunken nest in the prairie sod, watching her mate as he springs aloft and gives himself to the buoyant currents of the air. He swings in loose circuits and zigzags back and forth, singing gently at first, then, fluttering upward, rises by stages, taking each upward step at a steep slant, sailing, gyrating, mounting higher and still higher, pouring forth his whole soul in an ecstasy of song.

"Up and up he goes, swinging in dizzy spirals, pausing at one height after another to send back to earth his music; and so soars and sings until he fades from view in the clear blue canopy of heaven, and the song is wafted down sweeter and fainter until, like the skylark, he sings at 'heaven's gate.'

"Then, as the full flood of his ecstasy begins to ebb, and his strength wanes, he sinks slowly down; the far-away song swells on the listening ear, and, still fluttering and singing, he comes again into view. Swinging in wide aerial circuits he drops by slow stages until at last his hymn is ended, and, closing his wings, he drops like a meteor until near the earth, when he spreads his wings checking his headlong rush, turns, and swings along the sod until his toes touch the grass-tops as lightly as the summer wind, and he comes to earth again near the little nest, the center of all his hopes." (Forbush.)

Photo by Hegner

Prairie Horned Lark. The mother Lark has her feathers ruffled up so as to protect the young from the chilly night air; this is a flashlight photograph taken at 10 P.M.

Purple Martin. The Purple Martin is our largest Swallow. Like other Swallows, he is fitted for life in the air and for capturing insect food. His wings are long and powerful, but his feet are weak and of use only for perching. The original home of the Purple Martin was a hollow tree, but the Indians were accustomed to hang gourds on poles for them to nest in and this custom is still followed in certain regions. Martin boxes, in which a number of pairs of these colonial birds may nest at the same time, are a familiar sight in the yards of homes. They should be put up about fifteen feet from the ground and protected from cats and English sparrows. In cities the hollow ornaments on buildings afford Martins a safe nesting place.

Martins feed on the wing but sometimes alight on a branch

Courtesy, U. S. Bureau of Biological Survey

Purple Martins. They live amicably in colonies and readily accept a compartment house as a home.

of a dead tree. They gather together in flocks in the autumn and finally fly south for the winter. Like all Swallows, they are very beneficial because of the great numbers of harmful insects they destroy. A colony of Martins will join together for mutual protection and drive away hawks and crows that might molest them or their young, and incidentally, protect the poultry of the farmer wise enough to provide a nesting box for them.

The Martin in its flight "probably excels all our swallows, if not all other species. It often goes several miles from its nest for food and when returning directly it flies with amazing velocity. It is a common belief among country people that the Martin brings bedbugs to its nesting places, and that in this way houses and barns become infested. The only foundation for this belief lies in the fact that a peculiar bug, belonging to the same family as the bedbug, does infest Martins' nests and is doubtless carried from place to place by the birds. This insect, however, is not the bedbug and cannot live on other animals than swallows. There is therefore no danger whatever of its infesting dwelling houses." (Barrows.)

Cliff Swallow. The natural nesting site of the Cliff Swallow is a cliff, and colonies still nest on cliffs in the western part of the United States, but in many localities he has become an Eave Swallow, building nests in a row under the eaves of a barn. When protected from English sparrows, such a colony may occupy a site year after year. Sometimes they are destroyed because they are noisy or soil the side of the barn or are accused of bringing parasites into the home. Cliff Swallows do harbor parasites but they are not human parasites and will not live on human beings.

Photo by Hegner

Cliff Swallows. The mud nests of part of a colony that built on a cliff in northeastern Iowa.

The nest of the Cliff Swallow is a triumph in masonry. Pellets of mud are gathered from a wet place in the barnyard or from a near-by stream and plastered against the side of the barn and left to dry. Fresh pellets are added daily until a gourd-shaped nest results with the opening at the outer end facing downward. We have watched colonies both on cliffs and under the eaves, the air apparently being full

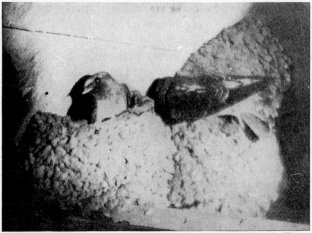

Photo by Hegner

Cliff Swallows. Two birds building their nests under the eaves of a barn; the sun was reflected on the birds while the photograph was being taken.

of Swallows flying to and from the nests, twittering continuously, and other Swallows remaining at home looking out from their nests. The nests are lined with grass and feathers, and from three to five speckled eggs are laid. If telegraph wires are present near a colony, they will be lined with Cliff Swallows sitting in rows, resting from their labors of building nests and capturing insects for themselves and their young.

Barn Swallow. Another Swallow that has changed its habits with the advent of human civilization is the Barn Swallow. His natural home is in a cave or under a ledge, but he prefers barns. He does not nest outside, as does the Cliff Swallow, but on a rafter inside. The nest is made of pellets of mud with grass and straw mixed in, and is lined with feathers. It is not entirely enclosed, as is that of the Cliff Swallow, but is an open, bowl-shaped structure.

The Barn Swallow is our most graceful Swallow. His tail is long and deeply forked, which makes it possible for him to perform his aerial evolutions with great skill. Swallows are very conspicuous birds and their arrival in the spring and departure in the fall are quite noticeable. They usually arrive in large numbers at one time, hence "one swallow does not make a summer" if it chances to precede the rest. "When the Swallows Homeward Fly" was written about the migration of the European

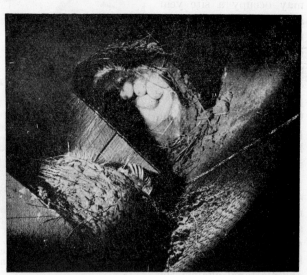

Photo by Hegner

Barn Swallow. This species builds a nest of mud and straw on a rafter inside of the barn and lines it with feathers; a mirror has been fastened above the nest and sun reflected from outside, the result being a photograph of the reflection.

relatives of the Barn Swallow away from home in the fall.   Barn Swallows are decreasing in numbers for several reasons, one being the tendency for farmers to build such tight barns that the Swallows are unable to get inside.

Bank Swallow.   One Swallow that has not been disturbed particularly by mankind is the Bank Swallow, or Sand Martin.   He still digs his nest hole in a bank, usually of a stream, at the end of which he rears his family in a nest of straw and grass.   This tunnel he digs with bill and claws, although they seem too weak for such work.   Like other Swallows, Bank Swallows are colonial and many pairs will nest together in a single bank.

Another Swallow that resembles the Bank Swallow very closely is the Rough-Wing Swallow.   We have captured many of these by digging out their nest-holes and picking them off the nest.   The edge of the outer wing feather is made rough to the touch by a series of small hooks, hence the bird's name.   The Bank Swallow does not have these rough feathers.   Rough Wings usually nest in small colonies or in isolation, but a Kingfisher may dig his nest hole near by and both species live in perfect harmony.   A crevice in a cliff may also serve as a nesting site for the Rough Wing.

Photo by Hegner

Bank Swallow.   The nest of grasses is built at the end of a hole in a bank; the mother sat on the nest while the hole was dug out.

Perhaps the most unusual nesting site on record is that of a pair of these Swallows that built a nest beneath the deck of a "transfer steamboat which made daily trips on the Tennessee River from Guntersville to Hobbs Island, a distance of 24 miles, leaving at 10 A.M. and returning at 6 P.M.   The birds, of course, followed the boat all the way to feed their young." (Howell.)

CHAPTER 31

JAYS, CROWS, ETC., AND BLACKBIRDS, ORIOLES, ETC.

Blue Jay. The Jaybird in his blue and gray and white uniform needs no introduction, since he is among our most noisy birds and introduces himself on every possible occasion with his challenging call of *jay, jay, jay, jay, jay.* "He appears to be among his fellow musicians, what the trumpeter is in a band." He is a

Photo by Allen. Courtesy, Nature Magazine

Blue Jay. A handsome rascal with a bad reputation.

beautiful, showy creature but has a bad reputation which is probably exaggerated because he is so conspicuous.

> *Mr. Blue Jay, full o' sass, In them base-ball clothes of his,*
> *Sportin' round the orchard jes' Like he owned the premises.* (Riley)

He bullies little birds and robs their nests of eggs and young. He is also fond of corn, but prefers insects, nuts, and seeds, a supply of which he stores up for winter use. His economic status is somewhat in doubt. To some he has "all the mis chievous, destructive, thieving traits of the Crow, and with a lot of audacity or 'cheek' thrown in for good measure." Blue Jays have a particular aversion for owls and will almost scream themselves to death even if the owl is stuffed. "And let anyone who supposes that Jays can't swear, and employ the most variegated vilification and the most fluent Billingsgate, just stand by and listen to the male-dictions of a flock of them as they mob their arch enemy, the Great Horned Owl." (Gladden.)

During the nesting season Jays become rather quiet. A pair that nested recently in the vines on our front porch were very seldom heard. They were very pugnacious when their nest contained young and struck us repeatedly on the head when we came near, on one occasion drawing blood. We have examined

Photo by Hegner

Blue Jays. These young are about to leave the nest.

the nests of a great many species of birds when they contained young, including large species such as hawks and owls, but have never actually been struck except by Blue Jays.

Canada Jay. Campers in the northern United States or Canada are familiar with this cousin of the Blue Jay and have given him many names, such as Whiskey Jack, Moose Bird, and Camp Robber. He is about the size of the Blue Jay, but less conspicuously colored, being dark gray above and light gray below. His call notes are blue-jayish, but include many discordant sounds peculiar to himself.

"Also 'Jack' has a distinctly uncanny air about him as he sits on a branch and regards you vacantly with his beady, black eyes, or flits noiselessly around your camp. But don't make the mistake of supposing that he is really preoccupied or absent-minded, much less timid, for actually he is about the cheekiest thing that wears feathers. All the time, probably, he has his eye on the bacon or the potatoes, which he will not hesitate to steal from under your very nose if he sees the oppor-tunity. Hence his well-deserved name, 'Camp Robber.' But the man who doesn't enjoy being robbed by such a thief, had better stay at home and sit in the parlor." (Gladden.)

The nest is built near the trunk of evergreen trees; it must be well lined with warm feathers, since the snow is still on the ground and the temperature often below zero while the eggs are being incubated.

Photo by Blickensderfer.   Courtesy, Nature Magazine

Canada Jay, or Camp Robber.   He is grayish in color and about the size of a Blue Jay; he is an inveterate thief and steals many things of great use to the camper but of no value to himself.

Crow and Raven. "As black as a Crow" and "Raven locks" are expressions familiar to everyone. Nothing certainly could be blacker than a Crow or Raven. The bird whose photograph is shown on page 478 is called a White-Necked Raven; only the basal parts of the feathers on neck, throat, and breast are white, and hence are effectively concealed. In England the common members of the Crow tribe are the Rook and the Jackdaw. These birds are frequently referred to in English literature, especially the Jackdaw probably because of its sociable nature.

Crows are among our most conspicuous birds. It isn't necessary to go to the country to see them, since their *caws* are often heard when they pass over the city on the way to better hunting ground. Those who have attempted to shoot Crows know that it is no easy matter to get within gunshot of them. Their cleverness is largely responsible for their continued existence, since every man's hand is against them. Farmers wage war on them because they pull up soft, sprouting corn; nature lovers object to their habit of killing small birds and robbing nests.

During the winter, Crows live in flocks and roost in colonies sometimes numbering several hundred thousand. "Early in the morning with regularly executed maneuvers, they start on the day's foraging, flying low, on the lookout for food. Late in the afternoon, they return at a much greater height — 'as the Crow flies' — and, alighting at some point near the roost, wait the coming of the last stragglers. Then, at a given signal, they all rise and retire for the night." (Chapman.)

The cawing of Crows is only one of their vocal accomplishments. They carry on "conversations" at great length and also may express their feeling in a musical little warble. Crows'

Photo by Cornelia Clarke

Crow. A jet-black bird that makes himself conspicuous with his caws.

nests are built in trees, often in woodlots, of sticks, twigs, grass, etc., and lined with roots and bark. Usually five eggs are laid; these are bluish-green, heavily marked with brown.

Ever since the time of Noah, the Crow has been considered an unclean bird not fit for human consumption. For this reason the expression "to have to eat Crow" is used to indicate any distasteful act either mental or physical, such as having "to eat one's words."

Courtesy, U. S. Bureau Biological Survey

White-Necked Raven. He is larger than a crow but otherwise an expert is needed to distinguish the two birds.

"Quoth the Raven, 'Nevermore,' " but the voice he used for this purpose was only a "hoarse, rolling *cr-r-r-cruck*." So similar are Crows and Ravens in appearance and habits that a close examination is necessary to distinguish them. The Raven is somewhat larger, reaching a length of about two feet, and the feathers on its throat are "narrow, lengthened, and pointed," instead of "normal, short, and rounded" as in the Crow. The White-Necked Raven lives in the Great Plains region, and like the Crow, is filled with curiosity. If not molested it is a friendly bird, but keeps its distance when once shot at. "The Raven frequently nests on cliffs and ledges of rock, but where such locations are not to be had it contents itself with tall trees, in which it builds a bulky nest, similar to that of the Crow. Probably the food of the Raven is almost as varied as that of the Crow, yet it is not known to attack cultivated crops." (Barrows.) The Raven is a symbol of bad luck.

Magpie. One of the most strikingly handsome birds that attracts the attention of visitors to the western states is the Magpie. It is not as large a bird as it appears to be because the tail accounts for about one half of the total length of twenty inches. The plumage is glossy, greenish- or bluish-black with iridescence; the belly and part of the wings are white as shown in the accompanying photograph. The relationship of the Magpie to the Crow-Blackbird, or Grackle (page 483), is quite evident.

Photo by Shanefelt.   Courtesy, Nature Magazine

Magpie. A long, slender bird with white and greenish, glossy black plumage; he is a noisy, mischievous rascal.

The Magpie "frequents the treeless or more sparsely wooded districts, being partial to the vicinity of streams and brushy valleys, but often wanders into the pine groves on hillsides.   While not exactly gregarious, it is sociable and usually seen in small, loose parties of from five or six to a dozen or more, and enjoys but weak powers of flight, being particularly bothered by high winds. It is very noisy, more or less quarrelsome, and one of the most mischievous and thieving of birds, nothing seeming to delight it better than to terrorize small birds by imitating the cry of a Hawk.   Ordinarily it is extremely shy, but if not molested it becomes quite tame, though always alert for possible trouble. It is very voracious, living upon carrion, insects of various kinds, berries, fruits, offal from slaughterhouses and refuse generally."   (Knowlton.)

The nest is a huge structure of sticks, sometimes three feet in diameter, lodged in a bush or tree usually not far from the ground.   The entrance is at one side and the inside is built of weeds and mud and lined with grass.   The difference between the nest of the Magpie and that of its relatives is worth noting. The eggs vary in number from six to ten ; they are not very beautiful, being drab or greenish in general tone and heavily spotted with brown and purple.   American and European Magpies are so nearly alike that they can hardly be distinguished one from the other.

Lyre Bird.   His tail is shaped like a lyre and displayed before his mate during the breeding season.

Lyre Bird.   Without its distinctive tail the Lyre Bird would probably remain practically unknown in the thick forests of Australia.   The tail of the male becomes fully developed during the fourth year.   It is shaped like the ancient musical instrument, the lyre.   The outer tail feathers form the frame of the lyre and the filamentous upper tail coverts, the strings.   The lyrelike tail is useful to the male as well as beautiful, since it is used to attract the female.   During the mating season, the male struts before the female with wings drooping and tail elevated over the back.

Lyre Birds are about the size of small chickens.   They live on the ground and their feet are adapted for scratching in search of insects, worms, etc.   The nest is a dome-shaped structure of sticks, moss, and fibers, usually built on the ground.   A single egg is laid.   The young bird is heavily covered with down.

Courtesy, N. Y. Zoological Society

Bird of Paradise. Brilliant colors, delicate filamentous plumes, and feathers like spun glass are some of the features that make these birds the most beautiful known.

Birds of Paradise. The supremacy of the Birds of Paradise in beauty of plumage cannot be successfully challenged. That is, the plumage of the males; unfortunately the females are rather dowdy and no match for their sumptuous mates. Nevertheless, during the courting season the males display themselves before their girl friends elaborately and at great length. The Blue Bird of Paradise when brought to the New York Zoo surprised everyone by posing upside down.

The colors and ornamental feathers of the various Birds of Paradise are too numerous and complicated to describe. Plumage like black velvet or burnished metal, long tail feathers of opalescent blue, headdresses like brilliantly colored spun glass, and side plumes like delicate filaments terminated by tassels, are part of the galaxy of splendor to be expected in one or another of these gorgeous birds.

Birds of Paradise are rather small, many of them being not more than six or eight inches long.   Such names as Great, King, Magnificent, and Superb have been applied to various species.   Like many other brilliantly colored birds they have limited vocal powers.   Their center of distribution appears to be in New Guinea and neighboring islands.

Probably closely related to the Birds of Paradise are the Bower Birds.   These peculiar species build "playing-grounds."   "The Gardener Bower-Bird builds a miniature cabin of various kinds of moss, and surrounds it with a tiny but perfectly kept lawn of moss, studded with brilliantly coloured flowers, fruits, and insects. Such as become faded are immediately replaced."   (Pycraft.)

Red-Winged Blackbird. Call notes that sound like *kongaree* announce the presence of Red-Winged Blackbirds. They also inform us that we are near a swamp or marsh and must look out for boggy ooze, since Red Wings are partial to well-watered territory. Their nests are usually built among the sedges and cattails only a few inches above the water, where they no doubt escape the depredations of various enemies.

"Mounting the topmost branch of a tree not far from the nest, the male becomes an ever-vigilant sentinel. His rich *kong-quer-ree*, which by association is so strongly suggestive of reedy marshes, is a signal that 'all's well.' He challenges all males of his kind by an inquiring *chut, chuck,* and with a long, shrill alarm-note, *chee-e-e-e-e*, circles out on fluttering wings, his gorgeous crimson epaulets showing conspicuously." (Chapman.)

The female Red Wing is a grayish-brown bird, heavily streaked with dark brown or black. The nest consists of grasses woven into a cup-shaped cradle. From three to five eggs are laid; these are bluish-white in color, with spots and lines of brown and purple, especially near the larger end. "Birds of a feather flock together" when Red Wings nest, and many pairs often occupy a marsh in common. Often the only way to get a close-up of their nest and beautifully marked eggs is to go wading.

Photo by Dawson. Courtesy, Nature Magazine

Red-Winged Blackbirds. The male, below, is singing *kongaree;* he has a patch of red on each wing; the females, above, are grayish-brown streaked with dark brown or black.

Cowbird. The Cow Blackbird, Cow Bunting, or Buffalo Bird, is a rather notorious character, but more interesting, perhaps, on that account, than many other common birds. Cowbirds, like European Cuckoos, are parasites during the breeding season, laying their eggs in the nests of other birds, usually species smaller than they are, and imposing on them the responsibility of rearing their young. The young Cowbirds are usually larger than the young of their foster parents and

Photo by Cornelia Clarke

Cowbird. This culprit looks as though he expected to be punished for the iniquities of his race.

crowd them out of the nest. From one to half a dozen eggs may be laid by Cowbirds in a single nest, but often one young Cowbird is large enough to fill the entire nest of such a bird as the Warbling Vireo. It is ludicrous, but also pitiful, to see a mother Song Sparrow feeding a young Cowbird four times as large as she is. Some birds, notably the Yellow Warbler, will build up the sides of their nest and put in a new bottom above the egg of the Cowbird.

Cowbirds are commonly found in the neighborhood of cattle, probably because of the insects that are stirred up as the animals move about through the grass. They sometimes alight on the cow's back. Cowbirds are not polygamous or polyandrous but practice free love, apparently without the difficulties that accompany this practice when attempted in human society. The male is an ardent wooer, as he puffs himself up, and spreads his wings and tail before the female, and makes vain attempts to sing to her. "Throughout the season the sexes intermingle promiscuously, from the time the females arrive in the spring. As usual with other species, the males come first. They perch in the tops of tall trees, and their only song is a long, thin whistle, high keyed and little varied. The common note is a *chuck*. The females soon arrive from the south, and then flocks may be seen in which they usually predominate. The eggs are deposited from April to June. An egg is dropped slyly when the owner of the nest is absent. Undoubtedly the food habits of the Cowbird are on the whole beneficial; but, as every Cowbird is reared at the expense of the lives of at least two other birds, the reputation of the species suffers accordingly." (Forbush.)

Cowbird. A Cowbird laid an egg in the nest of a Vireo; the young Cowbird pushed out the other young and now receives all the food brought by the foolish Vireos.

Photo by Hegner

Grackles. These large Blackbirds have many characteristics in common with the Crow and are sometimes called Crow Blackbirds. They are about twelve inches long, black all over with iridescent lines on the head, neck, and shoulders and with a long tail that assumes a V-shape when the bird is in flight. Grackles are familiar birds in country, town, or suburb when there are evergreen trees in which to build nests. They roam about during the winter in very large flocks, but break up into small groups in the spring. When they return from their southern winter homes, they make themselves conspicuous at once with their harsh, unmusical voices. They appear quite comical, as they strut about on the front lawn trying successfully to look dignified.

The nest is built near the top of an evergreen tree. It is a very bulky structure of twigs and grass. The four to six eggs are greenish-blue, marked with large blotches or wavy streaks of brown and black. The young are ludicrous in the extreme but soon develop into handsome birds. The Purple Grackle is an inhabitant of the Atlantic coastal region, whereas the Bronzed Grackle occurs farther west.

"Grackles are conspicuous, and when close at hand are unmistakable. The tail is often held with its outer feathers upturned like the sides of a boat, particularly when they fly, which they do usually at some height, in rather a labored manner, keeping about the same level. The ordinary note is a sort of hoarse, loud *chuck*, and the song sounds much like the rather musical creaking of a rusty hinge. They have also a metallic, jangling note, and when a number perch on a favorite tree and sing in chorus, the clanging and creaking they produce are indescribable.

Photo by Gleason. Courtesy, Nature Magazine
Bronzed Grackle. A stately bird about a foot long; the feathers on the back are metallic bronze.

"Crow Blackbirds destroy both gipsy moth and brown-tail moth; bugs, ants, and spiders are eaten also. Mice, birds and eggs, frogs, lizards, salamanders, snakes, fish, crustaceans, mollusks, and snails form a portion of the Grackles' food, besides corn and other grains, wild seeds, nuts, acorns, and weed seed." (Forbush.) Though destructive to corn, they are indispensable because of the vast amount of insects they destroy. In the west they are so numerous that the farmer often must defend himself against them.

Photo by Hegner

Bronzed Grackle.   The nest is usually built in an evergreen tree; the eggs are beautifully
blotched and streaked with brown and black.

Meadowlark.   No outing in the country is complete without the loud, clear,
melodious song of the Meadowlark.   As he sits on top of a fence post and pours
forth the clear tones of his repertoire it seems as though he must burst his throat.
He is undoubtedly doing the best he can and no opera singer ever sang with greater
abandon.

The Meadowlark is a bird of the fields.   He is plump, with a short tail, a long
bill, a black collar on a yellow breast, and white outer tail feathers that are revealed
during flight.   He flies on rapidly vibrating wings.   When he alights on the ground,
he flirts his tail vigorously.   He is one of the few birds that walk.

His nest is built on the ground among high grass and is often arched over.   Old
fields are favorite nesting places, probably in part because the dead and uncut grass
offers concealment for the nest, and in part because in such fields the nest is undisturbed by the mower.   Meadowlarks do not fly up directly from the nest but sneak
off for a few yards along a winding path first; they approach their nest in the same
fashion.   In some regions, Meadowlarks are considered game birds by certain
hunters.   They are no doubt good to eat, but should be vigorously protected not
only because of their beauty and melodious song, but because they destroy large
numbers of injurious insects.   The western Meadowlark resembles the eastern
form so closely that only an expert can tell them apart.   It is a much more accomplished singer with a beautiful warbling song.

"The Meadowlark's common alarm note is a rather sharp chatter, not loud, but shrill, which often follows or precedes a long, piercing call. The ordinary song is a rather plaintive but pleasing whistle of a few notes, the last usually held for several seconds. This song is uttered either from the ground, from a perch, or while the bird is on the wing. Rarely a talented individual soars aloft, uttering an ecstatic flight song, which compares favorably with that of the most celebrated songsters. I have heard this in full volume but once, and then found it difficult to believe that it came from the throat of a common Meadowlark. It was not at all suggestive of that bird's ordinary song, except in some of the last notes; it

Courtesy, Natural History Society of Maryland

Meadowlark. This bird is cleaning the nest and has a packet of excrement in her bill.

more resembled the music of the Bobolink, but was louder and not so hurriedly given." (Forbush.)

The Meadowlark is now quite generally protected by law at all times, and no bird more fully deserves such protection. It is practically harmless, and takes nothing that is of any use to man except a few small grains and seeds. On the other hand, it is one of the most useful birds of the field, perhaps the most valuable. In summer almost ninety-nine per cent of its food consists of insects and allied forms. It eats about all the principal pests of the fields, and is particularly destructive to cutworms, hairy ground caterpillars, and grasshoppers.

Photo by Hegner

Meadowlark. The nest is built in deep grass and partly covered over with a grassy roof.

Baltimore Orioles. Baltimore Orioles fully deserve the admiration they receive, because they are among the most gorgeous-colored of our summer residents, possess a song that is noteworthy, and weave a nest that is truly astonishing. The plumage combines black and flaming orange, the colors of Lord Baltimore, who founded the State of Maryland. The song is quite distinctive, and each male expresses his own individuality in his notes so clearly that one can recognize different birds day after day, and even year after year, by their songs.

Photo by Miller.   Courtesy, Nature Magazine

Baltimore Oriole.   This cleverly woven, hanging nest is fastened to the branch of a tree with string.

The nest of the Baltimore Oriole is also very distinctive, and differs widely from that of any of our other birds.   It is a pendulous bag ordinarily fastened near the end of a drooping limb of an elm tree about thirty feet from the ground. If an elm tree is not handy, a maple, birch, or weeping willow will suffice. Plant fibers, such as those from milkweed stalks, horsehair, and string are used in its construction.   These are woven together to form a pouch about ten inches long. It is lined with horsehair.

The sitting parent, and later the young, must find such a nest a rather violently rocked cradle when strong winds blow, but because of its depth, need have no fear of being thrown out.   The nests are so firmly built and fastened to the tree that they retain their identity for several years, and often two or three nests are present in a single tree, representing the homes of a pair of birds in successive breeding seasons.   The eggs, usually five in number, are bluish-white, with fine, irregular, or zigzag lines of brown or black.   The young are very noisy both before and after leaving the nest, for which reason they have been called the cry-babies of the bird world.

Starling. Unless examined closely the Starling might be classed with the Blackbirds, but he really belongs to an entirely different family of Old World birds, and every bird lover wishes he had neven been brought to these shores.   Starlings were introduced into New York in 1890; they have increased rapidly and spread far and wide since then.   They live both in the country and in the city, and travel about in large flocks most of the year.   In the fall of the year, they roost in trees or around buildings, often becoming a great nuisance.

Starlings are largely beneficial as insect destroyers, but are very destructive to native species of birds, and their numbers should be kept down as much as possible. They nest in any sort of opening in a building or in hollow trees and bird boxes. When Flickers have dug a hole for themselves, the Starlings proceed to take it away from them. They deprive other birds of nesting sites and of food, and their combined strength is too great for any of our native birds. Besides this they are able to withstand our northern winters and are already on the field when other birds arrive in the spring, which is half the battle.

In England the Starling is a universal favorite. "It is a sturdy, hardy bird on which the weather has very little effect, being partially migratory and partially stationary, breeding abundantly in central and northern Europe and during the cold season retiring more or less completely to southern Europe and northern Africa. Gregarious at all times, even during the nesting season, it frequents fallow fields, pastures, and meadows, often in company with its larger relative, the Rook, and during the winter and early spring subsists almost entirely upon various insects and their larvae, of which it destroys incalculable numbers. After the

Courtesy, U. S. Bureau of Biological Survey

Starling. An obnoxious bird introduced from the Old World that should have been left at home; the one shown here built a nest in a bird box and is bringing a beakful of insects to its young.

young are able to care for themselves they congregate with the parents in vast flocks, which resort each evening to some chosen roosting place, where they congregate in tens and even hundreds of thousands, resembling, as they whirl and turn, a gigantic black cloud. For an hour they may alternately alight and circle about before they finally settle for the night, with the accompaniment of multitudinous and almost deafening calls. The Starling enjoys the reputation of being an accomplished singer and great mimic, producing, it is said, with astonishing fidelity, the call notes of Goldfinches and other birds, or even the sounds of human activity, but Mr. Hudson insists that its supposed accomplishment is due, not so much to conscious imitation as to the fact that it naturally possesses a great variety and range of call notes from which it is possible to select ones resembling those of other birds. Its own more distinctive notes, which are most frequently heard during the breeding season, are clear whistled calls." (Knowlton.)

The Starlings that nest near our home seem to enjoy fooling us especially by their imitations of the bob-white and wood pewee.

Cedar Waxwing.   The well-groomed, jaunty appearance and smooth, delicately tinted plumage of the Cedar Waxwing make him one of our most beautiful feathered gems.   He is grayish-brown with a long crest, with yellow on the abdomen and tip of the tail, and secondary wing feathers that end in flattened elongations, scarlet in color, and resembling red sealing wax.

During most of the year Waxwings wander about in flocks.   Late in the summer they build a nest usually in an orchard tree about twenty feet from the ground. They feed largely on insects, but when cherries are ripe they show such a preference for them that they are sometimes called Cherry Birds.   In winter they eat large quantities of cedar berries.

Photo by Gross.   Courtesy, Nature Magazine

Cedar Waxwing.   A front view reveals her conspicuous black mask; how snugly she fits into the nest !

Shrike, or Butcher Bird.   Shrikes resemble Mockingbirds in general appearance and are sometimes called French Mockingbirds.   They are gray, black, and white and have a black stripe on the side of the head.   They do not resemble Mockingbirds in their habits, but may almost be classed with the Birds of Prey.   Their bill is hooked at the end, and in addition to insects, mice and other small mammals and small birds are captured by them and devoured.

Shrikes have a habit of fastening their larger prey in the fork of a tree or impaling it on a thorn or the barb of a wire fence, apparently because its feet are too weak to hold it while it tears it to pieces.   They do not go hunting for food as a rule but rest quietly on a perch until they locate a victim; then they fly down and seize it with their claws and kill it with their beak; no wonder a common name for them is Butcher Bird.   The indigestible parts of the food are disgorged.

Photo by Blickensderfer. Courtesy, Nature Magazine

White-Rumped Shrike, or Butcher Bird. She is keeping her eggs warm in the nest but looks alert;
note the hooked beak and black line through the eye.

The nest of the Shrike is built in a thorn tree or thicket about ten feet from the
ground. It consists of weed stalks, grass, and roots and is lined with wool, horsehair, and feathers. The young birds are as pugnacious as their parents.

CHAPTER 32

CHICKADEES, WRENS, WARBLERS, ETC.

Black-Capped Chickadee. Our commonest representative of the Titmouse family is the Chickadee, one of the most entertaining of our smaller birds that fortunately, in many regions, spends the entire year with us. This little black-capped midget greets us on a cold winter day with his *chick-a-dee-dee-dee*, or simply *dee-dee-dee*, and occasionally expresses himself with a *Febe* much like the call of the Phoebe.

Chickadees are often encountered in company with Nuthatches and Kinglets, flitting through the woods searching for insects. They like company, even that of human beings, and are fearless and confiding, being easily induced to accept food from one's hand. A piece of suet fastened to the branch of a tree has a great attraction for Chickadees and will make them regular visitors, and with such little effort.

Chickadees build their nests usually in the deserted nest-hole of a Woodpecker. Leaves, moss, and grass are used and a soft lining of horsehair, fur, and feathers is added. From four to eight eggs are laid. Economically Chickadees are very valuable because they devour enormous numbers of insects, including moths and their eggs, and especially tent caterpillars. One bird during the winter may destroy in the egg many thousands of potentially destructive insects.

Photo by Hegner

Black-Capped Chickadee. At the entrance to a cavity in a dead birch tree in which the nest was built; the black cap and black throat are very conspicuous.

White-Breasted Nuthatch. In winter, when most of our birds have departed southward, our permanent residents become not only more conspicuous, but also more dear to those of us who love the companionship of birds. A bit of suet tied to the limb of a tree is all that is needed to attract the White-Breasted Nuthatch.

This bluish-gray bird with his black cap on relishes a taste of suet, but spends most of his time running up and down and around the tree trunks, as often upside down as rightside up, searching diligently for insects. "Its readiness in descending topsy-turvy is due in part to the fact that, as the quills of its tail are not stiff enough to afford support, it is obliged to depend upon its legs and feet. As it has on each foot three toes in front and only one behind, it reverses the

Courtesy, Natural History Society of Maryland

White-Breasted Nuthatch. A bluish-gray bird with a black cap; he can perch as well as run up and down tree trunks.

position of one foot in going head downward, throwing it out sidewise and backward, so that the three long claws on the three front toes grip the bark and keep the birds from falling forward. The other foot is thrown forward, and thus with feet far apart the 'little gymnast has a wide base beneath him.'" (Forbush.)

The White-Breasted Nuthatch is about six inches long. His call note is a very distinctive *yank, yank*. The nest is built in a hole in a tree, usually that dug by a woodpecker a year or so before. Bark, leaves, hair, and feathers make a soft bed for the five to eight white, brown-speckled eggs to lie on.

Brown Creeper. A place between the Nuthatches and the Wrens seems quite appropriate for the little Brown Creeper. One of the few birds that live in the forest, the Brown Creeper may be discovered industriously minding his own business, which is hunting for insects and their eggs, larvae, or pupae in the cracks and crevices in the bark. He pays no attention to the observer but climbs up in a spiral path, and when he thinks he has mounted high enough, he descends to the base of another tree and repeats the performance. He advances up the trunk by little jumps or "hitches" and often passes entirely around the tree several times before he reaches the main limbs and enters the branches.

Photo by Bond. Courtesy, Nature Magazine

Brown Creeper. His long, curved bill helps him pick insects out of crevices in tree trunks.

One ornithologist watched a Brown Creeper constantly for an hour; during this period he visited forty-three trees, climbing up the trunk of each for about twenty feet.   By the end of the hour he had traveled about 100 yards but was still intent on properly guarding the tree trunks from harmful insects.

Brown Creepers breed in the northern United States and Canada.   The nest is usually built rather near the ground behind the loose bark of a tree, most often a conifer.   Moss, strips of bark, and wood are used in its construction.   The five to eight eggs are white, with a wreath of rufous-brown and lavender spots around the larger end.

Photo by Hegner
House Wren.   Jenny Wren at the entrance to a cigar box under the eaves of a barn in which she had built her nest.

House Wren. If you live in or near the country, usually only a slight effort is necessary to attract a pair of House Wrens to your home. A box or bird house about six inches square placed under the eaves of an outbuilding, or fastened to the side of the house or in a tree about fifteen feet from the ground, will in many cases induce the Wrens to become summer residents in your yard. Two or three houses placed in different types of locations are more attractive than only one, since House Wrens seem to like to build several nests before selecting one in which to lay their eggs.

In nature, Wrens will nest in almost any sort of cavity, hence their scientific name, which means "cave dweller."   The nest is made of dead twigs and lined with grass and feathers.   Usually from six to eight eggs are laid.

The House Wren is an elegant-looking little bird in a brown suit.   He is very nervous and excitable and moves about incessantly, with his tail up in the air. His song is a bubbling outpouring of a merry, exuberant soul, and is repeated at frequent intervals throughout the day.   It is certainly not very musical but makes up in cheerfulness what it lacks in beauty.

Photo by the Finleys.   Courtesy, Nature Magazine

Cactus Wrens.   Natives of our southwestern states that build their nests in cacti; our largest
Wrens, being over 8 inches long.

Jenny Wren is more shy and unobtrusive, creeping about like a little mouse
in nooks and crannies looking for food.   When the young are half grown, both
parents must work from "early morn 'til dewy eve" to keep them fed.   We once
found a pair already at work at four o'clock in the morning, and they kept at it
constantly until dark 16 hours later.   The average number of visits with food
for the young was about 30 per hour.   No strikes for shorter hours are allowed
in the Wren family.

The New World is the home of the Wren, since only about thirty of over 350
known species live abroad.   The Cactus Wrens of the southwestern United
States are our largest species, reaching a length of over eight inches.   They
build their nests in cacti and in bushes, gathering together a mass of twigs and
grass, with the nest proper in the center, and the entrance at one side.   The nest
is lined with feathers.   Marsh Wrens nest in marshes attaching a large mass of
vegetation to upright stalks several feet above the water.   The entrance to their
home is on the side.   One must don high rubber boots if he wishes to visit Marsh
Wrens in comfort.

Yellow-Throated Vireo. Vireos are interesting little birds that occur only in America. Most of the 75 species live in the tropics, but about a dozen have been reported from the United States. The Yellow-Throated Vireo is the handsomest species that makes its home with us. Not only the throat but also the breast is yellow in color, — a characteristic that distinguishes this species from all others.

The nest of the Vireo has a character all its own. It is cup-shaped and suspended between the arms of a forked branch. The walls are rather thin but compact. They are constructed of plant fibers, lined inside with fine grass, and covered outside with lichens. The depth of the cup inside is about two inches.

Photo by Forbush. Courtesy, Nature Magazine

Yellow-Throated Vireo. Throat and breast are yellow; the nest is a pocket-like cradle covered with lichens.

Usually the nest is placed near the trunk or close to a large branch of a tree from ten to thirty feet from the ground. The eggs are three or four in number, white in color, and spotted, especially around the larger end.

The Yellow-Throated Vireo moves about principally in the tops of the trees, where it diligently hunts for insects in crevices and under the leaves. It is "comparatively deliberate in both song and movement, and, though naturally shy when it was confined to the open woods, it has now become rather fearless, and may be readily watched with a glass as it moves along the tall trees. The song is a little louder than that of most Vireos, and may be easily distinguished from all others. It usually consists of two or three rich and virile notes, uttered interrogatively or tentatively, followed immediately by a few similar tones uttered decisively. The bird appears to ask a question, and then answer it." (Forbush.) The words "See me; I'm here; where are you?" have been suggested by way of imitation. The alarm notes of this species are harsh and unpleasant. Vireos should be carefully protected, if for no other reason, because they eat house flies and mosquitoes. However, they also devour vast numbers of such pests as the hairy caterpillars of the tent, gypsy, and tussock moth.

Redstart. A favorite candidate on every bird lover's list for first place among our Wood Warblers is the Redstart. He is the most conspicuously colored of this highly colored family, and added to this has the habit of spreading the tail so as to reveal the bright orange markings underneath, and vibrating the half-raised wings. He never stops for a moment, but with exuberant and boundless energy dances through the forest like a fairy endowed with perpetual motion, busily hunting insects that other birds cannot catch, as he dashes from limb to limb or flutters to the ground and back like a fiery flash. Redstarts are common in woodland districts. They usually build their nests in the crotch of a small tree, weaving a compact cup of vegetable fibers, bark, and grasses and lining it with fine grass, rootlets, hair, or feathers.

Louisiana Water-Thrush. One would hardly expect a Warbler to answer to this name, but he looks very much like a Thrush, with his back of grayish-olive and his white underparts streaked with the same color. You must visit small water courses and the wooded ravines that lead into them in order to see this shy bird or hear his rich, resonant song. He moves about with a dainty, graceful walk in a quick, nervous manner, bobbing his tail up and down much like a Spotted Sandpiper.

Photo by Peabody.   Courtesy, Nature Magazine

Redstart. She is seldom quiet except when sitting on her nest; the male is more brightly colored; Redstarts are warblers.

His nest is well worth examination. It is usually built in an indentation in a mossy bank and would be difficult to find if it were not for the owner's habit of building a large platform of leaves in front of the entrance. With this knowledge it is a simple matter to detect the site of a nest when some distance away. Water-Thrushes feed largely on the larvae of aquatic insects, but other insects, as well as seeds and fruit, are also eaten.

"Few birds are more particular in their choice of homes than this Water-Thrush. He lives where dashing brooks leap down wooded hillsides, or where quieter streams flow through the lowland forests. He is a wild, shy bird, and his never-ceasing alertness suggests the watchfulness of the savage. Approach as quietly as you will, the Water-Thrush knows of your coming. With a tilting motion he walks on ahead, springs from rock to rock, or with a sharp, metallic clink of alarm takes wing and darts through the woods so low you scarcely get a glimpse of him. From a distant

Photo by Hegner

Louisiana Water-Thrush. A Warbler that looks something like a Thrush; the mother is looking out from the cavity in a bank in which her nest was built (see the accompanying photograph).

limb near the ground he watches you, constantly teetering his body as though even when resting he must find some outlet for his surplus nervous energy.

Photo by Hegner

Louisiana Water-Thrush's Nest. The nest was built in a little cavity in a bank and a mass of dead leaves arranged in front of the entrance.

"As a songster the Water-Thrush is without a rival. His song is not to be compared with the plaintive chant of the Field Sparrow, or the hymn-like melody of the true Thrushes; it is of a different kind. It is the untamable spirit of the bird rendered in music. There is an almost fierce wildness in its ringing notes. On rare occasions he is inspired to voice his passion in a flight-song, which so far exceeds his usual performance that even the memory of it is thrilling." (Chapman.)

Somewhat resembling the Water-Thrush is the Ovenbird. His domed nest with the entrance at the side is a bulky affair built on the ground in the woods. His familiar call notes, are "teacher, *teacher*, TEACHER, TEACHER, TEACHER."

Hooded Warbler. A little green and yellow bird with black head, neck, and throat and a large yellow patch around each eye and across the forehead is a Hooded Warbler. "This beautiful bird is a lover of well-watered, rather densely grown woods. It is a bird of the lower growth rather than the trees, but is not a thicket-haunter, and its habit of flitting restlessly from bush to bush renders it easily observed. When on the wing, its white outer tail-feathers are conspicuously displayed, and, with the striking markings of the head, make an excellent field-mark.

"The song of the Hooded Warbler is sweet and graceful. It is subject to much variation, but as a rule consists of eight or nine notes. To my ear the bird seems to say, 'You must come to the woods, or you won't see me.' Its call-note is a sharper, characteristic *cheep*, frequently uttered when the bird is anxious for the safety of its nest of young, and accompanied by a flit of the tail, which reveals the white outer tail-feathers." (Chapman.)

Hooded Warblers are persistent insect hunters; they actively catch insects, darting out for them the way Flycatchers do. One was seen to catch two insects per minute, which amounts to almost a thousand for an eight-hour day. The nest is built only a few inches above the ground; it consists of leaves, bark, and grass and is lined with hair.

"Warblers are birds that assume the care of the trees from the ground to the topmost twig. Some walk daintily along the ground, searching among the shrubbery and fallen leaves; others cling close to the bark, and search its every crevice for those insignificant insects which collectively form the greatest pests of forest and orchard; others mount into the tree, skip from branch to branch, and peer about among the leaves or search the opening buds of the lower branches; others habitually ascend to the tree tops; while still others are in almost constant pursuit of the winged insects that dart about among the branches." (Forbush.)

Photo by Brownell

Hooded Warbler. The head, neck, and throat are black, but a large yellow patch surrounds the eye and extends across the forehead. A meal of insects is about to be delivered to the young.

Yellow Warbler. To most people the Yellow Warbler is confused with the American Goldfinch, or Wild Canary; the latter, however, has black on the crown, wings, and tail, whereas the Yellow Warbler is yellow all over with a more or less greenish tinge on the back, wings, and tail, and in the male, streaks of chestnut color on the sides of the body. He "plays about like a rich yellow flame among the pink of the apple blossoms." Common names for the Yellow Warbler are Summer Yellow Bird, or simply Yellow Bird.

Yellow Warblers are the most familiar of our Warblers. They frequent pasture lands where there are small trees and plenty of shrubbery, but may also visit the vegetation close to the house. They "keep to the middle of the road," neglecting the ground and the tree tops for moderate heights. The song is whistle-like in quality and may be translated into the words *we'-chee, we'-chee, wee'-oo.*

The nest is usually built in the upright crotch or fork of a small tree or shrub. Vegetable fibers, fine grass, and an abundance of plant down are used in its construction. Sometimes a cowbird lays an egg or two in the nest before the Yellow Warbler has had a chance to complete its own egg laying. When this happens, a new bottom may be laid over the eggs, resulting in a sort of double-decked nest.

The speed with which the female builds her nest seems hardly credible. "She first laid a foundation of a few straws and placed upon them the cotton or down from fern fronds. These she bound together with the silk from a tent caterpillar's web. Then she went alternately for the cotton and the silk, stopping occasionally at an apple tree and feeding for a moment or two on cankerworms. When I went past the nest at night I found she had it nearly complete; the lining only was lacking." (Mosher.)

Photo by Brownell

Yellow Warbler. The nest is firmly wedged in the crotch of a small tree; although it contains four young, "three is a crowd."

"It would be hard to find a summer bird more useful among the shade trees or in the orchard and small-fruit garden than this species. Almost entirely insectivorous, it feeds on many of the greatest pests that attack our fruit trees, vines, and berry bushes. Whenever the caterpillars of which it is fond are plentiful they form about two-thirds of its food. It is destructive to the small caterpillars of the gypsy moth and the brown-tail moth, and is inordinately fond of cankerworms and other measuring worms. Tent caterpillars are commonly eaten." (Forbush.)

Gnatcatchers. Gnatcatchers are small Flycatcher-like birds about five inches long, classified with the Kinglets and Old World Warblers. The species that lives in the warmer portions of the eastern United States is the Blue-Gray Gnatcatcher. He spends much of his time in the topmost branches of the tallest trees, "skipping nimbly from twig to twig, with lowering half-spread wings and nervous twitchings of the whole body, in eager quest of insects and larvae, now pausing a moment to pry more closely into a suspected crevice of the bark, then darting into the air to capture a passing fly, and regaining his perch after almost a somersault."

The nests of the Blue-Gray Gnatcatchers "are exquisite examples of bird architecture, being very deeply cup-shaped structures composed of strips of soft bark, thistledown, and the like, stuccoed outside with lichens, and firmly fastened in a crotch or on a branch, usually at a considerable height from the ground. The four to five eggs are bluish white thickly spotted with brown." (Knowlton.)

The Gnatcatchers of the western United States are similar in appearance and habits to their eastern relatives. The Plumbeous Gnatcatcher is shown in our photograph. Its eggs are pale greenish-blue spotted with reddish-brown.

Photo by the Finleys.   Courtesy, Nature Magazine

Plumbeous Gnatcatcher.   A small Flycatcher-like bird about five inches long; the nest is deep and well constructed of plant fibers and thistledown.

CHAPTER 33

THRASHERS, THRUSHES, SPARROWS, ETC.

Mockingbird. The Mockingbird, Catbird, and Brown Thrasher belong to a family of birds famous for their vocal ability. The Mockingbird is one of the most renowned singers in North America. Appropriately enough the scientific name of the Mockingbird means "many-tongued mimic." He imitates many other birds, such as the Robin, Wood Thrush, Bluebird, Wren, and Cardinal, and one observer in South Carolina reports having heard one mimic the notes of 32 birds in ten minutes. Besides this he has a remarkable song of his own, and on moonlit nights during the mating season "the inspired singer launches himself far into the air,

Photo by Squire. Courtesy, Nature Magazine

Mockingbird. A long, slender, ashy-gray bird with a grasshopper in her bill for the hungry babies in the nest.

filling the silvery spaces of the night with the exquisite swells and trills, liquid and sweet, of his unparalleled melody. The song rises and falls as the powers of the singer wax and wane, and so he serenades his mate throughout the livelong night."

Mockingbirds will even sing in a cage and were formerly trapped and sold as cage birds, but this pernicious practice has, of course, been stopped.

In the South the Mockingbird is a semi-domesticated dweller in village gardens, much as the Robin is in the North. His nest is built in a small tree, bush, or hedge, usually from six to ten feet from the ground. The parents defend their young with great courage.

Brown Thrasher. The Brown Thrasher, or Brown "Thrush," as he is sometimes erroneously called, is almost as famous a songster as the Mockingbird, and certainly excels the Catbird as a vocalist. He mounts to the highest twig of the tallest tree and sends his rich, musical melody over the countryside for all to hear. When

Photo by Cornelia Clarke

Brown Thrasher. Her back is reddish-brown, her breast streaked with black, and her bill long and sharp; the nest is built in a vine-entangled thicket.

he sings passionately to his mate, he works himself into a fine frenzy. "As the fervor increases his long and elegant tail droops; all his feathers separate; his whole plumage lifted, it floats, trembles; his head is raised and his bill is wide open; there is no mistake; it is the power of God. No pen can report him now; we must wait until the frenzy passes." (Cheney.)

The Brown Thrasher is a long, slender bird, reddish-brown above and heavily streaked with black below. His bill is long and curved downward at the end. He is less domestic than the Mockingbird or Catbird and more retiring, being partial to thickets near cultivated fields, where he shyly skulks away when approached. Much of his food is obtained on the ground with vigorous scratching, scattering of leaves, and thrashing of the tail.

He protects his nest with vigor, rivaling the Blue Jay in this respect. Like most birds, favorite perches are used again and again when the Thrasher brings food to its young. On one occasion the top of a fence post proved to be a rather constantly used resting place and a photograph was easily obtained by focusing the camera on the top of the post and snapping it the next time the parent approached the nest, which was located in a bush near by.

Catbird.   The voice of the Catbird is almost as fine and varied as that of the Mockingbird, but it includes many harsh notes and is interrupted by "cat calls"

Photo by Hegner

Catbird.   A slaty-gray bird with black crown and black tail and chestnut-colored feathers beneath the tail; the nest was built among the vines on the side of the house.

and hence is seldom fully appreciated. The Catbird is inconspicuous and male, female, and young are all alike in appearance both in summer and in winter. The plumage is slaty gray, the top of the head and tail black, and the under tail coverts chestnut.

Catbirds live in shrubbery and build their nests in tangled growths or in bushes. They are made of sticks, leaves, grass, and rootlets, and the eggs, usually four in number, are dark bluish-green. Both parents are very solicitous of their nest and young and even take part in the troubles of other birds. We have seen Catbirds as excited, when another bird's nest was being robbed, as though it were their own.

The nest shown in the photograph was built in some shrubbery against a house. The devoted parents returned to it with very little hesitation even though the branches had been removed so as to reveal the nest, and sunlight from a large mirror was reflected upon it so that a photograph could be made.

Robin.   Among the Thrushes are included the Robin and the Bluebird, the most familiar members of the family.   The Robin is perhaps the best-known bird in America.   He is fond of human society and may be considered semi-domesticated in the regions where he breeds.   We love Robin Redbreast especially well, since he is among the earliest harbingers of spring and entertains us so constantly with his cheerful warble.   He is fond of earthworms and makes a very interesting moving picture as he drags his prey slowly out of its hole in the lawn.   Fruit also finds a place on his bill of fare, and sometimes cultivated fruit suffers, but for the most part the Robin feeds on insects and wild fruit and is therefore very beneficial.

Photo by Hegner

Robin.   A partial albino bird sitting on her nest in the characteristic Robin attitude; many of the feathers are white that are ordinarily dark-colored.

The nest of the Robin is a bowl of mud with a lining of grass, and is usually placed in the crotch of a tree.   The masonry in the nest is concealed by grass; it is molded into shape by the mother so as to fit her body exactly; this must be a great comfort to her as she sits hour after hour with nothing to think about but her bodily aches and pains.

Occasionally animals of various types lack their usual coloring matter and are known as albinos.   One spring a partial albino Robin appeared and built a nest opposite our home.   We were fortunate to obtain several photographs which show the bird in characteristic Robin attitudes.   Probably on account of its conspicuous colors, this Robin was captured by a cat before the young were old enough to leave the nest; they perished there, since the father left them when their mother was killed. Cats are perhaps the most important enemies of birds, at least in settled communities, and should be eliminated entirely or confined during the nesting season.

Bluebird.   The Bluebird rivals the Robin as a harbinger of spring, but is an inhabitant of orchards and fields and therefore not often seen near our homes. He is a welcome tenant of the farm, and his presence is assured if a bird house is provided for him.   Bluebirds build their nests in cavities in trees and fence posts, often the old deserted nest-holes of woodpeckers; they are found only where there are nest sites.

The call note of the Bluebird is a plaintive melodious whistle and the song a rich, sweet warble.   In the fall their good-by notes *far-away*, *far-away*, may be heard as they fly by overhead to distant and warmer climes.   Bluebirds feed largely on insects and often fly down to the ground to catch a grasshopper and then return to their perch.   Sometimes, like a Flycatcher, they catch insects on the wing. In 1895, a severe cold wave developed after the Bluebirds had reached their summer

Photo by Hegner

Bluebird.   The solicitous parent has brought a grasshopper but the young bird does not respond, probably because he has been moved from a hole in a fence post to this perch.

nomes in the North and many thousands of them perished, but they have since regained their normal numbers.

"Gentle and lovable in disposition, he comes fearlessly about houses and gardens, having the 'blue of the sky upon his back and on his breast the tints of its rosy dawn,' a veritable harbinger of spring and messenger of good cheer. Although generally migratory everywhere, a few may occasionally be seen in winter even in the most northern states, but the majority spend the colder months in the south, where in companies they congregate to feed upon the berries of the mistletoe, red cedar, and other like fruits.   But in earliest spring, often in February and March, they suddenly appear in couples in their summer haunts in the

north, returning year after year to the same localities. As soon as weather conditions permit, they set about house hunting and after the inspection of all available sites select a nesting box, a hole in a tree, a hollow post or fence rail, and upon a scant lining of soft grasses deposit from four to six pale blue, rarely white, unspotted eggs. They are often annoyed and frequently dispossessed of their nesting site by the pestiferous House Sparrow, especially in towns and cities, though in country districts they manage to hold their own. After rearing several broods, they congregate in small parties in pastures, stumpy fields, and cleared woods, and seem loath to leave, but at last when the warning of approaching winter can no longer be unheeded, they start with sadly plaintive calls quite unlike their cheerful spring notes for their winter home." (Knowlton.)

Photo by Hegner

Bluebird. The father bird pays a visit to the nest-hole in a small tree.

Wood Thrush. The Wood Thrush combines handsome feathers with a beautiful voice and, what is even more important to some of us, has adapted himself to human habitations and is often to be found nesting in shade trees near our homes. We have been favored year after year in Roland Park, Baltimore, with Wood Thrush music during the summer season. We see the birds searching for beetles, bugs, and snails on the ground under the shrubbery in our yard. They have a plump body, bright, cinnamon-colored feathers above, and large, round, blackish spots on the breast and sides. The nest is a rather bulky affair resembling that of the robin. A shell of mud is covered with twigs, leaves, and grass, and lined with fine rootlets. The three or four eggs are greenish-blue, almost like robin's-egg blue.

The song of the Wood Thrush is equaled by that of few birds. "Its tones are solemn and serene. They seem to harmonize with the sounds of the forest, the whispering breeze, the purling water, or the falling of rain drops in the summer woods. At evening the bird usually mounts to the higher branches of the taller trees, often upon the edge of the forest, where nothing intervenes to confine or subdue his 'heavenly music.' There, sitting quite erect, he emits his wonderful notes in the most leisurely fashion, and apparently with little effort. *A olee*, he sings, and rests; then, unhurried, pours forth a series of intermittent strains which seem to express in music the sentiment of nature; powerful, rich, metallic, with the vanishing vibratory tones of the bell, they seem like a vocal expression of the

Courtesy, Natural History Society of Maryland

Wood Thrushes. The back of the bird is cinnamon-colored and the breast and sides bear large, round, blackish spots; both parents are visiting their young at the same time.

mystery of the universe, clothed in a melody so pure and ethereal that the soul still bound to its earthly tenement can neither imitate nor describe it. The song rises and falls, swells and dies away, until dark night has fallen." (Forbush.)

Hermit Thrush. Although this species of Thrush has both beauty of form and color, and a song of exquisite purity and sweetness to be proud of, he is so modest and retiring as to have earned the name Hermit. We are accustomed to see Hermit Thrushes early in the spring, identifying them easily because of their thrushlike characteristics combined with a reddish-brown tail, such as is claimed by no other Thrush. "It frequently descends to the ground, but is soon back again in the branches, making short flights from perch to perch, often with long, quiet pauses in the intervals. It may be known at sight by its habit of lifting its tail slightly, especially after alighting. This action is usually accompanied by the bird's customary note — a low *chuck*, which sounds scarcely thrushlike." (Chapman.)

During the summer, Hermit Thrushes bring up their families in the northern states and Canada. The nest is usually built on the ground. It is a rather bulky structure of leaves, grass, and moss, lined with pine needles and rootlets.   The three or four eggs are greenish-blue in color.

Much has been written regarding the song of the Hermit Thrush.   It has been compared favorably with that of the Wood Thrush and the Nightingale.   "Its

Photo by the Finleys.   Courtesy, Nature Magazine

Hermit Thrush.   This famous singer has a reddish-brown tail which distinguishes it easily from other thrushes; this nest was built in an evergreen tree.

notes are not remarkable for variety or volume, but in purity and sweetness of tone and exquisite modulation they are unequaled — in tranquil clearness of tone and exalted serenity of expression, go beyond any woods music we ever hear." (Bicknell.)

Nightingale.   Many birds sing at night, but the Nightingale has received more praise for its vocal powers than any other species.   It is a small bird only six inches long, colored rufous-brown above and grayish-white below.   During the winter, Africa is its home, and in the spring it migrates to southern and central Europe. Woodlands, groves, and hedges are preferred by it as a habitat.

> "'Tis the merry nightingale
> That crowds and hurries and precipitates
> With thick fast warble his delicious notes,
> As he were fearful that an April night
> Would be too short for him to utter forth
> His love-chant, and disburden his full soul
> Of all his music."   (Coleridge.)

Photo by Tuckett.   Courtesy, Nature Magazine

Nightingale. The most renowned singer of Europe; the back is rufous-brown and under parts grayish-white; the nest is in a shrub.

Bird lovers differ regarding the relative place among feathered songsters that should be accorded the Nightingale. One speaks of its smooth, deliciously melodious phrases "reminding us of the singing cadence of the night wind's gentle whistle, descending through almost imperceptible gradations of the chromatic scale." Another says "it is the only songster that has been too much lauded, with the inevitable result that its melody, when first heard, causes disappointment, and even incredulity."

Nightingales nest in shrubbery, building a home of leaves, grass, and rootlets. Four to six olive-brown eggs are laid.

Rose-Breasted Grosbeak. Grosbeaks are characterized by a very stout bill. Several of them are particularly handsome, and not the least elegant of these is the Rose-Breasted Grosbeak. The head, neck, and back of the male are solid black, the underparts are white, and on the breast is a triangular patch of beautiful rose-red. The female is a comparatively plain bird.

Rose-Breasted Grosbeaks are nowhere very common. We have found them nesting in the small trees along the borders of streams. The nest is a frail structure of twigs, grass, and rootlets. From three to five pale blue eggs, heavily blotched with brown, are laid. Both parents take part in keeping them warm, and the male is a devoted husband, remaining near the nest while his mate is incubating and later helping to care for the young.

Photo by Hegner

Rose-Breasted Grosbeak. This young bird seems very serious; it is colored like the adult female and has a white streak over the eye; the bill is very thick.

"The Rose-Breasted Grosbeak is a shy, retiring bird and not often seen. His call note, a thin, sharp *eek*, is very distinctive and once heard cannot be mistaken for that of any other species. His song is clear and melodious and strongly resembles the finest performance of the robin — only the warble is much more copious, continuously prolonged, and finely modulated with a peculiar richness, purity and sweet pathos in the tones. . . ." (Langille.) He sings during the middle of the day, when it is hot and most other birds are taking a nap, and may even sing while sitting on the nest. Finally, an outstanding feature of this species is its fondness for potato beetles, which are not eaten by most birds.

Cardinal. James Lane Allen's novel proclaimed the glory of the Kentucky Cardinal to the world most effectively. The Cardinal Grosbeak, or Redbird, is colored like the cassock of a Cardinal in the Roman Church. He has a black stripe around the base of the bill and a prominent crest on top of his head. The female is less brightly colored.

Photo by the Finleys. Courtesy, Nature Magazine

Gray Cardinal, or Pyrrhuloxia. A western species with a short, heavy bill; its habits are similar to those of the eastern Cardinal.

Cardinals are permanent residents throughout much of their range and are especially appreciated in the winter as they tune up at break of day or flash by against a snowy background. They are active and bold, and express their nature in no uncertain terms with a series of clear, resonant whistles, *What cheer! What cheer!* often repeated and ending with a long-drawn-out *e-eee.*

Cardinals favor the shelter of thickets in river bottoms, but many of them, fortunately for us, prefer to make their homes in the dooryards of villages and towns. Their nests are usually built in a bush a few feet from the ground. The male is a good husband, watching over his family with solicitude and taking charge of the young after they leave the nest.

American Goldfinch. Long after the other birds have finished rearing their young the American Goldfinch, Wild Canary, or Thistle Bird, begins to think of keeping house for a while. During most of the year Goldfinches are sociably wandering about in small flocks, hunting for seeds, like typical Sparrows, in fields and gardens. As July approaches they mate and build their nests. We have found many of them built in small saplings or in the crotches of large thistle plants.

Photo by Hegner

American Goldfinch, or Wild Canary. The nest was built in the crotch of a large thistle and consisted largely of thistledown; the day was very hot and the parent is panting for air.

They are compact cradles well lined with thistle down. The eggs are usually five or six in number, and pale bluish-white in color, without spots.

The body of the Goldfinch is lemon-yellow in color, and the wings, tail, forehead, and crown are black, the result being a striking contrast that makes him one of our most easily recognized Finches. Goldfinches are also characterized by a pronounced undulatory flight. Their call note is plaintive and their song much like that of the Canary. "Their love song is delivered with an ecstasy and abandon which carries them off their feet, and they circle over the field sowing the air with music." (Chapman.)

Vesper Sparrow. Among the plain-colored Sparrows, that group that is so hard to identify, is the Vesper Sparrow, whose other names are Grass Finch, Bay-Winged Bunting, and Ground Bird. Every boy who lives in the country is well acquainted with the Ground Bird, and its eggs are among the first to find a place in his collection. He is grayish-brown streaked with black, but is easily distinguished from other little brown birds by the two white outer tail feathers which are revealed when he flies. His shoulders are chestnut-colored, hence Bay-Winged Sparrow. He is a bird of the wide, open spaces, but is rather shy. Often he runs along the road ahead of one, flies forward for a short distance, and then alights in the road again.

His song is noteworthy and may be heard at any time of day, but especially in the early morning and evening. Perched on an elevation in the field, on a fence post or the low limb of a tree, he will sing again and again a short, simple, plaintive melody in a tender minor key. His nest is built in a cavity in the ground and is level with the surface. It consists of dried grasses, and is lined with horse-hair. As the mother sits on her eggs she can hardly be distinguished from the surrounding grass, so well do her markings blend with the vegetation. When she is startled from her nest of young, she uses all her arts to entice the intruder away, fluttering along the ground with white-bordered tail spread conspicuously, and dragging her wings as if sorely wounded,—a tempting bait to lead the disturber away.

Photo by Hegner

Vesper Sparrow. A grayish-brown bird streaked with black and difficult to see on its nest in the grass.

Lark Sparrow. The Lark Sparrow resembles somewhat the Vesper Sparrow in appearance and habits. He is handsome and more strikingly colored, with a chestnut crown through which runs a stripe of gray, a line of white over the eye, a white stripe below the eye, and a black button on a white breast. His tail feathers are tipped with white, so that when they are spread in flight, a white crescent appears, resembling in this respect the tail of the Mourning Dove.

Lark Sparrows live on or near the ground in open country. Like the Vesper Sparrow, they are often encountered in roads or perched on fence posts. The nest is built on the ground, usually at the base of a weed, such as a dandelion, as in the accompanying photograph. The song of the Lark Sparrow is so musical that the birds were formerly captured and used as cage singers. It is "one continued gush of sprightly music, now gay, now melodious, and then tender beyond description — the very expression of emotion. At intervals the singer falters, as if exhausted by exertion, and his voice becomes scarcely audible; but suddenly reviving in his joy, it is resumed in all its vigor until he appears to be really overcome by the effort." (Ridgway.) Lark Sparrows are famous "big game hunters," the prey consisting of grasshoppers. They deserve to be well protected.

Photo by Hegner

Lark Sparrow. The gray and white stripes on the head are distinctive markings of the Lark Sparrow; the nest was built under a dandelion plant.

Chipping Sparrow. These little Sparrows make up in friendliness what they lack in musical ability. They are birds of the farmyard, garden, and lawn, building their nests in vines and shrubbery, and especially in small evergreen trees. Rootlets form the outer structure of the nest, but so much horsehair is used as a lining that Chipping Sparrows are often called Hair Birds. Four or five eggs are laid, and two broods are often raised in a single season.

Courtesy, Natural History Society of Maryland

Chipping Sparrow. The chestnut-colored crown, grayish line over the eye, and black line behind the eye are the distinguishing marks of the chipping sparrow.

Chipping Sparrows are among the smaller Sparrows, measuring only about five inches in length. Their distinguishing marks are the following: the crown is deep chestnut; there is a grayish line over the eye and a narrow black line back of the eye; and the rump and tail coverts are ashy gray. "The song of the Chipping Sparrow is a mere string of dry chips, sometimes repeated very rapidly and almost running into a trill, sometimes more slowly. The ordinary notes are a variety of *chips*, a sort of squeak, and a series of querulous twitters, uttered when the bird is angry."

White-Throated Sparrow. Residents of the eastern United States know the White-Throated Sparrow only as a migrant, since he builds his nest north of our border. However, every bird lover is happy to welcome his spring and fall visits, since he is perhaps our most handsome Sparrow, and his song is a cheerful, piping whistle. Two clear notes are followed by three trills sounding much like the words "Old Sam Peabody, Peabody, Peabody." On this account White-Throated Sparrows are known as Peabody Birds.

There is no difficulty in distinguishing this species from other Sparrows because of the conspicuous white

Courtesy, Natural History Society of Maryland

White-Throated Sparrow. A handsome bird with a conspicuous white throat and a black crown with a white stripe down the center.

patch on the throat. The crown is black with a white stripe down the center. Above the eye is another white stripe which changes to yellow between the eye and the bill. The sides of the head and the breast are gray. The plumage on the back is brown, streaked with black. The birds are sociable during their migrations, going about in groups of a dozen or two. Their time is spent largely in scratching about among dead leaves in search of seeds and insects.

Song Sparrow. When you learn the call notes and song of the Song Sparrow, you can identify him easily without seeing him. Until that time comes, about all you need to know is that he looks like a sparrow and has black spots and streaks on the breast and sides and a large black blotch in the center of the breast.

His usual call note is a metallic *chenk*. His song may be heard at any time of the season, but is especially noticeable in March and April. It has been put to

Photo by Klugh. Courtesy, Nature Magazine

Song Sparrow. The spots on the breast unite to form a large blotch in the center, which is an easy mark for identification.

the following words: "Maids! maids! maids! hang on your tea-kettle-ettle-ettle."

Our earliest recollections of Song Sparrows are associated with fishing trips in the spring. One is almost certain to encounter these birds along rivers and on moist land near water. The nest is built usually on the ground, and well hidden in the thick grass or under an overhanging bank. It consists of grass, rootlets, and bark, and is lined with fine grass and hair. Four or five speckled eggs are laid.

Slate-Colored Junco. We especially appreciate the visits of the Slate-Colored Junco because he comes in the winter when the weather has driven most of our other feathered friends away.   This has gained for him the common name of Snow Bird. In company with other Finches, the Juncos wander about in flocks of a dozen or more, scratching away the leaves in search of seeds in fields, hedges, and dooryards. We can keep them near by for a longer visit by providing a supply of crumbs or seeds for them, and are well repaid by their gentle and friendly manner.

The Junco is a plump, slate-colored bird, about the size of an English Sparrow, with a white belly and a pink bill.   When he flies he flashes the white of his outer tail feathers.   His call note is a sparrow-like *tsip* and his song, which is heard to the best advantage in the breeding season, is described as "a prolonged tintinnabulous twitter — a more musical rendering of the monotonous strokes in the plain melody of the Chipping Sparrow.   Sometimes, however, one may surprise it in a soft, low warble, as if indulging in a musical soliloquy."   (Langille.)   Juncos breed at high altitudes or in the far North.   The nest is built on the ground of moss, grass, and rootlets and lined with fine rootlets or hair.

Slate-Colored Junco.   Some call him a Snow Bird; he is slate-colored and has a pink bill.

CHAPTER 34

MAMMALS — EGG–LAYING, POUCHED, TOOTHLESS, FLYING, AND INSECT–EATING MAMMALS

Mammals are popularly known as "animals" or beasts. We are all familiar with domesticated species, such as the dog, cat, horse, cow, etc., and with many of the wild forms. The term Mammalia was applied to the group because the young, which are born in a very immature condition, are fed with milk from the mammary glands of the mother. There are about 4000 species of living Mammals, but only a small proportion of these occur in this country. Mammals range in size from the shrew at one extreme to the whale at the other extreme. Among the simplest species are the egg-laying mammals of Australia and the opossum and kangaroo, which carry their young about with them in a pouch. Other well-known species are the moles, shrews, bats, dogs, cats, seals, rabbits, rats, anteaters, armadillos, camels, deer, horses, elephants, whales, monkeys, apes, and man.

Photo by Cornelia Clarke

Mole. The fore limbs are enormously developed for digging purposes. The nose is pointed and the eyes very small.

The great diversities exhibited by the Mammals are due chiefly to their various modes of life. Most of them live on the ground; but many are aquatic, others arboreal, and a few aerial in habit. The whales, dolphins, seals, walruses, and sea cows are aquatic, living almost without exception in the sea. They are not aquatic in the same sense that fish are, however, since they cannot take oxygen from the water but must come to the surface to breathe.

Among the arboreal Mammals are the monkeys, squirrels, and sloths. Some of the squirrels can even "fly" through the air for short distances; but, as in the case of the flying dragon, flight here is really only sailing through the air on outstretched membranes. The bats, however, possess wings and are as much air inhabitants as the birds.

A few species, like the mole, pass almost their entire existence underground, and the ground squirrels, woodchucks, prairie dogs, and similar species live part of the time in burrows.

Mammals, like birds, are warm-blooded animals and must be protected not only from their natural enemies and from the ordinary hard knocks of life but also from weather conditions, such as extreme cold, which would not injure cold-blooded creatures like the frog and turtle. Heat is kept in the body in various ways. Mammals that live in cold water, like the whale, possess a very thick layer of fat, the blubber, just beneath the skin, which prevents the escape of the body heat. The more usual method of protection from the cold is a thick covering of hair.

All Mammals possess hairs and may be distinguished from all other Animals by these peculiar structures. The hairs project out from pits in the skin, called hair follicles. The hair shaft broadens at the base, extending around a highly vascular papilla at the bottom of the pit. When hairs are shed, new hairs usually arise to take their place. Secretions from the sebaceous glands keep the hairs glossy.

The two main types of hairs are (1) contour hairs, which are long and strong, and (2) woolly hairs, which are shorter and constitute the under fur. In some animals the woolly hairs have a rough surface, as in the sheep, which causes them to cohere and gives them their felting quality. Certain of the stronger hairs may be moved by muscular fibers, which are responsible for the erection of spines or the bristling of the other hairs.

The air spaces between the hairs prevent the escape of heat, since air is a poor conductor of heat. Besides protecting the body from loss of heat, the hairy covering also prevents to a large extent injury due to blows. Human beings are almost entirely covered by hair except on the soles of the feet and palms of the hands. This covering is of practically no value except the thick growth on the head.

As a rule Mammals are not very highly colored, but many of them are characterized by stripes, as in the zebra and tiger, or spots, as in the leopard. The dull colors of Mammals and stripes or spots are all supposed to aid in concealing the animals amid their surroundings and thus to protect them from their enemies. Animals, like the arctic fox, that live in the colder regions of the earth change color in the winter, becoming white. This change is of advantage, since it renders them inconspicuous against the background of snow.

Mammals protect themselves from their enemies when in actual combat by means of their teeth, claws, nails, horns, and hoofs. The claws, nails, and hoofs are all modifications of the horny covering on the upper surface at the ends of the digits. The foot may rest partially or entirely on these structures, as in the case of the horse; but as a rule it is partly supported on the pads just beneath them. The horns of the rhinoceros and the horn sheaths of cattle are, like claws and hoofs, formed from the outer layer of the skin, the epidermis; but in many other animals the horns are of bone, and even in cattle the central core of the horn is bone. Some animals, like the deer and prong-horned antelope, shed their horns annually and new sets gradually grow out to take their place; others, like cattle and sheep, normally keep one pair of horns throughout life. In many cases only the male individuals of a species possess horns.

The habitat of an animal determines to a large extent its method of locomotion. Whales swim about easily in the water but are helpless on land. Seals and walruses

Photo by J. G. Allen

Porcupine. The hair of this gnawing mammal is not only very long but mixed with stout, sharp spines that can be erected by muscles in the skin.

are likewise excellent swimmers, but their flippers and heavy bodies make locomotion on land very slow and awkward. Most of the Mammals walk, run, or hop; but a few of them can sail through the air for short distances, and the bats, as previously stated, can actually fly.

The teeth of Mammals are among their most interesting possessions, since they vary considerably in the different species and indicate what kind of food is eaten by their owners. Most Mammals are provided with teeth; but the whalebone whales, the egg-laying species, and anteaters are without them in the adult stage, and in some forms they have never been found, even in the embryo.

The teeth are embedded in sockets in the bone. They consist of enamel, the outer hard substance; dentine, which constitutes the largest portion of the tooth; and cement, which usually covers the part of the tooth embedded in the jaw. The central pulp cavity of the tooth contains nerves and blood vessels. Teeth have an open pulp cavity during growth, which in some cases continues throughout life.

There are commonly four kinds of teeth in each jaw: (1) the chisel-shaped incisors in front, (2) the conical canines, (3) the anterior grinding teeth, or premolars, and (4) the posterior grinding teeth, or molars. In most Mammals, the first set of teeth, known as the milk dentition, is pushed out by the permanent teeth, which last throughout the rest of the life of the animal. The milk molars are followed by the premolars, but the permanent molars have no predecessors.

The relation of the form of the teeth to the food habits of the animal may be shown by the following examples: The dolphins have a large number of sharp, conical teeth adapted for capturing fish; the carnivorous animals, like the dog, are

Photo by J. G. Allen

Woodchuck. The large upper incisor teeth are worn down to a chisel-like edge by the lower teeth which rub against them; the incisors continue to grow throughout life.

provided with large canine teeth for capturing and killing their prey, small and almost useless incisors, and molars with sharp edges for cutting or crushing; herbivorous Mammals, like the ox, possess broad incisors for biting off plants, no canines, and large grinding molars; gnawing mammals, like the rabbit, have incisors that grow throughout life but are worn down by gnawing, thereby maintaining a serviceable length and a keen cutting edge; insect-eating Mammals, such as the mole, seize insects with their projecting incisors and cut them into pieces with the pointed cusps on their premolars and molars; and omnivorous animals are provided with teeth fitted for masticating both animal and vegetable matter.

The study of Mammals in their native haunts is rather difficult, since most of them are so badly persecuted by man that they conceal themselves as soon as they become aware of the presence of human beings. This situation can be overcome in part by the study of animal tracks. By an animal track is meant the footprint of an animal. When these footprints continue for some distance, they constitute a trail. Broken twigs and other signs are also of service in deciding what kind of animal was present and what it was doing. The character of the track depends somewhat on the way the animal walks. Bears, for example, walk upon the entire surface of the digits; they are called plantigrade. Cats and dogs rest only upon the outer parts of the digits (digitigrade); and the hoofed Mammals, such as the horse, are supported on the ends of the digits (unguligrade).

Snow records the movements of animals very clearly, and consequently winter is the best time to study animal tracks. Hard, dry snow, like a daily newspaper, is only a temporary medium; but tracks made in loose, wet snow may last for weeks or months. Wet sand, clay, or mud are also good recorders of animal tracks; but they can be found as a rule only near bodies of water.

To determine the kind of animal one is tracking, it is necessary to know something of the habits of the animals, the structure and size of their feet, and their methods of locomotion. Thus the tracks of the mink, least weasel, and wolverine are shaped alike; but that of the weasel is only an inch long, whereas that of the wolverine is five inches long, and the track of the mink may end in a hole in the ice. The direction in which an animal was moving may be determined by the claws.

Tracks frequently indicate emotions, such as fear, dislike, or anger. Fear or caution are most often expressed. For example, a rabbit came through a forest and was forced to cross a frozen creek before it could reach a swamp it wished to enter. The distances between its tracks as it neared the creek decreased from over three to less than two feet. It finally landed backward at the edge of the forest, facing its track to see if it was being pursued. Here it stayed long enough to melt the snow under its paws. Then it bounded across the creek, covering about five feet at each leap. Again it landed facing the track it had made. Being satisfied that it had escaped observation, it entered the swamp at a leisurely pace.

The problem of maintaining life during the winter is solved by most birds by migrating. Mammals, on the other hand, usually remain active, like the rabbit, or hibernate. During hibernation the temperature of the body decreases and the animal falls into a profound torpor. A cold-blooded animal, like the frog, can be almost entirely frozen without being injured; but warm-blooded animals must protect themselves from the cold. They therefore seek a sheltered spot, such as a burrow in the ground, in which to spend the winter. Furthermore, at this time the fur of Mammals is very thick and consequently helps to retain the body heat.

The temperature of the body of hibernating animals becomes considerably lower than normal; for example, a ground squirrel which hibernated in a temperature of 35.6° F. had a body temperature exactly the same, although its normal temperature is several degrees higher. Respiration almost ceases; the heart beats very slowly; and no food is taken into the body, but the fat masses stored up in the autumn are consumed and the animal awakens in the spring in an emaciated condition.

The woodchuck is the most profound sleeper of our common Mammals. It feeds on red clover in the autumn, goes into its burrow about October 1, and does not come out until April 1. The bear does not sleep so profoundly, for if there is plenty of food, and the temperature is mild, he will not hibernate at all. When the bear does hibernate, he scoops out a den under a log or among the roots of a hollow tree. The raccoon and gray squirrel sleep during the severest part of the winter; the skunk spends January and February in his hole; the chipmunk wakes up occasionally to feed; and the red squirrel is abroad practically all winter.   Many other Mammals hibernate for a greater or less period of time.

Comparatively few Mammals migrate; this may be due in part to their inadequate means of locomotion.   Among those that do migrate are the fur seal, reindeer, caribou, bison, bat, and lemming.   The fur seals in American waters breed on the Pribilof Islands in Bering Sea, where they remain from about May 1 to Septem-

Photo by Brownell

Tracks of Cottontail Rabbit in Snow.   The front feet are set down one almost behind the other and the hind legs straddle them, hence the forward pair of tracks in each set are made by the hind feet.

ber 15.   They then put out to sea, spending the winter months making a circuit of about 6000 miles.

The reindeer of Spitzbergen migrate regularly to the central portion of the island in summer and back to the seacoast in the autumn, where they feed upon seaweed.   The bisons used to range over a large part of North America, making regular spring and fall migrations.   They covered an area of about 3600 miles from north to south and 2000 miles from east to west.

The lemmings of Scandinavia are celebrated for their curious migrations. They are small, gnawing animals about three inches in length. "At intervals, averaging about a dozen years apart, lemmings suddenly appear in cultivated districts in central Norway and Sweden, where ordinarily none live, and in a year or two multiply into hordes which go traveling straight west toward the Atlantic, or east toward the Gulf of Bothnia, as the case may be, regardless of how the valleys trend, climbing a mountain instead of going around it, and, undeterred by any river or lake, keep persistently onward until finally some survivors reach the sea, into which they plunge and perish." They are said to march in "parallel lines three feet apart" and "gnaw through hay and corn stacks rather than go around."

The various species of Mammals and other animals are rather definitely restricted to certain regions on the earth's surface. The earth has an area of about 200,000,000 square miles, five eighths of which is covered by the sea. This vast territory is not uniform but presents a great number of sets of conditions. The principal habitats are the solid earth, the liquids upon the earth, and the atmosphere. The facts of geographical distribution have led to the formulation of the three following laws: (1) the law of definite habitats, (2) the law of dispersion, and (3) the law of barriers and highways.

Among the most important physical factors that determine the habitat of an animal are temperature, water, light, and food. The continent of North America has been divided by scientists into definite regions, according to the total of the temperature during the season of growth; and regions of a certain temperature, though widely separated, are likely to support similar kinds of animals. Winter is met by northern animals in one of four ways: by (1) dying, *e.g.*, adult butterflies, (2) migrating, *e.g.*, birds, (3) hibernating, *e.g.*, bears, (4) remaining active *e.g.*, rabbits. Animals living in tropical regions pass the summer in many cases in a torpid condition; *i.e.*, they estivate.

A certain amount of water is necessary for life, as the bodies of animals are made up of from 55 to 95 per cent water. Animals living in dry climates have thick skins, and thus evaporation is prevented. Light plays a leading role in the lives of animals; many species require it, but others shun it as much as possible, principally in order to escape their enemies. And finally food conditions are most effective, since carnivorous animals, *e.g.*, lions, must live where they may obtain flesh; herbivorous animals, *e.g.*, deer, must live where suitable vegetation abounds; and omnivorous animals must live where both flesh and vegetation of certain sorts exist.

Animals are confined to certain habitats by barriers and hence are prevented from entering a new region by mountains or lakes, by lack of food, and by the interference of other animals. Common barriers are mountains, bodies of water, open country for forest animals, and forests for prairie-inhabiting species. The reverse of a barrier is a highway. Apparently there are routes of migration that are especially favored.

Some species of animals have wide ranges; *e.g.*, some are found inhabiting practically every large land area on the earth's surface. This is true of many birds and of the bats. A number of species, on the other hand, are restricted to very limited areas. The mountain goat is found only in the higher Rocky and Cascade mountains of Alaska.   Islands are famous for the presence of restricted species; Darwin's descriptions of the animals he found in the Galapagos Islands read like fairy tales.

Scientists have divided the Mammals into Orders on the basis of structure.   A list of them may help the reader to obtain a bird's-eye view of the entire group.

Monotremes, or Egg-Laying Mammals, include the Duck Bill and Spiny Anteater.

Courtesy, U. S. Bureau of Fisheries

Fur Seals.   A male with part of his harem; they travel thousands of miles in the winter during the interval between breeding seasons.

Marsupials bring forth their young in a very immature condition and carry them for a long time in a marsupium, or pouch; examples: Opossum, Kangaroo, and Koala.

Edentates have no enamel on their teeth.   Most of them are rather curious animals, such as the Anteater, Armadillo, Sloth, and Aardvark.

Bats are the only mammals that can really fly.

Insectivores are small mammals with teeth fitted for grinding up the insects on which they live.   The Hedgehog, Mole, and Shrew are well-known species.

Rodents are gnawing animals with front teeth well fitted for this purpose.   Common species are the Rabbits, Pikas, Squirrels, Chipmunks, Prairie Dogs, Mice, Rats, Beavers, and Porcupines.

Ungulates are large hoofed animals.   The Horse, Ass, Zebra, Tapir, and Rhinoceros have an odd number of toes; and the Peccary, Wart Hog, Hippopotamus, Deer, Goats, Sheep, Camels, and Giraffes have an even number of toes.

Carnivores are flesh-eating mammals with sharp claws and teeth; examples: Wolves, Foxes, Cats, Dogs, Bears, Martens, Skunks, Seals, and Walruses.

Whales are adapted for life in the water.   Dolphins, Porpoises, and Sperm Whales possess teeth; the Right and Whale-Bone Whales have whalebone.

Primates possess nails on their hands and feet instead of claws; have the great toe and thumb opposible to the other digits and are provided with a large brain. In this group are placed the Aye-Aye, Tarsiers, Lemurs, Old World Monkeys, New World Monkeys, Gibbon, Orang Utan, Chimpanzee, Gorilla, and Man.

EGG-LAYING MAMMALS, OR MONOTREMES

We all develop from eggs, but in most of the Mammals, the eggs hatch within the body of the mother, and the young are born in a more or less advanced condition. In the primitive Mammals, however, the eggs are laid; the young that develop within them feed on yolk stored up in the egg, and finally hatch. After hatching, they feed on milk secreted by the mother, but the milk arises from a number of small pores and not from teats, as in other Mammals. The adults have no teeth.

The Duck Bill, or Platypus, and the Spiny Anteaters, or Echidnas, comprise the Egg-Laying Mammals. They live only in the Australian region.

Courtesy, Nature Magazine

Duck Bill, or Platypus. The "bill" is about 2½ inches long and 2 inches wide and serves to stir up the mud of the river bottom where worms and shellfish live.

Duck Bill, or Platypus. Such a queer animal as the Duck Bill, or Platypus, could come only from Australia, — a country that may boast of more strange and outlandish creatures than any other in the world. It has a ducklike bill, webbed feet especially adapted for swimming, and stout claws for digging, and it lays eggs instead of bringing forth its young alive, as every self-respecting Mammal should do.

The body of the Duck Bill is about fourteen inches long and the tail five inches long. The fur is brownish in color, with long curly hairs and a thick, soft, woolly under fur. The bill is about two and one-half inches long and two inches wide, and is used to stir up the mud at the bottom of the rivers, and for capturing the insects, worms, and shellfish thus uncovered. These are stored in cheek pouches. The young possess several teeth, but the adults grind up their food with horny plates, teeth being absent. There are no external ears, and the eyes are small. On the inner side of the hind leg of the male is a hollow, horny spur connected with poison glands which make it a formidable weapon.

Duck Bills live in burrows in the banks of streams, probably dug entirely by the females. These burrows may be 30 feet or more long and about a foot from the surface. At the end is a chamber about a foot in diameter in which a nest of weeds, leaves, and grass is built. Here from one to three eggs are laid. The young are naked when they hatch. The mother holds them to her abdomen with her tail so they can obtain milk from her mammary glands.

Courtesy, National Zoological Park
Spiny Anteater, or Echidna. The back bristles with sharp spines; the snout is like a long beak from the end of which a long tongue may be protruded for catching ants.

Duck Bills are excellent swimmers and divers, but otherwise rather helpless, hence their burrows are made long and tortuous, and are usually blocked with earth in several places to discourage enemies. One entrance is above the water, but the other is under the surface, which enables the Duck Bill to enter without exposing itself.

Spiny Anteater, or Echidna. The only other species of Egg-Laying Mammals are the Spiny Anteaters of Australia, Tasmania, and New Guinea. Spines resembling those of the European Hedgehog and Porcupine cover the back, and the animal may roll itself into a ball for protection, just as the Hedgehog does. There is an elongated beaklike muzzle, from which may be protruded a long, sticky tongue used for capturing ants and other insects. The feet are provided with strong claws which are used for tearing apart anthills or digging burrows in the ground.

Two eggs, about the size of a sparrow's eggs, are laid and placed in a pouch on the underside of the body. They have a white, leathery shell like the eggs of a Reptile. After hatching, the young remain in the pouch for a few weeks until they reach a length of three or four inches.

The Duck Bill and Spiny Anteater, being the most primitive of all Mammals, should give us some idea of where Mammals came from out of the dim and mysterious past. The formation of their flat beaks reminds us very much of Birds, but scientists tell us that their internal structure is more like that of the Reptiles. Apparently Mammals have evolved from reptilian stock.

Pouched Mammals, or Marsupials

Not quite as primitive as the Egg-Laying Mammals, but still low in the mammalian series, are the Pouched Mammals. In them, the eggs hatch within the mother's body, but the young are born in an immature condition. The mother places them in a pouch on her abdomen into which the mammary glands open. They attach themselves to her teats, where they remain for a long period, clinging tightly with their sucker-like lips.

One family of Marsupials, the American Opossums, occur in the New World; all the rest live in Australia, New Guinea and near-by islands. They include the Kangaroos, Wallabies, Phalangers, Koala, Wombats, Bandicoots, Tasmanian Wolf, Tasmanian Devil, Pouched Rats, Jerboa, Pouched Mice, Banded Anteater, and Marsupial Moles.

Courtesy, U. S. Bureau of Biological Survey

Virginia Opossum. He feigns death, or "plays possum," apparently so that he will be considered dead and hence left alone.

Virginia Opossum. The only Mammal living in North America that carries its young in a pouch is the Virginia Opossum. The Opossum is about the size of a house cat with a body about 20 inches long and a naked tail a foot in length. The snout is slender and the ears large and naked. The fur consists of long hairs and short, soft underfur and is gray in color.

Opossums live largely in trees, using their grasping feet and clinging tail much as a monkey does. During the day, they sleep in a hollow tree or log, or among branches, but at dusk become busy hunters for food. Almost anything is acceptable, but especially fruit, eggs, insects, and small birds and mammals. These are caught both in trees and on the ground.

In two respects the Opossum is especially noted. First, the young are born in a very undeveloped stage and crawl into the pouch on their mother's abdomen, where they feed on milk until they can creep out upon her back, scurrying in again in case of danger. From five to fourteen young are born at one time, and two or three litters are reared in a single year. Secondly, the Opossum when frightened seems to drop dead. However, it only feigns death, and is really "playing possum," a con-

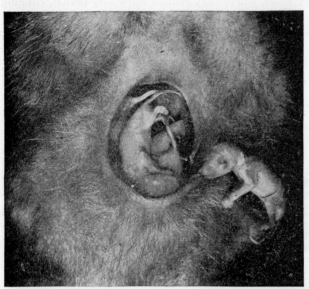

Courtesy, Nature Magazine

Virginia Opossum. The young are very immature when born and are kept in this brood pouch until able to cling to the mother's back.

dition which may lead to its escape later from one who does not understand this habit.

One may wonder how the Opossum, which is a slow, dull-witted animal and of value both as food for man and as a fur-bearer, can continue to exist. The reasons are its nocturnal habits, the large number of young that are well cared for in the mother's pouch, its climbing ability, its appetite for almost any kind of food, the fat it stores up under the skin that enables it to pass through the winter successfully, and its habit of "playing possum."

Among the enemies of Opossums are Great Horned Owls, Foxes, Wolves, and Wild Cats. In the southern section of our country many people hunt them at night with dogs and torches, and try to catch them alive so they can fatten them for several weeks before eating them. The Virginia Opossum occurs from New York to Florida and west to the Great Lakes and Texas.

Kangaroos. Nature has played a curious prank on the Kangaroo by adapting it so thoroughly for leaping that the front part of the body is about the size of a large dog and the hind part like that of a mule, with an enormous tail thrown in. The front legs are comparatively weak and used as hands or to support the body when the animal is feeding on the ground. The tail serves as the "third leg" on which the Kangaroo rests, which with the hind legs form a sort of three-legged stool.

The Great Gray Kangaroo is widespread in Australia and Tasmania, living on the grassy plains. It lives on vegetation, and has front teeth for cutting off grass, and hind teeth for chewing it. The old males reach a height of over five feet, and a weight of over 200 pounds. The tail is four feet or more in length. The natives call them "Foresters," "Boomers," or "Old Man Kangaroos." They are hunted for sport with rough-haired greyhounds trained for the purpose, and fight desperately before they are caught or killed. They often go about in "mobs" and will blindly follow a leader.

The females have a pouch in the abdomen into which the young crawl when they are born. The young are at first blind and naked and only about one inch long, resembling in appearance a red grub. They feed on milk from the mammary glands that open into the pouch. When about four months old, they begin to venture out, but scurry back again if frightened. The female, when pursued, will pull her young out of her pouch and throw it to one side. She is said to do this in order to save herself, but it may be a method of getting her baby out of danger.

Kangaroos are famous leapers. Ordinarily they move slowly, jumping about five feet, but when pursued may leap a distance of 25 feet and over fences five feet or more high. The Kangaroo is a natural pugilist and the males will pummel each other and kick their opponents with their hind legs, observing fairly regular "rounds" of action

Courtesy, N. Y. Zoological Society

Red Kangaroo. The tail is used as a third leg when resting; the fore limbs and shoulders are weak when compared with the hind legs and thighs which are used for jumping.

and rest. They are easily trained to wear gloves and to box with a man.

The Red Kangaroos have soft, woolly fur which varies in color from rufous to blue-gray. White patches occur at the base of the whiskers. They inhabit the western part of Australia. Wallabies are small Kangaroos; they have large feet and a long, tapering tail, which is more hairy than that of their larger relatives.

The Kangaroo when running, "springs from the ground in an erect position, propelled by its powerful hind legs and balanced by its tail, holding its short fore arms well in to the chest, after the manner of a professional runner. Thus it bounds lightly and easily along, clearing any obstacles, such as fallen trees, and even low fences, in its stride. The long tail materially assists them in running, and its measured thumps may be heard on the ground long before the kangaroo itself appears in sight in the thick forest. In general habits, kangaroos much resemble sheep and deer. Timid and shy, their senses of sight, hearing, and smell are acute. Like the hare, they appear to be unable to see an object directly in front of them when running. They feed early in the morning and at twilight, and I think also much at night. The kangaroo lies up by day, during the hot summer weather, in damp, thickly-scrubbed gullies; in the winter, on dry, sandy rises. Here, unless disturbed, they will remain quiet for hours; and it is a pretty sight to watch a 'mob' camped up, some of them playing with each other, some quietly nibbling the young shrubs and grass, or basking in the sun half asleep on their sides." (Old Bushman.)

Courtesy, N. Y. Zoological Society

Brush-Tailed Wallaby. This kangaroo is carrying a well-grown baby in her brood pouch.

Australian Native Bear, or Koala. This ludicrous little fellow is not a bear but a pouched animal nearly related to the Opossum and Kangaroo. Its bearlike characteristics consist of a podgy, tailless body and large, round, thickly-tufted ears. The eyes are small and close together. The legs are short and the five toes are arranged as in parrots with three opposed to the other two, making the grasping of tree limbs easy.

Koalas when full-grown are two and one-half feet long. Their fur is ashy-gray in color and thick and dense. It makes attractive, warm rugs, but the man must be cruel indeed who can kill such innocent-looking, harmless creatures. A wounded Koala crys piteously, like a child in distress.

Koalas are tree-dwellers. They live on the leaves of the gum tree, eucalyptus, and will remain placidly in one tree for days. During the day they sleep among the lower branches, but become active at dusk when they hop up the smooth tree trunk into the higher branches with jumps of four or five feet.

One young is born at a time; it remains in the mother's pouch for about three months, and then clings to her back, as shown in the photograph, for several months longer before shifting for itself. The droll and toylike appearance, fearlessness, and quaint, babyish expression of the Koala win for it the deepest affection of all who become acquainted with it.

Among the other Pouched Mammals is the Tasmanian Wolf, a fierce-looking species about the size of a dog that now occurs only in Tasmania. A near relative that is also found only in Tasmania is the Tasmanian Devil. Phalangers are small Pouched Mammals that live in trees. One of these, the Honey Mouse, is only about the size of a house mouse; it feeds largely on the nectar of flowers and on small insects. The Flying Phalangers are provided with membranes which they spread out much as do the flying squirrels as they glide from tree to tree. Bandicoots are about the size of rabbits and like them may have large ears and long hind legs. One species is actually called the Rabbit-Eared Bandicoot; another species is known as the Long-Nosed Bandicoot.

Courtesy, Nature Magazine

Australian Native Bears, or Koalas. When the young is large enough to leave its mother's brood pouch, it rides on her back for several months.

TOOTHLESS MAMMALS, OR EDENTATES

The scientific name, Edentata, applied to this group means "toothless," but many of the species really possess teeth. The front teeth, however, are absent in all of them. The Toothless Mammals are lowly organized, and are supplied with a small and poorly developed brain. The five families into which they may be divided are the Sloths, Anteaters, and Armadillos, all of which live in the New World, the Scaly Anteaters of Asia and Africa, and the Aardvarks of Africa.

Sloths. The jungles of Central and South America are inhabited by many peculiar animals but none more strange in structure and habits than the Sloths. These slothful creatures live in the trees, suspending themselves with their back downward, as they progress by slow motion from limb to limb. They cut a ludicrous figure when placed on the ground; they lie sprawled out and are not very successful in pulling themselves along.

Courtesy, National Zoological Park

Two-Toed Sloth. It has two toes on the fore feet and three on the hind feet with which it clings upside down to the branches of trees; the hair lies so that water runs off when it rains.

Sloths possess long, strong, curved claws with which they hook on to limbs. The hind feet have three toes, but the fore feet in some have three, and in others only two, toes. The fur is coarse and shaggy, and in certain species, green algae live in the longitudinal grooves in the hairs, giving the animal a greenish tinge that helps conceal it from harpy eagles, jaguars, and other enemies. The hair is arranged on the body, not like that of other mammals, but so that the water runs off when the Sloth is hanging upside down during the torrential tropical rainstorms. The head of the Sloth is round, the ears are very small, and the tail nothing but a vestige. Sloths are about as large as a small dog. They feed on leaves, from which they obtain moisture in sufficient quantities so that they need not descend to the ground to drink. Sloths range from Nicaragua to Brazil.

Armadilo. Central and South America support another group of Toothless Mammals called Armadillos, one of which, the Nine-Banded Armadillo, lives as far north as Texas. Old Man Armadillo has lost not only his teeth but also most of his hair. In place of the latter, nine transverse bands of bony plates have developed, which enclose the upper part of his body. The tail is long and covered with overlapping rings. When an Armadillo cannot escape to his burrow, he may roll up into a ball like a Hedgehog, in which condition he is difficult to injure.

The life of the Armadillo can hardly be considered exciting. Usually the day is spent in a burrow; this he digs in the dry soil with the two extra-long, middle claws on each fore foot. At night, and often by day, he busies himself digging for

Courtesy, American Museum of Natural History

Nine-Banded Armadillo. The shell is hinged so that the animal can roll up into a ball when attacked.

insects and pays very little attention to his surroundings, probably because his sight and hearing are so poor that he doesn't notice things. He has a small, narrow head, large ears, and short legs and "has in life an odd resemblance in both form and motion to a small pig." (Nelson.)

The tongue of the Armadillo is long, sticky, and protrusible, designed to entangle insects after they have been dislodged by the powerful claws. The young number four or eight. Each egg produces four young, instead of one as in most animals. Among human beings, one egg sometimes gives rise to identical twins. The Armadillo goes this one better by giving birth to identical quadruplets.

In Argentina dwells a Pigmy Armadillo only about five inches long, also called the Fairy Armadillo, or Pichiciago. Its shell is of a pinkish hue and its hair is pure white. The Great Armadillo occupies the other extreme, with a body about three feet long and a tail eighteen inches in length. It lives in the forests of Brazil and Paraguay. This species, however, is not as large as certain prehistoric forms that lived in South America and are now known

Lesser Anteater. This species climbs trees and has a prehensile tail; the snout is long and narrow and the fore feet fitted for tearing apart ant hills.

only from fossil remains. Some of these Glyptodons were as large as a hippopotamus and looked very much like gigantic turtles.

Scaly Anteater, or Pangolin. The body is covered with heavy scales which become erect when the animal coils up into a ball as a defense against its enemies. The tongue can be extruded from the long snout for catching ants.

Anteaters. Anteaters are confined to Central and South America. They are peculiar-looking beasts, especially their heads. A long snout has developed, in which is a tubular mouth and a tongue that can be extended from it for a considerable distance. Ants are collected by the sticky tongue and drawn back into the mouth. They are swallowed "as is," there being no teeth to grind them up with. In order to obtain enough ants to satisfy their appetites, digging must be resorted to. This is accomplished by a huge, overgrown claw borne by the middle toe of the fore feet.

The Great Anteater is the largest of the family, measuring about eight feet in length. It lives on the ground and has a long, bushy tail.

The Lesser Anteater shown in our photograph is only about half the size of its larger relative. It lives in trees and has a prehensile tail that aids it in clinging to the branches. Its hair is short, and its ears quite conspicuous. This species, which is also known as the Tamandua, has a broad, blackish band covering the back and sides between the legs. The tip of the tail and under surface of the body are naked.

Scaly Anteater, or Pangolin. The other side of the world also has its Ant-eaters. Java, Borneo, the Philippines and neighboring islands, China, and Africa are all provided with the type of Anteaters known as Pangolins. These are built on the same plan as the American type, but are covered on the upper surface of the body, and all over the tail, with an armor of very heavy scales.

When attacked, the Pangolin rolls itself up into a ball with its snout thrust between its fore legs and its tail held against the body between its hind legs. The bending of the body erects the scales so that they are presented edge-on to the intruder. In this condition the Pangolin can resist the onslaught of almost any kind of enemy.

As in the American Anteaters, the snout is long, the tongue is slender and can be thrust out for a considerable distance, and the fore feet are provided with strong claws that are used for tearing open the nests of ants and termites. Most Pangolins are from three to five feet in length.

Courtesy, Science Service

Aardvark. A native of Africa with an arched back, long ears, a long, piglike snout, and short legs; it feeds almost entirely on ants and termites and is an efficient digger.

Aardvark. The first animal listed in the dictionary is the Aardvark, also known as the Ant Bear or Earth Pig, a very peculiar mammal that occurs only in Africa and apparently has no very close relatives. It is adapted for digging in the ground and for capturing ants and termites, which constitute its entire and rather monotonous diet. The body is arched and about six feet long, including the long, tapering, cylindrical tail. The head is long, the snout long, and piglike, the mouth tubular, the ears long, the neck short, and the front part of the body near the ground because of the short legs. The hide is sparsely covered with brown or gray hair and is very thick, like pigskin.

The Aardvark is a remarkably powerful digger and has four very strong claws on the fore feet with which it gouges out the earth and passes it back between the hind legs. One will dig itself entirely out of sight in a few minutes even in hard ground. During the day the time is spent sleeping in a burrow, but at dusk the creature emerges in search of food. The nests of ants and termites are torn open and the wildly excited little insects are licked up by the long, sticky tongue. There are no front teeth and only twenty back teeth in all. These serve to crush the insects before swallowing them. These teeth have no roots but grow continuously throughout life. The Aardvark is very shy and very seldom seen, and will scurry quickly into its burrow if its keenly sensitive ears detect any unusual sound.

"At the Zoo, it lives half buried in the earth during the daytime. It shows itself, however, a very lively beast after dark when it will run and even jump in a clumsy fashion, and has swept more than one keeper off his feet with a single blow of its long cylindrical tail. At the Pretoria Zoo a dog-cart puts out twice a week for the sandy wastes, and brings back in a zinc tank a consignment of termites for their dozen or so 'earth-bears' who combine monastic seclusion with a love of good living." (Boulenger.) Termites are destructive insects with a type of family life that gives them great advantages in the struggle for existence (see page 140). Fortunately Anteaters and Aardvarks keep them under control.

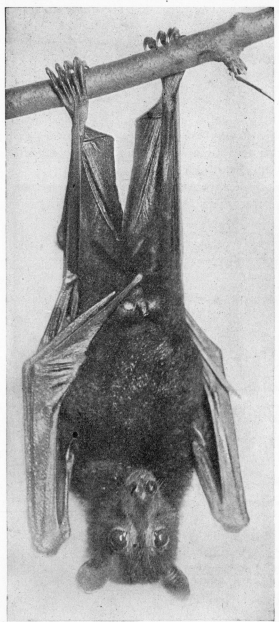

Courtesy, N. Y. Zoological Society

Fruit Bat, or Flying Fox. He hangs head down when at rest, with wings folded; his face looks somewhat like that of a fox.

FLYING MAMMALS, OR BATS

Bats are the only Mammals capable of true flight. Other animals may glide through the air for a short distance, like the Flying Squirrel, but never really fly. The fore limbs of Bats are provided with four very long fingers, between which is stretched the wing membrane. This membrane also extends along the side of the body, between the fore and hind limbs, and between the hind limbs and the tail. The thumb is free, ends in a claw, and is used for clinging purposes. The hind toes are also free; they terminate in sharp, strong claws which are used to suspend the body head downward from a support when the Bat is at rest.

Courtesy, American Museum of Natural History

Javelin Bat. When the wings are spread, the extremely long fingers are revealed, and also the the way the wing membranes are attached to the body and legs.

Bats may be divided into two types: (1) Insect-Eating Bats are usually small; they may have large ears and leaflike rosettes of skin around the nose. They occur practically all over the world. About 600 species and subspecies are known; these are placed in about sixteen families. They include the Mouse-Tailed, Tomb, Fish-Eating, False-Vampire, Horseshoe, Leaf-Nosed, Vampire, and Typical Bats.

(2) The Fruit-Eating Bats are much larger, and limited in their distribution to the tropics and subtropics of the Old World. Most of them belong to one family of Flying Foxes, about 90 species of which are known. These Bats have foxlike muzzles, are gregarious in habit, have no tail, and may reach a wing spread of five feet.

We became acquainted with Fruit Bats in the Philippines, where, at certain times of the year, they congregate at night in large numbers in orchards searching for fruit. The natives hang lanterns in the trees to discourage these visits, but in spite of this, many Bats could be seen flitting about. Specimens were shot as they flew above us, silhouetted against the sky. They were not killed for sport, but in order to obtain their parasites for study.

In the Zoo at "night — or on a dull day — the bat collection wakes up and performs extraordinary antics, when they engage in fierce arguments with each other over the dinner-table. Their fights to secure the most comfortable places from which to 'strap hang' — head downwards — are responsible for a greater uproar than has ever been emitted from any rookery." (Boulenger.)

Little Brown Bat. The Little Brown Bat is one of the smallest but most widely distributed species of Bats in this country. Its flight is a noiseless fluttering, and rather erratic. Its insect food is captured during the twilight hours while in flight, the mouth-opening being very wide as is that of birds, such as the Nighthawk and Chimney Swift, which also capture insects on the wing. "Their apparently erratic zig-zags, loops, turns, and twists appear meaningless unless one understands that at the end of each of these little irregularities of course, the flyer has probably captured one of the insects on which it preys." (Nelson.)

Bats are accused of many misdemeanors of which they are innocent. They do not take refuge in, nor enjoy becoming entwined, in a lady's hair. They do not harbor nor distribute bedbugs. They are not "blind as a Bat," but can see very well in semi-darkness and fairly well in broad daylight. Their eyes look wicked, but they are perfectly harmless. Formerly they were considered evil spirits, and dragons and devils are usually represented with Bats' wings.

During the day Bats rest, hanging head downward in a cave, hollow tree, old building, or attic. One or two young are born at a time. They cling to the body of the mother until they are old enough to be "hung up" in a safe place, while she goes foraging for food. The Little Brown Bat is about three and one-half inches long, including the tail. The fur is colored dull brown and is very soft and silky. A single Bat is covered with about a million and a half hairs; each hair is made up of funnel-shaped segments.

The head of a Bat looks something like that of a mouse. In Germany Bats go by the name Fledermaus, meaning "flying mouse." The voice of the Bat is squeaky and very high, so high-pitched that some people are unable to hear it. During the winter the Little Brown Bat may hibernate or move further south.

Photo by Klugh. Courtesy, Nature Magazine

Little Brown Bat. When asleep, he clings to a vertical limb with head down, — a very uncomfortable-looking position.

Vampire Bat. The nocturnal habits of Bats, and the "blood-sucking" behavior of certain species, are responsible for the name Vampire that is applied to some of them. Much confusion has existed, however, with respect to which species are the real Vampires. Fruit Bats were for many years mistaken for Vampires, but we now know that the guilty "bloodsuckers" live in the forests of tropical America. They are only about three inches long and are covered with reddish-brown fur.

The Vampire Bat visits human beings, horses, and other animals at night. He is able to cause bleeding without awaking

Courtesy, Dr. H. C. Clark

Vampire Bat. He is only about 3 inches long and doesn't look very ferocious, yet he is the real Vampire among the bats.

his victim by cutting the skin horizontally instead of vertically; this severs many of the small blood vessels without producing pain, as a vertical cut or puncture would do. The front teeth (incisors) and canines are large and sharp and well fitted for this purpose; whereas the grinding teeth are small and weak, — because none of the food needs grinding. Vampires usually attack the large toe of human beings, because this is a part of the body often exposed. The blood they lap up is stored up in a large pouchlike extension of the stomach, a reservoir that holds such a large quantity that a long time may elapse between meals. How grateful a housewife would be if the members of her family possessed this enormous storage ability.

Courtesy, Science Service

Javelin Bat. A close-up of this species reveals a mouth full of sharp teeth and an unpleasant disposition.

Recently it has been discovered that a disease of horses and mules that is prevalent in Panama, and is due to a minute protozoon, a trypanosome (see p. 17), is transmitted from infected animals to clean animals by the bites of Vampire Bats. This is the first time transmission of this type by a Mammal has ever been recorded.

The vampire legend is of eastern European origin. The ghost of a human being, preferably of a suicide or sorcerer, was supposed to leave the body at night and suck the blood of living persons. When the grave was opened, the corpse was declared to be fresh. Such a vampire could be kept at home by driving a stake through the body of the corpse.

INSECT-EATING MAMMALS OR INSECTIVORES

Many species of Mammals feed on insects, but one group contains such a large number of species adapted to this type of food that they have been named Insectivores. They are the Cobegos, or Flying Lemurs, the Shrews, Tree Shrews, and Jumping Shrews, the Moles and Mole Shrews, the Hedgehogs and Rat Shrews, the Tenrecs of Madagascar, and the Golden Moles of Africa. Only two families have representatives in the United States; these are the Moles and Shrews.

The Insectivores are mostly small Mammals with a long snout and with many sharp teeth fitted for cutting up the hard bodies of insects. Their fur is usually

Courtesy, U. S. Bureau of Biological Survey

Mole. Here we see the wedge-shaped head, large fore feet for digging, velvet-like fur, and naked tail; the eyes are too small to show in the photograph.

thick and soft. Spines are present in some species. The eyes and ears of Moles and Shrews are small; their feet have five toes, each with a claw; and glands are present that secrete musk.

Our acquaintance with the curious animal known as the Flying Lemur was made in the Philippines. An expedition to the Island of Bohol was successful in obtaining a load of Flying Lemurs, each about the size of a cat. These animals do not really fly, but, like the Flying Squirrel, sail from one tree to another on their outstretched "wings" for distances of 200 feet or more. The skin is extended on all sides, from the head to the fore legs, from the fore legs to the hind legs, and from the hind legs to the tail, so that when the legs are spread out, a large surface is provided that supports the animal like a parachute as it glides through the air.

The fur of the Flying Lemur is short and soft and covers not only the body but also the wings. When we examined our specimens closely, we found several naked babies clinging closely under the armpits of the mothers.

Courtesy, U. S. Bureau of Biological Survey

Mole Ridges. Moles often burrow close to the surface, throwing up ridges such as these that disfigure the landscape.

Common Mole. Life underground demands many modifications and these the Mole exhibits to a remarkable degree. Like an animated plow, the head is wedge-shaped for penetrating the soft earth. The enormously enlarged fore legs are armed with long, broad nails, and with an extra, sickle-shaped bone on the outside of the thumb, forming all together an effective living chisel for gouging out the earth; they are extended forward, then pushed out, and drawn back with their burden of earth. The fur consists of short hairs so closely packed as to resemble velvet, and like velvet, does not become wet easily nor allow the penetration of earth to the skin.

The sense of sight is not needed underground and consequently the eyeballs are only about as large as the head of a pin. The ears are likewise small, but very sensitive to sound waves passing through the soil. The sense of touch is remarkable; the snout is abundantly supplied with nerves and wonderfully sensitive; and the tail, which is naked and looks somewhat like a pink worm, is also very sensitive and guides the Mole as it moves backward through its tunnel.

The tunnels are just beneath the surface, and often the earth is pushed up into unsightly ridges, interrupted by an occasional mound of excess earth that is brought to the top. These tunnels serve as the Mole's hunting ground, where insects, worms, and other small animals are captured and cut up by the sharp teeth. An enormous amount of food is necessary to supply the energy for such an energetic animal; it has been estimated that one will eat its own weight in insects in a single day.

The rate at which a Mole can dig a tunnel is almost unbelievable. If placed on the surface, it will dig out of sight in ten seconds, and will tunnel at the rate of one foot in three minutes. One Mole is reported to have dug a tunnel 68 feet long in 25 hours, and another Mole dug a tunnel 100 yards long in a single night. To do a proportionate amount of digging, a man would have to make a tunnel about 50 miles long and large enough for him to crawl through.

Moles are only about six inches long, but in spite of their small size, their skins are used for making wraps. The fur is blackish brown and has no "set," that is, it can be brushed either backward or forward. About 1000 skins are necessary to make a long evening cloak.

Moles are seldom seen above ground. They are highly beneficial because of the obnoxious insects eaten by them, but make unsightly ridges in lawns and elsewhere. They can be captured by watching for movements at the end of the tunnel and striking the surface at that point; this stuns the Mole, which can then be dug out easily.

Courtesy, Nature Magazine

Shrew. Shrews are among our smallest mammals. They are shy and seldom seen.

Shrew. The name Shrew seems entirely out of place for such a small and harmless-looking animal, but size does not determine disposition and the Shrew is really a fiendish killer. His ordinary bill of fare consists of insects, but he will give battle to mice which are several times his size, and after killing them proceed to feast on the victim. If two Shrews are placed together in a cage, a terrific fight ensues, and not uncommonly one kills and eats the other.

The Common Shrew is one of the smallest Mammals in northern North America. The body is very slender and the tail long; its total length is four inches. The Pygmy Shrew is even smaller, being the smallest Mammal in North America; its body is about two inches long and its tail about one inch long. Shrews are abundant but so small, secretive, and active that they are among our least-known Mammals. When they are encountered, they are often thought to be moles or mice.

The Common Shrew lives on the ground and seeks concealment under rocks, logs, and roots or in tunnels in the grass or under leaves. He is grayish-brown in color, has small eyes and ears, and an elongated nose. The end of his snout is flexible and very sensitive, and is no doubt very useful in finding food.

Shrews live a fast life.   They are very nervous and active and their digestion is so rapid that a comparatively large amount of food is necessary to keep them alive.   It is said that they will starve to death in a few hours if nothing to eat is provided.   Since Shrews are active in winter as well as in summer, earning the daily bread must be a real chore for them.

Hedgehog.   Many methods of gaining protection from their enemies in the struggle for existence have been developed among animals, but none more remarkable than that of the Hedgehog.   In this species, some of the hairs have changed into sharp spines.   When attacked, the animal rolls itself into a ball; this erects

Courtesy, N. Y. Zoological Society

European Hedgehog.   His back is covered with sharp spines, which are erected when he rolls up into a ball for protection; the American Porcupine is not a Hedgehog.

the spines, which then completely cover the body, presenting a defense superior to a barbed-wire entanglement.

Hedgehogs are inhabitants of western Europe, where they frequent hedgerows. They are about the size of a small cat, and possess short legs and small, black eyes.   In the autumn they become fat, and when winter comes, they hibernate in a nest of dry leaves.   Although they belong to the group of Insect-Eating Mammals, they vary their menu by adding slugs, worms, frogs, snakes, and mice when these are available.   The Porcupine is often called a Hedgehog, but belongs to an entirely different group, the Gnawing Mammals.

CHAPTER 35

GNAWING MAMMALS, OR RODENTS

World-wide in their distribution, the Gnawing Mammals are not only the most numerous in species, but also in individuals, of all the mammalian groups. They are mostly small or medium in size. You must look them in the mouth if you would know their most distinctive character, that is, their peculiar teeth. There are no canines present and a wide gap, where the canines ought to be, exists between the incisors and molars. The incisors are two in each jaw, except in the

Photo by Cornelia Clarke

Cottontail Rabbit. Rabbits live in one locality throughout the year, and during the cold winter, hide in a "form" under bushes where they are protected from the weather.

Rabbits and Pikas, which have four in the upper jaw. These long incisors grow continuously at the root and are worn off at the outer end by gnawing. Since in most species the hard enamel covers only the outer surface of the incisors,

542

the inner, softer material wears away more rapidly, leaving a broad, sharp, chisel-like edge of enamel, admirably suited for gnawing vegetation. The molars are of the grinding type, and the lower jaw is hinged to the skull in such a way that the molars of the two jaws can be moved against one another backward and forward, and from side to side, as well as up and down, thus facilitating the grinding of vegetable food.

Gnawing Mammals live in a great variety of habitats. Most of them are ground dwellers, many live under the ground, others spend most of their time in trees, a few may be said to be aquatic, and several have developed flaps of skin with the aid of which they can glide through the air from one tree to another. Some of the more common Gnawing Mammals are the Tree Squirrels, Flying Squirrels, Ground Squirrels, Chipmunks, Prairie Dogs, Marmots, Beaver, Rats, Mice, Voles, Porcupines, Jerboas, Hamsters, Chinchilla, Agouti, Cavy, Capybara, Hares, Rabbits, and Pikas.

Photo by Hegner

Cottontail Rabbit. This youngster could not run fast enough to evade capture; his fur is untidy and his ears held back as though he were not certain what is going to happen next.

Cottontail Rabbit. The Cottontail is perhaps the best-known Gnawing Mammal in North America, and the most numerous representative of the Hare and Rabbit family. He has long hind legs adapted for leaping, long ears, and a short tail, the underside of which is white, hence the name Cottontail. Brer Rabbit, as every child knows, lives in a brier patch. If no brier patch is handy, he seeks the hedgerows or brushy cover anywhere and everywhere on the countryside. Occasionally we see him hopping about our lawn in a suburb of Baltimore, and how he escapes the numerous dogs and cats, and raises a family in such a thickly settled district, is a mystery.

Cottontails, however, live on green things and hence have little difficulty finding food, and are very prolific, giving birth to several litters of from three to seven young each year. They are mostly nocturnal and spend the day hiding in a snug "form" under a bush or in the grass, or in a burrow in the ground, or in a hole under a log. When dislodged from their "forms," they do not attempt to escape by speed alone, but after a short, erratic series of hops, either crouch suddenly as motionless as a stone, or dive into a hole if one is available.

Many predatory animals, including Man, hunt Cottontails, and a large part of the food of such species as the fox, coyote, lynx, and certain hawks and owls, consists of fresh Rabbit. They are, nevertheless, able to hold their own in their struggle against these enemies, as well as against agricultural progress.

Black-Tailed Jack Rabbit.   The temptation to call an animal with extraordinarily long ears a Jackass led to the common name of the Jackass, or Jack Rabbits.   Of the several groups of Jacks, White-Tailed, White-Sided, and Black-Tailed, the last named ranges over the largest area and is the best known.   Black-Tailed Jacks are large and conspicuous, being 28 inches long, with huge ears and very long hind legs.   They are inhabitants of the treeless area of middle North America, where existence depends on the ability to eat almost any kind of vegetation and to run with great speed.

Photo by J. G. Allen

Jack Rabbit.   His ears are almost as large as those of a jackass and his hind legs are very long.

Young Jacks try to escape from their enemies by crouching quietly and allowing their protective coloration to conceal them, but the adults are famous for their quick get-away.   Their sight and hearing are extremely keen, and they are ready to go long before the animal or human hunter wants him to. An alarmed Jack "leaps away in quick, springy, and graceful bounds, now and then making a high soaring leap as if to command a better view. These occasional high leaps mark the first stages of alarm. In greater stress, when pursued by a coyote or other swift-footed enemy, the Jack Rabbit indulges in no such showy performances, but gets down to serious work, and developing marvelous action in a combination series of rapid, low-stretching leaps, with ears lying flat along the shoulders, it skims over the ground almost as swiftly as a bird. Coursing Jack Rabbits with greyhounds was for many years a favorite sport in different parts of the West.

No other dog has much chance for success in the open pursuit of these animals." (Nelson.)

Jack Rabbits sometimes become so numerous that they ruin alfalfa fields in summer and attack haystacks in winter. "Drives" by many neighboring ranchmen have resulted in corralling as many as 20,000 Jacks at one time. Apparently the Indians hunted them by this method long before Columbus discovered America. Besides the Cottontail and Jack Rab-

Photo by Finley and Pack. Courtesy, Nature Magazine
Pika, or Cony. He looks like a Meadow Mouse, but his ears are very large and rounded; his home is among the rocks.

bits, the Hare and Rabbit family includes among its commonest species the Arctic Hare, Varying Hare, Pygmy Hare, and Swamp Rabbit.

During the summer Arctic Hares are dull grayish-brown in color, but when winter comes, they change to a snowy white, all except a small spot at the tip of each ear which is black. The fur of this species becomes very thick in winter.

Pika. A curious little relative of the Rabbits is the Rocky Mountain Pika, or Cony, also known as Rock-Rabbit, or Little Chief Hare. Its habit of living in rock piles is responsible for the name Cony taken from the Bible. "The Conies are but a feeble folk, yet make they their houses in the rocks." (Prov. XXX, 26.) This is true also of the Pikas, and that such soft, gentle little creatures can live permanently above timber line at an elevation of from 8000 to 13,500 feet seems remarkable indeed.

Pikas are shaped like Meadow Mice and are about the size of a small Guinea-Pig. Their ears are large and rounded and their eyes bright and saucy. Their palms and soles are thickly covered with hair, and at the base of each toe is a naked pad; this arrangement enables them to scamper about over the rocks without slipping and to dive to safety into a crevice when danger approaches. The

Pika is an accomplished ventriloquist and its clear, penetrating call is difficult to locate. Pikas believe in making hay while the sun shines. At harvest time, they gather together an immense pile of grass and other plants, sometimes as much as a bushel, on which they feed during the winter.

Red Squirrel. The second group of Gnawing Animals are known as Squirrels. Some of them, including the Red Squirrel, Fox Squirrel, and Gray Squirrel, spend

Photo by Middleton.   Courtesy, Nature Magazine

Red Squirrel.   This saucy fellow is taking his own picture by pulling on the nut which is attached by a string to the shutter of a camera.

most of their time in trees; Chipmunks are known as Rock Squirrels because of their fondness for rocky crevices; Woodchucks, Prairie Dogs, Striped Gophers, and Pocket Gophers are some of the common Ground Squirrels; and although the Flying Squirrel is a tree-dweller, it occasionally takes to the air and "flies" from one tree to another.

The smallest of the Tree Squirrels is the Red Squirrel, or Chickaree. He is a spirited little beggar, busily gathering pine cones or chasing his friends up and down and around the tree trunks in his exuberance. Instead of keeping himself concealed, as most wild animals strive to do, he deliberately seeks you out and then barks and scolds as though you had done him some injury. Like the Pika, the Red Squirrel is active throughout the year and must store up food for winter. This consists principally of cones, which are buried in some safe place, one by one, or cached in large quantities under a log or at the base of a tree.

Red Squirrels probably favor evergreen forests to other types of woodlands because they furnish an abundance of desirable food. Their nests of twigs and leaves are usually built in a cavity in a tree. A pair recently reared a family in a recess under the roof of the porch of our summer cottage in Maine, and we had the delightful experience of watching the mother bring her four young down along the side of the fireplace chimney and carry them to a near-by tree. She grasped them in her mouth by the skin of the belly, and they put their cute little fore limbs about her neck, as though they were quite confident of being delivered safely into the outer world.

It is certainly too bad that animals so charming to watch should be guilty of robbing birds' nests. Warblers, chickadees, thrushes, and many other birds that nest in localities inhabited by Red Squirrels fall an easy prey to their depredations, and those who have studied the situation carefully advise that most of the Squirrels be killed, since each one may destroy a dozen or more eggs or young every year.

Gray and Fox Squirrels. Two other species of Squirrels share popularity with the Red Squirrel; these are the Gray Squirrel and the Fox Squirrel. Both species occur in the deciduous forests of the eastern United States as far west as the Great Plains. The Red Squirrel is hardly large enough to be considered game, but both the Gray and Fox Squirrels are much larger; their flesh is excellent, and shooting them with a rifle is a pastime that may almost be called "sport."

Courtesy, American Museum of Natural History

Gray Squirrel. In city parks and suburbs, Gray Squirrels often become quite tame, since they are not molested by human beings; however, they must look out for dogs and cats.

One of our ambitions when young was to "bark" squirrels, that is, to shoot the bark on which the Squirrel was resting in such a way as to stun the animal without actually hitting him. Usually the bullet embedded itself in the limb beneath the Squirrel and the Squirrel scampered away out of gunshot.

These Squirrels often become quite tame and are pleasant inhabitants of city parks and suburbs. Their nests are built in hollow trees of twigs and leaves or in the tree tops. The Gray Squirrel may occur in two color phases and black individuals may be born in the same litter with gray ones, much as Screech Owls may be either gray or red. Fox Squirrels vary much in color according to locality, being rusty-yellowish, clay color, or blackish. They are about twice as large as the Gray Squirrel, some of them reaching a weight of almost three pounds.

Fox Squirrel. A large species often rusty yellowish in color; like the Gray Squirrel, it is easily tamed.

Chipmunk. In many localities a day in the country is certain to be made more enjoyable by the presence of Chipmunks, especially if the journey includes a visit to a region where rocky ledges, stone walls, or brush piles abound. With ears erect and tail extended, often straight up but not held over the back like a Squirrel, the Chipmunk scuttles about with sharp, high-pitched chirps. Although timid, he is full of curiosity, and when he learns that you mean no harm, but are prone to provide new and wonderful items to his menu, he loses his fear and becomes quite tame.

Chipmunks live in crevices in rocks, under logs, or in burrows in the ground. Their tunnels may be several yards in length and include several branches. They end in a nest chamber several feet underground and about a foot in diameter. Chipmunks are bright, handsome little fellows and very active, especially on bright sunny days. Food is carried in pouches inside of their cheeks, and, since Chipmunks are more or less active all winter, nuts and seeds are stored up for winter use in a hollow log, or in burrows in the ground, or under leaves. They have many enemies, such as snakes, hawks, foxes, and especially weasels. Like most small boys, we were once fond of hunting for Chipmunks in brush piles, and have captured many of them as they tried to escape when one of us jumped up and down on top of the pile.

About sixty different kinds of Chipmunks have been described, but they resemble one another so closely that only a specialist can possible tell them apart.

Striped Ground Squirrel. Every country boy in middle North America is familiar with the Striped "Gopher," or Thirteen-Lined Ground Squirrel. He is yellowish-brown in color with thirteen stripes on his back and sides, some of them dotted with rows of yellow spots. His body is small and slender, and his cheek pouches rather large. He has many enemies and keeps a very watchful lookout when out of his burrow, often standing rigidly upright on his hind legs to increase the field of vision. If danger threatens, he rushes quickly to the entrance to his burrow and dashes in, uttering a shrill, trilling whistle, often both before and after reaching a safe place underground.

We have spent many pleasant (for us) days snaring Gophers. A noose on the end of a string is placed around the inside of the burrow just below the top and the small boy lies in wait a few yards away at the end of the string. The Gopher, usually within a few minutes, comes to the top of the burrow and sticks his head out to see if the coast is clear. A pull on the string tightens the noose around his

Courtesy, U. S. Bureau of Biological Survey

Chipmunk. A bright and handsome little creature that can be coaxed close by with food, depending for safety on his quick get-away.

neck and one more Gopher is added to the menagerie. The Gopher's burrow is a rather complicated structure, often with several entrances, and not infrequently the Gopher sticks his head up from one of the holes other than that containing the noose.

A less refined method of catching Gophers is to stop up all the holes but one, and then pour water down into the burrow until the Gopher makes his way to the surface. He can then be grasped by the back of the neck without much danger of being bitten. Striped Gophers hibernate during the winter, sometimes

Photo by Hegner

Striped Ground Squirrel, or Gopher. He is about to dive into his hole in the pasture; when outside, he frequently stands up on his hind legs to see if there is any danger near.

for five or six months. They eat insects, mice, and other animal food, as well as seeds, grain, and other vegetation.

Pocket Gopher. Like the Mole, the Pocket Gopher is an animated steam shovel, modified for digging subways in which he shuttles back and forth in Stygian darkness. He is said to be a stupid animal, and he may seem so when taken from underground into the open air where he is like a fish out of water, but any animal that is as successful as is the Pocket Gopher can hardly be called stupid. He has a robust body about ten inches long, with a broad head, short neck, and powerful shoulder muscles. His fore feet are provided with long claws with which he digs tunnels, aided by strong, broad, incisor teeth. The loosened earth is pushed out of the hole with the head and palms of the feet. When walking, the claws are folded back against the palms. The tail is about three inches long, rather thick, and with few hairs; it is very sensitive and is used to guide the Gopher as it shuffles backward through its tunnels.

Photo by Hegner

Pocket Gopher. This specimen came to see why the plug had been removed from the entrance to his hole in the ground.

Courtesy, U. S. Bureau of Biological Survey

Pocket Gopher Mound. Earth is pushed out of the hole into a pile; the entrance to the hole is beneath the little circular elevation at the right-center of the mound.

Pocket Gophers occur only in North America where they range from sea level to an elevation of over 13,000 feet. Many species and subspecies have been described, varying in size from that of a large mouse to that of a muskrat.

The Gopher subway is usually about six inches underground; its progress can be traced by the mounds of earth brought to the surface. Often an enormous amount of earth is excavated. According to one report, three Gophers threw up 103 mounds in twelve days. The hole is always plugged up, but its position is indicated by a circular groove surrounding a convex little elevation. If one digs through this, the tunnel is soon reached. We have caught many Pocket Gophers by placing a trap in the floor near the opened hole; the Gopher soon comes up to close up the hole and if the trap is not sprung by the earth he pushes ahead of him, he is caught by the leg.

Pocket Gophers have large pockets, or pouches, in their cheeks in which they carry food. They live on vegetable material mostly gathered underground, such

Photo by Klugh. Courtesy, Nature Magazine

Woodchuck. The sun is evidently shining, hence, according to tradition, this "Ground Hog" will see his shadow as he emerges from his hole and go back again for six weeks.

as roots, bulbs, tubers, and bark. They work both by day and by night, but seldom leave their holes by day. In the winter they eat food stored up in special underground chambers, and also go foraging in tunnels under the snow. Pocket Gophers are sometimes so numerous as to be injurious to crops; they can be destroyed most easily with poison bait. Badgers, weasels, coyotes, snakes, hawks, and owls aid in keeping down their numbers.

Woodchuck. The Ground Squirrel that we call the Woodchuck, Ground Hog, or Marmot, is much larger than the Pocket Gopher and spends much more of his time outside of his hole. For this reason he is one of the best known of the group. He digs a burrow in the ground under a pile of rocks or even in an open field, and is frequently seen standing upright on his hind legs, motionless as a statue, survey-ing the surrounding country.   When approached, he runs clumsily to his hole and scrambles in with a loud, piercing whistle.

Woodchucks are frequently encountered in woodlands, and we have observed a number of them as much as six feet or more above the ground in trees that they succeeded in climbing.   They are solitary and rather surly animals, and, as our old dog could testify, fierce fighters.   Farmers consider them a nuisance and destroy them whenever possible, using traps and poison bait or fumigating their burrows with carbon bisulphide or the exhaust from an automobile.

Woodchucks hibernate during the winter and hence do not store up food the way the Pocket Gopher does.   They eat large quantities of grass, clover, and field crops, including onions, and be-come very fat in the fall, living on this fat during their winter sleep.   February 2 is "Ground-Hog Day."   According to tra-dition, if the Woodchuck comes out and sees his shadow on that day, that is, if the sun shines, he retires for another period of six weeks.   Woodchuck fur is coarse, but is sometimes dyed and sold as mink or sable.

Photo by Hegner

Prairie Dog.   A large part of his time is spent sitting on his hind legs and looking around at his neighbors. His barking is probably his way of spreading gossip.

Prairie Dog.   A trip through the Great Plains region is much enlivened by the appearance from time to time of Prairie Dog towns.   These sociable little ani-mals are not Dogs, but Ground Squirrels that have earned their name by their explosive, yapping "barks."   They are about the size of a small woodchuck, but although they live in holes in the ground, differ radically from woodchucks in disposition.

Companionship is necessary for the happiness of Prairie Dogs, and colonies covering from a few acres to many miles are scattered through the plains country.   One colony was reported in Texas that covered an area 100 miles wide and 250 miles long and was estimated to contain 400 million "Dogs." They are bright and active by day, visiting one another, digging burrows, and searching for grasshoppers, roots, grass, and other vegetation.   When danger threatens, they scamper to their burrows, stand bolt upright on their hind legs at the crater-like entrance until the last moment, and then dive in head first.

According to certain storytellers, Prairie Dogs, Burrowing Owls, and Rattlesnakes live happily together in the same burrow, but the snakes and owls feed on the baby dogs. Eagles, badgers, coyotes, and other carnivorous animals depend largely on Prairie Dogs for their food and levy a deadly toll on Prairie Dog towns. In spite of their many enemies, however, the Dogs seem to keep right on enjoying themselves.

Flying Squirrels. Unique among the members of the Squirrel family are the Flying Squirrels. These graceful, dreamy-eyed forest waifs have a fold of skin on either side of the body from wrist to ankle stiffened by a rod arising from the wrist. When the Squirrel launches itself into the air with legs widespread, it may glide to a neighboring tree as far as fifty yards away, guiding its "flight" with its broad, flat tail.

Courtesy, U. S. Bureau of Biological Survey

Flying Squirrel. Being a nocturnal creature, his eyes are very large; his tail is bushy, his fur fine and velvety, and his "wings" folded along the side like a lace ruffle.

Like the flaming youth of today, Flying Squirrels come out to play at sunset, their large eyes making it possible for them to see well in the dark. During the day they roll up into a furry ball and sleep the time away in a cavity in a tree, in a nest

Photo by Cornelia Clarke

Flying Squirrel. When one pounds on the tree in which a Flying Squirrel has his nest hole, he sticks his head out to get a look at the intruder.

of leaves in a tree, or occasionally in a bird box or the attic of a house. Sometimes many flying Squirrels live together in a single nest. They are active all winter, feeding on nuts, grain, berries, and insects.

Captive Flying Squirrels become very friendly and affectionately attached to their caretakers. They are exquisite little fellows with velvety fur as fine and soft as silk, and when at rest, their folded "wings" look like the edge of a lace ruffle. Flying Squirrels are the only nocturnal American Squirrels and on this account are very seldom seen. They spend more time in trees and less time on the ground than other species of Squirrels do.

Rats and Mice. The Rats and Mice occupy a prominent place among the Gnawing Mammals, not only because of their numbers, but also because of their economic importance as destroyers of food products, and as disseminators of disease germs such as those of the plague. The Old World Rats and Mice are placed in one family, which includes our most destructive species, unfortunately introduced from abroad. The House Mouse and Norway Rat are the worst offenders; the latter is also known as the Wharf Rat, Gray Rat, or Brown Rat. Two other introduced species, the Black Rat and the Roof Rat, have been driven out of most of the United States by the Norway Rat.

The family of Native Rats and Mice is separated into two subfamilies. The first subfamily includes the Harvest Mouse, White-Footed Mouse, Rice Rat, Cotton Rat, and Wood Rat, and the second subfamily, the Lemming, Red-Backed Mouse, Meadow Mouse, Pine Mouse, Water Rat, and Muskrat. A third family contains the Pocket Rats and Pocket Mice, and a fourth family the Jumping Mice. The name Vole is frequently applied to certain species of Rats and Mice. The Japanese Dancing Mouse was probably originally a native of China. It differs from the House Mouse in various details, especially in the structure of the inner ear. Dormice are natives of the Old World. The Dormouse of England is similar in size to the House Mouse but is colored bright yellowish-buff. Occasionally one reads in the daily press about the capture of a Singing Mouse. One of these was brought to us some years ago in Ann Arbor, Michigan. It could be heard from about twenty feet away. "The sound is best described as a rapid whole-toned trill involving the tones c and d. . . . The quality of the tone resembled somewhat that of a fife or flute, but each tone ended with a slight throaty click." This singing ability has been recorded in a few cases; it is probably due to some structural modification of the vocal apparatus.

The extraordinary migrations of the Brown Lemming have puzzled observers for centuries. This species lives in arctic and subarctic regions; it resembles the Meadow Mouse in size and general appearance, but has a short tail. When normal enemies are few and breeding conditions favorable, the food supply becomes too scanty and vast numbers start to march, evidently seeking new feeding grounds (see page 521). They march by night and sleep by day, devouring everything in their path, and overcoming all obstacles in their way. Rivers and lakes are crossed by swimming and the march continued on the other side. In Norway they are said to reach the ocean, which they likewise attempt to cross by swimming, and those that had not previously fallen a prey to predatory animals and disease are finally drowned.

The Pocket Rats and Pocket Mice possess external, fur-lined cheek pockets. Pocket Mice, of which there are many species and subspecies, live on the plains or deserts and burrow in the ground. They use their cheek pouches to carry seeds. The common Pocket Rat is also known as the Kangaroo Rat (see page 556). Related to it is the Dwarf or Pigmy Pocket Rat, a species that resembles in general appearance a large Pocket Mouse, being about six inches long.

Photo by Chace.   Courtesy, Nature Magazine

Mouse and Nest.   No more cosy nest could be imagined than the fluff of a ripe cat-tail.

Meadow Mouse.   Meadow Mice are "a feeble folk, comparatively insignificant in size and strength, holding their own in legions against a host of natural enemies, rapacious beasts, and birds."   This is made possible principally because they are mostly nocturnal, are able to eat almost any sort of food, and are extraordinarily prolific.

Meadow Mice, or Field Mice, are called Voles in England.   They are about the size of House Mice, but live in fields and meadows practically all over North America.   They are more active by day than many other species of mice, making runways through the grass leading from their burrows to their feeding grounds. Their nests are usually placed at the bottom of a burrow about one foot deep. From two to six litters of from six to thirteen young are brought forth each year. No wonder they continue to exist in spite of the constant depredations of predatory animals such as snakes, foxes, weasels, coyotes, skunks, hawks, and owls.

Courtesy, U. S. Bureau of Biological Survey

Meadow Mice.   They seem less unpleasant than House Mice but may be very injurious to crops and to trees which they girdle during the winter.

Meadow Mice are economically very important.   The injury done by a single Mouse seems insignificant, but large numbers do almost incalculable damage. Studies have shown that one Mouse in captivity will eat about half its own weight per day.   If one acre of hay land supports ten Mice, certainly a very low estimate, the 65 million acres of land in this country devoted to hay would furnish at least five million tons of hay each year for the Field Mice.   Occasionally favorable circumstances result in a sudden increase in the numbers of Mice, and 12,000 per acre may occur during these Mouse "plagues."   In winter Meadow Mice tunnel under the snow, and frequently gnaw the bark away from the base of orchard and other trees, thus girdling and killing them.

Kangaroo Rat.   That those who give names to animals pay very little attention to their relationships is well illustrated by the Kangaroo Rat, which is not a Kangaroo and not a Rat.   He is a Gnawing Mammal, however, and, although comparatively small, is shaped somewhat like a Kangaroo.   He is perhaps the most handsome of all of our Rodents, with long, beautifully shaded fur as soft as silk, and with large, expressive eyes with which he is able to see well at night. His fore legs and feet are small and used for holding food, whereas his hind legs and feet are very long and fitted for leaping, much as a Kangaroo leaps. Some Kangaroo Rats are able to jump six feet or more. The tail is very long, and terminated by a tuft; it is employed as a balancer while jumping. The Jerboa of Africa resembles the Kangaroo Rat very closely in appearance and habits, but belongs to an entirely different group of Mammals.

On each side of the mouth of the Kangaroo Rat is a cheek pouch in which food is carried to the burrow to be eaten at once or stored for future use. These pouches have given him the name Pocket Rat. The more or less desert regions of western North America are the habitat of Kangaroo Rats. Here they riddle the ground with their burrows, especially in sandy areas; these burrows become very long

Courtesy, U. S. Bureau of Biological Survey

Kangaroo Rat. The hind legs are long and serve for leaping like a kangaroo; the tail is a long balancer with a tuft at the end.

and twisted and the earth brought to the surface often forms large mounds. Sometimes a number of pairs live near together, forming a sort of colony. Kangaroo Rats can live where other animals would die of thirst, since they do not drink water, although they live mostly on dry food, such as seeds and desert plants. They are nocturnal, becoming active at nightfall. Although harmless-looking, they are pugnacious when pitted against each other. Tracks that they make after a night of activity "have been referred to as the 'fairy dances' of these beautiful little animals, but the truth revealed proves them to be really 'war dances.'"

Muskrat. A Meadow Mouse that kept on growing after it reached its usual size until it became as large as a cat would look very much like a Muskrat. But the Muskrat is an aquatic animal, with his hind toes partly webbed and his tail flattened vertically and hence useful as a rudder. Muskrats occur only in the New World; they may be found almost everywhere in North America, along streams, ponds and lakes, and in marshes.

In certain regions Muskrats are considered a delicacy and are sold in the markets under the name of Marsh Rabbits, but their principal value lies in their fur. They are the most important of our fur-bearers. Their fur consists of a fine, dense under-coat concealed by longer, coarser hairs. It is waterproof and hence prevents water from wetting the Muskrat; it serves also to keep warmth from escaping from the

Photo by Cornelia Clarke

Muskrat.   Not a very handsome fellow but a fur-bearer of great value and also good to eat, being known as "marsh rabbit."

body during cold weather.   When the long hairs are plucked out, and the underfur is dyed, the manufactured product is known as Hudson Seal.

In spite of persistent trapping, the Muskrat has held his own.   This is largely due to his fecundity, since the young number from three to thirteen and the number of litters per year ranges from three to five.   Muskrat houses are familiar sights in marshy regions.   They are conical structures about five feet wide and three or four feet high, built of mud, roots, and stems in shallow water, with an oval chamber inside above the water line and one or several entrances under water.   They are built primarily for a winter home, the summer nest being made of grass.   In many

Photo by Denmead.   Courtesy, U. S. Bureau of Biological Survey

Muskrat Houses.   Piles of vegetation are gathered together in a marsh in which the muskrats make their home.

Photo by Kellogg. Courtesy, Nature Magazine

Beaver. A flashlight photograph taken at night showing a Beaver at work on his dam.

regions a burrow is dug in a bank with the entrance under water and a chamber above the water line. These burrows, when dug in dams or the sides of irrigation ditches, often lead to considerable damage.

Muskrats are active throughout the year and store up food for the winter. They eat roots and stems, but are very fond of clams, also, and occasionally make a meal of frog or fish. They possess glands that give off a penetrating, musky odor, hence their name.

Marshy areas may be converted into Muskrat "farms" without much difficulty and a constant income can be derived from what would otherwise be waste property. One area in southern Louisiana suitable for this purpose contains more than one million acres. About fifteen million pelts are taken annually in the United States. Muskrats have been introduced into Europe and have spread there with remarkable rapidity.

Beaver. To "work like a Beaver" is an expression that implies indefatigable and long-continued effort, and is based on the amount of work and engineering skill required of the Beaver in felling trees, making dams and lodges, and building canals. Beavers add to their lodges, or houses, year after year until they may reach a diameter of 20 feet or more. Sticks are cut the desired length with their

Courtesy, U. S. Bureau of Biological Survey

Beaver. He has a large, flat tail covered with scales which helps in swimming; his fur is thick and valuable.

Courtesy, U. S. Bureau of Biological Survey

Trees Felled by Beavers. The tooth marks are very distinct. Beavers are said to be able to fell a tree in any direction desired.

chisel-like teeth, laid criss-cross, and cemented together with mud. The flat tail is not used to dig mud nor as a trowel, but serves as a propeller in swimming. The nest chamber, like that of the Muskrat, is a cavity in the lodge above the water line and is reached by an underwater doorway.

Beaver dams are built according to the best rules of engineering; for example, if very long they curve upstream, which increases their strength. They usually consist of sticks four or five feet long and one or two inches in diameter, laid at various angles and covered with mud. Large ponds and even lakes are formed behind these dams; in these bodies of water lodges are built and a food supply can be obtained easily by swimming.

Various kinds of vegetation are used as food, especially bark, twigs, and wood of aspen, cottonwood, and willow. Trees more than a foot in diameter are felled, it is said, in the direction desired. Grooves are cut around the tree and the wood in between is then chiseled out. Lack of space prevents us from giving an extended account of the many interesting phases in the lives of Beavers, that would easily fill a book.

Capybara. The first Capybara we ever saw was in the London Zoo. We were more surprised to see him than he was to see us, because we had no idea such an enormous Gnawing Mammal existed. The Capybara is, in fact, the largest species of Gnawing Mammal in the world. He is a sort of aquatic guinea-pig, but is as large as a small real pig, reaching a length of four feet and a weight of about 75 pounds. He has webbed feet, small ears, and coarse brown hair, and like the guinea-pig, has no tail. He is an excellent swimmer and diver, and when alarmed, takes to the water. When among water plants with just the tip of his nose above the surface of the water, he is not easy to find. Why the Capybara should be so large and its cousins so much smaller is a question that cannot be answered. Perhaps life in the water requires less exertion than that on land, and a luxuriant food supply, such as exists in its tropical home, provides an extra abundance of vitamins.

Courtesy, U. S. Bureau of Biological Survey

Beaver Dam and Lodge.   The dam consists of sticks and mud and the lodge was built in the pond created by the dam.

Photo by Hegner

Capybara.   The largest living gnawing mammal known, reaching a weight of 75 pounds; a water-loving species with webbed feet.

Capybaras live on vegetation growing both in and out of the water. According to some writers they are not good to eat, but we took part in a Fourth of July banquet in Panama several years ago at which the *pièce de résistance* was roasted young Capybara captured in Darien. Everybody agreed that it was delicious. Capybaras are inhabitants of rivers in Central and South America, but specimens may be seen in the larger zoological parks.

Photo by Hegner

Cavy. A gnawing mammal from Patagonia that lives in a burrow, has large ears and a short tail, and is gray or rufous in color.

Cavies. Closely related to the Capybara are a number of smaller South American Gnawing Mammals known as Cavies. Some of these resemble guinea-pigs, and from one species that lives in Peru, our domestic guinea-pigs were derived. A much larger species that lives on the plains of Patagonia has large ears and a short tail. It is shaped somewhat like a hare and is of about the same size. The Agouti and Paca are also South American Gnawing Mammals similar in many respects to the Capybara and the Cavies. Their toes are hooflike and their tails are either very short or entirely absent.

Porcupine. Perhaps the most peculiar and distinctive of the Gnawing Mammals is the Porcupine. This is the result of his unique method of defense, that is, his quills. These are long, stiff, and sharp and provided with barbs, and are distributed over the back and tail. Muscles at the base of the quills serve to erect them when the animal is alarmed, and if a dog or other invader gets too close, a flip of the tail drives them into its face. The barbs firmly fasten the quills into the enemy's flesh and heroic efforts are necessary to extract them. The quills are loosely attached to the Porcupine, but are never "shot" at a disturber.

Like other animals with excellent methods of defense, the Porcupine shows little fear of attack and therefore seems rather slow and stupid. His home is in a hollow log or in a cavity among the rocks. He is a forest-loving animal, and fond of climbing trees whose foliage, buds, and bark constitute a large part of his food. He is especially fond of salt and will chew up most anything that has on it the least trace of this substance. The Porcupine is sometimes called a Hedgehog, but differs from the European Hedgehog. He is one of our largest gnawers and may reach a length of three feet and a weight of 35 or 40 pounds.

Photo by Brownell

Porcupine. He is noted for his spines but is not a hedgehog; he may reach a length of 3 feet and a weight of 40 pounds.

CHAPTER 36

HOOFED MAMMALS, OR UNGULATES

The principal characteristic of these Mammals is the enclosure of the toes in hoofs. They all live on the ground and move from place to place by walking or running. Their food consists of vegetation. Hoofed Mammals are usually separated into two groups, those with an even number of toes and those with an odd number of toes.

The even-toed species never have more than four toes to each foot. Often only the two middle toes are developed and these are equal in size. This group contains the majority of the "game" animals and includes the pigs, hippopotami, camels, giraffes, deer, antelopes, sheep, goats, cattle, etc. The term ruminant has been given to the animals belonging to the camel, deer, giraffe, and ox families since they ruminate, or chew, their cud. The food of these animals is swallowed without sufficient mastication; it is later regurgitated in small quantities and thoroughly chewed. This method of feeding enables "these comparatively defenseless animals to gather nutriment in a short time and then retreat to a safe place to prepare it for digestion." A typical ruminant possesses a stomach consisting of four chambers. The food is first taken into the rumen chamber, where it is moistened and softened; it passes back into the mouth as "cuds" and is ground up by the molar teeth and mixed with saliva. When the cuds are swallowed, they are received by a second chamber, then pass into a third chamber, and finally into the fourth chamber.

The deer constitute the majority of the American Hoofed Mammals. The prong-horned antelopes are confined to the open country of western North America. The ox family contains the gnus, Rocky Mountain goats, sheep, goats, musk oxen, and bison.

The odd-toed Hoofed Mammals are the horses, asses, zebras, tapirs, and rhinoceroses. They are characterized by the presence of an odd number of hoofed toes. The horses, zebras, and asses of the horse family have but one functional toe on each foot and two lateral splints. The common horse, of which over sixty domesticated races exist, is not now known in a wild state. The Nubian ass is probably the parent of the domestic donkey. The zebras are confined to Africa. The tapirs live in tropical America and the Malay Peninsula. The rhinoceroses are large, thick-skinned mammals with one or two epidermal horns on the nasal and frontal bones; they live in Asia and Africa.

Traditions and ancient fables picture the Unicorn as an animal usually having the head and body of a horse, the hind legs of an antelope, the tail of a lion, sometimes the beard of a goat, and always a long, sharp, twisted horn set in the middle of its forehead. Unicorns have always been associated with India but no such animal has ever been reported from there or anywhere else.

According to an ancient belief, the horn of the Unicorn was an antidote for poison, and for this reason has been used frequently to decorate drinking cups. However, a horn drinking cup was once tested by the Royal Society and was found to have no effect on poisons, hence this old superstition was disproved. In the court ceremonial of France as late as 1789 instruments of Unicorn's horn were still used for testing the royal food for poison. The Unicorn has been frequently employed in heraldry. After the union of Scotland and England, it became a supporter of the royal arms, a royal crown being added to its head.

Photo by Hegner

Collared Peccary. Obviously a member of the Pig family with a grayish color. Peccaries go about in droves and may prove dangerous; their flesh tastes like pork.

Collared Peccary. The aphorism "United we stand, divided we fall" is the motto of the Collared Peccaries, which are practically never observed alone but travel about in droves of up to 30 or more. Very few animals that live in the dense forests and low jungles of tropical America are as greatly feared as the Peccaries. One Peccary would be scoffed at, but the sharp, knife-edged tusks of an infuriated drove have forced many a man up a tree and kept him there for hours.

Peccaries look like small pigs and are called Wild Pigs and sometimes Musk Hogs, because of a gland on the rump which gives off a musky odor. We have been served the flesh of the Peccary in Central America and have found it to be much like pork, but the musk gland must be removed as soon as the animal is killed or the flesh will be tainted.

Around the body, where the neck joins the shoulder, is a grayish band or collar; the rest of the hair is grizzled black. Peccaries are accustomed to feed in the morning and evening; they eat various kinds of animals, such as insects, worms, snakes, and frogs, as well as roots, fruit, and nuts. Frequently the presence of Peccaries is indicated by their peculiar odor or by the rooted-up soil.

Wart Hog and Wild Boar. The most hideous-looking member of the Pig Tribe is the Wart Hog of Africa, but he is not nearly as fierce and dangerous as his appearance would lead one to suspect. His head is extraordinarily bizarre-looking with its broad, flat face, conical warts under the eyes and between the eyes and tusks, and enormous incurved tusks. These tusks may be over a foot long and are capable of inflicting severe wounds; but are ordinarily used to dig up roots.

Photo by Lang.   Courtesy, Nature Magazine

Wart Hogs. The warts on the face and the large curved tusks give them an ugly look but they are not very fierce.

The skin of the Wart Hog, especially of older animals, is almost devoid of hair. When excited the tail is held upright. Wart Hogs travel about in family groups, except the boars, which don't seem to get along well with their wives and children, and live by themselves. They spend most of the day under cover of thickets, coming out in the evening to feed in the open.

We are accustomed to consider pigs as indolent and harmless, but Wild Pigs are noted for their speed, strength, and ferocity. Hunting Wild Boars has been a favorite sport for centuries in European countries. Dogs are used and the Boar is given the *coup de grâce* with a spear. Not all Wild Pigs are "wild"; many of them are merely the descendants of domesticated pigs that escaped from the barnyard. However, these soon become as wild as their savage relatives. The young of true Wild Pigs are dark-brown in color and are decorated with longitudinal stripes of a lighter color. The young of domestic pigs rarely have these stripes.

Photo by Baynes.   Courtesy, Nature Magazine

Wild Boar.   The young of Wild Pigs have longitudinal stripes on their bodies.

Hippopotamus.   The largest of the Pig Tribe and one of the heaviest of all living Mammals is the Hippopotamus.   His scientific name and common name are the same; it means "river horse," and refers to the horselike appearance of the head as seen from the side when emerging from the water.   A large Hippo measures twelve feet long and four and a half feet high and weighs about four tons.

Hippos occur only in Ethiopian Africa.   They spend most of their time in the water, and in spite of their huge bulk, are champion swimmers and divers.   Their

Courtesy, National Zoological Park

Hippopotamus and Young.   The mother may weigh four tons but the baby looks like a toy.

legs are so short that the body almost rests on the ground.   The head is the most striking feature, being huge and much flattened with very small eyes and a cavernous mouth.   It seems a real waste of effort for such an animal to open its enormous mouth to receive a little peanut, yet we enjoyed feeding one in the London Zoo with one peanut at a time, and we got tired before he did.   Inside of the mouth are tusks ten inches of which may be exposed to view, the greater part being hidden in the jaws.

The hide of the Hippo is about an inch thick and is used for making various articles, including shields and whips.   What a godsend a hide like this would be to certain politicians. The flesh resembles beef rather than pork and that of the young is said to be very good.   Lard made from Hippos is of excellent quality and is called "lake-cow fat."   One young is born at a time; the mother is devoted to it and will defend it courageously. Hippos are herbivorous animals, living principally on grass and weeds.   In Liberia lives another species, the Pigmy Hippopotamus, which is half as long as the other and only 30 inches high.   It looks more like a baby Hippo than an adult of a separate species.

Courtesy, N. Y. Zoological Society

Hippopotamus.   The jaws look rather thin when he opens his mouth; the tusks are about 10 inches long.

It is a little difficult to think of Hippopotami as "Pigs" living in herds up to forty or more in number and eating grass and aquatic plants to build up their gigantic mass of flesh.   They are nocturnal in habit, foraging for food principally at night; and when, as often happens on the banks of the Nile, they reach cultivated ground, they do immense damage to growing crops.   An ordinary Hippo has a stomach over ten feet long that will accommodate five or six bushels of grass. Where they are not disturbed by man "they put their heads boldly out of the water to blow, but when rendered suspicious by persecution, they become exceedingly cautious, only exposing their eyes and nostrils above the water.   They are said to walk with considerable rapidity on the bottoms of rivers, beneath at least a foot of water."   (Lydekker.)

Moose. The largest and most grotesque-looking of the Deer family is the Moose. His body is too short for his long, gangling legs; his front legs are longer than the hind legs, resulting in an ungainly and awkward gait; his huge head has a long, hairy muzzle and large nostrils, and bears broad, palmate antlers which may have a spread of over six feet; and from his neck hangs a pendulous bell. No beautiful, graceful deer could acknowledge him as a relative without a pang of regret.

Courtesy, U. S. Forest Service

Moose. The largest member of the Deer family and monarch of our northern forests; the antlers are palmate; a bell hangs from the neck of the male; the tail is very short.

Nevertheless he is the monarch of our northern forests, and as he plunges through the woods seems the embodiment of irresistible force.

Moose love water plants and seek for them during the summer along the banks of lakes and ponds and streams. In the winter, vegetation provided by shrubs and trees takes the place of aquatic plants. For several weeks during the fall of the year the usually shy bull Moose becomes bold, and his roars and bawls of desire or defiance sound through the forest. It is the mating season, and at this time he becomes a vicious fighter, using his antlers and fore feet with great efficiency. He can be called within gunshot with a horn made of birch bark, if the love call of the cow is imitated. Moose have disappeared in many places, but are protected now, and may still be encountered in certain parts of the country.

The Irish Elk, an extinct Mooselike animal, is of special interest to scientists because its antlers became so large as to hinder rather than help in the struggle for existence. The result was its extinction. Remains of this species are common in the peat bogs of Ireland. Their antlers were enormously palmated and reached a span of over eleven feet.

Photo by Russell. Courtesy, U. S. Forest Service

American Elk, or Wapiti. A male is bugling in the snow; the antlers are provided with sharp tines, which are formidable weapons.

American Elk, or Wapiti. The Elk is exceeded in size and strength among American Deer only by the Moose. He is a mighty "monarch of the glen, lord of the wilderness, king of the red deer tribe" that once roamed over most of the United States and southern Canada, but is now restricted to certain western states and Canada. The hunting of bull Elks in order to obtain the large canine teeth in the upper jaw for use as an emblem of a fraternal order brought about the destruction of large numbers. The name of the Elk is unfortunate, since it is not closely related to the European Elk, although the Moose is an Elk. The name used by the Shawnee Indians, Wapiti, is now in general use for him.

The Wapiti stands as high as a horse and his regal presence is enhanced by his huge, branching antlers. These antlers are as dangerous as they are beautiful, the upper branches probably being used as guards when fighting, while the deadly blows are given by the sharp tines on the forehead. Bull Elks live by themselves most of the year. They are polygamous and during the fall is the time to hear them "bugle" a challenge to one another. Their bugle has been described as "a shrill shriek, like an English locomotive whistle, sliding down the scale into a terrific bawl." The strongest bull is master of all the cows and a jealous Brigham Young he is, driving away all competitors.

After the mating season the Wapiti collect in large bands, and as winter advances. descend into the feeding grounds in the lowlands. In the spring they

Courtesy, American Museum of Natural History

Caribou, or Reindeer. Reindeer are domesticated Caribou; they live in the far North; a drove of this size furnishes a forest of horns.

scatter out on the higher ranges and in May the hinds leave the herd to give birth to the young. The mother defends her infant or her twins from bears, wolves, and other enemies most nobly, and if danger arises, she bellows for help and the neighboring herd rush to her rescue. Wapiti are good swimmers, and in summer when mosquitoes and flies are troublesome, they enjoy standing in the water. Sometimes they migrate for long distances.

Caribou and Reindeer. If Caribou had not been domesticated by the people of northern Europe and Asia centuries ago, and been transformed into Reindeers, our memories of Santa Claus and his faithful Blitzen and Dixon might be very different from what they are now. Barren Ground Caribou live beyond the tree limit in the desolate Arctic barrens, and the Woodland Caribou replace them in the forested regions further south, but mostly north of the United States. Reindeer are the domesticated descendants of Caribou.

Caribou are not the graceful creatures we usually expect a Deer to be, but are rather heavy and short legged. Both male and female bear antlers, the latter the only female Deer in North America that can claim this honor.

Social life among the Caribou is rather peculiar. During the summer the bulls gang away by themselves, as though too proud to associate with the cows and calves, but as winter approaches, they become good friends again and congregate in herds. These herds formerly contained hundreds of thousands of Caribou, but are now much smaller, due to widespread destruction by white men with guns. Caribou are of inestimable value to Eskimos and Indians, whose lives often depend on a supply of these animals for food.

Courtesy, National Zoological Park

White-Tailed or Virginia Deer. The female does not have antlers; she should be able to hear well with those enormous ears; she is descended from one of the oldest Virginia families.

"The Reindeer is of especial value to the Laplanders, whom it serves as a substitute for the horse, cow, sheep, and goat. It is capable of drawing a weight of three hundred pounds, and its fleetness and endurance are remarkable. Harnessed to a sledge it will travel without difficulty one hundred miles a day over the frozen snow. During the summer the Lapland Reindeer feeds chiefly on the young shoots of the willow and birch." (Lydekker.) In winter its food consists of "Reindeer moss" and other lichens.

White-Tailed or Virginia Deer. Perhaps the game animal that is known best to American big-game hunters is the White-Tailed Deer. Although not nearly as large as the Moose, Elk, and Caribou, it is one of the larger Deer. The male is about six feet long and three feet high at the shoulder, and weighs up to 300 pounds or more. Venison is excellent food and an edible animal of this size was a god-send not only to the Indians but also to our own pioneers, providing them both with their principal article of food. Many of the young riflemen in the Continental Army acquired their knowledge of woodcraft and their skill as marksmen while hunting Deer. Deer hide, or buckskin, was likewise extremely useful for many purposes.

Virginia Deer are reddish-brown in color in summer and grayish-brown in winter, with a tail that is white on the under surface. The male bears antlers with branches directed forward and with five or six points. The antlers are shed during the winter, and a new pair grow in during the spring and summer; they are covered with fur (velvet) at first, but this is rubbed off in September.

As a result of proper protective measures, Virginia Deer seem to be holding their own. They feed on various types of vegetation, including grass, leaves, and aquatic plants, and find shelter especially in the second growth that grows up when the primeval forests are cut down. Usually two fawns are born at one time; at first they are decorated with a series of large white spots, but these are lost when the gray winter coat is acquired.

Photo by Swan.
U. S. For. Serv.

Fawn. Young Deer are cute little creatures with spotted sides and back; the spots are lost as they grow older.

"The White-Tail moves with an indescribable spring and buoyancy. If surprised close up, and much terrified, it simply runs away as hard as it can, at a gait not materially different from that of any other game animal under like circumstances. . . . But normally its mode of progress, whether it trots or gallops, is entirely unique. In trotting, the head and tail are both held erect, and the animal throws out its legs with a singularly proud and free motion. . . . In the canter or gallop, the head and tail are also held erect, the flashing white brush being very conspicuous. Three or four low, long, marvellously springy bounds are taken, and then a great leap is made high in the air, which is succeeded by three or four low bounds, and then by another high leap. A White-Tail going through the brush in this manner is a singularly beautiful sight." (Nature Lovers Library.)

Black-Tailed Deer. From Alaska to central California in the heavily wooded portions of the Pacific coast states one may expect to encounter the Black-Tailed Deer. They are in some localities relatively tame, especially in the National Parks. They are heavier than the White-Tailed Deer; their ears are larger; their tail is tipped with black instead of white; and the tines of their antlers are pronged instead of undivided.

The Black-Tail is at home in broken country, open plains, or brushy, partly wooded terrain and does not care for heavy forest or swampy regions. It moves about with the season, feeding during the summer well up into the hills and mountains and spending the winter in the more sheltered lowlands, often traveling a hundred miles or more to do this. During the winter the Deer congregate in good-sized bands, but when the snow melts in the spring and the animals are free to move about, they scatter and are usually seen as individuals or as small parties of two or three. In the summer the bucks and does do not mingle, but the

Photo by Hegner

Black-Tailed Deer. A western species common in some of our national parks; the tail is tipped with black.

sexes keep by themselves. The bucks may be found in small bands up to ten in number.

The home of the Columbia Black-Tailed Deer "on the abruptly rising slopes of the islands in the Alaskan archipelago is so restricted that both in summer and winter they fall an easy prey to native and white hunters. It has been reported that formerly there has been much wasteful killing of the deer on these islands for commercial purposes. When the heavy snows of winter force the deer down to the shore, great numbers of them are also killed by wolves.

Black-Tails commonly have two or three young, and this fecundity, combined with the effective protection given by the dense forest where many of them live, will aid in their perpetuation. At the same time they have not developed the mental alertness of the Virginia deer, and there is imminent need for effective action in safeguarding them in the Alaskan part of their range if they are not to be exterminated on some of the islands. Fortunately, under the present Alaska game law the wanton destruction, once operative, has ended and a vigilant game commission is actively guarding their interests. In this northern region the black-tails share their range with strange tribes of coastal Indians, whose huge seagoing canoes, totem poles, and artistic carvings are unique among native Americans." (Nelson.)

Photo by Hegner

Black-Tailed Deer. The antlers are at first covered with fur (velvet) as shown here, but this is rubbed off in course of time.

"The Black-Tailed Deer when alarmed runs with a peculiar high-bounding gait, taking off from all four feet and landing on all fours. Although spectacular, this gait does not cover ground as rapidly as the rush of the White-Tailed Deer. The real value in such a gait is correlated with the broken country in which these bounding Deer live, where such a method of progression carries them safely away from enemies much fleeter on the plains but incapable of great leaps over rough country." (Anthony.)

Prong-Horned Antelope. If being a unique animal is desirable, the Prong-Horned Antelope should be very grateful to Mother Nature. He is so different from the Antelopes that live in Africa that scientists put him into a family all by himself. He is the only Antelope with branching or pronged horns. His horns grow around a bony core and are therefore not antlers; nevertheless, they are shed like antlers annually. He is smaller than the White-Tailed Deer and has a shorter tail, but his rump patch of long, white hairs can be erected and "flashed."

Once Pronghorns were common on the plains of the western United States, but they are now rare except in certain localities. Besides contending with coyotes, eagles, and other predatory animals, the Pronghorn has had to withstand the more effective attack of Man. The old saying, "Curiosity killed a cat," applies perfectly to these beautiful creatures, since anything unusual will intrigue them within gunshot of a wily hunter. The only thing that prevents their speedy extinction is the protection they are now afforded by the government.

The young are beautifully marked with white and brown, and are practically invisible, as they crouch beside the sagebrush or in the dry grass. Many of the young are captured by prowling coyotes. During the winter, the Pronghorns roam about in large bands.

Photo by Swan.   Courtesy, U. S. Forest Service

Prong-Horned Antelope. The horns have a prong in front; the rump is clothed with long, white hairs.

The name Antelope has been applied to various species of Hoofed Mammals, most of them inhabitants of Africa. This name was derived from that of the Unicorn, Anthalops. The following are some of the animals that are usually called Antelopes: Hartebeests, Bonteboks, Gnus, Diukerboks, Klipspringers, Dik-Diks, Reedbucks, Waterbucks, Impalas, Blackbucks, Gazelles, Springbucks, Oryx, Bushbucks, Nyalas, Kudus, Bongos, and Elands. Space will allow us to describe only a few of these, namely, the Waterbuck, Gnus, Lechwe, and Gazelles. The others are, of course, also of interest since each species exhibits its own peculiar characteristics. The Eland has long, twisted horns.

Photo by Lang.   Courtesy, Nature Magazine

Waterbuck. The male has long, curved horns. In the background are several baboons. Waterbuck are Antelope that live in southern and eastern Africa.

Waterbuck. An antelope that inhabits southern and eastern Africa is the Waterbuck. The male bears slender, ringed horns that may reach a length of over three feet. They spread out from the top of the head and then curve slightly toward each other at the ends; they also bend a little forward in a graceful curve. As weapons of defense, they are very effective. The coat of the Waterbuck is grayish-brown, somewhat relieved by a white band on the throat and an elliptical white ring on the buttocks. Small herds of Waterbucks are to be found in hilly country near water. The females keep constantly on the alert for possible danger, which they recognize with their keen senses of smell and hearing.

Gnus. If we were to combine the head of a buffalo with the legs and hoofs of an antelope and the tail of a horse, and give the creature a Hottentot name, we would have something resembling a Gnu. These curious Antelopes once roamed over a large area in Africa, but have been killed off for their skins and for other reasons until very few remain alive except in captivity.

The head is nothing to be proud of, with its broad muzzle, and with tufts of hair on the face. Horns are present in both sexes. They are smooth and not ringed, broad at the base, and bend first downward and then curve upward. In some, they reach a length of thirty inches measured along the curve. The neck bears a mane that stands erect. The tail is long and bushy, white in color, and may reach a length of three feet. The face is black and the rest of the body dark brown in color.

Courtesy, N. Y. Zoological Society

Brindled Gnu. Antelope with a buffalo-like head and horselike tail; they are natives of Africa.

Gnus look somewhat like oxen, hence the Dutch in Africa named them Wildebeests. The White-Tailed Wildebeest stands about 42 inches high at the shoulders and a trifle lower at the haunches.

Gnus can run very swiftly and for long distances. Their sight is keen. When excited, and they are very excitable, they cut up curious capers, leaping and prancing about with no evident end in view. The Brindled Gnu, or Blue Wildebeest, is somewhat larger than the White-Tailed Gnu.

Lechwe Antelope. The Lechwe is an Antelope discovered by Livingstone in south central Africa. The horns are about two feet long; the general color of the body is pale brown; the ears are fawn-colored; and white rings surround the eyes. It lives in swamps and may often "be seen standing knee or belly-deep in the water, lazily cropping the aquatic plants, or reposing close to the water's edge." When Lechwes "first make up their minds to run, they stretch out their noses,

Courtesy, N. Y. Zoological Society

Lechwe Antelope. A water-loving African species with long, sharp horns, fawn-colored ears, and white circles around the eyes.

the males laying their horns flat along their sides and trot; but on being pressed they break into a springing gallop, now and then bounding high into the air. Even when in water up to their necks they do not swim, but get along by a succession of bounds, making a tremendous splashing. Of course, when the water becomes too deep for them to touch bottom, they are forced to swim which they do well and strongly, though not so fast as the natives can paddle; and when the country is flooded, great numbers are driven into deep water and speared." (Selous.)

Gazelles. To one group of Antelopes the pleasant name Gazelle has been applied. Gazelles are medium-sized animals, very few of them reaching a height at the shoulder of over 30 inches. They live in northern and eastern Africa and in parts of Asia. "The gazelles are among the most elegant of all antelopes, and are characterized by their sandy color and the presence of a white streak on the side of the face from the base of the horn nearly to the nose, thus cutting off a dark triangular patch in the middle of the forehead, while the streak itself is bordered externally by a diffused dark line. The horns, which are generally present in both sexes, are lyrate or re-curved and are compressed, oval in section, and completely ringed throughout the greater part of their length. The knees are generally furnished with tufts of hair. Glands are present in the feet, and the gland below the eye, if present, is small and covered with hair. Most of the gazelles do not exceed thirty inches in height, although the mohr reaches thirty-six inches. There are about twenty-one living species belonging to the genus Gazella, which are mainly found in the deserts

Courtesy, N. Y. Zoological Society

Addra Gazelle. An African Antelope small in size and delicate in appearance; he has long sensitive ears and a white necktie.

of Asia and North Africa, although the group is represented in South Africa by the springbok. Two of the Asiatic species are found at great elevations." (Lydekker.)

In certain parts of Africa, Gazelles are extremely numerous. The Springbok,
for example, which has the peculiar habit of suddenly leaping into the air, formerly
occurred in vast numbers. One writer says "on our climbing the low range of hills
through which the springboks had been pouring, I beheld the plains and even the
hillsides which stretched away on every side of me thickly covered, not with herds,
but with one vast mass of springboks; as far as the eye could strain, the landscape

Courtesy, National Zoological Park

Rocky Mountain Goat. In the high mountains he needs a thick, woolly coat to protect him
from the cold; his horns are short but sharp and his beard well defined.

was alive with them, until they softened down into a dim red mass of living creatures. To endeavor to form any idea of the amount of antelopes which I had that
day beheld was vain; but I have no hesitation in saying that some hundreds of
thousands were within the compass of my vision." (Cumming.) The small size,
graceful figure, and liquid eyes of the Gazelles have made them great favorites
among naturalists. Unfortunately, they are also favored by predatory animals as
well as by some big-game hunters. We hope they will hold their own until their
future is provided for by law.

Rocky Mountain Goat. The European Chamois and the Rocky Mountain Goat are both members of a tribe of Mountain Antelopes. Our representative lives among the higher peaks of the Rocky Mountains and Coast Ranges from Montana and Idaho to Alaska. He wears a long yellowish-white, shaggy overcoat with woolly underfur, and a short beard. Where patches of snow occur he blends into the landscape, but otherwise he is quite conspicuous. Poor Billy is considered something of a moron, because when pursued, he has a way of stopping to peep around the corner to see if the hunter is really following him, — a habit that is very bad for his health.

"Unlike mountain sheep, the goats do not appear to dislike the fogs and saline winds from the sea, and at various points along the coast of British Columbia and Alaska they range down precipitous slopes nearly to the shore. They are much more closely confined to rugged slopes and rocky ledges than the mountain sheep, which in winter commonly descend through the foothills to the border of the plains. Through summer and winter, goats find sufficient food in the scanty vegetation growing among the rocks, and their heavy coats of hair protect them from the fiercest winter storms." (Nelson.)

The Mountain Goat lacks the grace of the Pronghorn, but can travel over the steepest crags and most dangerous ice-covered slopes; in fact, he is the most expert and daring rock-climber of all American Hoofed Mammals. His hoofs are "an ingenious combination of rubber-pad inside and knife-edge outside, to hold the owner equally well on snow, ice, or bare rock." The Goat's horns are slender and blackish and almost a foot long. They are used by the Pueblo Indians as a model for decorating their sacred dolls or katcinas.

Mountain Goats, like the other Hoofed Mammals of the West, are preyed upon by predatory animals, but they really have few enemies because they live in such inaccessible regions; their flesh is not particularly good, hence they are not hunted very persistently.

Courtesy, N. Y. Zoological Society

Chamois. This Goat of the mountains of southern Europe can be distinguished from all others by the backward curve of the tips of the horns.

Chamois. The wariness and agility of the Chamois, and the character of his habitat, high up in the mountains of southern Europe, have stimulated sportsmen to test their ability in his pursuit, until now he is absent from many localities where he was once common. The Chamois can be distinguished easily from other goats by the character of his horns; these extend straight up from the head and have the tips bent sharply backward. His ears are pointed and stand erect and his tail is short and black.

Photo by Blickensderfer. Courtesy, Nature Magazine

Rocky Mountain Sheep, or Bighorn.   The horns are massive and much curved.

The race of Chamois that lives in the Alps is chestnut-brown in summer and grayer in winter. Under the longer brown hair is a thick, woolly fur, gray in color. Chamois are famous for their ability to leap from rock to rock and across chasms; this **is** due largely to the character of their hoofs. The outer edges of the hoofs extend beyond the bottom of the toes and hold firmly to slight irregularities in the surface of the rocks. A Chamois can stand on a base just large enough for all four feet to meet together.

Chamois live together in herds of a dozen or more, all except the old males, who prefer to live alone except during the breeding season. In October the old males join the herd, drive away the young males, and test their superiority with one another until the fittest survives as head of the family. Thus, as in many other species of animals, the strongest member of the clan is the one that leaves offspring, and in this way maintains the vigor of the species.

Chamois like cold weather. They live at the snow line in summer, feeding on plants. In winter, they descend to lower altitudes and feed on pine shoots. Leather made from their hides is the well-known Chamois skin, although nowadays much of the "Chamois skin" comes from other species of animals. The flesh of the Chamois is valued highly as venison.

Rocky Mountain Sheep. To most of us the Rocky Mountain Sheep, or Bighorn, is known only from western stories or from specimens in museums or zoological gardens. He rivals the Mountain Goat as a sure-footed mountaineer, but can now be observed in a state of nature only among the higher peaks. This is largely due to persistent hunting and to the disease known as scabies, which was brought to them by domestic sheep and has destroyed large numbers of them. However, man is now controlling scabies and also aiding the Bighorns by killing off large numbers of their natural enemies, such as cougars, lynx, wolves, and eagles, which carry away lambs. The flesh of the Mountain Sheep is said to be delicious, and the massive curled horns are much-prized trophies of the hunt.

"The Rocky Mountain Sheep, like other species, appears to feed on nearly every plant growing within its domain. In spring many lambs are killed by bald and golden eagles, and in winter, when driven down to lower levels by snow, it becomes easy prey for mountain lions, wolves, and coyotes.

"The sure-footedness with which a band of these sheep will dash in full flight up or down seemingly impossible slopes, where a misstep would mean death, is amazing. Even the old rams, with massive sets of horns, bound from point to point up a steep rock slope with marvelous grace and agility. Mountain sheep living among the rugged summits of high ranges possess the courage and prowess of skillful mountaineers, so admired by all, and the mere sight of one of these animals in its native haunts is an adventure achieved by few.

"No other big-game animal carries with it the romantic glamour which surrounds this inhabitant of the cold, clear, upper world. Big-game hunters prize above all others their mountain sheep trophies, which form vivid reminders of glorious days amid the most inspiring surroundings and bear witness to their supreme prowess in the chase." (Nelson)

Musk Ox. About the least desirable place anyone would want to live in is the bleak, frozen, windswept Arctic regions, yet the Musk Ox has chosen this area as a habitat, and gets along very well indeed, except when wantonly slaughtered by human beings. He combines the characters of both Ox and Sheep with a few of his own added. His long, matted hair gives him a very shaggy appearance, and his curious downward-slanting horns curl up at the ends like the mustachios of a city slicker. Under the outer long hair is an underfur so dense that neither moisture nor cold can penetrate. Both ears and tail are concealed by the hair.

Musk Oxen are gregarious and travel about in herds of a dozen or more. When attacked by their principal enemy, the wolf, they form a circle with their heads pointed out that no wolf can hope to penetrate. The milk of the Musk Ox is as good as cow's milk and the flesh is said to be of excellent flavor. The Eskimos and also Arctic explorers owe much to the Musk Ox. According to Peary, "In 1899, in Independence Bay, the finding of a herd of Musk Oxen saved the lives of my entire party."

Courtesy, U. S. Bureau of Biological Survey

Musk Oxen. When they face an enemy, they are difficult to conquer; the hair is long and matted, giving them a shaggy appearance.

Bison. The history of the Bison, or "Buffalo," that once held sway in countless thousands over the best grazing lands in this country should be known to everyone, and should serve to teach us that none of our natural resources are really "inexhaustible." His range once covered an area about 3600 miles long from north to south and 200 miles wide. On the Great Plains, as late as 1870, the migrating herds blackened the landscape as far as the eye could see, and trains were stopped by them. Then came the slaughter, and "buffalo robes" were familiar possessions in the average home in the East. Within 20 years the Bison had been exterminated in his wild state. At present one can see Bison in many zoological parks, and several herds exist in Yellowstone Park and in Canada.

The Bison was the Lord of the Plains, a dignified but rather stupid animal with a massive head, a hump on his shoulder, and a heavy body averaging about 1800 pounds in weight. In spite of their heavy coats, Bison were pestered by flies and loved to take mud baths in "wallows," thereby acquiring a coating of mud that furnished an armor, not beautiful, but very efficient as a protection against insects. Some of the old "buffalo wallows" still keep their pioneer names to remind us of the former Proprietors of the Great Plains.

Courtesy, U. S. Bureau of Biological Survey

Bison, or "Buffalo." The deposed Lord of the Plains now on a game preserve; his horns, shaggy coat, beard, and hump are well shown in this photograph.

"The Bison was one of our Mammals that was accustomed to migrate for considerable distances. Herds containing millions of animals set out on regular spring and fall journeys, sometimes hundreds of miles long, in order to reach satisfactory feeding grounds. Distinct trails were worn by these immense herds, trails that were later used by our engineers in laying out roads and railroad lines.

Water Buffalo. The wild Buffaloes of Asia and the East Indies are dangerous and destructive animals, but fortunately some of them have been domesticated, and no other species is quite as valuable to the natives in that part of the world.

Photo, Bureau of Science, Manila

Water Buffaloes. In the Far East rice cultivation is made possible by these slow but exceedingly strong animals; they are shown here plowing a rice field.

This is due to the fact that Water Buffaloes make rice culture on a large scale possible. They are extremely powerful and capable of wading through mud almost up to their thighs, dragging a plow behind them. They move very slowly and

Photo by Hegner

Water Buffaloes. They spend a large part of their time in the water with as much of the body covered as possible.

must be allowed to wallow in the mud or soak themselves in water a considerable part of the day. They love to lie in the water with only their nostrils and horns above the surface, as shown in the accompanying photograph.

Even when domesticated Water Buffaloes are dangerous. They recognize their owners and may be controlled even by little children, but strangers are not safe from attack. Wild Buffaloes do not hesitate to charge an elephant or a tiger and are the most dreaded of the large jungle animals. Their sense of smell is acute and aids them in hunting down an adversary. Being gored to death by one of them is certainly a very unpleasant business.

Yak. The peculiar hollow-horned Hoofed Mammal known as the Yak is an Asiatic relative of the Bison. If you have not seen domesticated specimens in a zoo you may have seen a caricature of him on the comic page of a newspaper. The Yak lives at a high altitude in the mountainous region of Tibet. He is a massive animal with very long, black hair over the shoulders and thighs, and a

Courtesy, National Zoological Park

Yak. He loves the cold of the Tibetan mountains; his long, black hair almost conceals his legs; his horns are black and widespread.

flowing fringe along the side covering the lower part of the body. At the end of the tail is a tuft of fine hair said to be used by Indian Princes as fly-whisks and called chowries. His horns are heavy, black in color, and curved upward and forward. Yaks appear to love the cold, dry air of the high mountains. They are great travelers, moving from place to place in search of the grass on which they feed. In India they have been domesticated, a process that apparently has resulted in a decrease in size.

Camel. The "ship of the desert" that now lives in a state of domestication in Asia and Africa is the most valuable beast of burden in those countries. The species with one hump is the Arabian, or True Camel, of which those bred for riding purposes and for speed are called Dromedaries. The Bactrian Camel, often erroneously called Dromedary, has two humps.

Camels have long legs and a long neck; they can reach food on the ground or in trees. The skin of the lips is hard and fitted for breaking off sharp or spiny desert plants, which are then chewed by the powerful teeth. The humps consist almost entirely of fat, which serves as a reserve food supply. Water can be consumed in large quantities, stored in cells in the paunch, and used little by little as needed, hence Camels can travel for several days without drinking, and for several weeks if juicy plants are available.

Camel with Young. The Arabian Camel has one hump, which consists largely of fat and serves as a reserve food supply; the young is light-colored but will become as dark as his mother.

In traveling, the legs on one side are moved together, giving the body a rolling, shiplike motion. The feet have broad callous pads which do not sink into the sand, are insensible to heat, and not easily injured by sharp stones. A pack Camel can carry a load of 500 pounds 30 miles a day, and a riding Camel can travel almost 100 miles in a day. Camels rest on callous pads at the joints of the legs and on the chest. Their hair is woven into cloth; their flesh is edible; their bones are sometimes substituted for ivory; and their milk is rich and thick. Camels were once introduced into the western United States as beasts of burden, but the experiment was unsuccessful.

The Bactrian Camel is an inhabitant of Central Asia. His two humps are enough to identify him, but he differs in certain other respects from the Arabian Camel. He is not as tall, has shorter legs and feet, and an abundance of long hair, especially on the humps and on the neck, shoulders, and top of the head. He is large enough to ride when three years old but does not reach his full size until five years of age. This species still occurs in the wild state in the more remote regions of Turkestan. Camels are usually given credit for being docile but sometimes they become very surly and show violent outbursts of temper. Apparently they have not lost all of their savage nature as a result of domestication.

Llama. The American members of the Camel tribe are restricted to western and southern South America, where two wild species and two domesticated species occur. The Vicuna is the smallest species; it inhabits the higher mountains of Peru, where it still exists in its native state. The Guanaco is somewhat larger and extends southward into Patagonia. From it the Alpaca and Llama have been derived by domestication. The former is bred for its wool, which is fine and long.

Llamas. These members of the Camel family are bringing loads of grain into the city of La Paz in Bolivia; they live only at high elevations in South America.

The Llama was domesticated by the Indians before the Spanish conquered what is now Peru and Bolivia. It is smaller than a camel, and has longer ears, smaller feet, and a shorter tail. The humps so characteristic of the camel are absent. Llamas are regularly employed as beasts of burden in Peru and Bolivia; we saw trains of them coming into La Paz daily with loads on their backs, and in Cuzco almost every native visitor seemed to be accompanied by his Llama.

These animals have certain very peculiar habits. Agustin de Zarate, treasurer-general of Peru in 1544, mentions several of these. "When they are weary they lie down upon the ground; and as there are no means of making them get up, either by beating or assisting them, the load must of necessity be taken off. When there is a man on one of them, if the beast is tired and urged to go on, he turns his head round and discharges his saliva, which has an unpleasant odor, into the rider's face." This disagreeable habit is practiced whenever the animals encounter anyone they don't take a fancy to. Knowing this, we were careful to keep well out of range when Llamas were near.

Giraffe and Okapi. The Giraffe belongs among the Hoofed Mammals some-where near the Deer family. He is the type of beast that when seen for the first time startles one into exclaiming, "There ain't no such animal." His extremely long legs and neck give him a height up to 19 feet and make him the tallest of living animals. This is of distinct advantage, since it enables him to obtain leaves high above the ground. In fact, his entire figure seems to be designed for this purpose, his fore legs being longer than the hind legs, his upper lip being long and capable of grasping, and his tongue adding about 18 inches to the distance he can reach.

Giraffes live in open forest country in Africa, including desert-like areas, since they can exist for long periods without drinking water. When they walk, they shuffle along, and when they gallop, they move the two legs on one side together. In a zoological garden the Giraffe is a conspicuous animal, but his form, his spots, and his behavior really serve as an excellent camouflage when in his native haunts.

Photo by Lang.   Courtesy, Nature Magazine

Giraffes. A group of adults with young; the long fore legs and elongated neck give them a height up to 19 feet; the spots on the body tend to conceal the animals from view.

Giraffes would long ago have become extinct if they had not been properly protected from big-game hunters. The authorities in Africa make it so difficult for the sportsman to hunt them that the number killed is limited. The animals are well able to protect themselves from ordinary enemies by powerful kicks with their fore feet, and also, to a lesser extent, by blows with their hair-clad horns.

"There are few sportsmen who have hunted in localities where Giraffes are found, but have been deceived by their tall, motionless figures. They stand perfectly still, not even swishing their tails like wildebeeste, and thus bringing about instant recognition; their mottled or dark colour, great height, and comparatively narrow bodies give them a striking resemblance to the many old vari-coloured relics of the forest, blasted by lightning or by bush-fires. . . . And the deception is often the other way, tree stumps being mistaken for giraffes. . . . Few animals are so easily lost sight of, if once the attention is taken from them, their bodies being always concealed behind the thick foliage of the trees, their long legs merely doing duty for tree stumps." (Kirby.)

Rather closely related to the Giraffe is the Okapi, an animal that is limited to the dark forests of Central Africa. It seems strange that an animal as large as the Okapi should not have been known to science until 1900; this was no doubt due to its restricted distribution. Okapis are smaller than Giraffes and have shorter legs and neck. They are about five feet high at the shoulder. The male only has horns.

Courtesy, American Museum of Natural History

Eohippus. A group of prehistoric Horses restored from bones found in Wyoming and New Mexico; they had four toes in front and three behind and were about the size of a fox.

They are shy, retiring creatures, with colors that effectively conceal them among the trees. They are in general purplish-brown, but the hind quarters are transversely barred with black and white stripes; the legs below the knees are white.

A Fossil Horse — Eohippus. The Horses now inhabiting America are descendants of domesticated animals which were brought to this country by the early settlers from Europe, but in prehistoric times the ancestors of our modern Horse were native here, and some of the finest fossil remains of these ancestors have been found in America.

The evolution of the Horse has been traced back through at least twelve distinct stages extending through the Cenozoic Era, or the Era of Mammals. The structural features that became modified during this era of about 3,000,000 years were such as to adapt the Horse to life on the open plains, where its food consisted of dry, siliceous grasses.

The feet gradually lost the side toes, and only the middle toe and splints of the second and fourth digits remain in our modern Horses. The limbs became longer, enabling the animal to move about more rapidly; this change was correlated with an elongation of the head and neck, which was necessary in order to reach the ground. The front teeth were modified as chisel-like, cropping structures, and the back teeth evolved from simple molars into wonderfully effective grinding organs with tortuous ridges of enamel and with supporting and protecting layers of dentine and cement. During the later periods the molars elongated, and thus became

Photo by Hegner

Zebra. An African member of the Horse tribe famous for his stripes; at night, when he is most active, he is said to be very inconspicuous.

adapted for grinding the dry, siliceous grasses which caused them to wear down more rapidly than the softer vegetation. During this evolution the body gradually increased in size from that of the earliest known form, which was about as large as a domestic cat, to that of the Horse of today.

Eohippus lived during the Lower Eocene Period. It was named from remains found in Wyoming and New Mexico; its fore feet have four complete toes and the splint of the fifth, and the hind feet have three complete toes and the splint of the fifth. The modern Horses have lost the first and fifth digits entirely, and the second and fourth digits are represented by splints. The third toe alone sustains the weight of the body.   The crowns of the molar teeth are much elongated, the skull has lengthened, and the body is considerably larger than that of any of its ancestors.

At the present time true wild Horses occur only in Asia.   The Mustangs and Broncos of our western plains and South America are not true wild Horses, but are descendants of domesticated Horses brought over from Europe.

Zebra.   In Africa the Horse tribe is represented by the Zebras.   A number of species are recognized, differing in distribution, in the size of body and ears, and in the arrangement of their stripes.   Among them are the True or Mountain Zebra, Burchell's Zebra, Grant's Zebra, and Grevy's Zebra.

"No more conspicuous animal can well be conceived, according to common idea, than a zebra : but on a bright starlight night the breathing of one may be heard close by you, and yet you will be positively unable to see the animal.   If the black stripes were more numerous he would be seen as a black mass ; if the white, as a white one ; but their proportion is such as exactly to match the pale tint which the arid ground possesses when seen by moonlight."   (Galton.)

Zebras live in herds and feed at night.   They are preyed upon by lions and other carnivorous animals.

Tapir.   Students of zoogeography cite the Tapir as an interesting illustration of discontinuous distribution, since one species lives in the Malay Peninsula and all of the rest in Central and South America.   We have seen them in Honduras feeding on the luxuriant vegetation in dense reed thickets along the water courses. They are somewhat piglike in form, but much larger, and the snout is extended into a sort of proboscis or trunk. Tapirs are excellent swimmers and divers and are said to be able to walk on the bottom of a body of water that is over their heads. They no doubt escape from some of their enemies by diving out of harm's way, but when they reach apparent safety they must be on guard against the anaconda which lies in wait to strangle them and must protect themselves from the blood-thirsty fish,

Courtesy, National Zoological Park

American Tapir. Tapirs love water. This view shows clearly the characteristics of the head and proboscis.

the "cariba," which may swarm around them and tear them to pieces with their razor-edged teeth.

Tapirs are not noisy but when properly aroused may utter shrill cries.   They are

American Tapir.   A harmless inhabitant of the American tropics; his body is rather piglike, and his snout is prolonged into a short proboscis.

timid creatures and quite harmless.   When captured, they become real tame and gentle.   However, they are not always tractable.   One specimen is reported to have disliked going to bed, but would gallop about its quarters in the Zoo for some time before giving in.   Their flesh is said to be well flavored and their thick hide is used for various purposes for which a heavy, strong leather is needed.

Tapirs "confine themselves exclusively to the thickest parts of the forests, forming regular pathways along which they travel in search of food and water. They are fond of rolling in soft mud, their hides being often thickly plastered with the latter, probably as a protection against the bites of insects. These animals are slow and deliberate in their movements, usually walking with their snouts close to the ground, and by the aid of scent or sound detecting the presence of foes with extreme acuteness. When frightened, however, they rush blindly forward, crashing through bushes or splashing through water in precipitate flight." (Lydekker.)

Young Malay Tapir.   Young Tapirs are curiously ornamented with longitudinal stripes and spots.

Rhinoceroses. The largest Mammal now living on land, with the exception of the Elephant, is the White Rhinoceros of Africa. One other species of Rhinoceros lives in Africa and three species occur in the Asiatic region. The Rhinoceroses that once lived in America became extinct long, long ago.

Rhinoceroses are huge, ungainly creatures with a very thick skin that in some species is conspicuously folded. The one or two median horns are fibrous in structure and derived from the skin. The skin is mostly free from hair; the eyes are small and the sense of sight poor; the ears are erect and prominent and the sense of hearing acute; the sense of smell is also acute.

Rhinoceroses sleep during most of the day, but in the cool of the evening they become active, feeding on leaves, grass, and other vegetation. They love to wallow in the mud and bathe. They are ordinarily timid but when hunted and brought to

Courtesy, Science Service

Indian Rhinoceros. The skin of this species is divided into distinct areas by heavy folds; the horn on the nose of this specimen was short.

bay are very ferocious. The Indian Rhinoceros is about five and one-half feet high at the shoulder and has a horn one foot long. White Rhinoceroses are five feet eight inches high and fifteen feet long. They are "often accompanied by rhinoceros birds, which, by running about their heads, flapping their wings, and screeching at the same time, frequently give them notice of the approach of danger. When disturbed they go off at a swift trot, which soon leaves all pursuit from man on foot far behind; but if chased by a horseman they break into a gallop, which they can keep up for some distance. However, although they run very swiftly, when their size and heavy build is considered, they are no match for an average good horse. When either walking or running, the White Rhinoceros holds its head very low, its nose nearly touching the ground. When a small calf accompanies its mother it always runs in front, and she appears to guide it by holding the point of her horn upon the little animal's rump; and it is perfectly wonderful to note how in all sudden changes of pace, from a trot to a gallop or vice versa, the same position is always exactly maintained." (Lydekker.)

Elephants. The two species of Elephants living at the present time are the largest four-footed animals. One species lives in Africa and the other in India. They can be distinguished by various characters, including the following: size, African larger, up to $11\frac{1}{2}$ feet high at the shoulder, Indian up to 10 feet at the shoulder; ears, African larger, up to 9 feet across, Indian up to 5 feet across; trunk, African with a series of ridgelike folds, with 2 "fingers" at the end, Indian with smooth trunk and one "finger" at the end; tusks, African in both sexes up to $11\frac{1}{2}$ feet long and about 230 pounds in weight, Indian smaller and lighter in the

Photo by Hegner

Indian Elephant.   The ears are small and the back is arched.

male, absent or small in the female; nails, African 4 in back feet, Indian 3 in back feet; back, African hollowed, Indian arched.

The tusks of Elephants are the incisors of the upper jaw. The molar teeth are huge and very effective for grinding the vegetation on which the animals feed. The nostrils are at the end of the trunk. The trunk, as everyone knows, is used for many purposes and is almost as effective as our hands. Elephants possess a keen sense of smell and are said to be able to detect a human being at a distance of several miles when the wind comes from that direction. Their hearing is not so good, however, and their eyesight is poor.

Elephants are placid animals with the motto "slow but sure." They are easily caught and tamed and learn to perform various tasks that require great strength. Various rulers, especially in Asia, have used them as an indication of power and might and as an aid in warfare. White Elephants are albinos; they have a pinkish skin and white hair, and are worshiped in Siam and Pegu. Probably

Courtesy, Nature Magazine

African Elephant.   The ears are very large, the tusks long and heavy, and the back hollowed.

the best-known Elephant that ever lived was Jumbo, an African specimen of very large size. In their native haunts, the old bull Elephants live a solitary existence a large part of the year, but when migrating in search of food, they all join together in herds of a few to a hundred or more.

Mammoth. The word *mammoth* is often used as a synonym for huge or colossal. Thus when an extraordinarily large cave was discovered in Kentucky, it was named "Mammoth Cave," and when a department store features an especially large event, it is called a "Mammoth Sale." As a matter of fact, Mammoths were no larger than many of our present-day elephants; they were closely related

Courtesy, American Museum of Natural History

Mammoth. Restoration showing the shaggy hair, small ears, and long, curved tusks.

to the elephants now living in India. Most of them were probably smaller than Jumbo, being about nine or ten feet high. The tusks of the Mammoth grew to a length of from eight to ten feet, and large specimens weigh about 200 pounds. They extend downwards and outwards and then bend upwards, the tips curving somewhat inwards.

The remains of Mammoths occur in many parts of the Northern Hemisphere. "Mummies" have been discovered embedded in the frozen soil of Siberia, and enough of them have been rescued from dogs, wolves, and bears to prove that they possessed long, coarse, reddish-brown hair and thick, woolly underfur that fitted them for life in a cold climate. Mammoths and early Man appear to have lived at the same time, from 10,000 to 50,000 years ago, and the latter are accused by some of having exterminated the Mammoths, just as modern Man has exterminated a number of species of animals within recent times. So many Mammoth tusks have been recovered that they form an article of commerce; it is estimated that at least 20,000 pairs have been brought to market within the last two centuries.

Mastodon. It is painful, but necessary, to debunk the Mastodons as we have the Mammoths, since the evidence derived from fossil remains indicates that

Courtesy, American Museum of Natural History

Mastodon. Restoration of a species that once lived in the United States.

Mastodons were probably not as large as the elephants living today. Their legs were shorter and their bodies were more heavily built. They differed also from modern elephants in the structure of their teeth. Some of the Mastodons possessed tusks in both jaws instead of in the upper jaw only, as in elephants and mammoths. These tusks varied in size and shape according to the species. One of these species roamed over most of the United States, but the best-preserved remains have been obtained in New York State.

Whether Man and Mastodon lived together in North America is still uncertain. Why Mastodons became extinct is also a problem that has not yet been solved. The glacial epoch has been suggested as too strenuous for them, although there are serious objections to this theory. Certainly at that time life in North America was anything but pleasant.   Mark Twain in his discussion of organic evolution gives us the following humorous, but rather unscientific, account of what the creatures of that period had to endure.

"During the next thirty million years the bird arrived, and the kangaroo, and by and by the mastodon, and the giant sloth, and the Irish elk, and the old Silurian ass, and some people thought that man was about due.   But that was a mistake, for the next thing they knew there came a great ice sheet, and those creatures all escaped across the Bering Strait and wandered around in Asia and died, all except a few to carry on the preparation with.   There were six of those glacial periods, with two million years or so between each.   They chased those poor orphans up and down the earth, from weather to weather, from tropic temperature to fifty degrees below. They never knew what kind of weather was going to turn up next, and if they settled any place the whole continent suddenly sank from under them, and they had to make a scramble for dry land.   Sometimes a volcano would turn itself loose just as they got located.   They led that uncertain, strenuous existence for about 25,000,000 years, always wondering what was going to happen next, never suspecting that it was just a preparation for man."

CHAPTER 37

FLESH–EATING MAMMALS, OR CARNIVORES

"That the Carnivore may live Herbivores must die." (Spencer.) In other words, Carnivorous Animals kill and eat the flesh of other animals; they may prey upon one another, but their victims are usually species that live on vegetation. The most prominent characteristics of the Carnivores are their sharp claws, their teeth for seizing and cutting up flesh, and their fierceness and active behavior. The front teeth, or incisors, are small and of little use; the canines, or eyeteeth, are very large and pointed, enabling the animal to capture and kill its prey; the premolars and the first molar in the lower jaw have sharp cutting edges; the other molars are broad, crushing teeth; and the fourth premolar of the upper jaw and the first molar of the lower jaw bite on one another like a pair of scissors.

Some Carnivores are terrestrial and others aquatic in habit. Dogs, martens, and cats are terrestrial. The dog family is represented in North America by the wolves, coyotes, and foxes. The hyenas, which live in Africa and Asia, are closely related to the "dogs" of this country. The marten family contains a large number of small fur-bearing animals. The otter, mink, weasel, marten, wolverine, skunk, and badger are well-known North American species. The cat family includes the cat, puma, leopard, lion, tiger, lynx, and cheetah. The principal species inhabiting North America are the wildcat, Canada lynx, puma, and jaguar.

The aquatic Carnivores are greatly modified for life in the water. The hands and feet are fully webbed and serve as swimming organs, and the body has acquired a fishlike form suitable for progress through the water. The sea lion family includes the sea lions and fur seals. The walrus family contains the Atlantic walrus and the Pacific walrus. The seal family contains a number of species; among them are the ringed seal, harp seal, and harbor seal.

Gray or Timber Wolf. Our daily speech contains many expressions that indicate what we think of the Wolf. "Big bad Wolf," "Hungry as a Wolf," and "The Wolf at the Door" are examples. Although cousin to the Dog, and therefore of high intelligence, the Wolf exhibits a disposition very different from the "friend and companion of Man." He seems to us cunning and merciless, and mean and treacherous. Our attitude toward wolves is no doubt largely due to the fact that in the Old World they do not hesitate to attack human beings when other game is lacking. This seldom happens in this country.

When North America was colonized, Gray Wolves were abundant everywhere that they could obtain game. Now their normal prey has been destroyed over much of the country and Wolves can be found in relatively few localities. In the West, they formerly depended largely on bison, but since these animals have been exterminated, except for a few that are protected, they prey on deer and livestock. In some regions they are so destructive that cattlemen and the government have united in efforts to destroy them.

Photo by Hegner

Gray or Timber Wolf. A doglike wild beast with a bad disposition and treacherous ways.

Wolves are excellent hunters. They have a keen sense of smell, excellent eyesight, and good hearing, are very cautious, and when hunting as a pack, can conquer almost any kind of animal. The howling of the Wolf is supposed to have something sinister about it but can hardly be distinguished from that of a large dog. The den of the Gray Wolf is a cave, hollow log, or hole in the ground. The burrow is usually dug in a hillside. Often a natural den among the rocks is selected. The number of young is usually six or seven.

Werewolf. According to an old superstition, human beings might voluntarily, or with the aid of the devil, change themselves into wolves and remain in this form as long as they desired. During this time they retained their human intelligence. Beastly acts, including cannabalism, were supposed to be committed by these Werewolves; and in Europe men were tried for this offense as late as the seventeenth century. Witchcraft was held responsible for changing others into temporary or permanent Werewolves, but these were not responsible for their change and hence were not so dangerous and might even do kind deeds.

Coyote. The Coyote, or Prairie Wolf, is a sort of small edition of the Gray Wolf. The word Coyote is derived from his Aztec name Coyotl. He is an inhabitant of open plains, where he finds jack rabbits, mice, ground squirrels, lizards, snakes, birds, and insects on which to feed. His den, like that of the wolf, is a hole in the ground or among rocks Being highly intelligent, proverbially fleet of foot and of great fecundity, he is able to hold his own against both natural

Courtesy, U. S. Bureau of Biological Survey

Coyote, or Prairie Wolf. He is singing his evening song, beginning with short barks and ending in a long squall.

enemies and Man. The millions of dollars paid out in bounties for the destruction of Coyotes have been largely in vain. Coyotes are not easy to kill or capture. They know enough to keep out of gunshot and are usually too cunning to enter a trap. Poisoned meat destroys many of them.

The Coyote is famous for its voice. It is "the only wild animal that habitually barks." "Most of the many calls of the Coyote are signals to its companions, but some of them seem to be the outcome of the pleasure it finds in making a noise. The most peculiar of its noises is the evening song, uttered soon after sunset, close to camp. This is a series of short barks, increasing in power and pitch until it changes into a long squall. One Coyote begins and undoubtedly two or more join in, making so much noise that newcomers think there must be a hundred Wolves out there. It is kept up for perhaps a minute or two, then ceases until some new impulse seizes them." (Seton.) The vesper song of the Coyote is delivered from a singing perch, and on moonlit nights when many animals join forces, the landscape rings with their weird music.

Foxes. The wiles exhibited by the Red Fox for the purpose of outwitting his pursuers or capturing his prey are proverbial. In the Joel Chandler Harris stories, Brer Rabbit always out-smarted Brer Fox, but this does not happen in nature. Most of the Fox stories we hear refer to the Red Fox of Europe, but "the American Red Fox is an animal far superior to the English Fox, in speed,

Courtesy, N. Y. Zoological Society

Red Fox. The fur of the Red Fox is rusty red and the tail bushy; Brer Fox is the size of a small dog and is famous for his speed, endurance, and cunning.

endurance, cunning, and resource, when in front of a dangerous pack. He laughs an inferior pack to scorn." (Ellzey.)

Red Foxes live both in forested regions and in rolling country where the vegetation affords protection. They dig a "den" in a hillside, or use a hollow log or cavity among the rocks as a home. They make several kinds of noises, the commonest of which is a short, yapping bark. Foxes probably mate for life. They eat many kinds of food, but especially birds and small mammals.

Red Foxes are about the size of a slender, small dog. The fur is rusty red, and the tail long and very bushy and tipped with white. The nose is thin and long and the sense of smell keen. Litter mates may be of several colors. The Black Fox has jet-black fur, the tail being tipped with white. The Silver Fox resembles the Black Fox, but its hairs are white near their ends, giving the animal a silvery appearance. The Cross Fox has a black stripe down the back and

Photo by J. G. Allen

Silver Fox. His fur is black but the hairs are white near the end, giving the animal a silvery appearance.

another across the shoulders. The fur of Foxes is very valuable, and fox farming has attracted considerable attention. Some farms have been quite successful, but many have not.

The Gray Fox resembles the Red Fox in size and shape, but is grayish in color, and has a longer body, longer legs, and a longer tail. It enjoys the warmer parts of the country, and occurs in forested regions as well as on the open plains. Gray Foxes are not as mentally alert as their red-colored relatives. However, they have one peculiar accomplishment, that is, their ability to climb trees. The fur of the Gray Fox is inferior to that of the Red Fox.

Arctic Foxes live in the far North, coming southward to the tree limit. They are smaller than the Red and Gray Foxes. During the summer their fur is brownish in color, but in winter it becomes entirely white. A color phase of this species is known as Blue Fox. Arctic Foxes manage to exist under very severe conditions and to leave offspring for the continuance of their race. They feed largely on wild fowl, such as ducks, geese, and gulls and also on small mammals, such as mice, lemmings, and hares. They are less suspicious of Man than their southern relatives probably because they are not as well acquainted with him.

Photo by Hegner

Gray Fox. He has gray fur and longer legs and tail than the Red Fox but is not as clever.

Hyenas. Very few animals impress us as being cowardly, but there seems to be no question regarding the Hyenas. Not only are they cowardly, but they apparently prefer meat killed by some other animal than to kill it themselves. Their teeth and jaws are particularly strong and well fitted for crushing bones. Hyenas are notorious scavengers. "They will visit the Eastern villages at night and feed upon carrion; while skeletons that have been picked clean by other creatures are not disdained by these ungainly-looking beasts. With one crunch of their powerful jaws they will break in half the thigh-bone of an ox, so as to obtain the marrow, and their digestive powers are so great that they can swallow whole a knuckle-bone without fear of suffering very ill results." (Berridge.)

The Striped Hyena is about the size of a wolf. The fur is grayish-brown in color and bears stripes of a darker shade along the sides. The ears are large and pointed; the mane is erect and extends along the back to the tail; the fore legs are longer than the hind legs; and the claws, unlike those of cats, are nonretractile. He is a solitary, nocturnal prowler, that utters blood-curdling cries likened to demoniac laughter.

The three species of Hyenas are the Striped, Brown, and Spotted. The Striped Hyena occurs in North and East Africa, Asia Minor, Persia, and India. The Spotted Hyena ranges in Africa from Abyssinia to the Cape.

"Many fabulous stories have been related in regard to the hyenas, not the least remarkable being that they changed their sex every year. Should their shadow fall upon domestic dogs, the latter would become dumb; while they have even been credited with the power of imitating the voices of men, and even of calling them by their names." (Berridge.)

Spotted Hyena. A cowardly creature that feeds on bones and scraps left by lions and other animals; the jaws are efficient bone-crushers.

Lion. The leader of the Cat tribe and the undisputed "King of Beasts" is undoubtedly the Lion. No zoo is complete without a pair of Lions, but big-game hunters must go to Africa or southwestern Asia to find them in their native haunts. Here they live on the dry, open plains or in the swampy lowlands, resting by day and hunting for antelopes, zebras, and other prey at night, often in companies of several to a dozen. The Buffalo appears to be the most dangerous enemy he is apt to encounter.

The male Lion differs from other Cats in the presence of a heavy mane which drapes itself over the back of the head and forequarters. At the end of his tail is a tuft of hair which conceals a small, horny spur, the use of which is problematical. Lions are famous for their roaring voice. Their roars are not the result of their bloodthirsty nature, but like the voices of most animals, are love calls or challenges to their rivals. They are often uttered on dark nights or in cloudy weather.

"Generally a Lion begins to roar in the evening gloom, and continues with shorter or longer intervals through the whole night; a roaring Lion, as already mentioned, not being always hungry. The roar of the Lion is especially meant for its fellows; but other sounds, audible only when in close proximity, are much more alarming, as, for instance, the uninterrupted growling, when the animal, when surprised in its haunts, puts down its ears, waves its tail in an uneasy manner, and, hesitating between flight and attack, examines the situation, and tries to warn off the intruder by its attitude. Neither is the angry grunting of a partially satiated Lion, when surprised at its meal and unable to flee, calculated to induce any confidence. Most terrific, however, are the short, coughing sounds of a Lion when preparing to attack." (Lydekker.)

Only under unusual conditions do Lions become man-eaters. "A man-eater is invariably an old lion; and when he overcomes his fear of man so far as to come to villages for goats, the people remark, 'His teeth are worn; he will soon kill men.' They at once acknowledge the necessity of instant action, and turn out to kill him." (Livingstone.) Cases are on record, however, of man-hunters among young Lions. For example, when the Uganda Railway was being built, two young Lions killed 38 Indian coolies and many natives, and held up building operations until they were killed. Lion cubs, of which there may be three or four at a birth, play with their mother much as kittens do. "The lioness is usually an exemplary mother — solicitous, playful, and yet stern as occasion demands. She is no believer in sparing the rod, and can if necessary enforce discipline with a firm but gentle tap that to the human ear suggests the knock-out at a prize fight. Like the domestic cat she often carries her young about with her in her mouth. Baby lions grow apace, for the year-old cub is as big as a Newfoundland dog and ten times as strong. At this age it still retains its 'birth marks' of spots." (Boulenger.)

Courtesy, National Zoological Park

Lion. The King of Beasts lives in Africa or southwestern Asia, especially on dry, open plains or in swampy lowlands; the male has a heavy mane.

Tiger. Next to the Lion in size and power among the Cats is the Tiger, and in any beauty contest the Tiger would certainly be given first place. The black stripes on a ground color of rufous yellow are not designed for beauty, but really conceal the animals as they lie asleep amid the narrow shadows cast by the brush or reeds surrounding their lair.

Tigers. These Indian Tigers are powerful beasts, reaching a length of 10 feet and a weight of 400 pounds; they are active at night, preying on deer and other animals including Man.

Tigers are particularly abundant in India and parts of southeastern Asia. Like the Lion, they hunt principally at night, and prey on deer, antelope, cattle, monkeys, etc. They usually do not attack man unless they are old or other food is scarce. Then they exhibit great cunning and are more than a match for the natives. It has been estimated that Tigers kill about 1000 human beings every year. Tigers pair for life and appear to breed at any season; from two to five cubs are born at one time; these become mature in about three years. A large Tiger measures about ten feet long, the tail making up three feet of this, and weighs about 400 pounds. The female is smaller than the male and her head is lighter and narrower. There is no mane, as in the Lion, but the old males may grow a ruff of long hair around the neck and throat.

A common belief in India is "that the spirits of men killed by a tiger are its servants afterwards, sitting on its head and not only warning it of danger but helping it to destroy other human beings. Considering these superstitions, it is not surprising that tigers themselves, or images representing them, are objects of worship among many Indian tribes, that in former times oaths were sworn on a tiger-skin in Indian tribunals and that various parts of the body, as for instance, the front teeth, claws, and whiskers, are kept as amulets and charms." (Lydekker.)

Saber-Tooth Tiger. Today there are no Tigers in North America, but in prehistoric times this country was a happy hunting ground for animals that must have resembled present-day Tigers in general appearance, although they had a short tail and shorter and more massive legs and feet. The most striking peculiarity of these extinct Tigers is the enormous development of the upper canine teeth. In some species these were six or eight inches long, and shaped like curved daggers.

Courtesy, American Museum of Natural History

Saber-Tooth Tiger. A Tiger that once roamed over the United States; the enormous saber-like canine teeth in the upper jaw suggested his name; the picture is of a restoration.

Saber-Tooth Tigers probably had to feed on animals with a thick skin and hence needed formidable weapons such as these scimitar-like teeth. How they were used is in doubt, but the jaws of the beast were probably opened very wide, like those of a rattlesnake when it strikes, and the teeth used to slash or stab like reptilian fangs. The fossil remains of many species of Saber-Tooths have been discovered, especially in the La Brea asphalt beds at Los Angeles, California.

Leopard. The Leopard seems in many ways like a small edition of the Tiger. He is gorgeously colored and his famous spots, that he cannot change if he would, serve the same purpose as the stripes on the Tiger, since they render him invisible among the branches of trees. Unlike both Lion and Tiger, he climbs trees with great agility and strikes terror into the hearts of the monkeys on which he preys. Besides these, birds, reptiles, and other mammals, especially dogs, make up his bill of fare. After breaking the neck of his victims, he carries them away to be devoured in some safe hiding place.

Leopards are even fiercer, and have acquired a worse reputation, than Tigers. They cannot be trusted and will attack human beings though entirely unprovoked. Leopards occur in forested country all the way from South Africa to China. In

Leopard.   He cannot change his spots; his specialty is climbing trees after monkeys; he is also fond of dogs and may become a man-eater; he may be found from South Africa to China.

India, large Leopards are called Panthers. When old they become man-eaters. Leopards are smaller than lions and tigers, the head and body measuring about four feet and the tail about three feet in length. Sometimes a black Leopard is encountered, but in certain lights the characteristic markings are still distinguishable. The cubs number from two to four and become fully grown in three years.

A dwarf race of Leopards, paler in color than their larger relatives, lives in Somaliland. But no matter how small he is, a Leopard is still a Leopard with all of his blood-thirsty, feline characteristics. The Snow Leopard, or Ounce, lives in

Courtesy, National Zoological Park

Cheetah, or Hunting Leopard. A long-legged, leopard-like beast with small, round spots; he is a native of Asia and Africa and can be trained for hunting deer and antelope.

the high mountain ranges of central Asia. He also is paler in color. His fur is long and soft and his tail is very long and provided with a thick covering of hair.

Cheetah, or Hunting Leopard. The Hunting Leopard, or Cheetah, can be distinguished from its larger cousin, the Leopard, by noting the spots, which are small and solid instead of in circles or rosettes. His head is more rounded and his legs are comparatively long. Unlike other Cats his claws are not retracted into sheaths when not in use. Cheetahs live in various regions in Africa and Asia where they are able to find deer and antelope.

Their most interesting characteristic is the ease with which they can be tamed and used for hunting. After they are caught, they are kept among human beings until they become accustomed to human companionship and are quite tame, a process that requires about six months. Then they are taken blindfolded into the country, and when a deer or antelope is sighted, are released. They can run remarkably fast for a short distance, and can bring down the fastest deers. As a reward the Cheetah is given a drink of the victim's blood.

Courtesy, N. Y. Zoological Society

Jaguar, or "Tiger." The largest cat in America lives in the tropical jungles; his coat is golden-yellow spotted with black "rosettes"; he is about 6 feet long but afraid of Man.

Jaguar and Ocelot. The largest American Cat is the Jaguar, or "Tiger," that ranges from the southern part of the United States to southern Brazil. In color he resembles the Old World Leopard, with a golden-yellow coat spotted with black "rosettes." His head and body are massive, and his legs short and exceedingly strong. Jaguars wander through the jungles of tropical America looking for deer, peccaries, monkeys, birds, fish, and any other small animals that may come their way. Although fierce and formidable, they are afraid of human beings, only exceptionally attacking Man. The male is about six feet long and about two feet high at the shoulder, with a tail about twenty inches long.

"Jaguars are very destructive to the larger game birds and mammals of their domain and to horses and cattle on ranches. On many large tropical ranches a *tigrero*, or tiger hunter, with a small pack of mongrel dogs, is maintained, whose duty it is immediately to take up the trail when a jaguar makes its presence known, usually by killing cattle. The hunter steadily continues the pursuit until the animal is killed." (Nelson.)

A near relative of the Jaguar, and also an inhabitant of tropical America that ranges north into Texas, is the Ocelot, or Tiger Cat.   This species is considered by many the most beautifully colored of all mammals because of its wonderfully

Photo by Walker.   Courtesy, Nature Magazine
Ocelot, or Tiger Cat.   A beautifully colored inhabitant of tropical America, smaller than the Jaguar.

developed spots or ocelli.   It hunts at night for birds, small mammals, snakes, etc.   Also, it is hunted at night with a light.   In the jungles of Panama we encountered it in trails that we had made for the purpose of studying the behavior of monkeys.   One that we shot was suffering from a bad infection of the lungs.   Incidentally, monkeys and other wild animals suffer from various physical ailments, such as abscessed teeth and diseases of the lungs and other internal organs.   Tiger Cats reach a length of four feet and a weight of from twenty to thirty-five pounds.   They are shaped much like our house cats.   The fur is short and the tail fairly long.

Puma.   Next in size to the Jaguar among American Cats is the Puma, also known as the Mountain Lion, Cougar, or Panther.   He ranges from Canada to Patagonia wherever small mammals and birds are available for food, and forests and rocky ledges furnish hiding places.   His body is long and slender and tawny-brown in color; and his tail is also long.

The reactions of the Puma to man are very peculiar.   He actually seems to want to be friendly and in South America was called by the Spaniards "Amijo del Cristiano," the Christian's Friend.   This has led to the charge that he is a coward, but no beast that habitually attacks and kills moose, elk, and other powerful animals can be considered a coward.   "It is notorious that where the puma is the only large beast of prey it is perfectly safe for a small child to go out and sleep on the plain. . . .   The puma is always at heart a kitten, taking unmeasured delight in its frolics; and when, as often happens, one lives alone in the desert, it will amuse itself for hours fighting mock battles or playing hide-and-seek with imaginary companions, or lying in wait and putting all its wonderful strategy in practice to capture a passing butterfly." (Hudson.)   During the mating season the female Puma screams like a woman in distress.   "It is loud, piercing, prolonged, and has the agonized voice qualities of a boy or a woman screaming from the pain of a surgical operation.   To one who does not know the source or the cause, it is nerve-racking.   When heard in a remote wilderness it must be truly fearsome." (Hornaday.)

"A mountain lion usually secures its prey by a silent, cautious stalk, taking advantage of every cover until within striking distance, and then, with one or more powerful leaps, dashing the victim to the ground with all the stunning impact of its weight. The mountain lion often kills calves, but is especially fond of young horses. In many range districts of the western states and on the tableland of Mexico, owing to the depredations of this animal, it is impossible to raise horses. Unfortunately, the predatory habits of this splendid cat are such that it cannot continue to occupy the same territory as civilized man and so is destined to disappear before him, except in remote wilderness areas." (Nelson.)

Courtesy, National Zoological Park

Puma, or Mountain Lion. A powerful Cat ranging from Canada to Patagonia and preying on small mammals and birds; he is friendly toward Man.

Courtesy, U. S. Bureau of Biological Survey

Young Pumas. They resemble young kittens but seem to suspect the intentions of the photographer who found them in this tree.

Photo by the Finleys. Courtesy, Nature Magazine

Bobcat, or Wildcat. He differs from the house Cat in his bobbed tail, large ears and feet, and ruff of hair on the side of the head; besides, he is wild.

Bobcat. The Bobcat, Bay Lynx, or Wildcat, looks like an overgrown tabby with a bobbed tail. He is rather stout and has large ears and feet and a ruff of hair on the side of his head. His thick fur is colored pale rufous-brown. He is largely nocturnal in habit, shy and furtive and hence not often seen. At night he yells and caterwauls with great abandon, even more loudly than our tame back-fence musicians. He hunts mostly on the ground and is very destructive to game birds, such as grouse and quail. His strength and fierceness are hardly necessary considering the weakness of his prey, but he has a great reputation as a fighter, and if you want to make a he-man happy, all you need do is to tell him he can "whip his weight in wildcats." Give a Bobcat catnip, however, and he reacts as foolishly as a house cat. Wildcats are active throughout the winter. They make

Mongoose. A carnivore of India famous for his ability to kill cobras; in his cobra fights he usually wins by crushing the head or neck of the snake.

their home in a hollow log or cave in the rocks, where they raise from two to four young.

A larger brother of the Bobcat is the Canada Lynx, a species that can be distinguished from the Bobcat by his brownish-black ear tufts, over one and one-half inches long, his very short, unringed tail, his larger feet, and his color, which is light gray, grizzled with brown. A full-grown male measures three feet long and weighs about 35 pounds. The Canada Lynx ranges from the northern part of the United States into Canada.

Indian Mongoose. The Indian Mongoose, or Mungoose, is a weasel-like carnivore about sixteen inches long and with a tail almost as long as its body. Its brownish-gray fur is long and loose and can be erected by muscles in the skin. In India, the Mongoose is considered a very valuable animal because it kills poisonous snakes, rats, mice, and other "vermin." For this reason Mongooses were introduced into Jamaica and other islands in the West Indies. They acted as expected until they had killed off so many rats and mice that not enough remained to supply them with food; then they turned their attention to birds. As a result, what had been a beneficial rat destroyer became a menace to all bird life and a recognized nuisance. This is just another instance of the danger of introducing a foreign species of animal.

The Mongoose is not immune to snake poison but avoids being bitten. An eye-witness describes a fight between a Mongoose and a cobra as follows: When a cobra and a mongoose were put together in the same room, the mongoose would round "his back, and making every hair on his body stand out at right angles, which made his body appear twice as large as it really was, he would approach the cobra on tiptoe, making a peculiar humming noise. The snake, in the meantime, would show signs of great anxiety, and I fancy of fear, erecting his head and hood, ready to strike when his enemy came near enough. The mongoose kept running backwards and forwards in front of the snake, gradually getting to within what appeared to us to be striking distance. The snake would strike at him repeatedly, and appeared to hit him, but the mongoose continued his comic dance, apparently unconcerned. Suddenly, and with a movement so rapid that the eye could not follow it, he would pin the cobra by the back of the head. One could hear the sharp teeth crunch into the skull, and, when all was over, see the mongoose eating the snake's head and part of his body with great gusto."

Photo by Hegner

Black Bear. At the end of August, when this photograph was taken, Bruin had become so fat he didn't care much whether we gave him something to eat or not. He is a resident of Yosemite National Park and a favorite with motorists.

Black Bear. Nowadays the easiest way to see Black Bears in nature is to visit a National Park, such as the Yellowstone or Yosemite, where protection has transformed these wild animals into friendly and harmless companions of man. The fur of the Black Bear is not always black, but may be brown, in which case he becomes a Cinnamon Bear.

Forested regions, where food is available, is the habitat of this species, and his ability to maintain himself in spite of the encroaching hazards of human civilization is truly remarkable. The character of his food has much to do with this, since he eats almost anything, — berries, ants, honey, roots, fish, frogs, mice, birds, etc. What an easy husband he would be to cook for! When food is abundant late in the summer, he becomes a fat little roly-poly, and when, at about this time, it begins to get too cold for comfort, he hies himself to a hollow tree, or hole in the earth or among the rocks, where he follows the example of Rip Van Winkle and sleeps peacefully until the weather becomes pleasant again in the spring.

The cubs, usually two in number, are born in midwinter in a very undeveloped condition, but are able to run about in the course of a couple of months. Their playfulness exceeds even that of kittens. They box, wrestle, play hide-and-seek, and tease their mother in every possible way. Anyone who makes a pet of a cub knows how the mother Bear must feel at times. It has been well said, "If thine enemy offend thee, present him with a Black Bear cub." From time to time the mother drives the cubs up a tree, where they remain until she tells them to come down, — like laying the baby on a shelf while mother takes a little nap.

Photo by Hegner

Grizzly Bear. Old "Silvertip" has brownish hair with light-colored tips, which gives him a grizzly appearance; the claws on his fore feet are 3 inches long.

Grizzly Bear. Much larger than the Black Bear, and with a very different disposition, is the Grizzly Bear. He is called a Grizzly, or Silvertip, because the light-colored tips of his brownish hair give him a grizzly or silvery appearance. His face is distinctly concave, and his fore feet are provided with three-inch curved claws like hooks of steel. He is not an aggressive beast, but is highly dangerous if trifled with, and one blow from his sledge-hammerlike paw means sudden death. When Bison were plentiful on the western plains, he regularly preyed on them. Now he is restricted to the less accessible Rocky Mountains extending north into Alaska. One of his near relatives, the Kodiak Bear, reaches a weight of about 1500 pounds and is the largest Flesh-Eating Animal in the world.

The hunting range of a Grizzly is said to be indicated by tusk and claw marks made as high up on trees as possible, while standing on his hind legs. Any other

Photo by Hegner

Polar Bears. They love to swim in cold water and have a slender body, a long neck, and a pointed head; the fur is very dense and well oiled so as to shed water and retain the heat.

Bear that can make his mark as high or higher is entitled to remain. "The method of challenging all comers is common to a great many wild beasts, large and small; and I am inclined to think that when the house-cat stretches up to sharpen its claws on the trunk of a tree, it is a similar challenge for other cats to read." (Stone and Cram.)

"From the days of the earliest explorers of the Rocky Mountain region, grizzly bears have borne the undisputed title of America's fiercest and most dangerous big game. In early days, having little fear of the primitive weapons of the Indians, they were bold and indifferent to the presence of man, and no higher badge of supreme courage and prowess could be gained by a warrior than a necklace of grizzly claws." (Nelson.)

Polar Bear. An animal that can live his entire life on the ice, as does the Polar Bear, must differ from other animals both in structure and habit. The fur of the Polar Bear is very dense and full of air spaces, and hence a poor conductor of heat, thus keeping the warmth of the body from escaping; a layer of fat just beneath the skin has the same effect. The fur is kept well oiled by glands in the skin and sheds water easily, preventing the body from becoming wet.

Polar Bears are excellent swimmers and actually capture fish in the water. The body is more slender than that of most bears, the neck is long and the head slender and pointed, giving the freedom of action necessary to catch swimming animals. Heavy fur on the soles of the feet keeps them from slipping on the ice. Polar Bears live around the North Pole and range as far south as the pack ice. They feed on aquatic animals, such as fish, seals, and shellfish, as well as on land animals, including caribou, foxes, birds, etc. In summer the larder is easy to fill but it is certainly remarkable that they can find enough to eat during the long, dark winter months.

Courtesy, National Zoological Park

Otter. An "India rubber" Marten and expert swimmer and diver that can catch fish with ease; he has webbed feet, a rudder-like tail, and dense fur.

Otter. One of our most aquatic Martens is the Otter. He is a marvelous swimmer and diver, with a body almost as flexible as India rubber, broad, webbed feet, a rudder-like tail, dense fur, and a layer of fat beneath the skin to keep the heat of the body from escaping. He has slitlike nostrils that can be closed while under water, ears that are hidden beneath the fur and can be closed by a fold of skin, and teeth that are unusually sharp for seizing and tearing smooth and slippery prey.

The Canadian Otter, which is the species that ranges throughout the United States, Canada, and Alaska, is dark brown in color and about three and a half feet long. He and his wife and children are all fond of playing, especially sliding down snow banks in winter and down slippery clay banks into the water in summer. In the winter, when fish and crayfish are more difficult to find, the Otter family takes overland journeys, capturing ducks, muskrats, and even barnyard fowls. The three or four young Otters are born usually in a hole in the bank of a stream, the front door often being under water and thus effectively concealed from possible enemies.

Mink and Weasel. Martens, Weasels, Ferrets, and Minks form a group of Flesh-Eating Mammals of similar characteristics. The Mink is one of the most interesting and valuable species. He may be said to live a double life, since he goes hunting for mice and birds on land, frequently raiding chicken roosts and killing a number of fowls before selecting one to carry away with him, and appears equally at home in the water, where he catches fish and crayfish like an Otter. He kills not only for food, but because he is a bloodthirsty little beast and loves to kill.

Minks are slender animals, about as thick as a man's wrist and about two feet long, the tail making up about one third of the total length. The body is very

Photo by Bell.   Courtesy, U. S. Forest Service

Weasel. In winter the fur is entirely white except the black tip of the tail; in summer the color is brown; he is a bloodthirsty little beast about a foot long but very slender.

supple, enabling them to catch fish under water. Because their feet are short, they walk slowly and clumsily, but they can run very swiftly in a series of rapid bounds. Minks are solitary animals, active and restless. They travel from stream to stream and have a real home only during the breeding season. Then they find a cavity in a bank, log, or tree or among the rocks in which they make a nest of leaves and grass lined with feathers and hair. Here from four to twelve young are reared.

Mink fur is glossy brown, of high quality, and very durable. Large numbers of animals are trapped annually, but they still maintain themselves over nearly all of North America. When trapped, they are a "triple distilled essence of fury and red-eyed rage," and are apt to discharge a powerful and disagreeable musky liquid from a scent gland under the tail. Minks prefer thickets in the vicinity of water and bottomland forests for their happy hunting grounds. Here they are well protected from their enemies and can saunter out at any time in search of fish or fowl.

No more bloodthirsty or courageous animal for his size exists than the Weasel. Combined with these traits are a cunning and wariness that put him in a class by himself. He is very active at night and kills for the love of killing. Birds and small mammals are his usual victims. He sucks the warm blood from the neck, then eats the brains, and finally the flesh of his prey. His lust for blood is unbounded; he will kill as many animals as possible, leaving them uneaten. "To catch a Weasel asleep" is such a noteworthy accomplishment that the expression is often applied to any difficult feat resulting from an unexpected or especially clever piece of strategy. Among human beings the term Weasel means a "lean, mean, sneaking, greedy fellow," and anyone with a thin, sharp face is said to be "weasel-faced."

Weasels are about a foot long and very slender. Their fur consists of long, glistening hairs and soft, dense underfur. They are brown above in summer, but entirely white in winter, except the tip of the tail, which is black. They can travel very swiftly by silent, gliding leaps and can almost "dodge a bullet." Their young number from four to six per litter.

Black-Footed Ferret. One of the most deadly enemies of prairie dogs is the Black-Footed Ferret. This minklike invader might be able to exist without prairie dogs, but certainly without such a full dinner pail. He occurs on the Great

Photo by Hegner

Black-Footed Ferret. He is about a foot and a half long with reddish eyes, yellowish-white fur, and a "burglar's" mask over the eyes; he is often used to drive rabbits out of their burrows.

Plains where the prairie dogs live and often makes his home in their burrows. His body is more robust than that of the mink, his tail is short, and his face bears a black mask across the eyes like that sometimes worn by the midnight invaders of our own homes.

The domesticated Ferret is a descendant of the Polecat. He is a yellowish-white animal about a foot and a half long with reddish eyes. Rats and mice are his particular prey and a sufficient excuse for his existence. For many centuries, at least since the time of Pliny, Ferrets have been used to drive rabbits out of their burrows. We used them for this purpose many years ago in Iowa.

Skunk. Very few animals are less popular when alive and more highly desired when dead than our common large striped Skunk. Our dislike for him is due entirely to the extremely powerful, disagreeable musky odor of the liquid that he can eject so effectively from the two scent glands beneath the tail. These glands are filled with a clear, yellow fluid and supplied with muscles to force it out at the will of the owner. Skunks do not discharge this fluid if they can help it, — only when sufficiently provoked.   No danger need be feared as long as the Skunk faces you or the tail is held down ; but when a rear view is presented and the tail raised, it is advisable to beat a hasty retreat.   The fluid is discharged in a fine spray to a distance of about ten feet, the tail being held up so as to escape contamination. Several discharges may follow one another in quick succession.   The result is most gratifying to the Skunk, since the odor can be detected for half a mile or more and most animals give the animal a wide berth.   The fluid is strongly acid and burns the skin ; if it gets into the eye, temporary or permanent blindness may ensue.

The conspicuous coloring of the Skunk, that is, the white stripes on a black background, are supposed to warn other animals to keep their distance.   The Skunk seems to know that his defensive measures are effective, because he shows very little fear and is very deliberate in his movements.   He has not yet become

Photo by Hastings.   Courtesy, Nature Magazine

Skunk.   The "Wood Pussy" has a white crown, two white stripes along the back, and a thin white stripe down the center of the face ; his scent glands are under the tail.

accustomed to motor cars, however, and his failure to hasten out of the road brings about the death of large numbers every year.

Skunks occur throughout most of the United States and Canada except in deep forests and desert plains.   They are about the size of a house cat and the name "Wood-Pussy" is very appropriate.   Since they are most active at night, they are smelled more often than seen.   They seem to enjoy human association and often live under the porches of houses in the country.   The young are born in a nest of grass usually built in a burrow on the ground.   They are playful and affectionate and can be denatured easily by removing the scent glands.

The young Skunks do not separate as soon as they can run about, but remain together throughout the first winter.   During the coldest part of the year in the northern part of their range, they hibernate for several months, and from eight to a dozen of them may sleep together in one den.   When spring arrives they leave their brothers and sisters and set forth in search of a mate.

The odor of the Skunk has led to the general use of his name for certain particularly base human beings.   Skunk cabbage is a plant that grows in moist places and gives off a fetid odor.   The fur of the Skunk is excellent and popular.   Skunk farming has been attempted in various localities with more or less success.

A species that is less well known, although it occurs almost all over the United States, is the Spotted Skunk. This form is more slender than its larger relative and about the size of a half-grown house cat. The head is small, the legs short, and the tail bushy. The long fur is black and white, but the white is arranged in short stripes or in spots. Spotted Skunks are nocturnal; they are quite active as they hunt for insects and any small animals that are so foolish as to be out at night. In certain districts their bite is supposed to result in hydrophobia, hence they are sometimes called Hydrophobia Skunks, or Phoby Cats, a name which they don't deserve since they rarely transmit this disease. However, they defend themselves in the same obnoxious fashion as the species we are all familiar with. According to an old Indian proverb, if a skunk walks in your trail and leaves a stink there, do not go out of your way to prove that it is not yours.

Photo by Sherwood. Courtesy, Nature Magazine

Spotted Skunk. Widely distributed in the United States, but little known; his white stripes and spots are differently arranged from those of the common Skunk, but his scent is just as offensive.

In South and Central America a type of Skunk occurs that has a long nose evidently used for rooting in the earth for insects. For this reason the name Hog-Nosed Skunk has been applied to it. A single white stripe extends along the back and tail.

Badger. The slender gracefulness which we usually expect in a member of the Marten family is entirely absent in the Badger, which, on the contrary, is heavy and clumsy and looks almost as flat as a door mat. He is pre-eminently a digger and has a small, flat head, a short neck, and very powerful front legs with claws over an inch long. He not only digs burrows in the ground for himself and his family, but makes his living by digging out the burrows of other animals, such as prairie dogs, ground squirrels, and pocket gophers, spending his evenings traveling from one hole to another, digging out and devouring the unlucky occupants.

The plains and open forests of the central area of North America are his hunting grounds. So many are found in Wisconsin that this state is known as the Badger State and the natives as Badgers. The courage, viciousness, and endurance of the Badger are his principal peculiarities. We recently encountered a Badger in Colorado away from his hole and when we got close to him, he turned on us with a savageness and fury that would put a wildcat to shame.

This fierce nature coupled with a remarkable endurance led to the barbarous sport (?) of badger-baiting, which was regularly indulged in in Great Britain before it was prohibited about the middle of the nineteenth century. Badger-baiting was also practiced to a certain extent in our own western states.   A Badger is placed in a barrel so that he cannot be attacked from the rear and dogs sent in to drag him out; then he is put back and a second set of dogs substituted. This practice has

Courtesy, U. S. Bureau of Biological Survey

given rise to the use of the word "badger" for worrying or teasing. The expression "badger-legged" is sometimes applied to a person one of whose legs is shorter than the other, in allusion to the supposed inequality in the length of the Badger's legs. The long, bristly hairs, with which the Badger is thickly clothed, are grizzled gray in color and make excellent brushes, especially those used for shaving.

Badger. His body is stout and flat and his front legs and feet are adapted for digging out ground squirrels; his grizzled-gray hair is especially valuable for making brushes.

Raccoon and Coati. Closely related to the Martens is the Raccoon, more familiarly known as Coon. He is a rather stout Flesh-Eating Mammal with long, loose, yellowish-black fur, a black mask across the eyes, and a long, bushy tail ringed with black. Raccoons are widely distributed over North and Central America, especially near ponds and streams in which they go fishing. Usually their fishing is done from the edge in shallow water and small fish, fresh-water mussels, frogs, etc., are welcome trophies. They hunt also on land, and capture birds, mice, reptiles, and insects. These are sometimes flavored with fruit and especially green corn, which they seem to consider a great delicacy. If water is available, the Coon washes his food before he eats it, even, it is said, if it was recently captured in the water.

Courtesy, U. S. Bureau of Biological Survey

Raccoon. This animal furnishes us with coonskin coats; he has a black mask across his eyes and a bushy tail ringed with black; fishing is one of his accomplishments.

Coon-hunting is an exciting sport which we delighted in when of high-school age. It is practiced at night with dogs, which find the animal and soon chase him up a tree. Some member of the party climbs the tree and shakes the Coon out or the tree is chopped down. The dogs kill him, but not without a courageous fight on the part of the Coon. The average Coon weighs about fifteen pounds and furnishes a delicious meal when parboiled and then fried.

Coons hide by day; they nest in hollow trees, in cavities among rocks, or in burrows in the ground. They make interesting pets because of the innate curiosity that urges them to examine carefully every new object that comes their way. Coonskin caps, with tails as tassels, and coonskin coats have been favorite articles of clothing, especially with college boys, since the time of the pioneers.

Courtesy, U. S. Bureau of Biological Survey

Raccoon. He has the curious habit of washing his food before eating it, even if it is a fish just captured in the water.

Several relatives of the Raccoon inhabit the forests of tropical America. The Kinkajou is about the size of a cat. Kinkajous are nocturnal in habit and dwell in trees. They feed on small animals, eggs, fruit, etc. Their disposition is gentle, hence they make good pets.

Photo by Gross. Courtesy, Nature Magazine

Coati. A near relative of the Raccoon that lives in tropical America; his snout and tail are both very long; he makes an interesting pet.

Anyone familiar with the Raccoon will recognize at once the relationship of the Coatis of Mexico, Central and South America. The Coati has a much elongated piglike snout, and a long tail which he often carries straight up. He is very playful and makes an excellent pet. We found Coatis in the households of many foreigners as well as natives in Central America.

Fur Seal. Among the principal Flesh-Eating Mammals that are especially modified for an aquatic existence are the Seals, Sea Lions, and Walruses. Of these the Fur Seals are perhaps the most widely known because of the value of their fur. The Alaska Fur Seals are good examples of the group. They live on the Pribilof Islands and in other localities in Bering Sea. Their migrations are noteworthy. "In spring they leave the northwest coast and many of them travel steadily across more than two thousand miles of the North Pacific. For days at a time they swim through a roaring gale-swept sea, under dense, low-hanging clouds, and with unerring certainty strike certain passages in the Aleutian Islands, through which they press to their breeding grounds, more than 100 miles beyond, on the small, fog-hidden Pribilof Islands." (Nelson.) These islands were discovered by Gerassim Pribilof in 1786 and taken over by the United States in 1867. The number of Seals was greatly reduced by killing too many animals, but in 1911 the slaughter was regulated, and the herd grew from 200,000 in 1912 to nearly a million in 1927.

The home life of the Fur Seal would hardly be tolerated in human society. Polygamy is practiced, the bulls fighting fiercely with one another to establish a harem, which may contain up to 75 cows. The bachelors are forced to associate together until old enough and strong enough to displace one of the bulls. The cows occasionally enter the sea to feed, but the bulls neither eat nor drink for several months during the breeding season, but spend their time, both day and night, guarding their harem and ferociously battling with neighboring bulls in order to acquire more cows. Some animals apparently are never satisfied. Anyway, the strongest and most aggressive bulls leave offspring and in this way the vigor of the race is admirably maintained.

The fur of the Alaska Fur Seal consists of long, coarse hairs which conceal the dense, yellowish-brown underfur. The latter is the sealskin of commerce. "Fortunately, the conduct of the seals on land permits of the catch being made with the least possible attendant depletion of stock. The young males, or bachelors, 'haul out' to rest and sleep on the beaches adjacent to, but distinct from, the breeding-grounds. Here they are surrounded at night by the sealing gangs, rounded up in droves of from 1000 to 3000, and driven inland to the killing-grounds. The large droves are broken up into successive 'pods,' or groups, from 20 to 50, of which the 'killable' seals (animals of three years of age or approximating to such a size) are knocked down with clubs, those too large or too small being allowed to escape. The skins are removed, salted in kenches and, when cured, are exported." (E. B.)

The Fur Seal family differs from others in the presence of small external ears, and are hence called Eared Seals. While on land their hind feet turn forwards and not backwards as in other Seals. Besides the Fur Seal, this group includes the Southern Sea Lion, Steller's Sea Lion, and the California Sea Lion, which is the species usually seen in captivity.

Fur Seals on a Pribilof Island. Each large male has a harem of smaller females which he guards jealously.

Sea Lion. Anyone who has watched Sea Lions at play would award them the highest honors for their skill and agility as swimmers and high divers. As in the Fur Seals and Walruses, the body is streamlined so that it offers the least possible resistance to the water. The feet are completely webbed, forming flippers; those in front are used as oars and those behind as a rudder. Sea Lions are ungainly creatures on land but that doesn't worry them, because they like nothing better than to spend their time in the water hunting for fish, crustaceans, and squids or just gamboling about for the fun of it.

Photo by Bonnot. Courtesy, Nature Magazine

Sea Lions. The females are retreating into the water but the large male is more courageous.

The California Sea Lion is distributed along the Pacific coast of North America. The small Seals that occur along the coast of the North Atlantic are Harbor Seals. The Sea Lion is yellowish-brown to dull black in color and has no underfur. During the breeding season, the large bulls form harems containing up to a dozen cows. One pup is born at a time. The natives of the North make excellent use of the Sea Lion. The flesh is used for food, the blubber for fuel, the skin for making boats and boots, and the sinews for thread. Sea Lions would lead an exceedingly carefree life if it were not for these natives and the terrible Killer Whales.

Sea Lions can be trained with comparative ease. At the San Diego, California, Zoo their trainer gives an exhibition every day. They climb ladders, walk across a horizontal bar, balance balls on their noses, and do many other stunts. Here many of the animals that are exhibited on the stage and in circuses receive their training. "The sea lion has a big brain, and vast capacities for cunning and resource. He can escape from almost any kind of enclosure or packing case unless the most vigorous precautions are taken. On the other hand he will protest loudly at being required to pass through a doorway to which he has taken a dislike. The animal usually objects to negotiating any aperture the sides of which he can touch with his flippers, unless there is some object in his doing so, when he will squeeze through a fissure that threatens to crack his ribs." (Boulenger.) Sea Lions were used during the early part of the Great War to detect the presence of submarines. They were taught to react to vibrations by barking.

Harbor Seal and Elephant Seal. Along the Pacific coast and Atlantic coast north of the Carolinas, occur small seals that prefer harbors and the mouths of rivers to the open sea, and are hence called Harbor Seals. Their fur is coarse and hairy, which gives them the name Hair Seals, and their color is grayish to black with yellow or brown spots, which is responsible for a third name for them, Leopard Seals. They do not form large rookeries but usually assemble in small herds.

The largest of all Seals is the Elephant Seal that is now restricted to the Island of Guadelupe near San Diego, California. The long proboscis of the male gives it its name. The males reach a length of about eighteen feet, and are very massive;

Photo by Hegner

Harbor Seal, or Hair Seal. He prefers quiet harbors to the open sea; his coarse fur is spotted with yellow or brown, hence he is sometimes called a Leopard Seal.

the females are much smaller. Another species of Elephant Seal lives in the neighborhood of certain islands in the Antarctic Region. That they do not molest birds is evident from the photograph on page 382 where Sea Elephants and Penguins are shown living together in perfect harmony.

"The breeding season of Elephant Seals extends from February to June, and during this period these seals are far more numerous on shore than at any other time. They are gregarious in habits and formerly hauled up in herds on the islands or on remote and inaccessible beaches of the mainland. On shore they are sluggish, having none of the alertness shown by many other seals. They lie supine on the sand and permit a man to walk quietly up and touch them without showing signs of fear. When attacked by sealers or otherwise alarmed, however, they become panic-stricken and make ungainly efforts to escape, but quickly become exhausted. Their only natural enemy appears to be the killer whale.

Courtesy, San Diego Zoological Park

Walrus. This baby has a remarkably long mustache for one so young; the tusks so characteristic of the adults are still to grow out.

"Between 1855 and 1870 the great numbers of Northern sea-elephants, combined with their helplessness on shore and the value of their oil, attracted numerous sealing and whaling ships to the coast of Lower California.   The resulting slaughter reduced these animals from swarming abundance to a few scattered herds. Since then their numbers have steadily decreased.   The Mexican Government is now making laudable efforts to protect the small remaining herd." (Nelson.)

Walrus.   While in the water the Walrus is the monarch of the Arctic, but on land he is just a clumsy mountain of protoplasm easily approached and killed. Walruses "resemble distorted, mortified, shapeless masses of flesh; the cluster of big, swollen, watery pimples, which were of yellow, parboiled flesh color, and principally located over the shoulders and around the neck, painfully suggested unwholesomeness."   (Elliott.)

Adult Walruses are about ten feet long and weigh up to 3000 pounds.   The skin is yellowish-brown and from one-half to two inches thick.   The canines of the upper jaw form large tusks from twelve to fifteen inches long, and the bristles around the muzzle serve as a soup strainer to separate the clams, which they dig up with their tusks, from the mud that comes up with them.

"The adult bull Walrus like the adult bull elephant is apt to be troublesome and in Alaska an old bull walrus will often develop a penchant for killing seals. This makes him a marked beast and the Esquimos do not rest until the criminal has been killed. The walrus is fast diminishing in numbers, especially off the coast of North America where it is much hunted for the oil it produces and for its valuable tusks. According to American official reports recently published, 2,000,000 gallons of walrus oil is the annual yield, representing the destruction of more than 100,000 animals." (Boulenger.)

Eskimos hunt the Walrus in canoes of sealskin that hold one man and are called kayaks. A harpoon is embedded in the victim's body, followed by the death blow with a lance. Every part of the body is used for some good purpose, just as is that of the Sea Lion, and prosperity in the far North depends largely on the Walrus crop.

Chapter 38

AQUATIC MAMMALS

Many species of Mammals spend a large part of their time in the water, and some of these, such as the Seals, are modified for an aquatic life. Only the Sea Cows and Whales, however, are so wonderfully adapted to life in the water that they are supposed by most people to be fish.

The body of these Mammals is fishlike in shape; the fore limbs have become modified as paddles; and the hind limbs have disappeared entirely. Hair is present but very scanty; it occurs usually only as bristles on the snout. There are no external ears.

Four species of Sea Cows are recognized; they live along the seacoast, and each has its own habitat, namely, South America, North America, West Africa, and the Red Sea and Indian Ocean.

The Whales belong to two distinct groups, the Whalebone or Baleen Whales and the Toothed Whales. To the former belong the Right Whales, Gray Whale, Humpback Whales, and Rorquals. The Toothed Whales include the Sperm Whales, Beaked Whales, River Dolphins, Dolphins, Porpoises, Killer Whale or Grampus, Beluga or White Whale, and the Narwhale.

Courtesy, Shedd Aquarium, Chicago

Manatee, or Sea Cow. The front limbs are flippers; the hind limbs are absent; the tail is fishlike; he eats aquatic vegetation and grows to a weight of a ton or more; he lives along the coast of tropical America.

Manatee, or Sea Cow. Any self-respecting Mermaid, if there were such a creature, would hardly feel flattered if she knew that the Sea Cow probably served as a basis for her origin. "When suckling her young the Manati rises to the surface, her head and shoulders out of the water, and with her flippers holds the nursling partly clasped to her breast. This semi-human attitude, together with the rounded head and fishlike tail, may have furnished the basis on which the ancients built their legends of the mermaids." (Nelson.)

The Florida Manatee lives along the coast of Florida, where he grazes on the aquatic grass that grows in the sea pastures of the shallow lagoons and estuaries. He has a huge body weighing up to over 2000 pounds, and is more thoroughly adapted for life in the water than the Seals. His fore limbs are modified into broad flippers; his hind limbs are entirely absent, and his tail is broad and horizontally flattened; it serves as a powerful propeller. Very little hair is present on the skin, but the muzzle is covered with stiff bristles. The nostrils are valvelike and can be closed at will, which accounts for the fact that the Manatee may remain under water for five or six minutes. The lips are thick and the halves of the upper lip can be moved separately, which helps them grasp grass.

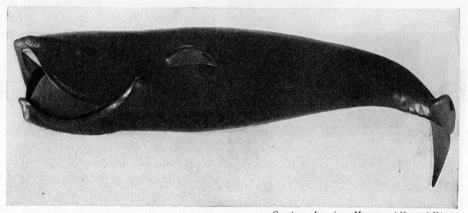

Courtesy, American Museum of Natural History

Right Whale, or Bowhead. One of the largest living mammals; his mouth is full of whalebone; his fore limbs are flippers and his tail lobes are called "flukes."

The Manatee is a gentle, fearless creature when not molested and a sluggish vegetarian. He is very sensitive to cold and many are killed by Florida cold snaps. This and their inoffensive nature may result in extinction, although efforts to protect them may save them for posterity.

Right Whale, or Bowhead. The word *whale* is a synonym for anything very large, and quite appropriately, because the Sulphur-Bottom, or Blue Whale, reaches a length of over 100 feet and a weight of over 150 tons, which means that it is the largest living animal and probably larger than any animal of the past. The Right Whale is not so large, but reaches a length of 65 feet, which ought to satisfy almost anyone. Since this species was one of the most valuable of all Whales, it was considered by Whalers the "right" whale to pursue, hence its common name. The name Bowhead is derived from the fact that its head, which is enormously large, being about one third of the total length, is strongly arched. This large size is necessary to hold the whalebone for which this species is famous.

Whalebone is not bone, but consists of a horny material, called baleen. This forms two parallel rows of thin triangular plates, sometimes fifteen feet long, that hang down from the roof of the mouth. The inner edges form a brushlike forest of long, hairlike bristles which serve as a strainer. Minute animals are taken into the open mouth with water; then the mouth is closed and the water is forced out again through the strainer by raising the tongue. The food is retained by the strainer and swallowed. It seems strange that such an enormously large body could be built up with minute animals almost microscopic in size. One mollusk occurs in the sea in such overwhelming numbers and is eaten so persistently by Whales that it is called by whalers "whale food." A single Right Whale furnishes about a ton of whalebone. Formerly enormous quantities of whalebone were imported into the United States. In 1853 whalebone was worth about 35 cents per pound.

The nostrils of this species are paired and called blow-holes. When the Whale rises to the surface, it expels warm air through them and the lookout in the "crow's nest" calls out, "There she blows!" Warm, moist air is thrown out when a Whale spouts, and not water, as generally believed. The fat, or blubber, of the Whale lies beneath the skin and is about a foot thick; it keeps the body heat from escaping. The tail is flattened horizontally and the two lobes are called "flukes." They have a rotatory movement somewhat like the screw of a steamer. The finlike fore limbs are used for steering.

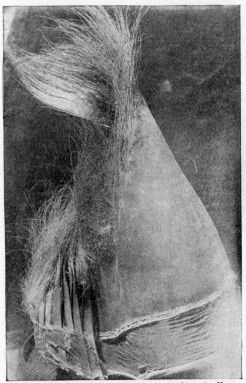

Photo by Hegner

Whalebone. A group of thin triangular plates frayed out at the end into a brushlike strainer.

Sperm Whale. The Right Whale is a Whalebone Whale and the teeth which appear in the embryo are not present after birth, whereas the Sperm Whale is a Toothed Whale and retains its teeth throughout life. Sperm Whales lack the whalebone, which is responsible for the large head of the Right Whale, but due to a huge oil-filled reservoir, the head of the Sperm Whale is proportionately just as large. The lower jaw seems absurdly small in comparison with the rest of the head; it alone bears teeth. The single blow-hole is at the front of the head and is shaped like the sounding-hole in a violin. Since the throat is large and Sperm Whales were well known to the ancients, having been mentioned in Assyrian cuneiform inscriptions dating from 885–860 B.C., it seems probable that one of this type was supposed to have swallowed Jonah.

The food of the Sperm Whale is quite different from that of the Right Whale. Huge squids and cuttlefishes of various species are captured and swallowed. Sperm Whales, it is said, may follow a boat day after day without sleeping; but there is some doubt about this story since other Mammals require a certain amount of sleep.

Two valuable commercial products are furnished by Sperm Whales, sperm oil and ambergris. Crude sperm oil is chilled to separate out a waxy substance known as spermaceti. The oil is an excellent lubricant and the spermaceti is used chiefly in the manufacture of face creams. Ambergris is a grayish substance secreted by the intestine, and is obtained from dead Whales, or found afloat, or thrown up

Courtesy, American Museum of Natural History

Sperm Whale. The enormous head contains a reservoir of oil; the single blow-hole at the front of the head is shaped like the sounding-hole in a violin. Did a Sperm Whale swallow Jonah?

on beaches. It has been used for many purposes; for example, by certain Asiatics as a spice in cooking, and by pilgrims as an offering to Mecca; but its principal value is to prevent the fragrance of perfumes from being quickly dissipated after use.

Killer Whale. The wolf of the seas is the Killer Whale, or Grampus. Endow an animal thirty feet long with twelve pairs of powerful sharp teeth in each jaw, and with a bloodthirsty disposition, and he becomes a menace to all other animal life. Killer Whales occur in all seas from the Arctic to the Antarctic. They are black, except for regions on the sides and under surface, which are white. The fin on the back is especially large, sometimes reaching a height of six feet.

"The killer usually travels and hunts in 'schools' or packs of from three to a dozen or more individuals. Unlike most whales, the members of these schools do not travel in a straggling party, but swim side by side, their movements as regularly timed as those of soldiers. A regularly spaced row of advancing long black fins swiftly cutting the undulating surface of the sea produces a singularly sinister effect. The evil impression is well justified, since killers are the most savage and remorseless of whales. The jaws are armed with rows of effective teeth, with which the animals attack and devour seals and porpoises, and even destroy some of the larger whales.

" Killers are like giant wolves of the sea, and their ferocity strikes terror to the other warm-blooded inhabitants of the deep. The Eskimos of the Alaskan coast of Bering Sea consider killers as actual wolves in sea form.   They believe that in the early days, when the world was young and men and animals could change their forms at will, land wolves often went to the edge of the shore ice and changed to killer whales, and the killers returned to the edge of the ice and climbed out as wolves, to go ravening over the land.   Some of the natives assured me that even today certain wolves and killers are still endowed with this power and, on account of their malignant character, are much feared by hunters.

Killer Whale.   A toothed whale, the giant wolf of the sea, that travels in "schools" and kills seals, porpoises, and other whales.

" Killers are known to swallow small seals and porpoises entire and attack large whales by tearing away their fleshy lips and tongues.   When attacking large prey they work in packs, with all the unity and fierceness of so many wolves."   (Nelson.)

Dolphins and Porpoises.   Not all Toothed Whales are "as large as a Whale"; many of them are quite reasonable in size, such as the River Dolphins, Dolphins, and Porpoises.   The River Dolphins range from five to nine feet long.   They are sociable creatures, going about in herds and favoring bays and estuaries of rivers rather than the open sea.   One species lives in certain rivers of India, especially the Ganges; another in the Yangtze Kiang of China; a third species in the Amazon; and a fourth in the La Plata River.

The Common Dolphin reaches a length of about eight feet, and is especially well supplied with teeth, since there are forty to sixty pairs in each jaw.   It is a wise fish that manages to steer clear of such a battery of sharply pointed stilettos.   The fin on the back of the Dolphin is well developed and triangular in shape.

The Common Porpoise is about six feet long.   It is dark above and white below; has a well-developed triangular fin sticking up from the middle of the back; and possesses about twenty-five pairs of teeth in each jaw.   It is a voracious creature

Dolphin. A small whale only about 8 feet long, but well supplied with sharp teeth.

and very fond of salmon and mackerel. Porpoises occur in herds and often swim along beside a steamer, easily keeping pace with the fastest boats. They leap out of the water from time to time as if to get a better view of the monster that has invaded their ocean, but usually all one sees of them is the arch-shaped back and dorsal fin.

The Beluga, or White Whale, lives in the Arctic region and reaches a length of about twelve feet. It is milk-white in color and has rounded flippers but no dorsal

Common Porpoise. A toothed whale about 6 feet long; he is very voracious and destroys vast numbers of salmon and mackerel.

fin. Usually from three to a dozen or more Belugas travel about together, frequenting shallow waters, often spending their time in bays and estuaries and sometimes swimming for some distance up the rivers.

"During the twilight hours of the Arctic summer night, glowing with beautiful colors, the ghostly white forms of these whales breaking the smooth blue-black surface of a far-northern bay add the crowning effect of strange, unworldly mystery to the scene."   (Nelson.)

Courtesy, N. Y. Zoological Society

Porpoises.   A familiar sight when on an ocean voyage is a school of leaping porpoises; the arched back and triangular dorsal fin are often in view.

The Narwhale also lives in the Arctic region.   It is a curious species because one of the incisor teeth of the male grows into a long, spirally twisted, horizontal tusk that may reach a length of nine feet or more.   The only other tooth it possesses is a second incisor, but this is merely a vestige.   The flippers of the Narwhale are short and no dorsal fin is present.   The body is about fifteen feet long.

CHAPTER 39

PRIMATES

The Primates live in tropical and subtropical regions, but can be seen in almost every zoological park, and some of them are brought to us by organ-grinders. The West Indies, Pacific Islands, New Guinea, New Zealand, and Australia have no indigenous species. Most of the Primates agree in certain characteristics, but, as usual, there are exceptions to almost every statement that can be made about them. If we ignore these exceptions, we may define them as follows: Primates are mammals covered with a hairy or woolly coat; five fingers and five toes are present; the large toe is opposable to the other toes; each finger and toe bears a well-formed nail; the eye is situated in a socket surrounded by a ring of bone; the brain-case is large and the brain is highly developed; and the mammary glands are two in number and located on the breast.

The Order Primates is usually divided into two Suborders and these into families. The more primitive types belong to the suborder of Lemurs. Here are placed a family containing one species, the Aye-Aye; a second family with seven species of Tarsiers; and a third family of True Lemurs containing many species that live in Africa, Madagascar, India, and the Far East.

The second suborder contains four families; these are the Marmosets and Tamarins, the New World Monkeys, the Old World Monkeys, and the Apes. The family of New World Monkeys may be subdivided into four groups: (1) the Night Monkeys, Titis and Squirrel Monkeys, (2) the Saki Monkeys, (3) the Howling Monkeys, and (4) the Capuchins, Woolly Monkeys, and Spider Monkeys.

The Old World Monkeys belong to a single family; here we find many species with names that are more or less familiar to us and many others that we have never heard of. Among these are the Baboons, Mandrills, Macaques, Barbary Ape, Mangabeys, Guenons, Langurs, and Guerezas.

The largest and most highly developed Primates are the Anthropoid Apes, all of which are placed in one family and given the highest position in the animal series. The more primitive Apes are the Gibbons and Siamangs; the higher Apes comprise the Orang-Utan, the Gorillas, and the Chimpanzees.

An excellent region for the observation of Monkeys is Panama, especially a jungle area between Panama and Costa Rica which has not yet been developed by white men. Here we have spent many days tramping through the jungle in search of them, or seated on a log waiting for them to pass by. In this region Spider Monkeys, White-Faced Monkeys, Howling Monkeys, and Titis are particularly abundant. Night Monkeys, Squirrel Monkeys, and Marmosets may also be encountered; they are sometimes brought to Panama City by the natives.

Aye-Aye. For many centuries the bamboo forests of eastern Madagascar have been inhabited by the most primitive of the Primates, the Aye-Aye, but it was not until 1780 that civilized man knew of its existence, when one specimen was brought to Europe, and 80 years more elapsed before a second specimen was brought to Europe. Since then many of them have been exhibited in zoological parks.

Aye-Ayes are about the size of a cat, but are quite thin and weigh less. Their fur is dark brown to blackish in color and consists of long, shaggy hairs and a woolly underfur. The head is round; the naked ears are very large; the fore feet are also large; the thumb bears a flattened nail, but the other fingers are provided with claws; the third finger is especially long and thin; the tail is much elongated and

Photo by Berridge.   Courtesy, Nature Magazine

Aye-Aye. An inhabitant of the bamboo forests of eastern Madagascar; this most primitive Primate is about the size of a cat, has large ears, a long, bushy tail, and large clawed fingers.

extremely bushy, — the kind of tail that "wags the dog"; and the teeth resemble those of a gnawing animal.

By day, Aye-Ayes remain curled up in their nests. These are lodged in the forks of trees; they are large, round structures of dry leaves with an entrance in one side. At night, the animals sally forth to capture insects. Wood borers seem to be considered a delicacy; the Aye-Ayes apparently hear them boring by means of their large, sensitive ears; their burrows are opened with the long gnawing teeth; and the borer extracted with the long, clawed middle finger.

Tarsier. Tarsiers are also among the most primitive Primates. They are to be found in Borneo, Java, Sumatra, the Philippines, and certain other islands of the Indo-Malayan archipelago. We succeeded in obtaining some of them alive on the island of Bohol in the Philippine group. They are about the size of a rat, but look as though they had been constructed from what was left over after the other mammals had been created.

The head is round; the eyes are extremely large and owl-like; the ears are very large; the tail is very long and ends in a tuft of thin long hair; the hind legs are much longer than the fore legs and built for leaping; the fingers and toes are long and all bear nails except the second and third toes, which have claws; and the tarsal part of the hands and feet is extraordinarily long, hence the name Tarsier.

The Tarsier is a nocturnal animal, coming out at night to search for insects and lizards. He moves through the trees leaping from branch to branch, and clinging to the bark with disklike pads on the ends of the fingers and toes, much as a tree frog does. He is rather rare and only the fortunate few among naturalists ever see him in his native haunts. Like a squirrel, he holds his food between his hands while eating it.

Ruffed Lemur. Only in Madagascar can one see True Lemurs in their native haunts. Here the forests are inhabited by troops of them belonging to a number of species. Lemurs are about the size of a house cat. The snout is much like that of a dog. The fur is soft, thick, and woolly and the tail long and bushy. A broken wreath of hair extends out from the cheeks and chin. The ears are tufted and the eyes large. The colors of the Ruffed Lemur are black and creamy white, distributed over the body as indicated on page 644.

The hind legs are only slightly longer than the front legs and hence Lemurs "are quadrupedal in their actions, walking on the ground or running along the branches of trees on all four feet, but also jumping with marvelous agility. They are gregarious, living in small troops, are diurnal in their habits, but most active towards evening, when they make the woods resound with

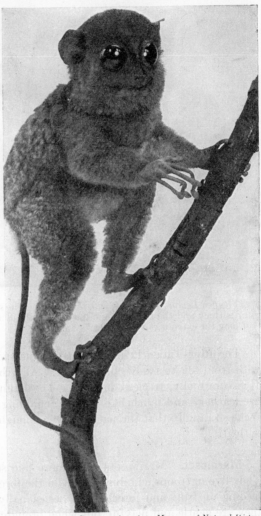

Courtesy, American Museum of Natural History

Tarsier. A nocturnal Primate of the Far East about the size of a rat, with large, staring eyes, a long, slender tail ending in a tuft, and long, thin fingers and toes with disklike pads on the end.

their loud cries. They feed not only on fruits and buds, but also on eggs, young birds, and insects. When at rest or sleeping they generally coil their long, bushy tails around their bodies, apparently for the sake of the warmth it affords. They have either one or two young ones at a birth, which are at first nearly naked, and are carried about, hanging close to and almost concealed by the hair of the mother's belly. After a while they change their position and mount upon the mother's back, where they are carried about until they are able to climb and leap by themselves." (Lydekker.)

Ruffed Lemur. A primitive Primate about the size of a cat that lives in Madagascar; the fur is thick and the tail long and bushy; the head is doglike and the ears tufted; a wreath of long fur extends out from cheeks and chin.

The Ring-Tailed Lemur is a handsome species with a pearl-gray tail decorated with from ten to twelve black rings. All other Lemurs possess tails of one color. It favors rocky, treeless districts. The palms of the hands and soles of the feet are leathery and much like suckers, enabling it to climb easily over the slippery rocks so rapidly that the natives, even though barefooted, are unable to keep pace with it.

Marmoset. Marmosets seem more like squirrels than they do like monkeys. They live in troops, climbing about in the forest trees in parts of tropical America, feeding on fruit and insects, and occasionally uttering chirping noises. As pets, they are gentle and playful, but when brought north do not live long.

The characteristics of the White-Eared Marmoset are evident in our photograph. The fur is thick and silky; the head is round; the face is flat and dark-colored, with a white spot on the forehead; the nose is flat and the nostrils far apart; the mouth is large; the eyes are large and gentle-looking; the ears bear a conspicuous tuft of white hair; the hind limbs are longer than the fore limbs; the toes all bear sharp, curved claws except the great toe, which bears a flat nail; the thumb is not opposable to the fingers but parallel with them; and the tail is bushy and banded with black. Marmosets bring forth two or three young at a birth. One Marmoset that was

Courtesy, Nature Magazine

White-Eared Marmoset. A little squirrel-like monkey that inhabits tropical America; the fur is thick and silky and forms conspicuous white ear tufts; there is a white spot on the forehead.

kept in captivity "never washed face or hands, and paid no attention to his coat, with one exception, — his tail. This apparently useless appendage, twice as long as he was, which usually hung straight down, or stood straight out, gave him much concern, and was evidently one point on which he prided himself. To dress it, he brought it up before him, held it with one hand and combed it violently with the claws of the other, — the wrong way of the fur." (Miller.)

The Tamarins belong to the same family as the Marmosets. The Silky Tamarin has soft, silky fur. The hair around the face and on the back of the neck is very long and forms a conspicuous ruff. This species lives in southeastern Brazil. Small troops of them travel about together, and because of their small size and light weight, they are able to ascend to the tree tops. They are quite intelligent and very playful. A smaller relative is the Maned Tamarin, a species with a body only seven inches long. The Moustached Tamarin has a well-developed moustache, and seems more like a squirrel than a monkey as it climbs about in the trees.

Howling Monkeys.   Visitors to the wilder regions of the American tropics are often treated to the vocal efforts of Howling Monkeys.   Sounds of remarkable depth and volume arise somewhere in the jungle and can be heard at a distance of a mile or two.   They are audible especially in the morning and evening, and we actually became so accustomed to hearing them, during our residence in Honduras and Panama, that life did not seem quite normal when they failed to greet our ears at the regular time.   The upper part of the windpipe in the Howlers is enlarged into a hollow sound box so that the throat is visibly thickened.

Howlers live in the jungles of Central and South America.   They are the largest of the New World Monkeys, reaching a length of about twenty inches, and bearing a tail about seventeen inches long.   The body is robust.   The tail is a powerful, prehensile organ with a naked area near the tip that is very sensitive to touch; it is used especially to cling to the branches of trees, constituting what amounts to a "fifth hand."

The Howler is considered to be the most ugly and repulsive of our Monkeys. The face is naked, the forehead retreating, and the muzzle protruding.   The hair on the forehead is directed backward and that on the back of the head is directed forward, a ridge being formed where they meet on top of the head.   Howlers vary greatly in color; some are brown and others black.   Seven subspecies are now recognized, but individual differences within one subspecies often seem greater than the differences between subspecies.

The following description of the behavior of Howlers made by an early explorer is not only historically interesting, but, for the most part, correct.   "The Monkeys that are in these Parts are the ugliest I ever saw.   They are much bigger than a Hare, and have great Tails about two Foot and a half long.   The under-side of their Tails is all bare, with a black hard Skin; but the upper-side, and all the Body is covered with coarse, long, black, straight Hair.   These Creatures keep together 20 or 30 in a Company, and ramble over the Woods; leaping from Tree to Tree.   If they meet with a single Person they will threaten to devour him.   When I have been alone I have been afraid to shoot them, especially the first Time I met them.   They were a large Company dancing from Tree to Tree, over my Head; chattering and making a terrible Noise; and a great many grim Faces, and shewing antick Gestures. Some broke down dry Sticks and threw at me; others scattered their Urine and Dung about my Ears; at last one bigger than the rest, came to a small Limb just over my Head; and leaping directly at me, made me start back; but the Monkie caught hold of the Bough with the tip of his Tail; and there continued swinging to and fro, and making Mouths at me.   At last I past on, they still keeping me Company, with the like menacing Postures, till I came to our Huts.   The Tails of these Monkeys are as good to them as one of their Hands; and they will hold as fast by them.   If two or more of us were together they would hasten from us. The Females with their young ones are much troubled to leap after the Males; for they have commonly two: one she carries under one of her Arms; the other sits on her Back, and clasps her two Fore-Paws about her Neck.   These Monkeys are the most sullen I ever met with; for all the Art we could use would never tame them. It is a hard matter to shoot one of them, so as to take it; for if it gets hold with its

Claws or Tail, it will not fall as long as one breath of Life remains. After I have shot at one, and broke a Leg or an Arm, I have pitied the poor Creature to see it look and handle the wounded Limb, and turn it about from side to side. These Monkeys are very rarely, or (as some say) never on the Ground." (Dampier, 1700.)

Recent studies by Carpenter of Howlers in their natural environment have furnished us with many interesting facts about them. Howlers live in dense forests

Photo by Gross. Courtesy, Nature Magazine

Howling Monkey. He has a naked face and retreating forehead with the hair directed backward; the muzzle is protruding and the throat thickened by the howling apparatus.

of tall trees and avoid scrub growth. They travel about in troops of from four to thirty-five, the average number being about seventeen. Subgroups exist within a group. "Groups of howlers tend to occupy a definite and limited territory. This region may be shared with other groups and there occurs from time to time some shifting of territorial range. Within their territories groups behave with reference to food and lodge trees. The groups travel at the average rate of about one hundred yards per hour and seldom move more than eight hundred yards per day. The groups move in an irregular column. There is a strong tendency for males to lead the groups and for females carrying infants to travel in the last positions of the column." (Carpenter.)

The females within a group live peacefully together and the males also seem to get along together without strife, co-operating in leading and defending the group. The mothers carry their young at first on their bellies and later on their backs near the tail. The young play together, hanging by their tails and wrestling in midair, or chasing one another along the branches and from limb to limb. Food is gathered from the terminal twigs of trees and usually the branches are drawn into the mouth with the hands and the food eaten directly from the tree.   Fruits, buds, and leaves are the principal items on their menu.

Howlers communicate with one another by gesticulations, by the positions they assume, and by sounds.   Their howls are well known, but other noises are produced by them, such as a deep metallic cluck emitted by the male while leading a group, the wail of a mother when she drops her baby, and a chirping squeal of the young

Courtesy, N. Y. Zoological Society

White-Faced Capuchin Monkey.   An inhabitant of tropical America; the nostrils are far apart; the canine teeth are well developed, and the tail is long and prehensile.

during play.   A number of individuals may howl at the same time, when the "tremendous roaring exceeds that of a lion or bull."   The barking, roaring type of noise is used as a means of defense and also to control the members of a group.   When several groups of Howlers meet in the jungle they attempt to out-howl each other.

Living in the same jungle area with the Howlers are a number of other species, such as the Capuchins, Spider, Owl, Squirrel, Titi and Woolly Monkeys.   The

Capuchins, Spider and Owl Monkeys are described here. The Squirrel Monkeys are often brightly colored. Their heads are round and their thumbs short. Titi Monkeys may also be conspicuously colored. Their hair is rather long. Woolly Monkeys are quite large and are covered with a dense coat of woolly fur. They are grayish or reddish in color and have a prehensile tail.

Courtesy, Science Service

Baby Monkeys. They combine the playfulness of kittens with the amusing antics of Monkeys.

White-Faced Monkey, or Capuchin. The White-Faced Capuchin Monkey, or Sapajou, has a stout body covered with rather woolly fur. The head is round and the eyes large and bright. The nose is broad and the nostrils far apart as in all New World Monkeys. The tail is long and prehensile, but clothed to the tip with hair. The thumb is opposable; in all other New World Monkeys it is not. He has been described as "looking like a little old man seen through the wrong end of a telescope."

Photo by Carpenter

Young Spider Monkey. Baby Spider Monkeys cling to their mother's back until rather well grown; this baby that we captured in the jungles of Panama is wondering what it is all about.

White-Faced Capuchins travel about in troops. We found their reactions quite different from those of Spider Monkeys or Titis. Instead of remaining together, thus allowing the hunter to shoot most of the troop, they scatter at once when one is shot and consequently are more difficult to collect. The food of Capuchins consists largely of insects. "It is incessantly on the lookout for insects, examining the crevices in trees and withered leaves, seizing the largest beetles and munching them up with the greatest relish. It is also very fond of eggs and young birds, and must play havoc amongst the nestlings. Probably owing to its carnivorous habits, its flesh is not considered so good by Monkey-eaters as that of the fruit-eating Spider-Monkey; but I never myself tried either." (Belt.)

The locomotion of Capuchins has been described as follows: "The troops consist of thirty or more individuals which travel in single file. When the foremost of the flock reaches the outermost branch of an unusually lofty tree, he springs forth into the air without a moment's hesitation and alights on the dome of yielding foliage belonging to the neighbouring tree, maybe fifty feet beneath; all the rest following the example. They grasp, on falling, with hands and tail, right themselves in a moment, and then away they go along branch and bough to the next tree." (Belt.)

Spider Monkeys. A light, slender body, very long, spindling limbs, and a long tail give these Monkeys their spider-like characteristics. They are more thoroughly adapted to life in the treetops than any other American Monkeys. A Spider Monkey "can do so many things at once that no juggler can equal it. It will hold fruit in one hand, pick more with one foot, place food to the mouth with another hand, and walk and swing from branch to branch with the other foot and tail, all simultaneously." The hair is long and rather coarse and no woolly underfur is present. A common species in Central America is about eighteen inches long and has a tail about twenty-one inches long.

Probably the best place in Central America to observe Spider Monkeys is in the Coto region between Panama and Costa Rica. Here a group of us spent a few weeks in the summer of 1932 studying their structure, behavior, and parasites. They travel about in troops, moving along through the treetops with marvelous agility. Just across the La Vacca River from our camp was a tall food tree which was visited by a troop of Spider Monkeys every day. Families consisting of father, mother, and young may be encountered almost any day hastening over the top of the jungle and talking excitedly to each other.

According to several observers, Spider Monkeys will break off branches and throw them down on any human invader, and one naturalist describes a troop that remained quietly in a nispera tree until he came underneath it; then they shook the hard, round fruit down on him. Whether these Monkeys actually throw objects at anyone is doubtful. Also in the category of romance is the tale about Monkeys that form a bridge across a stream, or between trees too far apart to jump across, by clinging to each other, swinging back and forth, and then, after acquiring a foothold on the other side, allowing the rest of the troop to pass over in safety, without getting their feet wet.

Considerable difference of opinion exists regarding the use of Monkeys as food by man. The early Spanish settlers in Central America considered them excellent; and both British and Spanish soldiers were no doubt often saved from hunger almost amounting to starvation by the large number of Monkeys they were able to obtain so easily in the jungle. We "feasted" on the flesh of young Spider Monkeys stewed with vegetables, and found that it compared very favorably with peccary, curassow, iguana, and other types of jungle food. Spider Monkeys are more gentle than some of the other species and make desirable pets if given the right kind of care. In their native haunts they are preyed upon by eagles and other predatory animals that make their lives less happy than their antics in the treetops would lead one to imagine.

Spider Monkey.   His name is due to his slender body, long, thin arms and legs, and long, prehensile tail; he lives in tropical America.

Owl or Night Monkey.   Most of the Monkeys are active by day but this little creature makes his whoopee after dark.   During the day he hides and sleeps in a hollow tree.   At night he roams abroad in search of insects, small birds, other small animals, and fruit, occasionally uttering "cat calls" to herald his coming.   The eyes of the Night Monkey are particularly noticeable, being extremely large and yellowish in color, a condition often developed by nocturnal animals.   The body is short and stout and about a foot long.   The bushy tail is about as long as the body.   The fur is thick and woolly.   The head is round, the muzzle short, and the face surrounded by a ruff of fur.

Night Monkeys range from Nicaragua to the Amazon.   "These Monkeys, although sleeping by day, are aroused by the least noise, so that, when a person passes by a tree in which a number of them are concealed, he is startled by the sudden apparition of a group of little striped faces crowding a hole in a trunk.   My own pet was kept in a box in which was placed a broad-mouthed glass jar; into this it would dive, head foremost, when anyone entered the room, turning round inside, and thrusting forth its inquisitive face an instant afterwards to stare at the intruder.   It was very active at night, venting at frequent intervals a hoarse cry like the suppressed barking of a dog, and scampering about the room, to the length of its tether, after cockroaches and spiders.   Although seeming to prefer insects, it ate all kinds of fruit, but would not touch raw or cooked meat, and was very seldom thirsty."   (Bates.)

Courtesy, N. Y. Zoological Society

Night or Owl Monkey.   A nocturnal resident of tropical America about a foot long; his eyes are very large and yellow, and his fur thick and woolly.

Baboons.   Baboons are inhabitants of certain parts of Africa and Arabia, favoring especially rocky hillsides in hot, dry regions.   They have a short body, and fore limbs and hind limbs are of almost equal length.   The palms of the hands and soles of the feet are applied to the ground in walking, the feet being particularly long.   The head is wolflike, the jaws being especially strong and armed with powerful canine teeth.   They are gregarious, going about in small or large troops. This habit, combined with a fierce disposition, massive jaws, and sharp teeth, makes

Arabian, or Hamadryas, Baboons. Their long hair is of a beautiful gray color; this species was venerated by the ancient Egyptians.

it possible for them to live on the ground in the same habitat with such carnivores as lions, leopards, and hyenas. When Baboons wish to threaten their enemies they open their mouths to the fullest extent as though yawning. This displays their formidable canine teeth which is enough to frighten almost anyone. When angry they may strike the ground with their hands.

"Of all quadrupeds, it is probable that the African baboons are pound for pound the most pugnacious, and the quickest on the draw. The old male baboon in his prime will fight anything that threatens his troop, literally at the drop of a hat. . . . His temper is hot, his voice raucous and blood-curdling, his canines fearfully long and sharp, and his savage yell of warning sufficient to keep even the king of beasts off his grass." (Hornaday.)

The Arabian, or Hamadryas, Baboon is stone-gray in color. "The old males are always most conspicuous animals, all the fore part of their body being covered with long hair. They usually take the lead when the troop is moving; some of them also bringing up the rear; others placing themselves on high rocks or bushes and keeping a sharp look-out after enemies. A troop collected on a rocky crag presents a most singular appearance. I several times saw large numbers assembled around springs in the evening in the thirsty Shoho country. . . . On such occasions every jutting rock, every little stone more prominent than the rest, was occupied by a patriarch of the herd, with the gravity and watchfulness befitting his grizzled hair, waiting patiently until the last of his human rivals had slaked his thirst and that of his cattle. Around, the females were mainly occupied in taking care of the young, the smaller Monkeys amusing themselves by gambolling about." (Blanford.)

Mandrill. A Baboon with grooved ridges on either side of the face that are intense blue in color; the central line and end of the nose are bright scarlet.

The Hamadryas Baboon "which was particularly sacred to Thoth, held a conspicuous place among the sacred animals of Egypt, being worshipped as the type of the God of Letters, and of the Moon, which was one of the characters of Thoth. . . . Sometimes a Cynocephalus (Hamadryas), placed on a throne as a god, holds a sacred Ibis in his hand; and in the judgment-scenes of the dead it frequently occurs, seated on the summit of a balance, as the emblem of Thoth, who had an important office on that occasion, and registered the account of the actions of the deceased. The place where this animal was particularly sacred was Hermopolis, the city of Thoth. In the necropolis of the capital of Upper Egypt, a particular spot was set apart as the cemetery of the Sacred Apes." (Wilkinson.)

Mandrill. The Baboon known as the Mandrill has a particularly heavy body, strong limbs, and a very short tail that is usually held erect. The brow ridges are very prominent, the eyes small, deeply sunk, and close together, and the canine teeth highly developed.

"The body generally is covered with a full soft coating of hair of a light olive-green above and silvery-gray beneath, and the chin is furnished underneath with a small pointed yellow beard. The hair of the forehead and temples is directed upwards so as to meet in a point on the crown, which gives the head a triangular appearance. The ears are naked and of a bluish-black colour. The hands and feet are naked and black. But it is in the face that the most remarkable disposition of vivid hues occur, more resembling those of a brilliantly coloured flower than what might be expected in the cutaneous covering of a mammal. The cheek-prominences are of an intense blue, the effect of which is heightened by deeply sunk longitudinal furrows of a darker tint, while the central line and termination of the nose are a bright scarlet. Notwithstanding the beauty of these colours in themselves, the whole combination, with the form and expression of features, quite justifies Cuvier's assertion that 'it would be difficult to design a more hideous animal than the Mandrill.'" (Lydekker.)

Macaques. The Bandarlog so graphically described in Kipling's *Jungle Books* are Bandar or Bengal Macaques, a species of Monkey that lives principally in northern India. Being an Old World species, its nostrils are close together and cheek pouches are present. To scientists it is known as the Rhesus Monkey and widely used for all sorts of laboratory studies. We have used them especially for experimental studies of parasites, since they appear in nature to be infected with the same species of parasites as those that live in man. We collected a large number of Macaques of a closely related species in the Philippines and found that they harbored "human" parasites.

The Rhesus Monkey is golden gray in color, about twenty-two inches long, and has a tail about ten inches long. Other species of Macaques have similar characteristics. They possess a robust body and limbs that are short and strong. The muzzle is prominent and the lips are thick and protruding. The eyes have prominent ridges above them. Cheek pouches are present; these the Monkeys cram with food, such as insects, seeds, and fruit, which can then be chewed up at leisure.

The emotions of Macaques are expressed, according to Tickell, as follows: "Anger is generally silent, or at most expressed by a low hoarse monotone 'Heu,' not so gular or guttural as a growl; ennui and a desire for company by a whining 'Hom'; invitation, deprecation, entreaty, by a smacking of the lips and a display of the incisors into a regular broad grin, accompanied with a subdued grunting chuckle, highly expressive, but not to be rendered on paper; fear and alarm by a loud harsh shriek, 'Kra' or 'Kraouh,' which serves also as a warning to others who may be heedless of danger."

Wild Macaques travel about in troops which include both males and females, and old and young. In captivity they are nervous and irritable and must be handled with care if painful bites are to be avoided. The young are quite docile. They are very playful and wrestle with each other for hours at a time.

Among the species of Macaques may be mentioned the Barbary Ape, the Celebes, Short-Tailed, Pig-Tailed, Bonnet, Philippine, and Crab-Eating Macaques. The last-named species lives on the shores of rivers, especially in mangrove thickets, and spends much time in the water swimming or diving in search of crabs. The Pig-Tailed Macaque has a slender, piglike tail which it carries erect. In Sumatra it is said to be trained by the natives to pick coconuts and bring them down to their masters. The Barbary Ape inhabits Morocco, Algeria, and Spain and occurs also on the rock of Gibraltar. The body is about as large as that of a moderate-sized dog. No external tail is present. Probably the "Apes of the Rocks" were brought over to Gibraltar by the Moors for sale and were thus introduced into Europe.

Courtesy, National Zoological Park

Japanese Macaques. Monkeys of the macaque type are native in various parts of the Far East but are much used in this country for scientific experiments; note the nostrils that are close together in this and other Old World monkeys.

The Japanese Macaques whose portraits are shown here have a face practically free from hair. The fur is long, soft, and silky; in general they are dark brown or yellowish-brown in color, but some parts are grayish. As usual, the group cling to one another as though for mutual protection.

Gibbons. The Gibbon occupies a position among the Apes similar to that of the Spider Monkey among the Monkeys. It is marvelously adapted for life in trees, with arms that are extremely long and hands that are likewise much elongated. The acrobatics of a captive female Gibbon have been described as follows: "Her movements may, indeed, be termed aërial, as she seems merely to touch, in her progress, the branches among which she exhibits her evolutions. In these feats her hands and arms are the sole organs of locomotion; her body hanging as if suspended by a rope, sustained by one hand (the right, for example), she launches herself by an energetic movement to a distant branch, which she catches with the left hand. But her hold is less than momentary; the impulse for the next launch is acquired; the branch then aimed at is attained by the right hand again, and quitted instantaneously, and so on, in alternate succession. In this manner spaces of twelve and eighteen feet are cleared with the greatest ease, and uninterruptedly for hours together, without the slightest appearance of fatigue being manifested;

and it is evident that if more space could be allowed, distances very greatly exceeding eighteen feet would be as easily cleared. . . .   Sometimes on seizing a branch in her progress, she will throw herself, by one arm only, completely round it, making a revolution with such rapidity as almost to deceive the eye, and continue her progress with undiminished velocity." (Martin.)

Photo by Hegner

Müller's Gibbon. A tree-dweller with very long arms, legs, hands, and feet and pronounced ability to use them; he and other Gibbons live in the forests of the Far East.

Gibbons are slender and about thirty inches long.   The head is small and round and the fur is soft and woolly.   Although most of the time is spent in trees, when on the ground the Gibbon walks erect, its long arms reaching to its toes, — the only Anthropoid Ape that habitually walks erect like a man.   The food of Gibbons includes fruit, leaves, insects, spiders, birds, and birds' eggs.   Gibbons drink like baboons, with their mouth in touch with the water.   They are delicate creatures and, unless conditions are very favorable, do not live long in captivity.   They are usually gentle and affectionate if treated well by their keepers.   The adults, however, may become ill-tempered just as most human beings do occasionally.

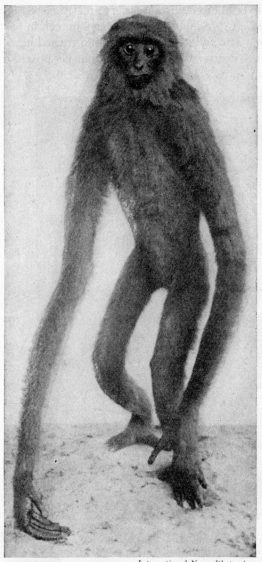

International News Photo, Inc.
Gibbon. "He glides through the air with the greatest of ease" as he swings from branch to branch with his extremely long arms, but walks upright like a man.

During the day Gibbons are quiet, but at sunrise and sunset troops of as many as 50 or 100 utter their terrific cries and evidently derive much pleasure from the exercise of their tremendous voices. In captivity they are gentle and affectionate, but rather delicate. One young is born at a birth. The baby clings to the underside of the mother's body for many months and the mother takes good care of her offspring.

Gibbons are the smallest of the Anthropoid Apes. They live in the forests of the Oriental region. About a dozen species are recognized; these are mostly black, gray, or light brown in color.

Orang-Utan. The "Man-of-the-Woods," as the Malays refer to the Orang-Utan, is restricted to the forested regions of Borneo and Sumatra. He is a shaggy beast with hair reddish in color and in some places as long as a foot or more, especially on the arms, thighs, and shoulders. The male is larger than the female, reaching a height of four feet six inches and a weight of up to 160 pounds. The body is stout, the neck thick, and the abdomen rounded and protuberant. The arms are long, reaching almost to the ankles; the hands are also elongated; the fingers are webbed; and the thumb is short. The hair on the arm is directed downward and that on the fore arm upward so as to meet at the elbow. The legs are short and bowed and the feet long and narrow. The great toe is small and may lack a nail.

The face of the Orang is naked and bears a rather doleful expression. The forehead is high; the nose is rather large; the lips are broad and very mobile; the ears are small, flat, and manlike; and the chin is practically absent. In the male, a fold of skin on either side increases the breadth of the face conspicuously, the face

Orang-Utan. A female bearing a rather disdainful expression; the lips are rather over-emphasized; the ears are small and manlike; and the hair long and reddish in color.

of the female being only six inches wide, whereas that of the male may be twelve inches in breadth. A beard is present but too thin to brag about.

"Of all Apes, the Orang has the brain which is most like that of Man; indeed, it may be said to be like Man's in all respects, save that it is much inferior in size and weight, and that the cerebrum is more symmetrically convoluted and less complicated with secondary and tertiary convolutions." (Mivart.)

Orangs move about from branch to branch and from tree to tree by means of their long, powerful arms and hooklike fingers. "I have frequently seen them swing along beneath the large limbs as a gymnast swings along a tight rope, reaching six feet at a stretch. When passing from one tree to another, the Orang reaches out and gathers in its grasp a number of small branches that he feels sure will sustain his weight, and then swings himself across." (Hornaday.) Locomotion on the ground is more difficult. His progress is awkward, the arms being used as crutches with which he swings himself forward, and his appearance resembling that of a man bent down with age.

Orangs are rather solitary animals. The male lives alone or with one female, who is accompanied by one or more of her offspring. Their food consists largely of leaves and fruit, especially the durian, probably the most evil-smelling of all fruits. The natives are also fond of durian, but we ate some in the Philippines which we could not swallow without a feeling of nausea, and hence do not envy the Orangs their choice of a diet. Drinking is accomplished by dipping the hands in water and letting the drops fall into the mouth or sucking them off the fingers.

The nest building of these Primates has often been described. "The Orang usually selects a small tree, a sapling, in fact, and builds his nest in its top, even though his weight causes it to sway alarmingly. He always builds his nest low down, often within twenty-five feet of the ground, and seldom higher than forty feet. Sometimes it is fully four feet in diameter, but usually not more than three,

Courtesy, San Diego Zoological Park

Chimpanzee. The lips are long and mobile and the large ears project out from the head.

and quite flat at the top. The branches are merely piled crosswise. I have never been able to ascertain to a certainty, but it is my opinion that an Orang, after building a nest, sleeps in it several nights in succession, unless he is called upon to leave its neighbourhood." (Hornaday.) Orangs are active during midday, remaining in the nest until the morning dew has dried away.

As a rule, Orangs are rather quiet, but when excited may express themselves by bellowing or roaring in a deep, bass voice. Very little success has been obtained in teaching them to speak, and "if these animals have a language it is restricted to a very few sounds of a general emotional significance. Articulate speech they have none and communication with one another is accomplished by vocal sounds to no greater extent than it is by dogs, with a growl, a whine, or a bark." (Furness.) "When wounded he betakes himself to the highest attainable point of the tree, and emits a singular cry, consisting at first of high notes, which at length deepen into a low roar, not unlike that of a panther. While giving out the high notes, the Orang thrusts out his lips into a funnel shape; but in uttering the low notes he holds his mouth wide open, and at the same time the great throat bag, or laryngeal sac, becomes distended." (Huxley.)

Chimpanzee. The Chimpanzee in the wild state is restricted to equatorial Africa. In many ways it resembles the Gorilla, but differs from the latter both physically and mentally. It has the most highly organized brain of all of the lower animals. The body is shorter and not as stout as that of the Gorilla. The ears are very large and stand out from the head. The lips are long, very mobile, and protrusible.

Photo by Hegner

Chimpanzee. A female with a baby that was born in captivity clinging to her abdomen in a characteristic attitude; note the extremely long, powerful arms.

Chimpanzees spend a large part of their time in trees. Their hands and feet are fitted for climbing among the branches. When on the ground they walk on all fours, with the hands closed and the backs of the fingers in contact with the ground. Young Chimpanzees are docile, but as they grow older they become dangerous and aggressive; they "don't know their own strength." Not only their muscles but also their voices are strong, and their shrieks and roars can be heard for long distances. Some of them seem to enjoy now and then a violent dance with vigorous stamping. In captivity a Chimpanzee may acquire the habit of filling its mouth with water, which, at an unexpected moment, it squirts into the face of anyone near the cage.

When Chimpanzees are cared for properly, they live well in captivity and even breed. At the Anthropoid Station near Jacksonville, Florida, where we spent some time studying the parasites of Chimpanzees, a number of young have been born and reared in captivity. In nature, Chimpanzees may form bands of from about a dozen to forty individuals, including males, females, and young of all ages. They are monogamous and often live in separate families.

Chimpanzees are active, nervous animals with an excitable disposition. They are given first rank among the Apes in intelligence. They love to play, exhibit great curiosity, are quite imitative, and have excellent visual memory, and considerable mechanical ability. Individuals vary in intelligence just as human beings do. They can be trained to perform in many ways, such as to skate with roller skates, and to ride a bicycle. Their faces are extremely expressive, indicating emotions such as affection, jealousy, fear, disapproval, anger, hunger, and contentment. Their voices are also used to express various emotions.

Photo by Hegner

Gorilla. One of the mountain Gorillas captured by the Martin Johnson expedition in Africa; he is black all over; when walking he places his knuckles on the ground.

Gorilla. The two highest Anthropoid Apes are the Gorilla and Chimpanzee. Comparatively few of these are maintained in zoological parks, the Gorilla being especially rare, since it does not ordinarily live long in captivity. One can distinguish Gorillas from Chimpanzees most easily by the size of their ears; those of the Gorilla are small and manlike, whereas those of the Chimpanzee are very large and project out from the sides of the head.

The Gorilla is the largest of the Apes, adult males reaching a height of over five feet and a weight of over 400 pounds. The body is broad and massive with enormous shoulders and chest which give tremendous power. The arms are long and muscular and the hands and feet broad. The head is large; heavy ridges extend out above the eyes; the mouth is wide; and the upper lip is short. The general color of the hair is black, but may be tinged with reddish on the head, and with gray on the back. The outer hair is long, straight, and coarse, the underfur being shorter and woolly. The canine teeth of the Gorilla are highly developed, becoming

Photo by Hegner

Gorilla. The ears are small and manlike, and the eyes are deeply sunk beneath prominent ridges; he is not snarling but only anticipating the gift of a banana.

formidable tusks. The upper molars differ slightly from those of the Chimpanzee and Man. The lower jaw has no true chin.

Gorillas also live in the dense forests of equatorial Africa, traveling about usually in family groups consisting of father, mother, and one or more children of various ages. They are active during the day, clambering about in the trees and feeding mainly on fruit. At night sleeping platforms of branches are built in the trees for the mother and young, the father remaining on guard at the base of the tree. These sleeping places are occupied usually for one night only.

When on the ground, Gorillas walk on all fours. "In walking they place the back of their closed fingers on the ground, or, more rarely, support themselves on the flat palm, while the flat soles of their feet are also in contact with the ground. Their gait is shuffling; the motion of the body, which is never upright as in Man, but bent forward, is somewhat rolling, or from side to side. The arms being longer than those of the Chimpanzee, it does not stoop so much in walking; like that animal it makes progression by thrusting its arms forward, resting its hands on the ground, and then giving its body a half-jumping, half-swinging motion between them." (Hartmann.)

Gorillas do not ordinarily attack human beings but will fight with great ferocity if brought to bay. Their vocal efforts take the form of grunts, which may develop into a scream or roar.   Another and curious form of emotional expression is the beating of the breast violently with both hands.   This is said to be done when the animals are angry, but we have seen them do it many times when two of them were at play together.   Gorillas appear to be less active mentally than Chimpanzees.

The Gorilla may be higher in the scale of life than the Chimpanzee, but we must end our Parade with one or the other, since the mentality of these great Apes and their physical attributes undoubtedly place them next to Man in the animal series. Noah must have heaved a sigh of relief when the Gorillas finally entered the ark and the gangplank was hauled in.   We hope they all had a pleasant time on board. We know that every species landed safely on Mount Ararat, since it has been our privilege to describe their descendants in this book.

INDEX